Best wishes

Much love

Janet Tyson

MEAT
ACTS

"History: n. An account mostly false, of events unimportant, which are brought about by rulers mostly knaves, and soldiers mostly fools."
Ambrose Bierce

MEAT ACTS

The New Zealand meat industry 1972-1997

Mick Calder & Janet Tyson

DEDICATION

This book is dedicated to 'the graders', Meat New Zealand's production supervisors. They are unsung heroes whose personal integrity and highly professional approach to their task assured the quality standards that give New Zealand meat its international competitive edge. Their role, a vital part of this history, has ended with the implementation of the new Meat Board Act.

First published by Meat New Zealand,
10 Brandon Street, Wellington,
New Zealand, 1999.

ISBN 0-9582052-3-X

Editor and Publisher: Fraser Books,
Masterton.
Front Cover: Hayden Doughty (design);
Lance Lawson (photography).
Design: Graham Kerrisk, Printcraft 81 Ltd,
Masterton.

Printed by Publishing Press Limited, 31 William Pickering Drive, Albany, Auckland, New Zealand.

CONTENTS

SECOND HALF – AGAINST THE WIND

FOREWORD

Sudden, turbulent and far-reaching change has touched every part of New Zealand society and the New Zealand economy in the past 25 years. Nowhere has the change been so extensive and dramatic as in agriculture as a whole, and the meat industry in particular. *Meat Acts* is a history of action, change, restructuring and reinvention, in which controversy is perhaps the only constant feature.

Over the 25 years, the industry has witnessed enormous change, from significant government involvement in the 1970s, through sharp swings in stock numbers, and finally to a deregulation of the industry and a complete free-market approach.

But it is also a story of survival and success, of achievement despite some severe growing pains. The New Zealand meat industry, from its farmers to its marketers, has performed extremely well in the environment it has had to operate in, at home and overseas. No other country exports such a high percentage of its product and has to depend so much on world markets as we do.

Most of our competitors still get government support to varying levels (through tariff and non-tariff barriers) while we have none. The world markets have been awash with not only red meat but, more significantly, white meat – pork and poultry – produced as industrial products at a fraction of the cost of red meat.

So it is a real success story that New Zealand lamb has been repositioned to be the highest priced red meat available in many markets, and New Zealand beef is starting to establish its own distinctive quality position. We have seen an enormous increase in productivity, both in the processing sector and on-farm. Huge strides have been made away from the commodity mindset towards high quality product, and from the dependence on the UK and US as markets. The meat industry consistently generates wealth for the New Zealand economy, with its growth trend steadily upwards.

Meat is a global business. New Zealand contributes nearly 10% of the world trade in beef and veal, and over 53% of the world trade in sheepmeats. Meat industries around the world have struggled with a hostile and distorted world market. Many Southern Hemisphere meat industries have not survived this period – New Zealand has emerged as leader of the pack.

To stay ahead, it is even more crucial that all the links in the marketing chain work harmoniously together. Having producer and processor representatives at the same decision-making Board table is a giant step forward, and positions us for the challenges of the new millennium. As Henry Ford said: "Coming together is a beginning, keeping together is progress, working together is success".

Neil Taylor,
Chief executive, Meat New Zealand.

AUTHORS' NOTE

"If you can't annoy somebody there is little point in writing."
Kingsley Amis

A lot can happen in 25 years. Dynasties can rise and fall, politicians can come and go and sometimes rise again from the ashes of past defeats, politics can swing from right to left and back again or at least back to the left or right of centre, entrepreneurs can wax and wane while institutions and their leaders can move into and out of the limelight. All of these and more have occurred in the New Zealand meat industry in the period 1972-97.

Our commission in writing this book was to chart, from the producer, processing and marketing perspectives, the course of these years, which began when the New Zealand Meat Producers Board celebrated its 50th jubilee.

The meat industry is uniquely demanding and unforgiving. Much more than the dairy industry with its dependable flow of the raw material milk, meat production is subject to the vagaries of climate, procurement competition, farmers' whims and politics. It is a business where customer preferences change quickly, and production response takes several years and animal generations to achieve, but if the price is right changes are made.

It's a business abounding in larger-than-life characters, where strong-minded individuals have made their mark. It's one that, despite the frustrations and the financial failures, gets into the blood of those who make it their career.

It's an industry where the parties are totally interdependent; but one where violent love-hate relationships exist between farmers, their representative bodies such as the Meat Board, and the meat processing and exporting companies. No wonder, therefore, that one of the biggest challenges that can be given to the New Zealand meat industry is to work collectively or in co-operation.

In this book we've aimed to give an overall picture of the main issues and key personalities of those 25 years, to pin down a very eventful period for New Zealand society as well as the meat industry. Inevitably, we've had to select and summarise and resist the temptation to fully explore some topics and people we know are worthy of books in themselves. To use a meat metaphor, this is a primal cut, and there is much further processing of the period to be done.

Inevitably, though our intention is to present a balanced picture, our priorities may not be universally approved, or indeed the perspectives we have taken. It could be said that the more crucial the major event, the more variations we have found in recollections of it.

Our thanks to all those people who have assisted us by contributing information, comment, photos and illustrations, have patiently answered our questions and helped unravel some tangled recollections.

Mick Calder and Janet Tyson,
September 1999.

ACKNOWLEDGEMENTS

Doug Archbold, Debbie Armatage, Gill Austin, Jeremy Austin, Margaret Baker, Mavis Barnett, Jean Begg, Alan Bott, John Buxton, Roger Chadder, Graeme Clent, Gary Donaghy, Gordon Dryden, Peter Elworthy, Pam Frith, Wayne Geary, Peter Gianotti, Terry Green, Ernie Greville, Barry Harcourt, Don Harwood, Colin Henderson, Sandra Irwin, Bruce Jans, Brian Lynch, Brian McCarthy, Christine McKenzie, Margaret McRae, Maria Martin-Smith, John Miller, Sue Miller, Chris Newton, NZ Cartoon Archive, Brian Peacocke, Gail Pope, Richard Prebble, Tim Ritchie, Daphne Robinson, Derek Robinson, Alan Royal, Martyn Saines, Barrie Saunders, Rod Slater, Paul Spackman, Ali Spencer, Gerry Thompson, Kemp Stone, George Troup, Chris Ward, Len Wood, Richard Woods.

And our interviewees:

John Acland, James Aitken, Trevor Arnold, Peter Blomfield, Mike Brooks, Robbie Burnside, Eric Cammell, Ron Clarke, Cheryl Craig, Ron Cushen, Lester Davey, Dick Davison, Rob Davison, Fred Dobbs, Harry Douglas, John Drayton, Peter Egan, Ross Finlayson, John Foster, Allan Frazer, David Frith, Darcy Freeman, Graeme Goodsir, Alan Grant, Peter Harris, Graeme Harrison, Athol Hutton, Ian Jenkinson, Richard Johnstone, Tiny Kirk, Blue Kennedy, Anne Knowles, Clive Lind, Graeme Lowe, Gray Mathias, Ian McKellar, John McNab, Norman McRae, Roger Marshall, Sandra Martin, Roger Middlemass, Derek Morten, Colin Moyle, Peter Norman, Catherine Petrey, Owen Poole, John Prendergast, John Russell, Bruce Ryan, Joe Ryan, Hassan Shaida, David Spence, Neil Taylor, Graeme Thompson, Jim Thomson.

Unless otherwise indicated, quotations from these people are sourced from interviews or conversations with the authors. Other material, unless specifically noted, originates from the annual reports of the Meat Board or Meat Industry Association or its predecessor organisations, and from the Meat Board publications *Meat Producer* magazine and *Meat Board News.*

And last but not least, our thanks also to Hilary Calder and Mel Tyson, for tolerating what was at times the invasive presence of this book in our lives over the past two years. And to Ian and Diane Grant of Fraser Books, surely the only publishers to encourage their authors with new-laid eggs as well as wise advice and an eagle eye for quotation marks.

The New Zealand Meat Producers Board, pictured just before Sir John Ormond's retirement, overseen by a picture of William Massey's cabinet at the time of the Board's establishment in 1922.
Back row: George Anderson, general manager; Adam Begg, government nominee; John Daniell; Len Keen, Board secretary;
Front row: Tom Carroll, government nominee; Crichton Wright; Charles Hilgendorf, deputy chairman; Sir John Ormond, chairman;
Frank Onion, Dairy Board representative; Bruce Ryan; John Polson.

A Game of Two Halves -
the 1970s Begin

"Sir John Ormond (chairman of the Meat Board) and my father (Sir Jack Acland, chairman of the Wool Board) were brothers-in-law. Uncle John was very charismatic, very definite, very thump the bloody table. Dad was much quieter, so they were an excellent combination. And when they really wanted something from government, they went up together. Once they went to see Henry Lang, who was secretary of Treasury, and (Finance Minister) Muldoon was there. He was very rude and abrupt and John Ormond said, 'Sit down, Muldoon, sit down. You do not control this country, Jack Acland and I control this country.' And it was so." John Acland.

As the 1970s began, leggy lambs were about to launch Mervyn Barnett of Dunsandel into national meat industry politics. Respected as a firm but fair rugby referee, he was also concerned to see farmers get a fair deal.

Frustration at legislation which had put a stranglehold on the building of new meat processing plants saw Graeme Lowe of Hastings practising his formidable lobbying skills, paying calls twice-weekly on his local MP, Duncan McIntyre.

Sir John Ormond, from Wallingford in Hawke's Bay, was preparing to step down after an unprecedented 21 years as chairman of the New Zealand Meat Producers Board.

Ormond's nephew John Acland was doubly linked to New Zealand farming traditions, and to the brokers of power through his father, chairman of the Wool Board. But he looked in new directions, and had spent his time as a Nuffield Scholar studying the British beef industry with its dairy cattle influence. At Mount Peel station, he and his brother Mark were laying the foundations of a new exotic beef herd, while also being among the first to take up the challenge of farming deer.

Signs of change to the established practices of the New Zealand meat industry were starting to appear, while many of the people who would influence it over the next 25 years were beginning to make their name. Around the world, first the deep freeze and then the microwave oven would accelerate one of the most significant social changes impacting on all providers of food and services – the increase in women in the paid workforce.

The pivotal point for many of the various activities in the meat industry came in the middle to late 1980s as political, economic and social attitudes in New Zealand changed.

As if a Southern Oscillation had struck, conditions swung from the warm, wet, centralised, interventionist and maternal La Nina climate of the early seventies to the hard, dry, ruggedly individual, deregulated market El Nino environment of the nineties.

To take a rugby cliché, it was a game of two halves, and the rules were changed at half time.

The players remained the same: the Meat Board, the farmers, the meat processing companies and the exporters. But their roles and relationships underwent both evolution and revolution.

For the first half, farmers were playing with the wind at their backs on a field tilted to their advantage. The Meat Export Control Act of 1921-22 and subsequent amendments gave the Meat Board a central position of power and authority to ensure this was so. Underpinned by government, the farming sector felt wanted; its contribution to the country was valued. A good proportion of the Ministers of the Crown, particularly from the National Party, came from farming backgrounds and government policies reflected that. There was a commonality of interest between them and the elected members of the producer boards to further the farming cause.

Hawke's Bay was a major powerbase for both the meat industry and New Zealand. Duncan McIntyre, who went on to become Minister of Agriculture, farmed there as did Tom Atchison, Electoral Committee chairman in the mid-seventies, while John Falloon who also became Minister of Agriculture, came from the nearby north Wairarapa. Prominent Federated Farmers leader Peter Plummer was a longtime chairman of the Richmond Meat Company and the Meat Export Development Company (DEVCO), established to develop lamb sales to North America.

Canterbury was another centre of influence, linked closely to Hawke's Bay. Many of the sons of Hawke's Bay farmers had been educated at Christ's College. More links were established on the rugby field through the annual quadrangular tournament between Christ's College, Wanganui Collegiate, Wellington College and Nelson College, and cemented by marriage.

The Meat Board of the 1970s maintained a distinctive culture, with clear expectations about behaviour and personal style. Norman McRae raised eyebrows when he arrived at his first meeting in a leather coat, while Warren Martin provoked apoplexy by appearing in walk shorts. Non-farmer Gordon Dryden, added to the Board by the Kirk Labour Government, bucked the blue-stripe shirt and tweed suit trend with a blue suit and pink striped shirt.

Some traditional rituals – natural to those used to the fagging system of boarding schools like Christ's College – sat less and less comfortably with external appointees and newer Board members. Fred Dobbs, welcomed to "the most exclusive club in New Zealand" by Charles Hilgendorf, refused to take on the 'new boy' role of filling the silver jug with water for the Board's drinks, saying there was no such thing as a junior or senior member on any of the other boards he was associated with. Among other traditions he determinedly ignored was the call to bring back thigh-rolled Cuban cigars from any overseas trip, and he chose not to stay with all the other Board members at the James Cook Hotel where the media could easily keep in contact.

Sir John Ormond had set the standard of using the Board's bar at Massey House in Lambton Quay as a meeting place for opinion-formers of all kinds, and Hilgendorf carried on the tradition of thrashing out significant debate at pre-meeting sessions over a whisky bottle. Even the meals were set pieces, centred round 'Andy's chops' prepared by Greek resistance veteran Andy Andriotis. The measure of a man was the number of chops he could consume. Fellow Board members presented Charlie Hilgendorf, an 'eight-chop man' with a necklace of chop bones on his retirement.

Peter Plummer, chairman of Richmond and also chairman of Pacific Freezing Ltd from 1977.

Celebrating the Board's Golden Jubilee in March 1972. Official speeches at Wellington's Majestic Cabaret. Sir John Ormond at the microphone. From left: Frank Kitts, Mayor of Wellington; Lady Judith Ormond; Wool Board chairman Sir Jack Acland; Prime Minister John Marshall; Leader of the Opposition Norman Kirk; Mrs Marshall; D Sinclair, chairman of the Apple and Pear Marketing Board.

Overall, farming times were orderly and comfortable in the early 1970s. A freezing works was a familiar landmark and source of employment in most New Zealand communities, except the central North Island and the South Island's West Coast. The works were a bricks and mortar expression of one of the most powerful motivating forces in each farming area, the need to ensure access to killing space for stock, at a time to suit farmers. Many plants had originally been built by farmer co-operatives around the turn of the century. Most had been transferred into private ownership during the 1930s, but that did not diminish the desire for farmers to co-operatively own plants.

The meat industry was generally structured along broad functional lines with a degree of separation of the processing and the selling activities, while a diversity of ownership existed which largely reflected the pattern of trade. Four major overseas-owned processing and exporting companies concentrated on the lamb trade to the UK and on the supply of beef to North America. The British companies were Thomas Borthwick and Sons (A/asia), usually known as Borthwicks, with four plants, the Vestey-owned W & R Fletcher with four plants under various names, and trading under the Weddel brand, and the Co-operative Wholesale Society (CWS) with two plants. The US-based Swift & Co Ltd had shares in two plants. The overseas companies controlled some 30% of the meat processing facilities, but had a much greater percentage of the marketing through arrangements with New Zealand companies.

Several New Zealand groups such as the New Zealand Refrigerating Co Ltd (NZR), Canterbury Frozen Meat Co Ltd (CFM), R & W Hellaby Ltd and Southland Frozen Meat Ltd (SFM) had multi-plant operations, and there were a number of other New Zealand-owned single plant operators, some of which were later to add plants to their portfolios. The latter included Gear Meat Co Ltd, Gisborne Refrigerating Co Ltd (part owned by Vesteys), J C Hutton (NZ) Ltd, Nelson Freezing Co Ltd, South Otago Freezing Co Ltd (SOFCO), Waitaki Farmers Freezing Co Ltd and T H Walker & Sons Ltd. NZR and CFM jointly owned NCF Kaiapoi.

Gear, NZR, SFM and Waitaki were publicly listed companies. The only true farmer co-operative was Auckland Farmers' Freezing Company (AFFCO), which owned three plants, but Hawke's Bay Farmers' Meat Company (HBFMC), which owned the huge six-chain plant at Whakatu, was also very influential. The one-plant Alliance Freezing Company in the South Island, established with "co-operative ideals" had not yet made the transition to co-operative status.

Central to the relationship between farmers and the companies that processed and marketed their meat was the weekly schedule of prices offered to procure the various weights and grades of stock for slaughter. It was the most important communication, as it told them how much they could expect to receive net of all processing and freezing charges for each grade of stock; transport costs and Meat Board levies were extra.

Schedule prices were calculated on the basis of an estimate of the overseas returns less 'intervening charges' of killing and freezing, transport and distribution, plus financing. The major companies conferred each week on the state of the markets and the livestock situation to determine their schedules. The prices were offered nationally and based on average returns and average killing and freezing charges, with some regional variations in Hawke's Bay and Southland. As John Prendergast, who joined W & R Fletcher in 1979, explains: "Borthwicks and Fletchers used to set the schedule for the whole of New Zealand each Friday. They advised the Meat Board what the schedule was and the Board published it."

An important function for the Board was schedule monitoring, checking the prices being offered against trends in market returns reported from its overseas offices, and verifying that they represented fair returns to farmers. Averaging was one of the main ways of ensuring 'fair' treatment for farmers wherever they lived, so similar philosophies equalised internal costs such as transport.

Because of the pattern of trade, and perhaps because of tradition, many New Zealand companies did not take ownership of all the product they procured or processed; some of the procurement was done by stock and station agencies. New Zealand companies sold some of their own product but relied heavily on other exporters, using the overseas companies to supply the main outlets of lamb to the UK and beef to North America. In 1971, 110 businesses held a Meat Export Licence (MEL).

Most New Zealand companies would process stock for any outside clients prepared to pay. Overseas companies were included in those using this toll-processing service, but generally did not reciprocate. Ron Cushen, former general manager of SFM, recalled that his company was quite happy to own only 50-60% of the kill, "and most of that was off-loaded to Borthwicks and Vestey's".

Two farmer-owned marketing co-operatives had been set up specifically to market product in competition with the majors – Producer Meats Ltd (PML) and Primary Producers Co-operative Society (PPCS). Other farmer-owned enterprises such as Richmond and the stock and station agents also provided a selling service; a newcomer in 1971 was Cattle Services, the co-operative group that would evolve into Fortex.

The separation of the processing and marketing functions, such as it was, could in part be attributed to the 'open door' provisions of Section 34 of the Meat Act 1964. One of the most effective tools for keeping power in the hands of producers, this gave farmers flexibility and choice in the methods of selling their stock for processing and, because it obliged licensed exporters to "accept certain stock for slaughter", attempted to guarantee access to killing space. In this environment PML and PPCS could flourish despite not owning processing facilities. These co-operatives and the 'open door' policy provided farmers with a means of comparing marketing returns and of keeping the processing companies 'honest'.

Processing capacity requirements were assessed from the farmer viewpoint of not having to wait any more than a week or so to present stock for slaughter, and on the ability to cater for seasonal peaks, especially in the South Island. Individual plant capacity was measured in 'kill days loading' – the number of days it would take to process the stock available if the plant operated at peak capacity. Any increase in capacity was achieved more by adding chains to old plants than by starting from scratch.

The Meat Board worked to ensure the companies could process stock as required and, in concentrating on peak killing capacity, probably promoted overcapacity for the balance of the season and, by today's standards, inefficient use of capital. In addition, the Board carried out an annual survey to determine the volume of cold storage to ensure there was sufficient to handle the peak of the kill and hold it until it was marketed later in the season.

The 'open door' policy was a considerable bone of contention between the export slaughterhouse licensees and the various owners of stock for slaughter, some of whom were represented by the marketing co-operatives. These owners sought access to killing space and to exercise their 'right' to selling methods other than on schedule or on a per head basis to the freezing company.

A popular alternative was the 'owner's account' arrangement which entitled any farmer to export 'small parcels' of product, sometimes only a few hundred carcasses. Most chose to ship lamb direct to the UK market. To facilitate owner's account, all the trading banks and stock and station agencies held export licences. Payments, deposited in accounts in the UK, could later be used to finance the new car only available with overseas funds or highly prized import licences.

Other selling alternatives included sale through the pools provided by the marketing co-operatives, freezing company pools and the freezing company 'nominated vessel' scheme.

The 'owner's account' method of sale was virtually eliminated by the introduction of a 'small parcels' surcharge in freight rates in the early 1970s. The main alternative to the freezing company schedule then became the various company pools. Farmers could nominate the pools and receive an advance payment based on the schedule, and then bear some of the market risk with the prospect of an end-of-season payout if the market returned a surplus above the schedule payout.

The fact that the product was in a pool did not necessarily mean that it was treated any differently in a marketing sense. The pool results could be manipulated to some extent and the companies showed a remarkable reluctance to seek recompense from the farmer if the market turned against them and pool returns were less than the schedule advance. When the Board's schedule monitoring suggested the prices offered were too low, it would indicate this to the

Meat companies and shipping companies advertised their services regularly in the early editions of the Meat Producer.

companies, and if they maintained the 'low' prices the Board could advise farmers to take one of the pool options.

Much of the uncertainty was taken out of the naturally risky business of farming. It was riding the tide of expansion, promoted by the 1963 Agricultural Production Conference, which targeted 100 million stock units by 1980. Land development loans at concessionary interest rates and other supports, such as subsidies on the price and cost of fertiliser, fuelled the growth, against an exchange rate so constant only economists gave it a thought.

For sheep farmers, apart from the occasional blip in the UK lamb market that the Meat Board would sort out, the grass grew guaranteed profitability. Wool prices fluctuated but almost as if synchronised to move up when meat prices were down. Beef farmers had experienced a 'golden decade' of demand-driven increase in trade through the 1960s, and had watched in delighted amazement as prices for their product in the US soared to dizzying heights.

Those in power understood the unique dynamics of this $500 million business which contributed almost 50% of total merchandise trade receipts. Decision-makers made sure the farmers' back pockets were full. The Prime Minister and Cabinet kept a close eye on the weekly schedule. The banks also recognised the significance of the industry and its distinctly seasonal demands for financing on a scale that called for syndicates to satisfy it. Farmers demanded payment for the stock they supplied within two weeks, while returns from overseas markets could take up to six months.

All the influential players were aware of the farmers' concerns – what happened to the meat when it reached the market; their dismay at the decreasing proportion of the final wholesale price that found its way back to them through the schedule; and their unquenchable suspicions about 'weak selling' – that New Zealand exporters were cutting each others' throats by lowering prices instead of cutting out other competitor countries.

The Board's mission was to improve returns to producers, and it kept a close eye on farmer financial health both behind and beyond the farm gate. It watched market prices through its network of overseas offices. The Meat and Wool Boards' Economic Service's regular survey kept its finger on the farming pulse, and gave independent advice on the financial impacts of price and cost changes. At a time when around 80% of sheepmeat was exported to the UK, it

Mervyn Barnett, indefatigable advocate for the farmer.

was possible, by deducting the intervening charges such as killing and freezing (K & F) costs, freight, insurance and distribution, to calculate what percentage farmers received of the wholesale price paid at London's Smithfield Market. As the 1970s began, it was up to 58%.

The Board also collated the K & F charges published by each meat company, and commented on any changes considered to be out of line. Fuelled by inflation and annual union demands, K & F charges tended to rise inexorably.

The Meat Export Control Act gave the Meat Board powers regarding licensing of exporters with special provisions for "development markets" and controls over the grading, shipping, marketing and promotion of meat for export. Its central role was typified by the fact that the shipping rates set by the Meat and Dairy Boards established the rates for all New Zealand exports, and had an influence on inward freight costs as well.

When lamb schedule prices dropped the Meat Board could step in to bolster returns. Similarly, when the US beef quotations plunged, Meat Board guarantees restored confidence. Making such largesse possible was the $100 million Meat Industry Reserve Account (MIRA), the legacy of the wartime UK Bulk Purchase agreement. It was designated for investment "for the benefit of the industry" and to underpin the rarely-used price support scheme authorised by the Meat Export Prices Act of 1955, and administered by the Meat Export Prices Committee (MEPC). Day-to-day funding for Board activities came from the levy collected on stock at time of slaughter.

The nine-member Board was adept at listening to its farmer constituents. But its direct pipeline to producer concerns came through the 26-man Electoral Committee which annually elected two Board members. Through the rigorous inquisition of each candidate, and the power of hiring and firing, the Electoral Committee could strike fear into Board members. Another conduit was the Meat & Wool Section of Federated Farmers. As well as regular formal meetings between the Board and the Meat & Wool executive, there was considerable overlap with the membership of the Electoral Committee.

Graeme Lowe, innovator and persistent agitator for deregulation.

A vast harness of regulations restrained the naturally unruly players on the processing side of the New Zealand meat industry. The Meat Act of 1964 virtually prescribed what they could and could not do. The Act set out the conditions for the slaughtering, inspection and export of meat in accordance with accepted health and hygiene practices under the auspices of the Minister of Agriculture and his department.

Getting a processing licence was almost like being selected for the All Blacks – it was hard to get in and even harder to get out – and those who joined the chosen immediately strove to keep their group exclusive. Any newcomer had to prove economic justification and downplay the possible effect on the performance of the other players before they could win a place on the paddock. Once they were on the playing field with a licence it was hard to depose them.

Before any action could be taken on a variety of issues, the Board had to be consulted. Innovators like John Neilson of Waitaki and Graeme Lowe of Dawn Meats, and the southern battler Alan Gilkison of SFM saw it as particularly invidious that the Board's consent was needed for any change of ownership of a company or for the building or extension of plants. These regulations ensured there had only been three successful applications to build new processing plants in the 50 years prior to 1972.

The majority of New Zealand's meat was commodity product shipped in bulk to the major markets – frozen carcass lamb to the UK, boneless beef to the US for the manufacture of ground beef for the hamburger trade and carcass mutton to Japan for 'ham' production. Little sheepmeat was further processed. The industry maintained a significant infrastructure of depots and cold stores for the UK lamb trade. The US trade, almost entirely boxed manufacturing beef, was much more arm's length, with importers playing the predominant role.

Export diversification was beginning to take off. The Lamb Market Diversification Scheme, introduced along with DEVCO in the sixties, was encouraging the development of sales to markets outside the UK. Exporters like Eric Cammell of AFFCO and the independents Ces Stevens, Ross Finlayson of Amalgamated Marketing, and Eric Miller of Dalgetys, were travelling to find new markets.

The Meat Board made a point of being the first to meet with any newly appointed Minister of Agriculture and to be among the first to congratulate the Prime Minister following an election. It provided an opportunity to remind the politicians about the issues of importance to the industry, to sort out the rules and their interpretation.

With some exceptions, meat companies did not enjoy such a direct entrée to the corridors of power. Some like Neville Thompson of AFFCO, Roger Golding of W & R Fletcher, Laurie Cameron of Gear and Peter Norman of Borthwicks, were adept at lobbying their own causes. Most based in Wellington, they were frequent attenders at the exclusive watering hole that was the Meat Board's Massey House members' lounge.

Representation of other industry players was more fragmented. The focus of the New Zealand Freezing Companies' Associations (NIFCA for the North Island and SIFCA for the South Island) was industrial relations, a consuming concern at a time when the meat industry outstripped all others in days lost due to strikes.

The larger meat processing and exporting companies did not have a separate forum for export-related matters until the formation of the Meat Exporters Council (MEC) in 1972. However the smaller exporters had the well-established forum of the Independent Meat Exporters' Association (IMEA).

Economic conditions, the strategic importance of the industry and collective bargaining strength gave the meat industry unions an effective lever in negotiations for better wages and conditions. With 30,000 workers the meat industry was one of the biggest employers. Its seasonal nature and the pressure from farmers to get their stock killed when they were ready or before the feed ran out meant that industrial action could be programmed for when the companies were most vulnerable. The ploy was usually very effective but if there was a deadlock the Minister of Labour would be on hand to jawbone the participants towards a solution.

The unions were also adept at leapfrogging conditions from one plant to the next, on the soundly based presumption that the companies would tend not to support one another by refusing stock that may have been destined for a rival who happened to have a strike.

The burden of increasing inflation and the escalating costs of maintaining the foreign exchange and import controls fell mainly on the export sector. The primary sector was the driving force of the economy. This justified a whole range of assistance and incentive measures to boost output and overseas earnings on the misguided assumption that New Zealand could sell anything that was produced. The mindset was quantity, rather than quality.

High inflation made it possible to recoup even loony land price payments, and earn a good living on a hill country family farm of 400 hectares with some 2500 stock units. It was a sheep numbers game… the head count was climbing from a low of 55 million, though productivity measures were modest. More production came from running more sheep per hectare rather than improving performance of the flock. There were 3.5 million beef cattle, but beef was less important politically.

As in rugby, New Zealand's achievements in meat exporting belied its size, and some of the rules set on the other side of the world served to baffle and frustrate the most passionate players.

A double dose of challenging bureaucracy was making its impact as the 1970s began. The industry, already absorbing the impact of new US meat inspection requirements, then had to meet the often contradictory interpretations of the veterinary regulations of the European Economic Community (the EEC, later to be the EC) as Britain's membership became a reality.

The US Meat Import Law carried the threat of an annual restriction on beef imports and the EC's Common Agricultural Policy clearly had the potential to impose restrictions on New Zealand lamb.

Sheep numbers began to climb, and more and more land was pressed into use for farming, as the subsidies built up over the 1970s.

These threats forced new relationships and attitudes to develop between the key players, particularly the Board and the Meat Exporters Council. And although the system changed with the election of the Labour Government in 1972, which emptied the Cabinet of farmers, it ironically brought to power in Colin Moyle an agriculture minister who did work the land and was to prove enduringly popular with the farming community.

It might seem that the Board and Federated Farmers, both representing producers, would be natural allies against the industry representatives of Freezing Companies' Association, the Meat Exporters' Council and the Independent Meat Exporters Association. But the reality of relationships was much more complex and combative.

And stringing the whole industry together was the network of contacts established and maintained at the meat industry equivalent of after-match functions, when the players replayed the games or re-organised the style of play. These connections enabled the industry to function even when there were serious and public disagreements or debates over issues that would otherwise stifle activities. Whisky served as a useful lubricant for the settlement of many arguments or disputes.

As well as the school connections, Lincoln College was a powerful link. Among others who attended the then agricultural college, and were already active in the meat industry, were Athol Hutton, of Hawke's Bay Farmers' Cooperative, John Buxton of Richmond, Ian Jenkinson at Hellaby's, Graeme Thompson of Cattle Services, and Allan Frazer and Mick Calder who worked for the Board. Former Lincoln lecturer Neil Taylor had just been enticed up to Wellington to join the Meat and Wool Board's Economic Service. There was a sprinkling of Lincoln old boys (but no girls) through the public service including Treasury, MAF and the Lands and Survey Department, which also helped when change was needed.

Federated Farmers formed another significant group. Progress through its structures – usually at a prescribed pace – was a step in a ladder that often also included membership of the Electoral Committee and the Board. At a time of compulsory military training, the army was another significant meeting place – people like David Frith and Robbie Burnside met this way.

Only John Buxton reached the exalted status of an All Black. But in an era where rugby reigned supreme, it was fitting that the 1970s were kicked off with a solo try scored for the farmers by Sir John Ormond.

The Shadow of the Sphinx
1971-72

"It is not for me to say what the Board could or should do next season or in any of the years ahead; whether it will again offer a schedule of its own to lift prices or whether it intervenes in any other way. But I do suggest that... the Board will not hesitate to eliminate any of the damaging elements from the markets if it is required, and it will not hesitate to inject itself on behalf of the producers further into the marketing scene if that is what is needed." Sir John Ormond, retirement speech, March 1972.

Even as he was preparing to retire from the Board, Sir John Ormond was still exerting his not inconsiderable influence on the industry.

John Ormond was an astute farmer politician who was given to making decisive moves if he considered that the situation called for it and it was in the best interests of the producers. A forceful personality with many influential contacts around the world, he acted as an executive chairman of the Board he had led since 1951, and determined many of its strategic moves.

Peter Norman, at the time general manager of Borthwicks, recalls: "He often said, 'Don't bother me with details, Peter, my mind's made up' – he instinctively knew what was the right thing to do for the New Zealand farmer. He didn't care how it was worked out – somebody, Fechney, or Frazer or de Gruchy (Board executives) would do that. He had this amazing ability to see through a problem and do something about it from the farmer perspective." As a result a large part of the chief executive's job was to sort out the details after John Ormond had departed for Hawke's Bay, often chauffeured by Andy Andriotis.

Ormond was the leading light in moving the Board to a position where it could use its powers to buy and sell meat for export from New Zealand. One of his last actions, instigating the urgent passing of legislation which added the acquisition of product to the Board's existing statutory powers, was to have lasting effect.

On the eve of Sir John Ormond's retirement the Board announced that, as a result of the low opening schedules advised by the companies, it would offer its own schedule of prices at which it would buy lamb on the open market. In essence this was a move which, in combination with various other changes that had taken place over the previous decade, would primarily focus the Board's activities on marketing through to 1985 and beyond.

In October 1971 the meat processing companies had followed up their advance warnings about the effects of cost inflation and an expected sluggish market for lamb in the UK, and announced opening schedules for export lamb the Board considered were too low.

The prices announced by the companies would cut returns to some farmers by as much as a half: $3.67 for meat and pelt from a prime 30lb (13.5kg) lamb in the South Island or $4.20 in the North Island. These were a far cry from the previous year's $6.81 for a similar grade.

The lifelong friendship between Sir John Ormond and Mr Denzo Ito of Itoham, was to prove crucial in the development of New Zealand exports to Japan. Pictured from left, Charles Hilgendorf, Denzo Ito and Sir John Ormond in the old Wellington Club. Mr Ito was the first foreigner to be honoured by the Queen with an OBE for service to New Zealand's interests in Japan. Sir John Ormond was instrumental in the awarding of the honour.

John Ormond and the other members of the Board took the view that the prices were below acceptable levels for producers to maintain production and that companies were taking an unduly pessimistic view of the state of the market. The Board decided to offer farmers a price of $4.50 per head for a 30lb prime export lamb and appropriate prices for other grades, unless the companies increased their schedules. This was the least that farmers needed to receive for a prime lamb to make their enterprises viable.

The low prices offered by the companies were attributed to a combination of external and internal factors, some of which they had signalled as likely to lead to a lowering of the schedule. The outlook in the major UK market was reported to be bleak as stocks of imported lamb had risen to 43,000 tons at the beginning of October 1971, or some 18,000 tons above the level then considered 'normal'. Arrivals of New Zealand lamb had been heavy in the late summer of 1971 and were competing with increased supplies of domestic and Irish lamb.

A 28% increase in the freight rate for refrigerated cargoes to the UK had been announced. Added to that was internal New Zealand inflation that gave rise to increases in killing and freezing charges of the order of 35- 40%.

Finally, there was the levy – or as Sir John Ormond bluntly put it, the tax – newly imposed on lamb by the UK as it made the transition towards EC membership. The levy had started in July 1971 at £9.33 per ton and was due to reach £28 per ton in July 1972 and eventually match the EC's Common Customs Tariff of 20%. Heartfelt argument by New Zealand Agriculture Minister Doug Carter led to a lower starting rate than originally intended. Sir John Ormond saw it as yet another cost for the producer – "getting on for 90 cents a lamb unless the British consumer is prepared to pay the extra".

The decision of the Board to announce its own schedule and purchase lamb for export was not part of a formal management plan. It was more a piece of Ormond's spur-of-the-moment acuity. His steadfast view was that the Board's purpose was "to control the whole of the exported meat of New Zealand so that it may yield the highest net return to the producer".

Peter Norman has written in his book *The Meat in the Sandwich* that "Ormond demanded that we pay at least $5 per lamb or the Meat Producers Board would assume ownership of the stock. We argued that $5 was not justified by the market indications and that we did not believe he had the authority to assume ownership.

"Ormond's reply was that if he did not have the authority he would get it. And he did – that same afternoon from the then National Government… This showed the power that John Ormond, the Meat Producers Board and thus the farmers had over a National Government."

The change in legislation went through in very short order. Kemp Stone, the Board's solicitor at the time, recalls that Ormond in particular, but also other Board members and the chief executive Harry Douglas, kept in very close contact with the Minister of Agriculture, Doug Carter, and other senior ministers.

The Board's position was summarised in a paper tabled at a special meet-

"I have always been impressed by your success in playing the sphinx – until you were ready to play your cards. You did not hesitate to take the dramatic steps to meet new problems head-on, with dynamic and often unprecedented measures. They usually worked and New Zealand's meat producers are indebted to you for your leadership through all these years." George Bronz, the Board's Washington lawyer, quoted in In the Chair *by P.S. Tait. The sphinx himself – Sir John Ormond – pictured with Minister of Finance Robert Muldoon.*

New Zealand High Commissioner Doug Carter, discussing the finer points of carving lamb with Gill Service, who conducted a number of promotions for New Zealand lamb during the early 1970s.

ing on 19 October 1971, which reviewed the fact that while the Meat Export Control Act gave the Board wide statutory powers these did not extend to taking ownership of meat except in very prescribed situations such as development markets.

"The legislation now requested from Government will enable the Board to acquire ownership of meat derived from sheep intended for sale in any export market, traditional or undeveloped. The power to acquire other types of meat will still be reserved only for undeveloped markets." The aim was to press the Government to give urgency to the passing of the legislation.

In vintage Ormond style, the request for urgency was put in person. Bruce Ryan, then deputy chairman of the Board, recalls: "Sir John and I went to Parliament Buildings to meet (Prime Minister) John Marshall and (deputy Prime Minister) Brian Talboys along with his private secretary, Harold Hewitt.

"John had this tremendous ability to talk what we called Hawke's Bay-ese. He would hum and ha, he was hard to follow and nobody would know what he was talking about. If someone asked him a question he would go into this Hawke's Bay language – 'Yes, of course, humph, you know, humph, ha, mumble…'

"He said: 'Of course, you know Prime Minister we need this legislation, for the benefit of the New Zealand meat industry and trade,' using his Hawkes Bay-ese. Marshall nodded and agreed saying, 'Yes Sir John, of course Sir John'. And John Ormond went on 'You know that we need it in a bit of a hurry, it's gone on for a while'.

Then straight after the meeting Harold Hewitt asked Ryan to return to Parliament without Ormond. "So I went back up and John Marshall said to me, 'Now Mr Ryan, could you please tell Brian and me what we have agreed to?'"

In the course of just two weeks, the necessary changes were pushed through Parliament.

The Board did not make these moves without reference to other parties. During the eight weeks from when the schedules were first announced in mid October, to mid December, there were seven full meetings of the Board and numerous consultations and negotiations. The Board met with members of the Government, with Sir William Dunlop and other executive committee members of Federated Farmers, and the Electoral Committee, chaired by Bruce Dryden, with meat processing companies and with meat exporters, separately and through their representative organisations.

Not only did they have to decide what to do about the lamb schedule; as the 1972 annual report notes, they also had to consider whether to make use of the Meat Industry Reserve Account (MIRA) and whether to call on government assistance "to restore confidence among sheep farmers".

On this latter point it reached agreement with the Government to pay $15 million from MIRA towards the Government's Stock Retention Incentive Scheme on condition that the Government contributed on a two-to-one basis – $30 million.

The incentive scheme aimed to pay farmers up to $1 a head for sheep held on their farms at 30 June 1972 as a means of encouraging expansion in stock numbers. The quid pro quo was an undertaking by the Government to meet two-thirds of any loss that might be incurred by the Board in its lamb trading activities; there was no apparent consideration of the possibility that the Board might make a surplus on trading.

The objectives of the Board were stated as: to get more money as quickly as possible to the farmer; to avoid as far as possible any disruption of the market; and to encourage exporters to raise their prices as soon as possible so that they, rather than the Board, would become the purchasers of lamb. The Board aimed to avoid dislocating established methods of trading.

This was not necessarily the view of others. In *The Keys to Prosperity* Clive Lind reports that Alan Gilkison, the chairman of Southland Frozen Meat, considered the situation in late 1971 had provided John Ormond "with the ammunition to get legislation passed which, in effect, creates the Meat Board as a trading organisation", adding "Sir John had been angling for such recognition for some years".

Peter Norman, general manager of Thomas Borthwick and Sons (A/asia) until 1982, chaired both the MEC and FCA at key times.

Peter Norman pointed out that the companies were jealous of their ownership and marketing role. In his view there was continual pressure from some farmers for the Board to get into trading and equal or greater pressure from the 'trade' to keep them out. "Not only did some farmers want a trading role for the Meat Producers Board, but some of their staff were also keen to see this."

Over the years the Board had made several moves relating to the market development and marketing of meat which gave it greater powers of intervention and control of these activities. But it is a matter of opinion whether the 1971 intervention was a planned step as part of a formal or even informal Board strategy, a natural progression of actions taken in the "best interests of the sheep and beef producers", or just a pragmatic move brought on by the political and economic circumstances of the time.

By the early 1970s the Board was using its powers to influence the marketing of New Zealand's meat by several different methods without it taking on any specific trading role. The system had evolved so that the processing and exporting companies worked under the overall direction of the Board, which acted for the benefit of the producer. In the Board's view, the producer had the benefit of the competition for his stock, but also had the chance to influence the sale of his meat through to the markets on the other side of the world. It was a facet of the industry that was to cause considerable debate 20 years later.

In his retirement speech in March 1972 John Ormond himself listed a series of stepping stones by which "the Board seems to have moved inevitably towards marketing involvement". His list included the actions by the Board soon after it was established in 1922 to regulate meat shipments, introducing a grading system and initiating a programme of promotion. He also referred to the scheme to diversify sales away from the UK, and the Board's promotion activities in support of the development of mutton sales to Japan and beef sales to the US.

He commented that over the years the Board had been involved in most of the elements that contributed to marketing. The decision by the Board to become an owner of product and market it through agents could be seen as a culmination of that.

So perhaps the Board's intervention was part of a longer-term strategy. However, circumstances and other actions were to take the Board further than John Ormond was indicating or perhaps contemplating at his retirement.

Meanwhile, it was clear that the companies were anxious to keep the Board out of marketing if at all possible.

The earlier moves to influence the marketing activities of the companies, other than the original decisions on shipping and grading, had included the establishment of the Meat Export Development Company (Devco) in 1960. This was only possible after the Board promoted a change in legislation (the Meat Export Control Amendment Act 1959 with some minor adjustments in 1960 and 1962) which enabled the Board to declare a region or country to be a "development market" on the grounds that "no market or no substantial market for New Zealand meat or for a particular class of that meat exists".

The development market clause in the legislation was used again in the early 1970s to declare first Peru (September, 1971), then Chile (February, 1972), Puerto Rico and Hawaii (May, 1972) as development markets. The Board's rationale for the announcement regarding Peru and Chile was principally to counter a single state buying organisation situation where any competitive pricing activity among New Zealand sellers tended to depress prices.

Exporters, however, interpreted it as a move by the Board to take up marketing activities more properly managed by established meat exporters. Ross Finlayson, then a member of the Independent Meat Exporters' Association (IMEA), recalls: "The industry was totally frustrated with the activities of the Board and Government. We felt we had to get together and stop the Board having the right to assume ownership of product."

In 1972 the IMEA, the major companies, and the producer marketing co-operatives set up their own marketing-focussed forum, the Meat Exporters' Council (MEC). John Buxton recalls that Bill Leonard of Producer Meats Ltd – headed at the time by David Ormond, brother of Sir John – was

Three long-serving executives of the New Zealand meat industry and active FCA members were farewelled on their retirement in 1975. From left are: FCA chairman John Fulton, of CFM, and the retiring executives, Darcy Freeman of Borthwicks, Keown (Bill) Cleland from NZR, and Jack Scandrett of SFM.

instrumental in setting up the MEC, and was its first chairman. He saw the need to have an industry body with a marketing focus, and in fact gained the support of Sir John Ormond "provided PPCS and PML were included".

One of the first actions of the MEC was to recommend suitable exporters to act as the Board's agents in Chile and Peru. As a result, the Board agreed to being the prime contractor in these single buyer markets, delegating its authority by the appointment of exporters as agents. Dalgetys were appointed as the agent for sales to Peru and Amalgamated Marketing for Chile. In the case of Hawaii and Puerto Rico, however, the Board decided not to restrict the market to any particular exporter.

Market diversification was another area of potential tension, in this case impacting particularly on the overseas companies which had been set up to supply meat to the UK. It became increasingly urgent to spread the market risk to reduce the effects of the restrictions which would be imposed when, rather than if, the UK joined the EC.

Warren Martin, producer representative from 1972-78, was an enthusiast for the increased use of air freight.

By the early 1970s the target under the Lamb Market Diversification Scheme, which encouraged exports away from the UK, was 22% . The penalty rate was set at 2.5 cents per pound and there was a bonus of 0.25 cents per pound for exceeding the target.

The scheme started the decline in influence of the British companies, particularly the Co-operative Wholesale Society (CWS). "Diversification practically killed them," Bruce Ryan says.

The British companies had bought plant in New Zealand to get access to stock to supply their chains of shops in the UK, and they did not want to have to supply other markets. But Borthwicks and Vesteys, which were close to the Board, soon took a more realistic approach. "To be in the trade, they had to take part in the whole New Zealand trade," says Ryan.

Peter Norman recounts that in the early stages of the scheme at least, companies tended to discount prices to diversification markets to meet the target and avoid paying the penalty that was greater than the level of the discount. "We merely dropped our price to say, Iraq, to 3 cents below what we were selling in England. You could sell into Iraq, you didn't have to pay the penalty, so you were no worse off… We got our diversionary percentage, which saved us from having to pay the fine. But it was crazy." However he does concede that it did get exporters to focus on other markets. "I suppose it got people into Jordan and Iraq."

There was also a tendency to load product on to DEVCO to meet the diversification targets. Sales to DEVCO were diversification sales and the Board guaranteed its funding, so market development plans sometimes took second place.

During November 1971 most of the principles of the Board's intervention and lamb marketing operation were decided with some assistance from the companies. The Board did not have any selling organisation in place and none of the staff had any real experience in buying and selling operations. A common criticism was the Board's staff "had never sold a pound of sausages, let alone a pound of meat in their lives".

The Board took advice from the exporters and processors and decided to appoint the companies as agents for the procurement of stock. It also de-

cided that the companies could continue to operate in the normal way; they could offer a meat schedule to match or exceed the Board's prices and at the time of kill they could decide if and what lambs they would take at those prices; any they did not buy would become the property of the Board.

The Board's price of $4.50 for a PM lamb was made up of a bare meat schedule price of 12.4c per lb (27.3c a kg) at the nearest port works (a return of $3.72 for the meat), plus a skin value estimated at 78c for a 1lb (half kg) wool pull. It was only offering to buy the carcass meat and left the companies the wool and pelt.

Some companies did subsequently match the Board's schedule but many did not, at least until later in the season. In the event, wool and pelt prices increased in the first few months so that the returns producers received were over $5.20 for a prime lamb even with the Board's meat schedule.

Initially, if they were prepared to match the Board's schedule, the companies had the pick of the lambs they thought they could sell, so as a result of its altruism, the Board was left with those grades considered less marketable. Later the arrangement was tightened up so that in any one week the exporter could take all or none of a particular grade of lambs, rather than taking their pick.

Charles Hilgendorf, as chairman of the Board's marketing committee, put a positive spin on this rather benign approach to intervention when he told the Electoral Committee in March 1972: "While this arrangement reduced the Board's chances of making a profit on the sale of its lambs, it left an opportunity for the exporters to raise the schedule price for individual grades above the basic level set by the Board. As a result the producer benefits even if the Board loses the chance of making a profit."

The Board appointed 26 agents to sell the lamb on its behalf mainly to the UK. The agents were paid a commission at rates set according to the point of sale. The commission rates were varied after discussion with the MEC. The aim was to encourage the agents to exercise more control over the flow of lambs onto the market in the UK – an early example of the

Board's concern to develop an orderly marketing arrangement.

Retailers were less than enthusiastic about the prospect of increased Board involvement in Britain, as the *Meat Producer* reported: "Meat retailers in Britain have come out strongly opposed to the Board doing its own marketing." Some suggested the Board, working in the interests of producers but not customers, wanted to rig the market – something "particularly easy to achieve with a frozen product" – an interesting comment in itself.

Subsequently though, the French market opened for British and Irish lamb supplies and this brought some easing of trading conditions and higher prices in the UK. Alliance general manager Ted Stanley, quoted in *A Cut Above* by Clive Lind, was still pessimistic when he reported to shareholders in December 1971. "The plain fact of the matter is that our internal and overseas costs, plus the UK lamb levy, and the 22% diversification penalty, have caused the total cost of the operation to rise at a far greater rate than the selling price, and this spells trouble."

The Board purchased 12.25 million lambs or some 48% of the total export kill with the majority of them coming from the South Island where exporters' prices did not rise above the Board's schedule as rapidly as they did in the North Island. Initial sales through the Board's agents resulted in small losses in the first three months of operation but later there was an improvement in prices on the UK market. The rise started early in the new year but took off in April/May when a dock strike over the de-stuffing of containers limited the volume of imported meat released to the market. Also, a decision by the European Commission to suspend duties on beef imports into the six founder members of the EC, as a means of lowering prices to consumers, caused a rush on UK beef supplies. The sharp increase in UK prices had a domino effect and there was concern that there might be buyer resistance in markets such as North America.

The improvement in market circumstances led to the Board recording a profit of some $8.5 million on its trading activities.

The Board claimed that making a profit was never a specific aim of the operation; it had been prepared to risk making a loss as demonstrated by the arrangements made with the Government at the start of the exercise. Under that arrangement the Government had agreed to cover two-thirds of any loss, so it was entitled to the same proportion of the profit. However, it was eventually agreed that the whole of the surplus would go into a separate 'Meat Marketing Research and Development Account'.

Funds in the account were to be used to underwrite any future deficits arising from Board intervention in marketing, or losses incurred in any other marketing operations by the Board where it was required to act as an intermediary in sales (development markets) and to finance research and development work – but not promotion.

The Board's intervention did more than make a profit. It provided a much closer insight into the strengths and weaknesses of the marketing system, and caused the Board to look at the adequacy of the minimum price support scheme and the level of reserves required to fund any future support operations. Both of these issues were the subjects of considerable investigation in the following 18 months.

Whetu Tirikatene-Sullivan Minister of Tourism, conferring with Charlie Hilgendorf at the dinner for the winner of the Board's 1973 'Chef to Europe' competition. John Batts, head chef of the Hermitage Mount Cook won with Lamb Aorangi. The competition was an early initiative to encourage chefs to make greater use of New Zealand beef and lamb in menus. The prize was an all-inclusive trip to Europe – in conjunction with Qantas.

Costs v Efficiencies
1972-75

"I thought this is the sensible way. We're facing all this expenditure, we're each going to want to be in every market, we've got old freezing works, we'll rationalise the bloody things... Neilson and I used the term 'rationalisation' of the industry, and we would have had a marketing arm and a processing arm, but we wouldn't have maintained all of the works."
John Drayton.

Virtually everything in the meat industry goes in cycles, including views on plant ownership and the need for rationalisation. Circumstances, people or driving forces may vary, but proposals for rectifying currently perceived problems are invariably similar. The common view expressed over the years is that the meat industry in New Zealand would mature and benefit from a concentration of ownership with fewer, bigger companies processing and marketing the bulk of the product. The model would then also provide for a reasonable number of boutique processors and/or niche marketers to sustain an element of competition and ensure that the big operators stayed honest.

Since the early seventies such views on restructuring or changing industry ownership as a means of improving efficiency in the processing and distribution chain have been advanced in one form or another at least five times, which suggests an average cycle of about five years.

In each of the circumstances, and despite its changing role, the Board was involved or exerted its influence. Its expressed aim was to achieve two broad objectives. First, a more rational, cost-efficient and competitive processing sector that gave producers a choice of selling options for their stock. A corollary was the economies of scale to be derived from larger works or groupings of works, although in time this idea would be the undoing of some companies.

While the Board called for a more competitive processing sector it also paid homage to the stringent conditions of the 1964 Meat Act that required prospective operators to provide "economic justification" for any new plant. Its urgings for competition were therefore directed at improvements in productivity and cost efficiencies rather than more competitors per se.

This aim for competitive processing efficiency was coupled with the Board's second objective of a co-ordinated or orderly marketing system in major markets to enable the exporting companies to capture more of the value of New Zealand meat and return it to New Zealand producers. It was a view also expressed by a number of other industry participants over the years. In an echo of the paradox that 'all farmers are capitalists behind the farm gate, and communists outside it', the Board promoted a strange dichotomy which required that companies should compete at home, but co-operate abroad.

John Drayton of CFM, who became its general manager in 1981. Later he managed Ngauranga Meat Processors.

Intervention was never regarded or claimed as a primary function of the Board during the 1970s, but it was prepared to step in if the circumstances warranted. Even so, Board members still supported and promoted the view that private enterprise was the best system for the industry, but with some measure of control exercised by the Board.

'Controlled private enterprise' became the theme, a concept in keeping with the philosophical stance of the new chairman Charles Hilgendorf.

Charles Hilgendorf took over in 1972. He was a more academic character than John Ormond, with an interest in cathedral architecture, but still very much a farmer politician. He had been a guide at Mount Cook in his early years, but for a former mountaineer was surprisingly clumsy on his feet. On more than one occasion he stumbled on steps and kerbstones and fell headlong, although he was equally agile in getting to his feet again and professing that he had come to no harm, despite occasional evidence to the contrary.

He had an amazing ability to mangle a written speech but when he spoke off the cuff was intelligent and intelligible. Gordon Dryden, who was appointed to the Board by the Labour Government in 1972 – the first non-farmer to any producer board – reckons, "Charlie Hilgendorf was the best democratic chairman I have ever met or seen in action. As a public speaker he didn't rate, but as a consensus chairman – brilliant. The Board very seldom put anything to the vote. Members would discuss each issue, then Charlie would sum up, 'it seems we generally agree...' If there was a major difference of opinion, he'd end by saying, 'I think we should do a bit more thinking about that'. And the issues would generally be resolved at drinks after that day's Board session or over dinner. As a result we didn't lock ourselves into factions or dogmatic positions."

In his address to the Electoral Committee in August 1972, reported in the *Meat Producer* of September 1972, Charles Hilgendorf took up the rationalisation theme. "The Board has no doubt that the path to efficiency lies through rationalisation that pulls some of the New Zealand companies into bigger units, although we do recognise that there cannot be a universal set of arbitrary rules for mergers."

He said there was a place for some smaller companies with special abilities or expertise. "It is in their overseas operation where the disadvantage of their smallness is most obvious. Too often they merely sell meat and do not market it at all. Too often they sell it in the UK on a consignment basis, which is probably the worst of all methods of marketing." He went on to say: "I am not one who sees no place for small enterprise; after all the corner store still survives in competition with the supermarket. All I am saying is that there is not room for 13 corner stores in this corner of the Pacific."

However, the processing industry still suffered from fragmentation and duplication and the producer was expected to "pay the premium for inefficiency". Until New Zealand companies recognise that "marketing strength can only be gained through unity", the Board, representing the producers, would not "stand by and see opportunities lost".

Gordon Dryden is pictured with Vatili Tora, assistant manager of the Trade Winds Hotel in Suva, during a joint Board/MEC promotional trip to Fiji and Tahiti. At the time Fiji was the eight largest market for New Zealand lamb. Tahiti, an important market for top quality table beef, air-freighted about half the total meat from New Zealand.

Earlier Hilgendorf had flown the kite of total producer control as an alternative to the existing complex structure. Speaking to the annual conference of the Meat & Wool Section of Auckland Federated Farmers he suggested that total producer control would mean co-operative ownership of all freezing works and a central marketing body with responsibility for marketing all meat and by-products both overseas and on the domestic market. In other words, the dairy industry model.

Personally, Charles Hilgendorf favoured more freedom, saying "the economy functions best in a basically private enterprise and competitive framework (but)… there have to be safeguards to protect both producers and consumers." He believed in producer control, but ownership of all the product was not the only way to achieve it. Monopoly control gave no yardstick for quality.

On the other hand, he said, while there had been some enterprising competition in the search for new markets, too many exporters were operating and there was some very poor marketing.

There was general disquiet about the dominance of the overseas companies in the trade and some Board reluctance to recommend approval to the Minister of Agriculture when they wanted to acquire shares in or build new meat processing facilities. The concern was also reflected in financial reporting. The New Zealand-owned companies were not required to fully disclose their accounts, particularly the amount of their taxes. It was a provision ostensibly designed to give them some protection from the overseas companies.

Peter Norman says: "I think that the 1922 Act establishing the Meat Board was largely brought into being because of concern amongst New Zealand meat companies, and presumably the Government, spurred on by farmers, that the British and Americans would gain such a strong foothold that they'd run the whole show." They had still managed to get a fair footing on the conductor's podium. Besides, a number of New Zealand companies preferred to use overseas-owned companies as their marketing agents, a type of co-ordination, but without New Zealand control of the product.

While the Board's intervention in lamb marketing in 1971-72 brought some short-term improvements in prices, returns to farmers were still low

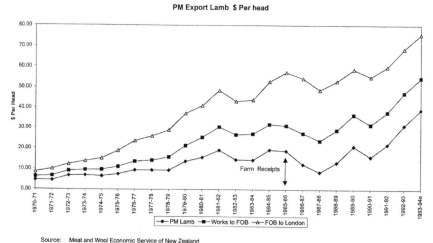

Farmers were very mindful of increases in intervening charges such as the cost of processing and transport to overseas markets during the 1970s. This graph from the Meat and Wool Economic Service shows how over that decade farm receipts took a decreasing margin as costs from works to fob and transport to the UK grew.

PM Export Lamb $ Per head

Source: Meat and Wool Economic Service of New Zealand
          Meat New Zealand

by historic standards. Low returns were in part attributed to steadily increasing processing and distribution charges, so the industry's efficiency and financial performance was the subject of considerable criticism.

From the producer's viewpoint companies had little incentive or need to increase efficiency. Many of the cost effects could be passed on in the form of higher killing and freezing charges so the companies could maintain a reasonable profit. In some instances that profit was considered more than reasonable.

One of the old-style plants. Ocean Beach, built for politician Sir Joseph Ward's company in 1890 and owned by the Co-operative Wholesale Society of Manchester in the UK from 1954. The Alliance Freezing Company bought Ocean Beach in November 1981 and closed it 10 years later. Photo: Otago Daily Times.

The Stabilisation of Prices Regulations had been introduced by the National Government in January 1972 as an anti-inflationary measure. The regulations included controls on K & F charges so that increases were limited to specified additional costs incurred since the introduction of the regulations. It was an invitation to entrench 'cost plus' attitudes.

Under the legislation, any increase in the K & F charges had to be approved by the Minister of Agriculture, acting on the recommendation of the Board. This ostensibly gave the Board a lever to gain what it had long aspired to, more information from the freezing companies about their charges and costs, to assist in its crusade against persistent increases. It hastened to advise the Minister and the companies that it could not make the required recommendations without adequate information and supporting factual evidence. Lengthy negotiations ensued.

The Board's 1972 annual report noted it had been agreed with the Freezing Companies Associations that "the Department's investigating officer would supply the Board, where an increase in charges is being sought, with costing figures in considerable detail – not for individual works, but for six groupings of works – namely small, medium and large works in both the North and South Islands."

It was one more example of the industry averaging system at work.

The arrangement was subsequently changed so that when an increase in K & F charges was applied for, the accounts and costings of four 'trend-setting' companies would be examined. If the application was approved then the other works in the trend-setters' region could alter their rates by the same percentage, subject to final checking of figures by the Ministry and a recommendation from the Board.

Approvals were given for the trend-setters to increase charges from 1 November 1973. The works were AFFCO 6.2%, Hawke's Bay Farmers' Meat Company 5.8%, New Zealand Refrigerating 6.2% and Alliance 1.8%. However, the new arrangement was to prove largely ineffective and the industry was soon making representations for the removal of the Board's responsibilities in that area.

There were other provisions in the price stabilisation regulations that curtailed the activities of just about any economic enterprise, including limiting the levels of dividends that could be distributed. Like the rest of the economy, the industry staggered like an overloaded camel under the weight of regulations and controls.

The expected cost of the necessary hygiene upgrades, combined with existing problems of financial performance, caused companies to review the viability of their operations. A round of ownership changes started, and two new players bid to enter the processing business.

In an early move Dawn Meats and Richmond Ltd both applied to build beef processing plants in Hawke's Bay. Despite the 'open door' policy both marketing companies had been experiencing difficulties in getting access, on behalf of their growing clientele, to killing space for beef cattle. They were determined to get into meat processing as a means of controlling their own destiny, but had come up against the Section 28 "economic justification" provisions of the Meat Act.

Consideration had to be given to the possible effects on the "ability of other licensees of export slaughterhouses to obtain regular supplies of stock sufficient for the reasonable requirements of their business". Existing operators could oppose any new application on the grounds that it would reduce their supply of stock. This approach had proved remarkably effective in excluding newcomers during the first 50 years of the Board's existence.

The Dawn and Richmond applications were based on the projected rise in stock numbers in the region but, despite the tireless and energetic lobbying of Graeme Lowe, had not made much headway against the established companies. However, shortly before his retirement Sir John Ormond indicated to both companies that the Board would probably be more sympathetic towards a joint application.

This suggestion was adopted, and a new company, Pacific Freezing Ltd, formed. Graeme Lowe of Dawn and John Buxton of Richmond jointly headed the company. However, shortly after its establishment John Buxton resigned to run Towers in England, with Rowan Ogg taking his place. Graeme Lowe brought in John Foster on the Dawn side. Lowe and Foster, who had previously worked together for Unilever, formed an unlikely but effective team, combining blunt energy with diplomatic determination.

To assist its deliberations, the Board initiated a study of meat processing facilities in Hawke's Bay, carried out by John Gillies of Invercargill, who was also the Board's appointee to the Alliance board. The Board's recommendation to the Minister in November 1971, was for a jointly owned slaughterhouse licence for beef processing, with a kill limitation of 250 cattle per day, and a packinghouse licence for all classes of meat.

Boneless beef being packed in the Richmond packhouse at Pacific Beef. A central wall created separate packing areas for the two partners in Pacific Beef, Richmond and Dawn Meats.
Photos: Graeme Lowe.

It would take until 1974 before the Pacific Freezing plant with a capacity of 500 head per day and two separate packing houses, was in operation. But the breakthrough had been made to develop new works instead of preserving and upgrading the large old style ones.

Also in 1971, after a long period of farmer agitation and negotiation, the Board recommended approval be given for a new export slaughterhouse licence so the Gear Meat Company could open a plant at Taumarunui. When no progress had been made by 1973, the approval was withdrawn.

Prompted by the economic pressures, the Canterbury Frozen Meat Company in 1972 proposed the merging of meat companies in the South Island. All were New Zealand-owned (apart from the Borthwicks plant at Belfast), and CFM believed that the merger would bring efficiencies and economies of scale. Savings could be made on hygiene upgrades, centralised processing of some by-products, and better management of stock transport. Coordination of the marketing of meat could also be achieved. The promoters went for the golden ring by advocating only one large company.

John Drayton of CFM recalls that talks proceeded, and working parties were set up. "I was totally for it." But despite numerous discussions and an indication of acceptance of the proposal from the chairman of the Board, it never really got off the ground. The South Otago Freezing Company (SOFCO) pulled out, followed by Southland Frozen Meat (SFM), and the whole deal fell apart. Nevertheless the issue had caused the South Island companies to review their situation.

Meanwhile, the tightening regulatory requirements had led to Swifts assessing its investment in the Wellington Meat Export Co's Ngauranga plant and the decision to close it in May 1973. The cost of upgrading to meet new hygiene and pollution control standards was given as the major reason. This brought an immediate reaction from farmers and unions resulting in Agriculture Minister Colin Moyle calling for an investigation of the future profitability of the works.

Farmers were perturbed that the decision would put pressure on the remaining works in the lower North Island at the peak of the season and the possible effects of labour disputes. The unions wanted to preserve employment for their members in the Wellington area. The report to the Minister vindicated the decision by the Swift directors – the location was not ideal and the costs of upgrading were excessive compared to a new works elsewhere.

This episode typifies not only the strong influence of farmers and the drive to maintain peak killing facilities, but also the heavy-handed regulatory environment. Companies could not take major ownership or operational decisions without the consent of the Minister, which invariably meant consultation with, or a recommendation from, the Board.

The Co-operative Wholesale Society (CWS) also decided to make a move in 1973 because of concerns about the cost of hygiene upgrades and the labour troubles they had experienced, which its CEO Alfred Wilson told Bruce Ryan were "the worst that CWS had to face anywhere in the world". In March the company proposed that the Board purchase their Longburn works on the understanding that CWS would continue to receive supplies of lamb from the plant.

The Board expressed interest, subject to acceptable conditions of purchase. It did not intend to operate the works itself, but as recounted in the annual report, proposed the formation of a company which would allow farmers in the district to acquire ownership over a "lengthy period". Negotiations with CWS continued for nine months, but eventually broke down over price differences in March 1974.

While the CFM initiative for the amalgamation of the South Island companies did not get off the ground, the need for some action was evident. As John Drayton explained, CFM had "three old rundown works, plenty of mana, prestige and loyal support, but no bloody money to improve them to meet the hygiene standards and no bank credit". It was decided to concentrate on processing, and a deal was made with Borthwicks. CFM sold their marketing operations and a 24% shareholding in the company in exchange for the Borthwicks' Canterbury works.

John Neilson, managing director of Waitaki Farmers Freezing Company Ltd, a strong advocate for integration of New Zealand meat processing companies. In 1972 he said, "The formation of a super-company comprising all the companies in the South Island has merit. Farmers would have no need to fear that there would be no competition, as there would still be the overseas-owned companies, and PPCS."

This transaction was subject to Section 73 of the Meat Act, which required the Minister to seek the Board's recommendation regarding the acquisition by a freezing company of shares in another freezing company. Board policy did not favour such acquisitions, but did allow there might be exceptions, and it recommended the Minister approve the share transfer. So Borthwicks added CFM marketing to the arrangement it had made with SOFCO back in 1946, as well as the less formal arrangements it had with other companies such as SFM and Alliance.

Waitaki now started to make some of the moves which were to take it from a single-plant operation based at Pukeuri near Oamaru into a multiplant business within 10 years, and to make the Waitaki name one of the best-remembered around the world for product innovation.

Waitaki general manager John Neilson was described as a man of great intelligence and vision. In a very conservative industry he was also regarded as a socialist, which roused suspicions on both ends of the political spectrum. As Kate Coughlan wrote later in the *New Zealand Times* of 23 September, 1984: "John Neilson doesn't fit. In the business community, the meat industry, Fendalton society and the world of politics, John Neilson stands out like a dead fly in a bowl of cream."

For example, she said, when he had the audacity to propose that the upstart Waitaki should take over CFM, the then chairman of the Meat & Wool Section of Federated Farmers, Alan Wright (later Sir Alan) declared, "It would be a tragedy if such an old-established and reputable firm as the Canterbury Frozen Meat Co Ltd had to succumb to modern commercial trends".

Neilson's means of ensuring both plant and people were employed for as long as possible through the year, rather than just for a short season, was to diversify into a range of 'related' investments. This started with the potato flake factory located within the Pukeuri plant. Other ventures would include textiles, hotel accommodation, concrete products, deer products, animal foods and printing.

Neilson's dream was to consolidate the fragmented industry and achieve critical mass to enable a New Zealand-owned and operated company to compete in the international marketplace.

In his view: "For the survival of the meat industry, structures of maximum effectiveness – that is a limited number of controlling owners – should be put in place."

According to Joe Ryan, assistant general manager of New Zealand Refrigerating (NZR) at the time: "Neilson did not articulate it publicly until quite late in his career, but he was a great advocate for New Zealand Incorporated. He saw that as the only solution to the meat industry, and that's why he says he pursued the acquisitions which he did."

Late in 1973 Waitaki put in a share swap bid to take over SOFCO which owned a large plant at Finegand near Balclutha, and made an offer to acquire Nelson Freezing Co which had a small multi-species plant at Stoke.

The Otago move drew the attention of SFM which put in a counter-offer to build its procurement and processing base. This led to a share price skirmish between the two offering companies and, as usual, both the Minister and the Board were involved. The Board's 1974 annual report indicated that while it did not object to the takeover by either party, it preferred the link-up of Waitaki and SOFCO.

The Minister gave his approval to Waitaki, and, as the SFM history *Keys to Prosperity* describes, indicated that influencing factors included: "The fact that the Meat Board, whose primary concern is the interests of the meat producers, was definitely in favour of the original Waitaki proposition as against that of the Southland Frozen Meat Company, and that the Board of the South Otago Freezing Company itself was of the opinion that, from a farmers' point of view, the Waitaki proposal was the better."

Sir Alan Gilkison, chairman of Southland Frozen Meat from 1961 to 1981.

SFM's final bid had been higher than the accepted offer from Waitaki. SFM Chairman Alan Gilkison commented, "For the first time to my knowledge shareholders have been prevented by the Government from disposing of their assets at the maximum possible price."

Waitaki's bid for the Nelson company was contested with CFM. The Board again expressed no particular preference provided certain conditions were observed. However the Minister required it to make a decision and the Board again advised that on balance its preference was for Waitaki. So Waitaki was well on the path to expansion by the start of the 1975 season, with little or no cash required.

In 1975 SFM and Waitaki locked horns again, this time over the ownership of NZR. The attraction of NZR was its spread of five strategically located processing plants, four in the South Island at Picton, Islington (Christchurch), Smithfield (Timaru), and Burnside (Dunedin), plus Imlay and the local trade company Tenderkist, a pioneer in cut beef, at Wanganui in the North Island.

NZR's long history dated back to the canning and preserving operation started by the then Christchurch Meat Company in 1869. In recent years, however, NZR had suffered some disastrous financial results and was vulnerable to any company in acquisition mode.

SFM and NZR had a close relationship through their joint shareholdings in Towers in the UK, a company which also came under financial pressure because of reduced volume of product, due in part to a decline in support from Gear, the other shareholder.

The principals of NZR and SFM met in secret at the offices of New Zealand Breweries prior to Christmas 1974 to discuss possible merger opportunities. They also discussed the possibility of getting CFM to join the talks but this never eventuated. However, early in the New Year, according to *Keys to Prosperity*, SFM became aware that some discussions were also taking place about a merger between Waitaki and NZR, that could have a detrimental effect on their investment in Towers. SFM put in a takeover bid for NZR without warning, which was considered a hostile move.

Joe Ryan recalls that early in 1975: "Suddenly someone, I can't recall whether it was a solicitor of theirs or not, walked into our secretary's office and banged an envelope on the desk. They were going to take us over. They'd heard enough talking. The chat, which I don't believe had any veracity to it, was that SFM got suspicious, that all we were doing was sucking their brains. We were absolutely flabbergasted. But that's how it all started. There were

The regular PPCS back page advertisement in the Meat Producer *around 1970. "Killing facilities at all 16 freezing works and drafting representatives stationed throughout the South Island." The 'open door' policy giving access to killing space made it possible for PPCS to increase its annual carcass throughput from an average of 131,000 in the early 1960s to nearly 2.5 million.*

friendly talks, wanting to do something co-operatively, they came in with a bayonet charge, we lobbed some mortar straight at them… and quite a fight ensued in public."

The recently retired general manager of NZR, Keown (Bill) Cleland, was instructed by his board to talk to Waitaki about merger prospects. So the SFM takeover notice aimed at halting the suspected, but non-existent talks, between NZR and Waitaki actually caused NZR to consider Waitaki as a possible 'white knight'.

The takeover bid required SFM to comply with the usual requirements of the Stock Exchange. Both SFM and NZR were listed companies, as was Waitaki. SFM also, as required, sought the approval of the Board and *Keys to Prosperity* reports Charles Hilgendorf expressed his delight at the news. The Board had apparently been discussing the whole question of plant ownership in the South Island and if SFM had not moved, a suggestion was to be put to them that they do so.

Waitaki got into the action with a proposal for a merger with NZR in March 1975. As Joe Ryan noted, "It was technically an NZR takeover of Waitaki" although the latter would emerge as the major partner. This set off a round of offers and counter-offers from the three parties involved.

Another diversionary development was a proposal for producer ownership of the NZR works by a group described in the March 1975 *Meat Producer* as "producer interests in the South Island and the southern part of the North Island".

According to John Russell, recently with AFFCO, who was working for the Bank of New Zealand at the time and acting as its banking adviser, PPCS was interested in changing the whole structure of the South Island. At the time, the Dunedin-based PPCS was purely a marketing company and did not own any processing facilities. However it had in chief executive Ian Jenkinson, who moved from Auckland at the start of 1973 after a career with Hellabys, an astute strategic thinker. 'Jenkie', as he was referred to, would establish strong financial backing for the company's assertively individual way of operating. He had an enthusiastic new team of directors, including Robbie Burnside, Max Naylor, Bernard Pinney and John Acland, the latter attracted to PPCS because of its co-ooperative philosophy and because of Jenkinson's ambition to get the farmer and the company as close as possible to the end customer.

John Russell recalls: "We made a bid for NZR. We were going to have PPCS as the marketing and treasury operation on a centralised basis, Burnside and Alliance (if they would join) in the southern province or region, Smithfield and Islington in the central region and Picton and possibly something else – we were looking at Kaiapoi – in the north. We would have ended up with two co-operative works in each area and PPCS orchestrating them on a regional basis."

The shareholding would have been sold down to farmers to create the co-operative works. PPCS needed access to Reserve Account money to put the whole deal together. Colin Moyle reputedly thought the proposal an excellent idea.

In May 1975 the Board set up a working party to examine the feasibility of producer ownership of freezing works. Under the chairmanship of Kemp Stone, the Board's long-time legal adviser, the working party was also required to report on methods of financing, modes of ownership, and hygiene requirements. The study was not to be confined to purchasing one or more NZR plants or the company itself, and the committee could recommend alternatives it believed could achieve the producers' objectives.

Adam Begg, as acting chairman, said this was in line with the Board's longstanding objective of having producer-owned processing works located strategically throughout the main meat producing regions of New Zealand – the 'key works' policy. This objective was to be the frequent focus of attention over the next 20 years.

The Stone committee recommended the Board should organise finance for producers to take over NZR. However, the Board decided against that and reaffirmed its key works policy, stating that it would not approve mergers and takeovers that negated the principle. "After full discussion... and considering all other aspects, including upgrading all New Zealand works to meet overseas hygiene standards, the Board does not consider that a Board-financed takeover on this scale is either desirable or practical – even if the shareholders of the NZ Refrigerating Company would agree to it."

It also announced it did not object to the takeover bid by SFM for NZR, but added the rider that it was expected farmers could acquire interests in a Canterbury works – presumably NCF Kaiapoi.

It declined to recommend to the Minister acceptance of the Waitaki/ NZR merger proposal "mainly on the grounds of the monopoly it would establish in some key areas". So while the Board favoured some rationalisation of ownership it was still promoting a competitive structure.

This view was reaffirmed at a July meeting of the Board and subsequently spelled out in a letter from Charles Hilgendorf to the Meat & Wool Section chairman of Federated Farmers, Tom McNab. Hilgendorf advised that the Board's support for the SFM bid was because the financial strength of the company would provide a stable base for upgrading and rationalising NZR. Also the SFM proposal offered the prospect of "unified control and assurance of supplies" which would provide the New Zealand-owned Towers with a strong base from which to make a major contribution to improved marketing.

The Waitaki merger was not favoured because it was likely to split Towers or at least alienate the strong support that SFM had given it. Also the geographic spread of works would be less desirable. An unspoken element was undoubtedly the fact that Charles Hilgendorf did not get on particularly well with John Neilson, the managing director of Waitaki, as their politics were at opposite ends of the spectrum. John Neilson was something of a left-wing maverick in the meat industry, while Charles Hilgendorf's right of centre leanings became more evident as his career progressed.

Despite the Board's recommendations favouring SFM, Agriculture Minister Colin Moyle opted for market forces and gave his approval to both SFM and Waitaki. The matter was left to the shareholders to decide. In the public relations battle that followed, NZR led the charge against the SFM takeover, seeking higher offers, and SFM promoted its financial strength

From left: Board general manager Harry Douglas, chairman Charlie Hilgendorf and producer representative John Daniell. Pictured at Australia-New Zealand-Argentina meat industry discussions held in Australia in May 1978.

and the competitive merits of its proposal. Eventually, after a series of bids and counter-bids and a dollop or two of mudslinging, the NZR shareholders accepted the Waitaki proposal, and the company became formally known as Waitaki-NZR.

Despite the fraught beginnings, Joe Ryan considers it was a very successful merger. John Neilson became managing director of the group with Harry Davis, the ex-general manager of NZR as the general manager of Meat Operations. Farquhar McKenzie from Waitaki became general manager of associated companies, which now included Tekau Knitwear.

The merger involved nine meat-processing plants spread throughout the South Island and the lower half of the North Island, giving the company the "strength of a multi plant operation". The group was able to introduce the techniques of directing selected stock to selected works and other transport rationalisation measures proposed earlier by CFM for the South Island, and embraced by John Neilson.

Despite the earlier concerns the takeover did not cause the immediate dissolution of Towers. In the first instance Waitaki proposed its investment in Stockbreeders Ltd in the UK be moved into the company. However that would have meant Waitaki/NZR held more than 50% of the company, which did not sit well with the partnership principle the company had operated on. Eventually the shareholding split was agreed with Waitaki holding 50%, SFM with 34%, Gear and Hawke's Bay Farmers Co-operative Association with 4% each, Allied Farmers of Northland with 0.8% and the balance of 7.2% held in trust for the two major shareholders. The aim was to have a structure in which no one shareholder held a dominant position, which was a hallmark of meat industry marketing alliances.

Pacific Beef at Hastings, one of the first new meat processing plants to be built since the 1920s.
'The Model T Ford' of what would be many construction innovations by Graeme Lowe, it was deliberately built with lightweight materials – "the papier mache plant" – and for a lifespan that might be less than 10 years. "I kept saying to my architects, the industry is over-designed. We're killing beef here, not elephants and we need to be flexible. Freezing might be out... there might be another method of preservation in 10 years time," Graeme Lowe recalls. The Pacific plant is still in business, now owned by Richmond.
Photo: Graeme Lowe.

The Hygiene Hydra 1972-83

"They said: 'You've washed your gear and you think it's clean, don't you? They'd take a swab of the knife or the pouch or the steel and put it in the incubator. Later they took us to look through the microscope, and we saw all these creepy crawly things, and we had a better understanding about why it was being done." Tiny Kirk.

The Wholesome Meat Act and the Third Country Veterinary Directive, known to all as the 3CVD, were two innocuously named pieces of legislation which had a huge and lengthy impact on the development and profitability of the New Zealand meat industry.

Until then, the industry thought it had the major issues covered. The major world threat, Foot and Mouth Disease (FMD), was isolated on other continents, and local systems seemed to be on top of concerns such as pesticide residues, the dangers of which had been highlighted by Rachel Carson's 1963 book *The Silent Spring*.

The United States' Wholesome Meat Act was enacted in 1967. The EC's 3CVD had been in existence for suppliers outside the Community since it was first established but became a significant concern for New Zealand as Britain's entry was confirmed in 1971.

The legislation meant that in future New Zealand would only be able to export to the US or EC from a plant 'listed' as having complied with the veterinary and meat hygiene requirements of each country. Gaining a listing to both meant meeting separate and in many ways conflicting sets of customer require-

US agriculture attache Roland (Bud) Anderson (right) with Meat Board supervisor Sid Parker inspecting lamb carcasses. Adam Begg at rear. During the hygiene upgrades every aspect of the processing operation was scrutinised by inspectors from both the EC and the US. It could be a fraught experience, as Joe Ryan recalls: "We'd had about 10 days notice of a visit by US inspector Art Eckert, and we had ourselves spic and span. But we suddenly had a huge ewe kill. We couldn't handle it all, and there were a lot of sheep actually being delivered dead. Some dimwits had just left about 200 dead sheep right beside the entrance to the works. As Eckert drove in three or four shepherds' dogs decided to have a feed. You couldn't think of anything worse! He was quite incensed, but he took my word that it was an isolated incident. We got quite a lecture about seeing that it never occurred again! That's probably the most indefensible position I've ever been in."

The US requirement for 'wholesome meat' led to a number of changes to ensure stock was cleaner on arrival. Washing every sheep on arrival began as the personal idea of the on-site US inspector at SOFCO's Finegand plant, but became a nationwide practice. In the 1990s swim-washing in particular has gone out of favour because it is stressful to the sheep and can spread bacteria between animals. Photo: MIRINZ.

ments at much the same time. Totally different philosophies underpinned each piece of legislation, even though both aimed at similar outcomes.

The US wanted clean meat free of residues; the EC wanted healthy meat, free of disease. The US took a macroscopic, 'scratch and sniff' approach to processes to achieve 'wholesome meat' whatever the species. The EC took the microscopic approach, focussing on hygienic construction, and species-specific inspections to detect disease. Each posed its own challenges for a production system based on volume throughput.

The New Zealand response to the hygiene requirements remade the country's meat industry, with a billion-dollar expenditure over more than 10 years. The freezing works where blue overalled, black-singleted workers stored their cigarettes at strategic points above the sheep chain (and the odd chook or duck might be knocked off during smoko), became a meat processing plant where white-coated and booted operators worked in a surgically clean environment.

It marked the end of the wooden stockyard and any use of permeable materials on any surface in any area where meat was being processed. The transition to stainless steel in most cases resulted in an almost complete refurbishment of plants, all but three of which had been built between 1882 and 1917.

Consisting mainly of new interpretations of existing rulings, the hydra-headed new hygiene requirements were difficult to define and all but impossible to plan for, as MAF approval was only given once work had been done. This led to costly patch-up solutions where, with hindsight, it would have been better to grasp the nettle and build new plants. As well, the regulatory and political environment of the times leant towards improving existing facilities, despite the dubious baggage some of them carried.

Over the years the cost of the hygiene upgrade served as a constant reminder of how importer countries could, without a shred of embarrassment, insist on standards far higher than those in operation for their own domestic market. Ultimately it was to put New Zealand in an extremely advantageous position as the new disease and food safety horrors of BSE and E coli emerged in Europe and the US.

Not surprisingly, when the need for change became clear, costs rather than the benefits of hygiene upgrades were most to the fore. No-one was under any illusions that big money would be involved, even if no-one envisaged the ultimate cost and duration of the upgrade.

Before 1971, it had been relatively easy to comply with the meat hygiene requirements of importer countries. The UK made fairly minimal demands, in keeping with what MAF's Derek Robinson recalls as the 'antediluvian' standards at its own domestic plants. The US had accepted procedures regarded as 'equivalent to' its own.

MAF, as the Department of Agriculture became from 1972, had the task of spelling out to the companies what the new rules would require, and shepherding their implementation in each plant.

Encouraged by Director-General Allan Johns, the Ministry was at the same time taking what was to prove a valuable strategic step, establishing and, in 1972, chairing new committees of meat hygiene and meat standards at the world food standards body, Codex Alimentarius.

The immediate reaction of most meat companies, once it was realised that the rules would become a reality, was to seek financial assistance, preferably as a grant.

There were two potential sources: the Meat Board, guardian of the $100 million dollar Reserve Account which, with government approval, had already made available substantial low-interest loan monies to New Zealand-owned (but not British-owned) companies, and the Government. The best hope of assistance from the Government was through the tax system.

The Board surveyed all companies on the costs they faced and how they hoped to finance them. With the help of a forward plan and cash flow projections, CFM convinced the Board to lend it $6.5 million (which, untypically, was repaid within three years). The Alliance Group increased its debenture from the Board to $6.3 million and AFFCO gained a guarantee for an additional $2.5 million. Other companies preferred to go it alone and the British companies had no choice.

The total cost was estimated at $90 million dollars and the first deadline was October 1972. The *Meat Producer* reported Peter Norman's announcement, as chairman of the MEC, of a three-phase upgrade scheme "for the whole New Zealand freezing industry".

Phase 1, expected to cost $10 million, included lengthening viscera tables and in some cases slaughterboards, separating edible and inedible processing, and upgrading tripe cleaning and processing areas. Phase 2, expected to cost $40 million and to be completed by October 1974, focussed on reconstruction. "For example, personnel in edible and inedible departments are to have separate amenities and dining rooms by then." Other requirements included mechanical ventilation for areas such as the slaughterboard and cooling floors. Bacterial testing was to be introduced in works laboratories, along with new testing for insecticides, pesticides and other residues.

Phase 3, also a $40 million outlay, would involve replacing with impervious material "all exposed timber interior construction in cold stores and freezers, and the demolition and reconstruction of all storage facilities".

The average spend per works would be $3 million. As Peter Norman pointed out: "No freezing company is able to absorb this huge outlay…This may be done to some small extent in our trading, but the bulk of these costs will have to be met by the New Zealand farmer." This, of course, explains the Board's wholehearted support for industry efforts in lobbying the Government for assistance.

Those first estimates were to be rapidly revised. It is relatively easy to estimate spending on stainless steel. But many other flow-on costs such as increased manning levels proved much harder to predict, as did the time it would take to find solutions acceptable to the EC or US inspectors – or indeed to MAF.

There was the additional requirement for inspection and veterinary supervision. Though MAF succeeded in arguing there was no need to go as far as Germany where all inspection was carried out by trained veterinarians, more vets had to be recruited, often from overseas. At Lincoln College, a new training course was set up. Inspector numbers trebled – by 1985 there were 1520 meat inspectors and 148 vets – a cost that was at first picked up by the taxpayer.

Many of the requirements increased manning levels and therefore costs.

Cattle being washed at the Whakatu plant in Hastings. As required by the EC, there are no permeable surfaces, hence the metal railings and concrete ramp.

John McNab – the "arch-bastard", the director of MAF's Meat Division during the hygiene upgrades.

"Because you now had to sterilise your knife to avoid cross-contamination if you switched from one task to another, extra people had to be put on," Tiny Kirk, now of the Meat Workers Union, recalls.

Numbers on each mutton chain climbed from around 37 butchers and labourers to total 58 or even 60. Not surprisingly this gave impetus to requests for the engineering experts at the Meat Industry Research Institute (MIRINZ) to speed up work on mechanical alternatives to the labour force, such as the rotary pelting machine.

In a situation John McNab describes as "shambolic" the mutton slaughterboards – processing up to 10,000 animals a day – were revamped one season only to be revamped again the next. The process continued, with all the attendant disruption, through to the early 1980s.

John McNab became director of MAF's Meat Division just as the regulations took effect. He acknowledges he was almost universally seen as the "arch-bastard" for bulldozing through the required changes which touched every aspect of meat processing operation from the arrival of stock through to the wrapping of the finished product and the cold storage it was held in. "The new hygiene regulations became the whipping boy for all kinds of things… industrial relations, shipping crises, it was all the fault of the hygiene regulations," he says.

A firm and even dictatorial approach was what the times called for, says Derek Robinson who was part of MAF's Meat Division management team. "McNab was a rock around which the meat industry circulated." Decisive but not a detail man, he was ably supported by Olle Sorensen in field operations and Jim Doidge in administration.

As part of the 1972 South Island rationalisation plan, the idea had been floated of having some plants licensed for the US and some for the EC. But John McNab was in favour of lifting standards to a level to meet both. To him, dual or treble standards spelt trouble, especially when it was likely different parts of one sheep carcass would be exported to different markets.

From the other side of the fence the hygiene requirements often seemed arbitrary and in conflict with practical realities. For example, udder removal and separate cow/heifer grading; and shiny-walled cold stores for boxed meat. The rules, or the interpretation of them, kept changing. "You were issued a directive to comply with… it was hard to find out what was an acceptable response to that directive… so you went ahead, and when you had finished and wanted approval to work with it, you were told it was not acceptable," retired SFM general manager Ron Cushen recalls.

Changing requirements for head inspections were one of the main frustrations for technical expert John Miller who joined the Freezing Companies' Association – now one combined organisation – in 1975 and initially spent much of his time assisting companies to comply with the regulations. "We'd go round with a checklist, and it would never be ticked right off… there was always something the companies hadn't thought of." Requirements later added by the EC were truck washing and covered yards for cattle.

Individual inspectors from both the EC and the US stamped their personal preferences on plant procedures. On the other hand, MAF kept some moral high ground and control over the process by delisting a plant themselves if an

Fred Ginsburg, veterinary officer at the NZ High Commission in London, maintained a comprehensive network of contacts with veterinary colleagues throughout Europe in the early 70s.

inspector looked likely to rule that way.

In November 1974 the FCA met with Minister of Agriculture Colin Moyle about the financial burden of the hygiene upgrade. $100 million had already been spent. The original EC deadline was regarded as impossible. The expected minimum spend was $200 million, calculating only above-the-line expenses, not other costs such as stoppages and rework.

The Minister was sympathetic, and successive governments promised to deliver the development plan both the industry and the Board were pressing for. But there was small comfort in the first official response which established two committees, one to discuss with each company how their expenditure would be funded and the other to consider "ways and means of giving financial assistance to the industry".

Speaking to a Lincoln seminar in 1975, the Board's Allan Frazer estimated farmers were paying an additional $1200 a year each to meet hygiene needs. In 1978, they gained a forum through which they could have their say. The Meat Hygiene Advisory Committee included representatives from MAF, the MEC and FCA, the Board, Federated Farmers and the unions.

It was not until 1979 – after the deadline for compliance with EC requirements had been extended to 1981 – that meat companies first saw the colour of the Government's cash. By 1980 the industry had received just over $1 million towards their costs that were now expected to total $382 million between 1971 and 1981.

As successive FCA chairmen summed it up in their yearly reports, the cost had been "phenomenal" and assistance from government "minimal". Some additional concessions in the form of increased depreciation on buildings had been won. Cash grants, on the other hand, increased tax liability.

Harry Davis' somewhat grumpy comments in the 1979-80 annual report are typical: "Because of the lack of revenue resulting from this investment, which the industry has expended in the national interest to comply with hygiene requirements, and the lack of realism in taxation allowances, the payback to companies for this type of expenditure is virtually non-existent.

"No commercial operator would, in normal circumstances, proceed with an investment with such a poor return." It was the cost of remaining in business.

Government was, however, strongly behind the push for upgrading. John McNab fought many battles to introduce what he saw as inevitable and overdue change, even if some of the actual requirements stretched technical credibility.

The National Government's new Minister of Agriculture Duncan McIntyre was particularly supportive of his department. John McNab recalls a discussion involving visiting UK veterinary official Roger Blamire, and the Minister – freshly lobbied by farmer voters disgruntled by various hygiene requirements.

"McIntyre said, 'The cockies tell me it's a load of bullshit.'

"Roger Blamire said, 'Well I buy New Zealand meat myself and I expect it to be clean and well inspected and up to standard, and isn't that reasonable?'"

On one point, however, John McNab and his Minister differed. "At one stage I told him that in my view the most efficient way to upgrade was to close down 13 of the oldest plants. His knees knocked... It was obvious his farmer

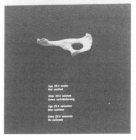

Pelvic bones from lambs of similar age showing different ossification (bone development). Part of a range of samples prepared for the Codex meeting in Germany, June 1973, to support New Zealand's case that the best means of defining 'lamb' is by the number of teeth (dentition), especially as it can be done on a live animal. Alan Kirton did the research and Allan Frazer presented what proved a successful argument.

voters wouldn't accept that."

Even as the FCA was lifting their lobbying effort with government, the issue of responding to hygiene requirements was becoming entangled with the need to upgrade for other customer requirements. And conversely, many of the upgrades MAF required, perceived at the time as of nuisance value only, were to prove farsighted for the New Zealand meat trade, especially as the move from carcass to cut lamb increased in pace.

Fundamental to the development of long-life packaging for chilled meat was a high standard of microbiological cleanness at every step in processing; meeting the EC and US demands had positioned New Zealand plants to deliver just that. The call for widespread use of accelerated conditioning and aging for lamb tenderness placed further demands to revamp the processing area to include conditioning tunnels. So did the explosion in exports to the Middle East and the requirement for slaughter that met both humane and halal requirements.

In March and April 1983, the FCA annual report noted, "One of the most important events in the recent history of the meat processing industry" occurred – the third and deciding inspection of processing facilities by a team of EC veterinarians. They were almost completely satisfied and listing could proceed. A time extension was allowed to resolve three major points: a substitute for stockinette packaging; whether more vets should be involved in doing ante mortem inspections; and how New Zealand's 'cool' boning procedures (not fitting the EC's definition of 'hot' or 'cold') could be made acceptable.

The final EC report showed 17 plants with problem areas for which additional assurances were required, and three listed for sheep and lambs only. Seven plants were not recommended.

Unlike the US, the EC would not allow a plant to be listed 'pending' a formal inspection, but problem plants were given until October 1984 to comply.

FCA executive director Peter Blomfield told the *Meat Producer* in March 1981 that over $382 million had been spent on compliance and $268 million on capital development to bring the industry to the point where 34 plants could be listed to export to member countries of the EC from 1 October 1983.

These were the above-the-line costs that had to be paid to keep the door to the two premium markets open. Below-the-line costs, in everything from increased manning to reworked meat, bought the tally closer to two billion dollars.

As John McNab reflects, "We made a lot of progress, but at too high a cost." Yet it was known already, and the future was to show, the industry had been moved forward to a position of advantage. It was poised for payback.

Controlled Private Enterprise 1971-74

*"After looking at the meat marketing systems in many importing coun-
tries and witnessing their complex nature, the Commission formed the definite opinion that New Zealand's interests in the marketing of meat would
be best served in the foreseeable future by a controlled form of private enterprise." Report of the Commission of Inquiry into the Meat Industry – 23
April, 1974.*

The plethora of ownership activity in the early 1970s occurred against a
background of disquiet over the financial viability of the meat companies,
the effect on returns to producers and the future of the industry. The Board
had been agitating for an investigation into the financial and physical state
of the industry since its intervention in 1971-72.

Charles Hilgendorf had always been somewhat ambivalent about the
viability of the industry. In mid-1972 he stated: "The overall efficiency of
the freezing industry is equal to that of any manufacturing industry in the
country – it is infinitely more efficient than most. This reflects great credit
on the workers and management." However, he said industry detractors had
a formidable and often well-founded list of complaints – wrong location,
failure to mechanise, labour intensive, poor labour relations, failure to recognise that meat should not be frozen while still warm, failure to find economical methods to produce primal lamb cuts or retail cuts, failure to use
many valuable by-products. In addition, the industry "had largely failed to
form big enough enterprises to cash in on economies of scale – either in
administration, and processing internally, or in marketing externally."

Later in the year, a Board review committee headed by John Daniell to
investigate meat canning and processing was critical of the lack of progress
in implementing a greater degree of further processing in New Zealand. It
said many processing firms were preoccupied with meeting hygiene requirements, rather than adding value, and lacked research into product development and consumer trends in overseas markets.

The industry activity that came in for the most attention from the Board
was marketing and returns to the producer. Various actions over the years
reflected the Board's view that better returns could be achieved from a more
efficient New Zealand-controlled and co-ordinated marketing system.

The idea of co-ordinated marketing was not shared enthusiastically by
all of the meat companies, although some of them had moved there to a
degree in specific markets. During the 1970s the New Zealand meat processing companies began to pay greater attention to the merits of exercising
more control over the sale or disposition of their own products in overseas
markets. They established their own sales offices in the UK rather than
selling to the New Zealand branches of the UK companies and, more importantly, they appointed their own agents in other major markets.

The Towers grouping of NZR, SFM and Gear, and later Hawke's Bay

*The New Zealand
Meatworkers Union
submission to the Nordmeyer
Commission was later
published.*

Farmers' Co-operative Association, in the UK, was the prime example of early market co-ordination. The Christchurch Meat Co. or NZR as it became later, had established an office in London in the late 1890s. It bought Towers in 1915. With subsequent changes of ownership and development, by the early 1970s, when John Buxton was recruited by Melville Pooley of NZR to "straighten the company out" after it had lost money on unwise abattoir refurbishments, Towers was importing 100,000 tonnes of meat. It had a turnover of £100,000 and employed 13,000 people in a chain of depots and a transport operation. By then the owners were principally Waitaki-NZR, SFM and Gear, plus Wesfarmers and F J Walker in Australia.

The early directors of CFM, on the other hand, had held the view that the meat belonged to the farmers and, if they did not like the selling methods used, it was up to them to do something about it. John Grigg, chairman of the company in the 1890s, is reported to have responded to one criticism of the lack of a CFM presence in London: "What! Are we to have some wretched hireling meddling with our affairs in London?" CFM waited until the 1950s to set up its UK operation, the Canterbury Frozen Meat Company, which profitably took advantage of any consumer confusion with Canterbury in Kent.

The Board's concerns regarding marketing efficiency had been heightened during its intervention in 1971-72, and resulted in the establishment of a Lamb Marketing Committee with Adam Begg, a recently appointed government nominee on the Board, as the convenor. Other members of the committee were Charles Hilgendorf and Bruce Ryan with "staff as appropriate".

Adam Begg was a South Otago farmer from a Scottish Presbyterian background, with an acute sense of the art of the possible in farming political circles. He was very knowledgeable, knew what he wanted and went about achieving it in a purposeful but generally quietly spoken manner. He had an even temperament, but when pushed a little too far his demeanour changed and he lived up to his name by becoming very adamant.

He would stand solidly with his feet firmly planted and present his points in a low-pitched voice and with a stony look on his face. He had an incredible memory for places, times and statements that he and/or others had made. It did not pay to get too far offside with him.

His abilities and his aspirations were to cause some political ructions within the Board itself, mainly to the disadvantage of Bruce Ryan.

When Adam Begg was elected deputy chairman in 1974, he displaced Ryan who was considered the natural choice and had been groomed by Sir John Ormond to eventually take over as chairman. A split in the Board's ranks when Wanganui-based producer representative John Polson also aspired to the title of deputy allowed Begg to come through the middle. The feisty Polson, an enthusiastic pilot despite his short-sightedness, had already outraged Sir John with an earlier challenge for the chair.

At the time of this vote the *Southland Times* suggested that Charles Hilgendorf supported Adam Begg to lessen the prospects of Bruce Ryan taking over as chairman sooner than he wanted. Some commentators dubbed the episode "the night of the long knives". The *National Business Review* of 1 May 1974 said, "Bruce Ryan's demise was totally unexpected either by the farming community, board officials, or, apparently, himself."

The *Southland Times* reported: "The Ryan story is one of success after success, brought about by the single-minded determination to work for the industry and to eschew politics. He won the respect and admiration of the former chairman Sir John Ormond; he won the confidence of both producers and the trade; and then faced a test by fire by resigning his sure seat on the Board as a government man and winning election by that fickle body of men known as the Meat and Wool Electoral Committee. Since then, Mr Ryan has headed the Board's shipping committee, its marketing and promotion committee, been a director of DEVCO, successfully negotiated contracts for the sale of meat to South American countries, become deputy chairman of the board, and gained appointment to the Government's Exports and Shipping Council, and chairman of the Trade Promotion Council."

Board deputy chairman Bruce Ryan pictured with DEVCO's 'New Zealand Spring Lamb' featuring the daisy symbol.

The newspaper went on to suggest that the Minister of Agriculture, Colin Moyle had been keen to see government appointee Adam Begg elected as the deputy chairman (although neither he nor his office could have had any direct influence). Finally it suggested that Begg might have to resign as a government appointee and test farmer opinion as Ryan had done.

Later in 1976, Adam Begg decided to do just that, as traditionally (apart from the first incumbent) the chairman of the Board had always been a producer member. Again he was in a contest with Bruce Ryan, whose three-year term of appointment as a producer member had expired, as had that of Crichton Wright. The result is rather blandly put in the Board's 1976 annual report: "The election held on March 24 resulted in Messrs Begg and Wright being elected as producers' representatives for a term of three years. This left a vacancy of one Government nominee and in July 1976 Mr N. D. McRae of Wyndham was appointed to fill the vacancy." Bruce Ryan accepted the result philosophically; some years earlier he had taken similar action and ousted a long-standing producer member and neighbour, Allen Thompson.

The aim of the Begg Committee was to study the longer-term future of lamb marketing in the UK and Europe, with a view to recommending actions to strengthen prices paid to producers and to streamline the operations. Its terms of reference were "to recommend ways and means of bringing about an improvement in the marketing of New Zealand lamb in the United Kingdom and Europe." There was still no specific reference to lamb markets outside Europe.

The task was split into a review of existing arrangements and canvassing the opinions of interested parties. The review was initially desktop research by staff at the Wellington and London offices, but the Committee also visited the UK and Europe to meet representatives of the different facets of the trade. The focus was on the ownership of product through the distribution chain as well as the volumes handled and the storage and selling facilities available to manage those volumes and the release onto the market.

The study was undertaken against the background of discussions at government level about the UK entry into the EC. The Board's view was that the industry should concentrate on keeping up the volumes of lamb shipped

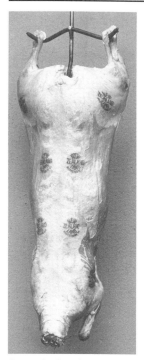

Storing lamb in the supposedly more natural 'squat posture' was one of the early techniques investigated by MIRINZ director Lester Davey to improve tenderness, and hopefully make the carcass more economical to stack. Unfortunately the side effect of a different-shaped leg and cuts bemused consumers.

to Europe and extract the maximum return from the market. This conflicted with Treasury's contention that consideration should be given to adopting the "higher price for a smaller quantity" position in negotiations, in effect – a lower tariff for a smaller quota.

This difference of opinion may have been the precursor to a continuing argument between the Board and the Government in which the former contended that the latter favoured lower lamb volumes and that during negotiations with the EC it tended to play off the access volume for lamb against the level of the butter quota.

The Begg Committee concluded that while there were many advantages to a centralised marketing set-up, the complex meat industry did not readily lend itself to such a structure. It did, however, consider that lamb selling in the UK and Europe was fragmented with too many agents handling the product and that this led to some price volatility. The Board should apply greater control through a reorganised and more precise meat export licensing system.

The Committee therefore recommended a tightening of conditions including requiring more commercial and market information from the licensee. It also suggested changes to the lamb market diversification scheme. The Board accepted the recommendations and started to draft legislation to change the licensing criteria, in consultation with the MEC which generally agreed on the need for tighter criteria for export licences but not with the provision of commercial information to the extent sought.

However, the Committee's findings and recommendations were superseded by the Government announcement early in 1973 that established the Nordmeyer Commission of Inquiry.

The Commission's order of reference covered the whole of the industry, so that the submissions it received and the investigations it undertook ranged over all aspects – marketing, economics, labour relations and training, physical facilities, and livestock production.

The Commission comprised ex-MP Arnold Nordmeyer (chairman), deputy chairman of the Board Adam Begg, Alan Hellaby of Hellabys, John Gillies who had earlier prepared the Hawke's Bay meat processing report, and Trevor Kelly representing the Meat Workers Unions. Their reporting date, originally 14 December 1973, was extended to April 1974.

In total, the Commission received 102 public and 28 private submissions. All the major meat export processing and marketing companies made submissions, as did a number of local processing companies, most Federated Farmers branches, sheep and beef breed societies, representatives of road, rail and sea transport, the unions, and government departments, along with a number of other businesses and representative organisations.

Charles Hilgendorf told the March meeting of the Electoral Committee that the Board welcomed any inquiry that would clarify or rationalise any problems in the industry and had been advocating a limited inquiry for some time. He hoped the wide-ranging Nordmeyer Commission investigation would "not get bogged down and unnecessarily delay the implementation of the Begg Committee recommendations." The Board's submission followed the Begg Committee in promoting co-ordinated marketing, particularly the merging of New Zealand-owned operations into bigger units.

Marketing was the first topic the Commission was required to review, principally, "(a) The present marketing system, both local and overseas, and the changes in the existing organisations concerned with marketing which may be necessary in the light of the future pattern of the trade; and (b) The means of obtaining continuing market intelligence and its dissemination to all sectors of the industry." This and the other topics were examined rigorously both in New Zealand and in the overseas markets.

The Commission's report contained 163 recommendations. As far as the Board was concerned the most important finding was "that the Meat Producers Board control over the export of meat has clearly been accepted as reasonable by most parties who have made submissions to the Commission" and the recommendation "that no changes be made to the constitution of the Board".

However the Commission did recommend that some functions be transferred to a proposed Meat Industry Authority, and the removal of the Board's responsibility for making recommendations to the Minister regarding proposed changes to the K & F charges. This could be seen as one of the first in a series of small steps to diminish the powers and role of the Board; there were a number of major strides later.

The recommendation on K & F charges was accepted by the Minister, which sparked Board protest, particularly when beef processing rates increased by 35% in Auckland.   In the debate with the Minister which followed, Charles Hilgendorf criticised the change as likely to give freezing companies "much less incentive to keep a tight rein on their costs particularly labour costs".

The Minister, Colin Moyle countered that: "The principle of a Board having in effect a veto over prices charged by an industry to that Board's constituents, does seem wrong." He considered that the best way to secure farmers' interests was to place responsibility directly on the freezing companies to observe the principles of price setting and proposed to use the investigating officers of the Ministry to ensure that it was done. Increases would be subject to a restraint on profitability, which was not to exceed the average rate in relation to turnover of the last four years.

The Board sought an undertaking that it would receive sufficient infor-

A 1978 meeting of the Lamb Promotion Co-ordinating Committee, an early attempt by New Zealand and Australia to help US producers boost consumption of lamb in their country.
From left: Board general manager Harry Douglas, deputy chairman Adam Begg, chairman Charles Hilgendorf, chairman Howard Derrick, USDA representative John Riesz and Peter Wood (AMLC).

mation prior to any increase to enable it to assure producers that the increase was justified. This was only partly complied with, and increases in K&F charges continued on a cost-plus formula. Freezing companies could increase charges at intervals of not less than six months, but not "in an unreasonable way". The Board commented that they now "merely had to prove retrospectively to the Minister's satisfaction that the increases were not what are termed 'unreasonable'." The protests were to no avail.

The Nordmeyer Commission's recommendations were made against a background of predicted growth in demand for both beef and sheepmeat products, in both the developed and developing world. The report included FAO consumption figures that showed a 38% increase in demand for lamb and mutton between 1970 and 1980. Also highlighted in submissions was greater competition from poultry and – a significant concern – artificial meats especially Textured Vegetable Protein (TVP).

The Commission made a number of recommendations to improve the economics of transport and plant siting and construction, saying the trend towards smaller plants which could remain open year-round should be encouraged. It recommended that to improve its overall status, the industry "should be recognised as a food industry and those employed in it should be encouraged to feel they are joining an industry which is making a worthwhile contribution to the satisfaction of the world's need for food." It promoted increased further processing, and a single grading standard for all meat processed in New Zealand, whether for domestic or export trade.

But it wanted to circumscribe the activities of overseas companies. While stopping short at forced sale of works, it stated: "No licence to build a new works should be issued to an overseas company not at present operating in New Zealand, and no additional export slaughterhouse licences granted to overseas-controlled companies already established in New Zealand." This portent for the swing to more New Zealand ownership and control was a far cry from the laissez-faire attitude that later developed.

On marketing, the Commission echoed the Begg Committee when it determined that meat marketing systems in many overseas countries were complex. In these circumstances New Zealand's interests would best be served by "a controlled form of private enterprise" marketing, rather than a "single-seller system" advocated in a number of the submissions. The Commission's view was that the meat trade depended on individual judgement, required a high degree of flexibility and was generally carried out on the basis of personal contact and mutual respect between buyer and seller.

The private enterprise system had certain inherent advantages with respect to these aspects which made it the most suitable for the meat trade. Even so, the Commission recognised that a different approach was necessary to deal with single-buyer or semi-state buying organisations. It commended the 'development market' system that had been developed by the Board and the MEC, with the appointment of a meat company as the selling agent.

As the Begg Committee had, the Commission recommended the licensing system be strengthened with emphasis on ensuring that exporters had adequate financial resources, proper distribution outlets, and the ability to

Lester Davey, director of MIRINZ from 1977 to 1987. In 1982 he was given the prestigious J C Andrews Memorial Prize for his contribution to the industry.

service sales. Various licensing conditions were proposed in the quest for more orderly marketing. The principal recommendation was that meat export licences should be issued, renewed, or revoked by the Minister on the recommendation of the Board and should be subject to "such conditions as to quantity, type of meat, market to be serviced, etc, as will ensure the orderly marketing of New Zealand meat around the world". Other recommendations proposed that licences should be reviewed annually in the light of exporters' performance, and that licensees should be required to supply marketing information to the Board detailing quantities sold and prices received in all markets.

In line with the earlier agreement giving the MEC a role in licensing, the Commission recommended that the MEC should co-operate with the Board on all matters relating to the export of New Zealand meat. This included establishing a "desirable pattern of shipment and sales and level of stocks" and "facilities for the storage and distribution of New Zealand meat" in overseas markets; and agreeing on the extent of co-operation in promotional activities.

The search for tenderness. At a Board/industry Field Day in 1974, Richard Bentley of MIRINZ demonstrates how electrical stimulation of muscle tissue accelerates the onset of rigor mortis and thereby reduces the conditioning time needed to tenderise lamb. DEVCO, supplying the US market, was the first to stipulate that lamb should be conditioned and aged.

The Commission had some far-sighted views on other aspects relating to marketing. It recommended containerisation of shipping should be promoted as a means of meeting future 'cold chain' requirements, and consideration be given to 'conditioning' frozen meat for the New Zealand trade, "to ensure its tenderness".

It advocated that alternatives should be encouraged to ensure 'fair' and adequate testing of the schedule setting system. It recommended that New Zealand farmers and locally-owned export companies be encouraged to retain ownership of a greater percentage of meat to the point of wholesale either through farmer co-operatives, company pools, or by taking a financial interest in companies representing them abroad, or sharing the marketing risk in some other way.

The Commission encouraged the Board to work towards this extension of ownership, using the Reserve Account funds if necessary. The restrictions on exports of lamb to the US should also be reviewed and in time the whole structure of DEVCO reorganised to ensure a more normal commercial enterprise.

The Commission noted there was a certain bias against the dominance of the overseas-owned companies in marketing, particularly of lamb in the UK. It also pointed out that the dominance was not exploited to the detriment of New Zealand and there was a considerable degree of co-operation.

Even so, the Commission suggested that New Zealand interests were capable of marketing a greater percentage of lamb exports. It therefore encouraged more New Zealand companies to establish their own outlets overseas to ensure more control of the sale of the product.

This possibly had the unintended consequence of encouraging more individual New Zealand exporters to get into the marketplace, which was contrary to the view that there were advantages in merging overseas marketing operations to reduce duplication, and promote more orderly selling.

Cresting the Cost Wave
1971-85

"The farmer pays the freight rate and should therefore control the shipping arrangements. It is only sensible, however, to have as great an input from the exporters as possible, and this is achieved by close consultation with the MEC. The degree of influence achieved by individual companies largely depends on the calibre of their representation on that body." Adam Begg to the Electoral Committee, 1981.

Of all the Meat Board statutory powers, it seems none was exercised with such enthusiasm as the control of shipping. The chairman himself usually chaired the prestigious shipping committee; others who chaired it were usually in line for higher honours. At least one other Board member was actively involved in negotiations, which guaranteed at least one annual trip to London.

Shipping was big business – as shown by the number of advertisements for competing companies in early issues of the *Meat Producer*. It was a hands-on commercial involvement relished by most of those who took part, an area where the Board took pride in its expertise and accumulated knowledge. Individual meat companies were consulted and involved in associated bodies, but the Board had the frontline role. Problems with shipping were, after all, one of the major reasons why a Meat Board had been established in 1922. Yet changing circumstances meant that shipping was to become one of the first of the powers to be extensively shared with the meat industry, then voluntarily surrendered.

Even while it was the dominant force, the degree of Board involvement in transport arrangements varied. At the peak of its influence, Board responsibilities included the scheduling of the use of all cargo space, as well as 'orderly arrival' programmes for key markets, and quality assurance/hygiene inspections.

Conference line representatives, at Tilbury Container Terminal, 1982 From left: Angus Hardy, Board shipping officer; a Port of London representative; Board general manager Darcy Freeman; Alan Bott of OCL; Board chairman Adam Begg; Alexander Macintosh of ACT, and Board European director Harry Douglas.

For the major traditional trading areas negotiations on the service conditions and freight rates were conducted with a conference of companies – the New Zealand Tonnage Committee for the UK and the New Zealand European Shipping Association (NZESA) for Continental Europe. Separate groups serviced the East and West Coasts of North America. This system was seen by the Board as the only means to guarantee a suitable frequency of service by the specialised ships required for the trade.

To those outside, the conferences were seen as anti-competitive cartels which had 'evicted' other contenders, and the negotiating arrangements as part of a series of exclusive behaviours such as the way that for much of the period meat companies and their representatives, the Meat Exporters Council, Independent Meat Exporters' Association and Freezing Companies' Association, though vitally interested and consulted, were not directly involved in major negotiations.

John Foster, then chair of the IMEA, saw it as a cosy and not particularly effective club. Why, for instance, did the customer ever have to make the effort to travel to London to negotiate the rates?

Despite the conference confines, the Board's annual report lists a total of 34 different companies as carriers for New Zealand meat in 1972. The Vestey organisation, parent of one of the major exporters, W & R Fletcher, was involved because it owned the Blue Star Line.

Outside the key trades serviced by the conference lines the Board's role was more of a watching brief; this applied particularly to the charters used by independent exporters to sell to regions like Russia and parts of the Middle East. It also applied to air freight, which the Board's powers had been extended to cover in 1959, where the normal practice was for individual companies to negotiate rates and service. As the national carrier in a regulated environment, Air New Zealand went to the Minister of Transport with its requests for freight rate changes.

Sir John Ormond was described in *Golden Jubilee,* the history of the Board's first 50 years, as an acknowledged master of the "refined horse trading" involved in the regular negotiations. His contacts, personal style and even his knighthood, all strengthened the Board's bargaining stance.

The Board's power in annual negotiations, often conducted in association with the Dairy or Apple and Pear Boards, lay in the large tonnages they could promise on behalf of the industry and in the support for improved logistics at either end.

Amongst the cards the shipping companies held was the fact that refrigerated ships designed specifically for the primary product trade (both conventional 'reefers' and containers) had no other use, brought little back cargo, and were expensive to build and replace. Possibly the fact that many negotiations were conducted in London counted in their favour. The balance of power had been somewhat equalised since the mid-1950s when the independent accounting firm Peat Marwick was engaged to assess and provide neutral advice based on financial information provided in confidence by both sides.

But it was a symbiotic relationship. Bringing significant change to many aspects of the New Zealand meat industry was as difficult as manoeuvring a massive container vessel. The shipping business and the meat business, besides

Much trial and error was involved before suitable shrink-wrapping was developed to meet the EC requirement for an alternative to stockinette to wrap carcasses. Pictured is 'Super Canterbury Quality' lamb with the Crossed Keys brand of Southland Frozen Meat, processed at ME22 Makarewa. Trials, which began in 1978, included the 'Lambrap' project based at Nelsons (NZ) Ltd's Tomoana plant but also involving other companies such as Affco, Mirinz, the Meat Board and Alex Harvey Industries. The Tri-Engle system was developed by Raph Engle Systems with Trigon.

Lambrap won a number of awards. The process involved placing a patented bag of plastic friction film called Fricfilm on a carcass, then heat-shrinking the bag around it. The bigger problem – eventually solved by containerised shipping – was how to control the shiny wrapped carcasses. The compromise was to put them in stockinette.

being interdependent, were prone to similar problems of over-capacity, and lengthy, expensive, gearing up to meet new market demands. The Board accepted some kind of premium was payable to ensure a regular flow of reliable shipping.

Shipping companies were amongst New Zealand's strongest supporters in terms of access to Europe. Without their initial investment, the first container ports in Auckland and Wellington, funded largely by the British and Germans respectively, would not have proceeded.

Individuals like Alan Bott, who represented the NZESA for over 25 years, and Geoff Perks and Bob Whyte of the New Zealand Tonnage Committee, became life-long friends of the meat industry. So did Roger Chadder of Peat Marwick in the UK. His loyalty to New Zealand was sealed when Charles Hilgendorf responded to his confession of a million-pound miscalculation, fortunately made in preliminary workings, with an invitation to come out to see and feel involved with the country he was supplying data for.

The considerable status of the staff involved in shipping is shown by the fact that Brian Jeffries moved on from shipping manager to become the Board's senior representative, first in the US and then in the UK. (Harry Douglas, general manager in Wellington and later US manager, was recruited from a shipping company, as was Gary Donaghy, who succeeded Brian Jeffries as shipping manager in 1978 and whose responsibilities expanded hugely during the period of Board ownership.)

The scope of Board responsibility for transport costs as they affected farm incomes stretched right back to the farm gate. As at October 1971, shipping costs devoured 29% of total export earnings, transport expert H B Smith wrote in the *Meat Producer.* One of the main reasons the Economic Service was set up was to provide data to back the Board's arguments during freight negotiations. Since 1967, under the 'port works' system, transport costs had been averaged out with farmers charged on their killing sheet only the cost for transport from the works closest to the port, like Westfield in Auckland.

Consequently, as the 1985 Pappas Carter Evans and Koop (PCEK) report pointed out, meat companies had no incentive to minimise the total transport distance, and were indifferent to major cost differences. Plants designated as port-works paid minimal freight costs (1.5c/kg) even if the product was shipped from a distant port. So they enjoyed lower transport costs than inland works, which might be closer to the actual port of shipment.

The artificial cost advantage amounted to a subsidy which allowed port-works plants and those close to port-works to offer premiums to attract stock. Aggregation and averaging schemes obscured where actual costs fell and redistributed some of the savings from containerisation.

Though the Board, over these years, steadfastly kept the industry at arms length from any freight negotiations, it worked closely and regularly with the Shipping Committee of the MEC, which also included members of the FCA. One of the roles of the Shipping Committee was to provide information to assist with the programming of ships, based on data from the Economic Service.

At the other end of the marketing chain, the Board had begun investing around $1 million a year, levied on all cargo, to improve unloading and distribution of conventionally carried cargoes at the UK end. This involved new facilities, mainly cold stores, at the ports of Avonmouth and Southampton. In 1971, the Board used Reserve Account funds to divert 60,000 tonnes of meat from London and Liverpool to the new facilities. UK director Derek Fechney devised a two-port loading and discharge system to avoid congestion.

Logistics and lobbying was the role of the Exports and Shipping Council (E & SC) which met monthly at the Board's Wellington office. Its membership included the Meat Board, Wool Board and Dairy Board, the shipping lines serving Britain, representatives of the freezing companies, railways, Harbours' Association, Chambers of Commerce and the Federation of Labour.

Sir John Ormond remained as chairman until 1973, though he had stepped down from the Board, and later he was to chair the New Zealand Shipping Corporation (NZSC). Likewise his successor, Bruce Ryan, chaired the E & SC as an independent after he was ousted from the Board and into the period when he became a government appointee to NZSC.

By general agreement, *Golden Jubilee* recounts, the Board had been very effective in holding cost increases from 1960-70 to single-figures. But a new environment of rapid cost escalation faced new chairman Charles Hilgendorf and his shipping committee, chaired first by Crichton Wright and then by Adam Begg.

The Board was keen to see the container revolution become a reality as soon as possible. Containers had much to recommend them for the transport of meat: less handling as they could be loaded at the plant, better temperature control, better security. In short, customers wanted them.

A major drawback was the lack of infrastructure, and the cost of providing it. The UK conference had promised to build four container ships, then, in 1971 pulled back. Escalating costs – from $50-80 million in one year – were given as the main reason for the decision, which was reversed a year later.

At the same time, negotiations on the new freight contract broke down. When they resumed, the agreement was for a record 28% increase, with new penalty charges to cover the extra handling involved in the 'small parcel' consignments (in the past as small as a single carcass) that were a feature of 'owners' account' exports.

Rates to Europe and North America increased 7% at the same time; those to the Caribbean, where frequency of service for a developing trade for hotels and cruise ships was a concern, went up by 13%.

It was a similar story year after year. As the proportion of cargo carried by container steadily increased – just over 23% in 1972, 35% by the end of 1974, with full containerisation of the boxed beef trade to the East Coast of the US, and to a high of 75% in 1979 – costs continued to climb. The oil crises added to increases by introducing bunkering surcharges which in 1974 were as high as 30%, and making it necessary to call at additional ports. Most agreements also included a currency adjustment clause which, through much of this period, led to adjustments of 11% or more, with the growing Japan trade one of the worst affected.

Auckland and Wellington were the first two container ports in the North Island, followed in the South Island by Port Chalmers and Lyttelton – neither

Unloading a varied meat cargo in the Caribbean in the early 70s.

the first choice of meat industry lobbyists.

As Charles Hilgendorf said in the 1976 annual report it is "now clear our overseas buyers want their meat in containers and the Board intends to see that their wishes are met as soon as it is practicable". This added to the argument, initiated by the MEC shipping committee, for a levy to centralise the costs of railing the freight to container terminals. Bruce Jans recalls coming to Wellington with John Foster one Christmas Eve to "thump the table" at Adam Begg about the $600 a container Hawke's Bay exporters were forced to pay to ship to Wellington.

The intention was to "enable every exporter to have equal opportunity to ship meat to any overseas market by a conventional ship on the same cost structure insofar as inland freight is concerned."

The focus on containerisation had a predictable adverse effect of starving the smaller regional ports. Yet, in the South Island, Timaru and Bluff, both equipped with special covered all-weather meat loaders, managed to attract a good share of conventional exports – for a while.

Berthing and storage at container ports around the world was increasingly overtaxed. Little wonder this was happening with the launching of ships like the *Resolution Bay* – which the Board's 1977 annual report noted was able to carry 2044 containers or "more than a year's output from the average New Zealand freezing works". Those wanting a prompt discharge of a perishable cargo like meat had to pay congestion surcharges – up to 17% in Japan and the developing market of Greece.

Other penalties came from delays and stoppages offshore, with the container lines coming via Australia vulnerable to labour disputes there. Lengthy industrial action at various times during the 1970s by US longshoremen and British dockers and truckers also had a negative effect. With 85% of meat shipped in containers to the UK and Europe by 1980 much of the benefit of port diversification was lost as cargo was once again concentrated at one port, Tilbury. This put new pressures on the distribution system.

Pre-shipment costs were also racing ahead. Contributing here were inefficiencies in freight handling and problems with the cargo flow on the wharves themselves, both issues the E & SC was actively involved in. Turnaround time at individual ports and for ships to complete their calls around the country had increased, and ship days lost to industrial action or 'unavailability of labour' numbered in the hundreds.

Both the Prime Minister and Minister of Labour were regular visitors to the Council, which met at the Meat Board's offices. So were representatives of the railways, which in pre-transport deregulation days had a virtual monopoly on long-distance freight haulage.

The Board's role in negotiating the annual shipping contracts with the British and European conference lines became increasingly contentious. The meat companies had long argued the Board should give more recognition to the requirements of the industry, and they were critical of the freight rates negotiated, which they considered had a direct impact on them. They had suggested that members of the FCA Shipping Committee should be part of the negotiating team but the Board had declined their request.

In the FCA 1978-79 annual report: "The MEC has from time to time re-

The Resolution Bay, *pictured going through the Panama Canal, could take 2044 containers or "more than a year's output of an average New Zealand freezing works".*

quested representation on the negotiating team, so far without success." It is "wrong that we the meat exporters, the owners of the product, do not have the opportunity to join the negotiating team that decides on the type of services (for which) we must pay."

Many apocryphal stories circulated about what companies considered to be the Board's lack of preparation for the negotiations and indulgence in the trappings of the UK visit like Ascot and Wimbledon. John Foster summed it up: "It was years of mismanagement, going back to Sir John Ormond I would suggest, if half the stories are almost correct!"

The ABC Containerlines Antwerpen. *Waitaki's attempt to ship meat on this vessel put the Board's shipping powers to the test.*

The issue came to a head in late 1979 when Waitaki, or more correctly John Neilson, decided to take on the Board. Waitaki had been shipping some of its non-meat products to Europe using the services of ABC Containerlines operated by Tsvi Rosenfeld, who had been trying to break into the major New Zealand refrigerated trades with little success.

The Board was aware that shipping meat on a non-conference line was being considered and discovered Waitaki was attempting to send 32 containers from Auckland on ABC's *Antwerpen*. As this contravened the contract the Board had signed with the conference lines, it was forced to take action. The only possible course, it believed, was to use the powers under Section 10 of the Meat Export Control Act and assume control of Waitaki's meat. In doing so the Board sought the assistance of the Customs Department to ensure the containers were not shipped on the ABC ship.

The intention had been to take only that meat intended for shipment on the *Antwerpen* but, with no way of knowing which specific meat was to be shipped, control was extended to all Waitaki's export meat, which could then only be shipped as the Board directed.

This resulted in considerable media publicity and debate, and the Board had to defend its actions. Charles Hilgendorf commented that, though Waitaki's action had been halted, it had raised questions in Europe about the Board's real ability to control the flow of product on to the market and had resulted in a brief reduction in confidence in the Board's powers.

It also highlighted the whole issue of shipping arrangements and publicised the fact that a third of the meat shipped from New Zealand was not covered by contracts and that the arrangements for North America and Japan were service agreements to meet the needs of the trade. In response to a call from Federated Farmers that freight covered by contract should be offered for tender, the chairman of the Board's shipping committee, Norman McRae, advised that it had sought alternative services. However, none of the applications offered advantages over the existing designated carriers.

In 1980, the Exports and Shipping Council hosted Forum 80 to look at future shipping and transport issues, including whether or not contractual arrangements with shipping conferences should continue and how internal costs could be cut. No immediate decisions were made.

The Board itself undertook a review into shipping and freight costs, against a rising chorus of criticism as reported by Adam Begg in the 1981 annual report: "The Board came under scrutiny from many sectors… on matters relating to its shipping policy and in particular with the arrangements being entered into with Conference Lines." The review covered pre-shipment activities and costs in livestock transport between farm gate and processing works, product movement from the supplying works to the port of loading, and cargo-related costs at the port. The aim was to identify ways of containing costs within current practices and/or changing practices to control costs.

Attention was focussed on the averaging arrangements under the Meat Industry Centralisation (administered by the MEC) and the Port Works Aggregation schemes that had been implemented when containers were introduced. The MEC considered that these schemes "assist the exporter to service the market at competitive rates, and subsequently pay the farmer a higher schedule than would otherwise be the case in outlying districts."

The review showed the claimed benefits were only achieved at the expense of farmers situated closer to the works and the ports. Also, in addition to the levies that were charged or the additions to the freight rates, the system had hidden costs. The report indicated that the schemes encouraged costly product crossovers between port regions, and offered little incentive for exporters to restrict their supply options to the cheapest alternative. This affected the competitive balance between different producing regions, and had an undue influence on the siting of new processing facilities.

The Board said it believed that a system almost totally reliant on cost averaging and cross-subsidies was incompatible with a delicensed industry and fundamentally flawed. Changes to correct the imbalance in the allocation of pre-shipment costs were proposed for introduction in the 1982-83 season, once the cost implications were assessed. But the assessment was to be overtaken by events.

By the end of the decade new shipping space was beginning to proliferate and frustrations with the existing systems was growing. Federated Farmers were vocal in their calls to allow in new carriers in the interests of competition and have at least 20% of cargoes shipped outside the conferences.

The annual MEC refrain about being kept on the 'outside' was reaching higher, if still politely expressed, levels of exasperation. "Despite repeated requests to the Meat Producers Board, it still concerns the Council that the owners of the product when it is shipped have no representation at all in the negotiation of the freight rates."

The MEC's 1979-80 report recorded: "Recently, the Industry was confronted with an increase in freight rates by the Lines operating the Middle East container service. The Industry refused to accept these increases. Consequently, following discussions, the Lines agreed to contain some increases. This involvement by the exporters who have the commercial expertise, made a strong impact on the Shipping Lines and hopefully will encourage consultation with the owners of the product on freight rate negotiations for the Conference services."

The legal action taken by Waitaki against the Board for the seizure of the company's products in 1979 was heard in the High Court in April 1981. Sir Ronald Davison ruled that the Board had been entitled to seize control of the product. He also determined that the Board had not exceeded its lawful powers in entering into an agreement that allowed the conference lines a monopoly on meat shipments to Europe for the period of the contract.

"I am not able to say that the decision of the Board to enter into this con-

The traditional method of loading frozen carcasses.

tract was unreasonable," Sir Ronald said, "The Board made a commercial decision to contract for a service which, in its view, was in the best interests of New Zealand and consistent with the purposes of the Act... There may be widely differing opinions as to whether the commercial decision is the right one or the wrong one but Parliament in this case has left the decision with the Board."

The court case did, however, raise again the whole question of the shipping arrangements and the need for the Board to consult more closely with the companies than it had in the past. And the incident provided lots more grist to the free-market mill of colourful *National Business Review* writers like Warren Berryman and his associates, including Rae Mazengarb who wrote a front page story on first-class fares and lavish entertainment by the New Zealand Shipping Corporation, then chaired by Sir John Ormond.

For Berryman the conferences were cartels. In April 1980 he wrote: "Producer Board contracts with shipping cartels are coming under fire from farmers and manufacturers now that this country has opted for export-led recovery. Soaring freight rates, traditionally worked out between producer boards and cartels without reference to manufacturers who now earn a quarter of our foreign exchange... A world-wide surplus of shipping tonnage has spawned a host of non-conference lines offering below-cartel freight rates. But the producer boards and the cartels are determined to ensure no exporter will have access to these cheaper rates of freight."

ABC Containerlines spearheaded the lobbying for the European trade, while Refrigerated Express Lines pushed the case for reintroducing break-bulk shipping on the North American runs. The Board, Berryman reported, turned down an offer by REL to service the US out of Napier, Timaru and Bluff at a saving of 15% on current costs. Containerisation, the companies argued, was most effective for door to door delivery, not for the US trade where 90% of meat was unpacked for inspection at the port of entry. Break-bulk offered something for everyone – even increased work for the waterfront unions, whose container handling rate was amongst the world's slowest.

Despite the fact that the 'US-New Zealand rate agreement' had attracted the attention of US anti-trust investigators, the Board in December 1980 renewed the conference-only service for another two years and rejected an application by ABC Containerlines, which offered reduced rates, and New Zealand Shipping Corporation. The ABC application had been supported by Waitaki, CFM, PPCS, Dawn Meat, C S Stevens, Mair, CWS, and the Hawke's Bay Farmers Meat Company and Co-operative.

Under the heading 'Meat Men Stew' Berryman said the decision sparked "angry reactions from the New Zealand-owned section of the meat trade" and accusations that the Board was acting in the interests of foreign-owned shipping and meat interests (like Vesteys as owners of Blue Port ACT) at the expense of local farmers. Adding insult to injury, the decision came the day after Transport Minister Colin McLauchlan had called for more competition in freight. Trade Minister Warren Cooper was publicly outraged on his behalf, blasting the Meat and Dairy Boards for "a certain degree of conservatism present in their attitudes, which prevents them from clearly perceiving some of the alternatives available in transport today... Some measure of competition is ultimately the most efficient way of regulating freight rates. For too long (the

Presenting the Manalytics Report, July 1982. From left: project leader, Bob Hanelt; Manalytics president Elliot Schrier, and Norman McRae, chairman of the Board's shipping and airfreight committee.

Boards) have been complacent, unquestioning, accepting shipping arrangements which have suited us in the past."

Explaining the decision, Adam Begg underscored the need for reliable service. He pointed out that giving ABC a portion of the trade had the potential to destroy the certainty of the whole business. He felt it wasn't possible to "trim any more fat" off the conference charges. "You can either make an agreement or not," he said. He also pointed out none of the 'rebel' companies had come to the Board, and the MEC endorsed the Board's actions.

"On shipping matters we deal with the official body. What a hopeless mess I would be in if I started talking to all meat exporters individually around the country."

Berryman had the last say, conjuring up an image which, like the word cartel, was to recur through his subseqent writings on meat industry issues. "Some of the New Zealand-owned meat companies are concerned about the 'London Club', an old boy's relationship wherein Producer Board executives and British meat and shipping interests gather in British county establishments socially. They fear their own nationalistic hopes might be forgotten amidst all this county opulence and cameraderie."

As a result of the Waitaki case and rising criticism the Board agreed to an in-depth investigation into the overall shipping arrangements for meat from New Zealand. The aim was to establish a direction for shipping for the future, and a policy for the next decade. Manalytics of San Francisco was appointed as review consultants and asked to investigate: (a) relative merits of shipping systems, such as containers, conventional shipping and roll-on roll-off services; (b) developments in meat cargo and handing methods; (c) vessel designs for the replacement of first and second generation container ships; and (d) methods of negotiating continuity of freight contracts.

The investigation pointed up potential cost savings, including rationalisation of shipping services, rationalisation of port calls both in New Zealand and overseas, review of the balance between container and conventional shipping services and co-operation with other cargo interests.

The results of the study were not disclosed on the grounds that they would prejudice the Board's effectiveness in negotiations with the shipping companies, which raised the ire of the MEC. They considered the lack of information made it difficult for the industry to make considered decisions on transport matters, particularly in view of the renegotiation of the Board's contract with the European lines in October 1983.

Norman McRae recalls the decision not to disclose the content of the report was particularly useful during negotiations with the shipping lines. "The report was done quite well but didn't have any earth-shattering recommendations, but there was never a leak out of the Board about it. The shipping companies were beside themselves to know what was in it. We went to North America and got back 21-22% that time. It was an enormous drop and they hardly talked to me afterwards. They were paranoid about the report and there was nothing in it. It was money well spent and one of the best paybacks we had."

Supporting Prices
1974-75

"We had a cost-plus environment but we also had rampant inflation... the Board and the industry came under severe pressure... because what government wanted to do was smooth farmer incomes... We also had a New Zealand dollar which was riding high, it's never been as strong as it was in 1974, the US dollar was about .6 something to the New Zealand dollar... We were living in cuckoo land. (Then the Zanetti Committee) came up with the most complicated piece of nonsense with regard to smoothing farmer incomes, and the Producer Boards had to respond to it." Graeme Harrison.

Another aftermath of the lamb marketing intervention in 1971-72 was the Board's decision to review the minimum price support arrangements.

The Board's intervention had been at prices above the minimum levels set by the Meat Export Prices Committee. This raised questions about the effectiveness of minimum prices determined by the existing formula in providing support to farmers when they needed it, and the adequacy of the reserve funds to provide such assistance.

A comparison of the funds required to purchase just half of the export lamb kill against the expected growth in stock numbers and rising industry costs, suggested the Meat Industry Reserve Account would not have sufficient funds to support any future intervention.

Price support was not reviewed in depth by the Nordmeyer Commission. It did, though, comment on submissions from both Treasury and MAF which were critical of the Board's conservatism in using Reserve Account funds. The departments recommended more active use of MIRA funds "both in meat export prices support, and in market intervention, as in the 1971-72 lamb market, where considered necessary by the Board."

The report noted that the Board believed that such intervention was more appropriate than the meat export price support system, because its minimum prices were set unrealistically low. For an effective price support scheme, it suggested more realistic minimum prices.

Alternatively, it suggested the price support scheme be abandoned and the Board use the Reserve Account for any market intervention deemed necessary. This was reinforced by the statement in the 1974 annual report that "it is the Board's policy to use the Reserve Account as gearing for market intervention operations and not for across-the-board deficiency payments or price support."

This statement conflicted significantly with the principal purpose of the MIRA, but it showed that the Board's attitude was pro-marketing and intervention.

The price support scheme had been established under the Meat Export Prices Act 1955. The scheme was to be funded by the Reserve Account, as Prime Minister Sidney Holland wrote on 31 October 1950 to the then Board chairman Gilbert Grigg. "The accumulated funds derived from meat and

Boning beef at Borthwick's Waingawa plant in the Wairarapa.

allied products (built up during the period of UK Bulk Purchase during and after the Second World War) are, in terms of the agreement between the Government and the Farmers' Organisation, held for the benefit of the industry and can only be spent by agreement between the Government and the Industry.

"The general understanding is that the funds will be available to cushion any sudden price falls or to spread any long term downward trend in world prices, and thereby support farmers' incomes at a higher level than would be the case while corresponding adjustments take place in other prices and costs."

The Act provided guidelines for the Prices Committee to determine minimum support prices at the beginning of each season. These were set on a 'free on board' (fob) basis (including all costs up to loading on the ship) and were generally at very conservative levels, at least in terms of providing any realistic support for producers.

As a result the scheme had only been triggered for beef in 1955-56 and 1956-57, for lamb in 1959-60 and 1961-62 and for mutton in 1958-59, 1959-60 and 1961-62. The 1961-62 support for lamb had been the most significant with payments totalling $4.6 million. There was no call on the scheme in the following 10 years.

Because of the way the scheme was structured, the minimum price provided less money for farmers as killing, processing and other charges to fob increased. At a time of rampant inflation, this explained why the scheme was considered ineffective. As well, both the Board and Federated Farmers advocated that minimum prices be set conservatively to minimise the danger of a substantial drain on Reserve Account funds through price support activities.

A series of *Meat Producer* articles in 1974-75 by Board economic research officer Graeme Harrison highlighted the escalation of costs and the impact on marketing. Harrison, a recent political science graduate whose thesis was on political restraints on the marketing of New Zealand agricultural products in the United States, had joined the Board to work on its Nordmeyer Commission submissions. He recalls; "The whole (minimum price) thing became meaningless because the level of reserves available to support the market was diminishing; inflation took care of that."

The operation of a price support scheme, and notably the effect of the time lag between procurement and marketing of export lamb and to a lesser extent mutton, was a particular concern to the Board. There was always the possibility of increases in market prices between payment of schedule, including any deficiency payments, for the purchase, and eventual sale. That delay could be up to eight months.

For example, in 1961-62 companies announced low early season schedule prices, which attracted deficiency payments. Later price increases in overseas markets meant company returns were substantially greater than the original minimum prices paid for product in the early part of the season.

In the Board's view the arrangements could be seen as providing price support to farmers while enabling export companies to reap windfall gains at the expense of the Reserve Account. It preferred, therefore, to intervene in the market to support lamb and mutton prices rather than funding deficiency payments. Intervention meant that if prices improved the Board would receive the benefit of higher returns that could be transferred to the Reserve Account. Beef trading arrangements were more transparent with a more rapid turnover of stock so that intervention was not considered as necessary.

The minimum price scheme failed to support producers' returns again in the 1973-74 season when beef prices plummeted. Beef cattle numbers had built up in most of the major producing countries in response to consumer demand and higher prices. There was also an element of self-fulfilling prophecy as the FAO and OECD had been projecting meat demand shortages and rising prices. This had led governments around the world to encourage production increases.

The subsequent increase in beef output swamped the market, where demand was soon tempered by the effects of the first oil crisis, currency devaluation in the US, and a revaluation in New Zealand.

Prices for 90% visual lean imported cow beef tumbled from a high of US120 cents per pound in August 1973 to 60 cents in May 1974. The fall in prices prompted some countries to impose import restrictions (EC) or quotas (Canada), which exacerbated the situation for net exporting countries such as New Zealand. The FAQ Manufacturing Cow schedule slid from around 63 cents per kg in December 1973 to 30 cents by April and 20 cents in June. Even so the minimum prices, which had been set at 48.5 cents per kg, did not operate.

The drop in prices brought a "deluge of criticism, most of it of a rather shotgun nature, suggesting that someone, somewhere, somehow, should have predicted the price falls and advised farmers accordingly", as Board chief economist Jack White wrote in the *Meat Producer* of June 1974.

Much of the blame was directed at the Board, but Jack White, in an article titled 'Meat Prices: Predicting the Unpredictable' commented that the Board had sounded warnings of the very large increases in cattle numbers in the US and Australia and the bearish effect this would have on beef prices.

"We would however, be the first to concede that the extent and rapidity of the drop is very much greater than we expected," he said. He listed a number of abnormal factors that had contributed to the crash, including the effect of Watergate on US policies and the President's price freeze in 1973, the oil crisis with its effect on consumer behaviour in Europe and impact on the Japanese balance of payments, industrial problems in the UK and the snap election, and the decline in supplies of animal feedstuffs following the El Nino-related shrinkage of the Peruvian anchovy catch. The juxtaposition of these unforeseen events had a profound impact, but clearly no market forecaster could have predicted all of them.

There was "naturally some pressure for the Board to intervene in the market" and to subsidise the retention of beef-type calves.

The Board took the opportunity to secure an Order in Council to enable it to buy and sell beef in case such action became necessary at short notice; this was an addition to the 1971 provision to buy and sell sheepmeats.

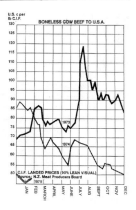

In 1973 a worldwide oversupply of beef led to a price crash in the US market which at that time bought nearly 70% of all beef exported from New Zealand. After a decade of demand-driven increase in production, the first oil shock caused increased grain prices and doubled production costs, leading to a massive beef slaughter in the US.

*Don Armstrong with one of
the hundreds of Friesian-cross
calves he has reared on his
Hauraki Plains property.
The use of Friesian and
Friesian-cross bull calves
revolutionised the New
Zealand beef industry.*

On this occasion, though, the Board decided not to intervene or pay a subsidy on calves. Instead it backed up its confident view of the long-term future of the beef market by announcing it would guarantee beef schedule prices for 1976-77 and suspend the producer levy on beef for the last three months of the 1973-74 season.

Subsequently, following representations from both the Government and the Dairy Board, the guarantee was brought forward to the 1975-76 season as a means of encouraging the retention of dairy calves suitable for beef production.

None of this resolved the twin problems relating to the minimum price scheme – the ineffective pricing and the inadequate fund levels. Even so, the Board had taken some action to alleviate part of the funding problem.

In 1973 the Board had initiated a review of the rate of levy on export meat. The rate had been set at the equivalent of 0.075 cents per pound in the early sixties, but levy income, which amounted to approximately $1 million in the early seventies, was insufficient to cover the costs of the Board's expanding promotion and market support activities.

The deficits (of the order of $3 million each in 1972 and 1973) were made up by way of transfers of some of the interest earned by the Reserve Account, such transfers being subject to ministerial consent.

The Board believed its normal annual expenditure should be derived from levy income and proposed that the rate of levy should be increased to 0.35 cents per pound carcass weight, which it expected would provide sufficient income to cover most of its projected expenditure over the following five years. Even so, it advised in its annual report that it still wished to retain some flexibility in its financing "so that, should unexpected changes in prices, costs or market conditions occur it would be able to act promptly to safeguard the interests of meat producers by reducing or suspending the levy, and making up income from interest on the Reserve Account".

The impact of this move on the status of the Reserve Account was also a consideration. The Board's stated intention was to keep drawings to a minimum so that "the reserve position of the producers in the future would be strengthened". The *Meat Producer* of April 1973 reports that the increase in levy rate had met fairly general support from producers.

Minister of Agriculture Colin Moyle said the Government felt the levy should be set at a level to cover the cost of the Board's operations and "go some distance towards rebuilding the Meat Industry Reserve Account to compensate for the $15 million that was withdrawn as part of the 1972 stock retention scheme."

The president of Auckland Federated Farmers, Don Middleton, was reported in the same publication as saying farmers would not begrudge any increase in the levy. In his view the Board had broadened its activities by popular request and this had made demands on the reserves: "The Board is in a position to carry out the wishes of the industry in market promotion and market development and has shown a willingness to shoulder extra responsibilities outside the norm."

A subsequent proposal by the Board to charge an ad valorem or percentage levy, to provide a more flexible means of building up funds in the better

*Friesian bulls – fast-growing
lean meat producers.*

times, did not get the same degree of support.

The Board's early confidence in the future strength of the beef market was not vindicated. Market prices slid again in late 1974 with the schedule for Manufacturing Cow dropping to 12 cents per kg in December.

To restore some confidence the Board established its own schedule of minimum prices for beef for the remainder of the 1973-74 season. These were significantly below the Board's guarantees for the 1975-76 season. For example, the minimum price for the benchmark M grade Manufacturing Cow carcasses over 140kg was 20 cents per kg compared with the 1975-76 guaranteed price of 40 cents per kg.

A further increase in the Board's prices of between one and nine cents per kg depending on grade was necessary in late February 1975 to encourage the required flow of animals to the works as farmers held stock back in anticipation of better guaranteed prices in the following season.

However, as a result of a supplementation scheme drawn up in conjunction with the MEC, the Board stopped buying in March and the trade resumed responsibility for marketing all export beef. Exporters were reimbursed for payments in excess of their own market-related schedules through a supplementary payment arrangement.

The arrangement, conceived by Graeme Harrison, relied on four regional beef schedules rather than the previous national rate and with one region nominated as the benchmark region. This meant the supplementary payments could be uniform over the whole country although the minimum returns would vary between regions. Beef supplements cost $32.8 million, which along with the Government's $1 per head on lamb, were covered from the newly established Meat Income Stabilisation Account (MISA).

Initial funding for the Stabilisation Account came from a government grant of $35 million plus the $8.6 million of profits from the 1971-72 intervention in the lamb market (ex the Meat Marketing Research and Development Account) and a $14.2 million injection from the Reserve Account.

The change to supplementing beef was in line with the Board's policy of favouring private enterprise marketing of meat wherever possible. However, the scheme put in place was a forerunner of the structure required for the Price Smoothing scheme that operated from 1976.

Mutton prices were also in the doldrums during 1974 and the lamb schedule dropped like a stone in January and slid for the rest of the season. To cap it all off, massive increases in intervening charges pushed schedule prices down even further, which led the Board to announce its own guaranteed prices for both lamb and mutton in November 1974.

The Board's lamb schedule price of 38 cents per kg for meat was aimed at providing a return of $6 for a PM grade lamb including pelt and wool. The Prices Committee had set the bare meat minimum price for lamb at 35.3 cents per kg at fob, still far too low to be effective, at the schedule level.

Even those prices were not considered sufficient to provide adequate levels of farm income. Agriculture Minister Colin Moyle suggested 38 cents represented "an unduly pessimistic view of the market" and suggested a Board price of 42c per kg to return $6.50 per lamb. The Government would

Boxed beef being loaded out.

share any loss after the use of the $8 million profit from the 1971-72 intervention.

The Board declined to raise its prices on the basis that it should not use farmer funds to subsidise costs largely caused by inflation which, it considered, was the Government's responsibility. The Board was more concerned with fluctuations in overseas prices; the escalation in internal costs was a separate problem. Farmers supported this stand as a telegram from Taranaki, quoted in the *Meat Producer* of December 1974, showed: "Endorse your action on meat schedule support. Farmers' funds must not be squandered defraying increased internal costs."

In January 1975 the Government announced further support measures which included a supplementary payment of $1 per head to ensure a minimum of $7 for a PM lamb. Other measures to be announced were guaranteed prices for wool, additional bounties for fertiliser and lime spreading, suspension of meat inspection charges and easier terms for seasonal financial support. Colin Moyle was very persuasive. He recalls: "During this period there was a huge drought so I was able to convince my non-farming colleagues that farmers needed all sorts of assistance, even subsidies for building hay barns, to increase the storage capacity for feed against the drought." It was also an election year.

The companies matched the Board's minimum prices for lamb during the early part of the 1974-75 season but when prices dipped in mid-January some exporters started passing lambs to the Board while others elected to retain some or all of them and continue their own marketing. The Board insisted that traders could not 'pick the eyes out' of the grades and pass on the balance; it had to be all or nothing.

Some 3.6 million lambs were acquired by the Board between January and March 1975. They were marketed on a commission basis by the companies as agents for the Board, or by direct sale from the Board to the exporters. A lift in market prices then saw the exporters re-enter the procurement market for lamb. However, the Board acquired the entire season's mutton production, as the guaranteed prices for mutton were double what the companies offered. Although there was some improvement in returns during the season the Board sustained losses of some $4.5 million on the mutton intervention, slightly offset by a $1 million profit on lamb.

The Board's price supports formed part of a spectrum of mechanisms which recognised the strategically important role that agriculture played in the economy of New Zealand and generally encouraged increased production. Introduced as part of a general farm prices and incomes policy over the years, by the early 1970s there were measures that affected product prices and production levels, farm income equalisation, subsidies on farm input costs, subsidies on livestock numbers, tax measures, suspensory loans and other credit arrangements and, if all else failed, changes in the exchange rates.

New Zealand's economic policies were largely protectionist towards domestic import competing industries as a means of maintaining the goal of full employment. Externally the terms of trade for exporters were rapidly deteriorating as a result of subsidised agriculture in developed economies coupled with restrictions on market access. As successive governments kept tight controls on the exchange rate in order to keep the value of the New Zealand currency above the market rate as an anti-inflation measure, agricultural producers, processors and exporters received lower New Zealand dollar returns for their export products.

The amalgam of measures was such that Agriculture Minister, Colin Moyle established a Farm Incomes Advisory Committee to undertake a comprehensive review. The Committee was chaired by Professor Giovanni Zanetti of Victoria University, with Neil Taylor of the Meat and Wool Boards' Economic Service, Graham Lindsay of Federated Farmers and Godfrey Gloyn of MAF.

The Committee was required to examine ways of reducing fluctuations in prices of the major agricultural products, achieving a more consistent level of farm incomes, and limiting the disruptive stop-go impact on the New Zealand economy as a whole.

The Committee reported in March 1975. It had determined there was a need for comprehensive and co-ordinated longer-term arrangements to stabilise prices of agricultural products and incomes to provide for consistent and orderly planning of production, marketing, investment, and growth in the farming sector.

This could be achieved by withholding some part of the earned receipts when demand and prices were at a peak to provide buffer funds to augment receipts when prices fell. Stabilisation prices were best determined on the basis of a moving average of past realisations with some element of discretion to counter some of the effects of a 'moving average lag'. Buffer stock systems, which would involve some authority in the purchase and storage of product in the expectation of a price improvement, were not favoured. But trading by an industry authority operating a commodity pool and price

Mutton being loaded out at Gear in Petone. The cold store, with its timber supports, is still to be upgraded to meet EC requirements.

stabilisation had much to commend it, according to the Committee.

The Committee also recognised that while price stabilisation was a necessary condition, it was not sufficient for any real benefit to farming. This could only come about if prices and incomes were high enough to enable average efficient farmers to achieve long term viability and the necessary increases in production levels required by the rest of the economy.

At the time the Committee was deliberating, inflation was rampant in New Zealand, directly affecting producers in the form of rapidly escalating charges for killing and freezing plus rising internal freight rates. As a result the increased market returns that were being recorded at fob did not translate into improved returns at the farm gate. A common complaint was that the farm gate return, as a proportion of the Smithfield price, had dropped to only 20-25%, whereas a return of over 35% had been the benchmark in the early seventies.

K & F charges were subject to the Price Stabilisation Regulations, but were still set on a cost-plus basis and costs were rising through the roof. Increases of between 20-30% per year were not uncommon. A continuation of this cost-price squeeze on agriculture would ultimately have an undesirable impact on the health of the economy as a whole.

The Committee suggested that "supplementary payments outside the stabilisation rules" be considered when necessary to maintain the industry's productive power. This was justified by "the key importance of the pastoral industry as a producer of foreign exchange, the inability of the pastoral sector to pass its cost increases on to markets, and the special position of the pastoral farmer as the final absorber of cost increases within the sector… But regard must also be had to the long term prospects of the industry." These recommendations would be the foundation of Supplementary Minimum Prices.

Finally, the Committee reviewed the role and functions of organisations involved with pastoral production and concluded there was a degree of fragmentation that was not conducive to efficiency. It proposed establishing a pan-industry Pastoral Industry Co-ordinating Authority (PICA) to provide a comprehensive overview and integrate all activities, including the setting of stabilisation prices and any supplements to those prices.

Until the PICA was established it proposed a Pastoral Industry Pricing Authority (PIPA) to co-ordinate the setting of commodity payouts through specific meat, wool and dairy industry price setting sub-committees.

The Zanetti Committee put forward a somewhat esoteric and complicated proposal involving a basic price for each commodity that virtually assumed continuing intervention by an industry authority. The Committee referred to the Nordmeyer Commission's recommendations supporting the controlled form of private enterprise, but considered "a single authority with the ability to purchase all meat" was the best way to administer price stabilisation. The Board would take over all meat "at the hooks" then pass it to selected exporters to sell on commission, to retain the expertise and experience in processing and marketing that existed in the industry.

This proposal was pronounced as being completely unacceptable to the Board or the industry. Graeme Harrison described it as "the most compli-

Splitting a beef carcass at Dalgety Crown's Aotearoa Meats, Cambridge. Skilled beef slaughtermen were amongst the highest paid meat workers.

cated piece of nonsense". Adam Begg, reported in the *Meat Producer* of May 1975, said it showed "a lack of practical experience in the marketing of meat and in the realities of New Zealand politics" and reiterated the Board's opinion that the best method of marketing New Zealand's meat exports was through private enterprise, not through a meat marketing commission or corporation.

The Board believed there were advantages in farmers receiving more stable prices and that this could be achieved without disruption to the established marketing system. It did not believe that complete stabilisation of prices was possible or desirable since "we are dealing with very large aggregates and sometimes quite major price fluctuations".

There was also a danger of divorcing producer prices from the market both within a season and between seasons. The Board had been making its own investigations into ways of smoothing out the short term extreme fluctuations in producer returns. These centred around a self-balancing Meat Income Stabilisation Account and a new Price Smoothing scheme.

The Board set two conditions to the scheme. It was adamant it was the Government's responsibility to ensure producers received an adequate income. Also the Board should be able to continue its policy of market intervention, regardless of the level of minimum prices, if it considered exporters' schedule prices unrealistic or felt it could improve market returns by taking action.

These two requirements were to have considerable consequences for the Board, successive governments, and the industry in the 1980s. Even so, the scheme was accepted with only minor modifications and formalised by the incoming National Government under the terms of the Meat Export Prices Act 1976.

Inspecting "the first consignment of New Zealand aged and conditioned frozen beef" from the property of Roger Marshall in Marton, imported into Japan by C Itoh & Co in the early 1970s. Pictured from left: Borthwicks' newly appointed representative in Japan, Pat Borthwick; Malcolm McSporran, the Board's Asian director; Mr Y Ichihashi of Itohs. Mr Iigarashi, president of Iigarashi Cold Stores, is obscured.

Pyrrhic Victories and Power Games 1972-79

"With the hygiene regulations we had to replace all wooden gratings in the stockyard with steel. Tradesmen couldn't do the dirty work of lifting the grating, labourers did that. The carpenters said it was traditionally their work. If the engineers could manufacture the steel grating, the carpenters should be the ones who put it in place... There was an argument (whether) engineers could weld, or anybody who had the basic capacity to do so...

"We had a court case over that... then found that the carpenters didn't want to do the work anyway. Fifty years of accumulated droppings were under the yards. We had to get outside contractors to do it." Anne Knowles.

"$8 a day." Every tree on the avenue leading to the Waingawa freezing works was wrapped in a sign saying "$8 a day". The same message emptied from every envelope in Borthwicks' managing director Peter Norman's mail.

His workers at Feilding and Waingawa were calling for equal treatment after the Gear Meat Company in Petone made the unilateral decision in 1976 to give its mutton butchers a raise of $8 a day. Their letters and placards were among the more good humoured industrial actions – and also the least effective. The company didn't pay, and some of its workers moved down to Gear.

A more typical scenario was confrontation, a bold headline in the papers or a bloody image on the nation's TV screens, where men like National Meatworkers' Union secretary Blue Kennedy and Meat Industry Association executive director Peter Blomfield became familiar faces.

Some of the enmity was for show, much was real. Officially condoned tactics included the throwing of eggs or mudballs, sugar in the petrol, and a high level of verbal intimidation; unofficial ones included psychological warfare such as threatening late night phone calls, physical violence and sabotage. Both sides used battle imagery, but many of the victories were pyrrhic.

'Malevolent obedience' or working to rule was honed to a fine art, as in the instance at Longburn, another very militant works, where the strategy to subvert a 'scab' supervisor was to split the department in two groups. As Roger Middlemass, then the branch organiser, recalls: "The most militant ones were to do exactly what they were told by this man, and the least militant ones were to tell him to go and get stuffed. So then he would sack them and he would be left with an absolute hard core...

"One freezer hand said, 'We can't put up with this... the next load-out we'll manoeuvre him under a shute and we'll just drop a quarter of beef on him'. And I said, 'That'll kill him'. He said, 'Of course. You know, a quarter of beef, frozen solid'. So I said, 'Oh no, no, we're not into that'."

Nobody suggested meat processing was a pleasant job, and people like Peter Norman who had spent time in the fellmongery or on the legging table at his company's Belfast plant, or union representatives like Graeme Cooke, a mut-

Peter Blomfield, executive director of the New Zealand Freezing Companies Association and its successor the Meat Industry Association, from 1974 to 1992.

ton slaughterman, always acknowledged the mix of monotony, exertion and gore.

The work by its very nature could be stomach-churning, and working conditions taxing. But the chance to earn a pay packet well above the national average for unskilled workers – even if only for a short period – had its appeal despite full employment. Training tended to be of the 'watch me, or watch out for yourself' style, with few national standards. Theft was rife as a way of getting even, the means as brazen as a barbecue out the back door of the plant. Blue Kennedy recalls seeing a frozen pig as pillion passenger on a motorbike.

But it was the high number of stoppages, with flow-on effects for farmers, and the escalating killing and processing costs, also passed back to farmers, which put labour relations high on the list of issues examined by the Nordmeyer Commission.

Over the previous five years, the meat industry had averaged 1197 stoppages per 1000 wage and salary earners, with other industries only 41. Freezing works employees at peak season represented 2.6 percent of the total labour force but in 1972 were responsible for 56.1% of all man-days and $1.5 million in wages lost.

New Zealand's industrial relations and wage-fixing structure had changed little since the Industrial Conciliation and Arbitration Act of 1894, with union membership compulsory from 1936. The Industrial Relations Act of 1973 formalised some recent changes to disputes procedures, and prohibited strike action while award negotiations were in progress.

Awards were negotiated annually. In the meat industry, the ritual dance of offer and counter-offer was staged in the knowledge that with each passing day more lambs were ready for slaughter. With the pressure from farmers to process their stock, plus the need to satisfy overseas markets and the potential impact on the economy, large disputes were a signal for external parties – particularly successive Ministers of Labour – to become involved, diminishing the incentive for management and workers to reach resolution. Compulsory conferences and other forms of conciliation would ensue but many issues were finally decided in the Arbitration Court, the decision inevitably being, as Peter Norman writes in *The Meat in the Sandwich*, that the companies should "Pay up!"

Agreement on the national award was just the start. Clause 13 of the award allowed for a second tier of bargaining to establish new payments for a myriad of conditions, effectively adding up to 60% of costs in an industry based on piece work.

The farmer ultimately footed the bill through steadily increased killing and processing charges. The annual wage bill doubled, from $232 million to $560 million between 1977 and 1983. Wages and salaries accounted for 60% of the costs of operating a meat plant, with freezing worker wages making up 75% of this.

Separate awards covered freezing workers, clerical workers and tradesmen, shift engineers and the meat inspectors who were part of the public service and represented by the PSA. The Freezing Industry Tradesmen's Wage Agreement (FITWA) covered the various tradesmen and the Freezing Workers' Clerical Award the clerical positions. Each group had its own union, in the tradesmen's

Manually removing pelts at HBFMC Whakatu plant, a task calling for considerable strength. Pelt removal was one of the first processes to be mechanised, ultimately opening up work on the slaughter chain to a wider variety of people, including women.

case with affiliations to the separate trades.

Workers coming under the Freezing Workers' Award were represented by two unions. The largest was the New Zealand Meat Processors, Packers, Pre-servers, Freezing Works and Related Trades Union. This union, led in 1972 by Frank McNulty, was based in Christchurch but covered 25 plants in the South Island and a large part of the North Island with four branches – Otago/Southland, Canterbury/West Coast, Marlborough, and West Coast North Island.

The Auckland Freezing Works and Abattoir Employees Union, the Taranaki Freezing Works and Related Trades Union, and Tomoana Freezing Works Un-ion divided up the remaining eight unionised plants. As far as possible, the Auckland Union, led by Frank Barnard, distanced itself from the other groups but, in Blue Kennedy's words, was prepared to "walk out with the spoils". Inter-union and inter-branch politics added another unpredictable element.

On the other side of the negotiating table, the employers were organised into the Meat Industry Employers' group through two separate associa-tions, the North Island Freezing Companies Association (NIFCA) and South Island Freezing Companies Association (SIFCA) with Jack Walton and Max Willyams respectively as general secretaries. In 1974, the organisations joined as the New Zealand Freezing Companies Association (NZFCA) un-der Jack Walton.

The split in union representation did nothing to diminish worker power or stop disputes from spreading like wildfire within plants, across companies and around the country. 'One out, all out' was the rule, and when the workers went out, the stock went back to the farm. Sometimes companies backed each other by refusing to take stock diverted from strike-bound works, sometimes they didn't.

Often the only management/union interaction was to solve a dispute. In Blue Kennedy's view: "One of the major problems was the people put in charge… how does a good loyal employee move into a position such as boardwalker? He's got as much show of handling human nature as he has of demolishing water with snowballs."

Joe Ryan's time as manager for NZR of one of the more stroppy workplaces, Burnside, had its moments. He was an expert in the 'human psychology' of the workforce, as shown by the occasion when, having travelled to Wellington and secured a ruling which gave the unions an increase that worked out as "five eighths of nothing" he then had a win at the Trentham races.

"I walked round the plant on the Monday morning. They were back at work, all very angry at all the money they'd lost. I went up to one particular fellow who was a good racing man, and I said, 'Now, you're not to tell, (but) I went to Trentham and I made $500 bucks as well!'

"It went round the works, and boy, did that make the union officials sour. Not only had Ryan had a great victory, but he also got to Trentham. You can have a little bit of fun. A freezing works is absolutely incredible; I guarantee you can start off a story in the sheepyards, and walk straight to the boning room, and it's there before you are."

In a climate where job 'ownership' was sacrosanct, demarcation lines were clearly drawn, not just between but within occupational groups. Slaughtermen could not share a lunchroom, let alone a toilet, with slaughterboard assistants –

Operations manager for Waitaki/NZR, Joe Ryan was well equipped with the old-fashioned people skills essential in keeping a meat processing plant humming. "He was a familiar sight on the slaughter floor, chatting to everyone, putting them in a good mood at the end of the week – then telling management 'now you can speed up the chain'," Chris Ward, now of MAF but formerly with Waitaki, recalls.

a ruling that, until successfully challenged in 1981, was used to stop qualified women at Ocean Beach from rising to the top paid ranks.

Absenteeism was a major problem, particularly on Mondays and Fridays, to the point that manning levels were set with additional 'floats' to cover for absentees. In one of the many distortions which had developed, a worker whose absenteeism was 'chronic' could – through the nominal amount of time he had been employed – claim seniority, while those who moved to a different area of work and gained new skills were likely to lose it.

A long-simmering issue was the payment for mutton slaughtermen, based on tally (numbers put through per hour), which acted as a benchmark for other pay relativities. Attempts to bring in mechanisation were seen as a threat, and new hygiene regulations introduced even more potential for discontent and demarcation disputes. For instance, the requirement that windows be closed at all times, and the increased use of hot water, turned some workplaces into a sauna in summer.

For employers, farmers and unions, the Nordmeyer Commission hearings provided a forum to air these frustrations. Ongoing developments such as the 1973 closure of Swift's Ngauranga plant (where workers managed to negotiate redundancy payments, despite the lack of a national agreement) further concentrated the mind. By the time the Commission reported, the national disputes committee had been out of action for over two years, following a union disagreement over who should be chairman.

Both employers and unions claimed in submissions to the Commission to be frustrated by continual disruptions, and keen to start afresh with award coverage and union representation. One side's wish to promote an extended season to provide more stability of work coincided with the other's desire for better plant utilisation.

Information tabled included an analysis of the causes of disputes between 1970-72: 24% over wages, 16% over special payments, 17% "alleged unsatisfactory working conditions", 9% safety or health. Dismissals or demarcation issues together resulted in 14% of stoppages. Worker militancy and the means by which it was expressed varied greatly; one plant accounted for 20% of all disputes over the past five years while plants affiliated to the West Coast union branch refused to use the disputes procedure.

Waitaki's original plant, Pukeuri, stood out as one where union and management largely worked co-operatively. As Joe Ryan commented, the socialist principles of John Neilson tended to rub off.

Negotiations were inclined to be unsubtle. Roger Middlemass, reflecting on alternative approaches: "We mainly just carried the big stick. We spoke fairly loudly."

The various awards included 250 different special rates of pay. Skilled beef slaughtermen were among the highest paid; some of the most lowly jobs were in the casings room. The incremental effect of annual settlements had in some cases widened the margins of pay between different classes of workers, and in others allocated similar rates for work of widely varying skill and effort.

The union-supported Canterbury quota had been introduced in 1948 with the intention of spreading the kill and the season over a longer period and more equitably among the eight plants from NCF Kaiapoi down to CFM's Pareora

Woman at work in the Dawn Meats boning room. Photo: Graeme Lowe.

There was equal pay in the meat industry from the late 60s, ahead of national legislation. Equal pay was brought in to help the big plants in regions like Southland which routinely had to import workers for the season – from the North Island, Australia and the Pacific Islands, and had to employ women.
Various strategies were used to ensure that only men could access the higher status and higher paid jobs.
"A clause in the Award said that women and youths could not work in the freezers, on the slaughterboard, and in the beef house without the specific consent of the local plant union," Anne Knowles recalls. "This is protecting them from the cold and the really heavy work, but that's also where the highest earnings were." A provision in the Freezing Companies Clerical Award, paid a loading of 25% for part-time workers, thus protecting the 40-hour week for men.

works. Now companies argued it meant truckloads of lambs were heading down to Southland for slaughter while smaller plants like Kaiapoi were restricted from growing their share of kill.

In its findings the Commission focussed on the frequent disputes and stoppages as a "matter of national concern". Even worse, it said, was "the incredibly frivolous, trivial and apparently insignificant nature of the causes of some disputes" and the fact that agreements were easily broken, with union leaders sometimes having little discipline over their members. It recommended stronger penalties along US lines.

The report tended to discount union claims that overseas-owned plants were the source of a disproportionate number of disputes, saying there was little relationship between ownership, size of plant or length of season. It said greater efforts should be made to settle disputes on the job, then at regional level, with reference to a national disputes committee the final resort. Normal work should continue pending the hearing of disputes.

It recommended a complete revision of the Freezing Workers' Award, after independent job evaluations. There should also be a review of the seniority system and the patchwork of incentive payments which existed, some formal, others not, many "born in circumstances which have long since changed" and "a fruitful and frequent source of disputes". More effort should be made to increase the numbers of women employed, then only 3% of the meat processing workforce. Women were entitled to equal pay, but enshrined in union rules and even the awards were a number of barriers to the higher paying jobs.

The Commission suggested having one North Island and one South Island union, with their activities formalised through on-site provision for meetings and record-keeping. Formal training and induction should be introduced, and there should be greater worker participation including a works council at every plant.

Many of the recommendations, including the new national disputes procedure, reflected the submissions put together on behalf of the New Zealand Meat Workers Union. They were presented by Frank McNulty, and later published as a booklet. However, the suggestions of worker involvement, including the right to be represented on any board or authority in the industry, fell short of the detailed proposals from the union.

As if a boil had been lanced by the Commission findings, 1974 was a relatively good year for industrial relations. Stoppages were down by 24% and discussions began on revising the Freezing Workers' award and incentive schemes. The Department of Labour chaired an employer/union consultative committee. Work began without problems at the new Pacific Beef plant.

Just after the Commission released its report, the new Accident Compensation legislation was introduced in April 1974. It was to add a fertile new source of costs and problems for an industry already leading the way with absenteeism and injury.

In November 1974 Peter Blomfield became the new executive director of the FCA, his main focus industrial relations and his brief to be a higher-profile spokesperson for the employers' cause. He appointed as legal adviser a young law graduate, Linda Hensley and, as industrial executive, Chris Ineson. In 1978, when Linda Hensley left, former Christchurch lawyer Anne Knowles became legal adviser, a role she combined with industrial executive from February 1981 after Chris Ineson moved on. Three days after joining the team Anne Knowles had passed the acid test… standing unflinching on the slaughter floor to debate the issues at the Mataura works.

The addition of a woman to the negotiating table cleverly altered the dynamics of discussions. Peter Blomfield recalls that Prime Minister Muldoon at one point asked for Chris Ineson to replace Linda Hensley, because with a woman present "the union couldn't swear to quite the same extent".

And the roll call of issues remained unresolved. In the words of John Foster: "By the late 1970s the industry was a hospital case with weak management, engineers building extravagant plant extensions, unions making insatiable demands, and the bills being added up and subtracted from the farmer."

Anne Knowles. Legal adviser and later industrial relations executive for the FCA and MIA from 1978 to 1990.

For all the wrong reasons, the meat industry dominated headlines in the *Southland Times.* Clive Lind, later its editor but then chief reporter, recalls "a dreadful, undisciplined time industrially".

What the FCA called the "archaic payment system" for mutton slaughtermen was a perennial problem with every attempted solution seeming to generate more trouble. Successful trials of mechanical pelting showed the automation issue was not going to go away. Compulsory conferences, productivity claims, loadout bans and walkouts followed one another in a litany of disruption.

Late in 1976, after nationwide plant closures, the Government brought down the Industrial Relations Amendment (No 3) Bill, which declared the freezing industry an essential one. Fourteen days notice had to be given of strikes or lockout, and there were fines for not killing out stock beforehand. They may as well have saved the printing ink. By mid-October thousands of workers were on strike or suspended.

Employers were grappling with the steeply climbing direct costs of Accident Compensation. By 1976-77 the requirement to pay in full for the first week following an accident cost $7 million (about 15c for each lamb slaughtered).

It was, therefore, a back-breaking straw when the Arbitration Court decided in September 1977 that the union was entitled to an 8.5% wage adjustment (while the Price Stabilisation Regulations set a nationwide ceiling of 7.5%). In a comment he must have counted well beyond 10 before writing, FCA chairman Ted Roberts said it was: "A decision… that should never have been made as I am sure it was not government's intention to restrict all sections of the country except freezing workers on piece rates."

He also said, "Surely it is time that management and unions came close together and try to resolve their differences by consultation rather than confrontation." In December 1977 Peter Blomfield tabled a paper suggesting consultants be invited to advise on a total restructure of payments for the meat freezing industry. It was, however, head-banging time, and seizing each party by the ears was Prime Minister Robert Muldoon.

By February 1978 the national award was still not settled but, as outlined in *Keys to Prosperity,* pay rates for slaughtermen were leaping ahead, in direct contravention of the wage regulations, with rates of between $55 and $60 a day quite common. Industrial mediator Walter Grylls had been called to chair a compulsory conference to find binding agreements on the proliferating points of concern in Southland.   A particularly bad drought was closing off the options for farmers to hold stock.

In March, meat export companies and union representatives were summoned to the Prime Minister's office along with the Ministers of Labour (Peter Gordon) and Agriculture (Duncan McIntyre). Among the unionists was Blue Kennedy, who had become national secretary in 1977. It was his first encounter with Robert Muldoon. To the surprise of many, there was an instant rapport between the two men.

"He tried his old sabre-rattling bulldust stuff," Blue Kennedy, who stood his ground, recalls. "(But) I had a job to do… and I had the figures to back up what I said." From then on Kennedy had what many described as a 'direct line' to the Prime Minister who described him as his "old mate"… In some union sectors this proved a 'kiss of death', but in other ways the relationship was fruitful.

"Because of the industry, he was always interested."

Peter Norman was another at the meeting. As he wrote in *The Meat in the Sandwich*: "After some stating of cases, when it was plain government wanted shipments to proceed uninterrupted (thus maintaining the balance of payments) the Prime Minister suggested his ministers leave and he would settle the matter. Muldoon's solution was pharaonic. He cut the problem into three."

According to the FCA annual report, the industry had to increase its offer by $3 million to $17 million, the union had to reduce its claim of over $22 million by a similar figure, and the Government would contribute a $3 million subsidy on an annual basis. The decision was enshrined in the Economic Stabilisation (Meat Processors, Packers and Preservers) Regulations. Companies could recoup their costs through increased killing and processing charges, and there would be an offset for the farmer with MAF absorbing meat inspection fees.

The rationale for this intervention was that farmers were facing an exceptional drought and were in no state to withstand further industrial action. "Why not look on the bright side?" Peter Norman recalls Muldoon saying. "We would have had every freezing works in the country closed today. We haven't."

As the deal was structured, the Government absorbed less of the cost than the other parties, and made only one payment. The companies were saddled

Sid Scales' Otago Daily Times *comment on the March 1978 three-way wage agreement brokered by Prime Minister Muldoon.*
Blue Kennedy is the blushing bride and Peter Blomfield the reluctant groom.

with the ongoing costs, and the dramatic gesture, or in the words of SFM chairman Gilkison, quoted in the *Keys to Prosperity,* the Government's hand-out to the union, achieved industrial chaos, instead of peace.

John Miller from the FCA and Ken Findlay from the union were part of a small group which spent a frantic Easter recalculating pay rates so an Order in Council could be issued. In the event, they forgot to include one $6^1/2\%$ increase and the whole Order had to be reissued. That was just the start of the calculation complications that flowed from the decision.

Anne Knowles took part in the downstream work of adding what started at 42.2 cents an hour into the Awards and Clause 13 second-tier agreements. "That particular clause stayed for a number of years with increases agreed at negotiation being added on and adjustments having to be made all the way through." Ultimately there was a move to insert increases into the actual hourly rates of pay, with a resulting reduction of piecework rates. That also led to a number of disputes over interpretation.

The ongoing implications from one move by Robert Muldoon in 1978, reflected in accelerating killing and processing charges, were to last for about seven years.

And industrial peace was still a long way off. Southland with its short production season was always vulnerable, particularly during drought. Farmer anger had been steadily building, especially since the *Southland Times* began to delve deeper into the background to some of the strikes: lunchroom conditions or the number of dogs in the sheds. Often the story was news to many of the workers. When the *Times* published a lengthy list, including previously unrecorded stops of a few minutes, the union was only able to challenge a few minor details.

"A lot of people started to ask questions," Clive Lind recalls. "Did you have all that stock heading home because of THAT? One day a woman who lived near Gore rang up. Her stock had come back and it was late in the season, it had been a terrible autumn, and they had no feed. Obviously their whole operation was marginal, they were going to have to buy in feed for these poor sheep, and pay for their transport. She was in tears."

The Ocean Beach plant, then owned by CWS, was particularly unsettled. In

Southland farmers protest delays in slaughter by releasing ewes in Invercargill's main shopping street then slaughtering them. Photo: Southland Times.

1977, payments to Ocean Beach workers, causing dissent at other Southland plants, had been ruled illegal by Labour Minister Peter Gordon, but reinstated after an urgent disputes hearing involving former MP Aubrey Begg in his capacity as local disputes committee chairman. Not long after, *Keys to Prosperity* recounts, 200 Ocean Beach slaughtermen flouted the new law by leaving carcasses on the chain when they walked out.

Consequently there was widespread local sympathy for Syd Slee and Owen Buckingham when in June 1978 they and 250 other farmers released 1500 skinny old ewes to devour the flowers in Invercargill's main street before being bloodily dispatched on a vacant section.

It put the issue on nationwide television but did nothing for the temperature of industrial relations in the region. A ban on slaughtering stock belonging to Slee and Buckingham stayed in place till the end of the year, with Buckingham finally winning the right through the Supreme Court to have his stock slaughtered at SFM's Makarewa plant.

Labour Minister (and Southlander) Peter Gordon had more success with the peace package brokered just before the start of the North Island season in October 1978. At a conference in Wellington in September, farmer, union and company representatives agreed to a five-point plan. The pending Ocean Beach prosecutions would be dropped and annulled by mutual request, a stock killing-out agreement signed, a comprehensive report by Secretary of Labour Gavin Jackson on industrial relations legislation would get under way and once all the foregoing were successfully completed, conciliation would begin.

As Clive Lind recalls, when Gavin Jackson asked for an adjournment of proceedings in the Invercargill Magistrate's Court so the peace package could be worked out, Crown Solicitor Laing offered no evidence against all the men charged and the magistrate dismissed all charges.

The meat industry share of nationwide stoppages dropped to an eight-year low of 36.9% in 1979, and the 1978-79 season was without major disruption, though Southland mutton rates continued to cause unrest.

The state of the New Zealand economy as seen by Eric Heath. Dominion, *22 November, 1976. NZ Cartoon Archive.*

Matching the Market
1972-83

*"Farmers respond quickest to price changes but, because animal pro-
duction is a long-term business, they need notification of any proposed
change. The Board can give notice of its intention to review grading standards, but it is in the way that exporters set their 'schedule offer prices' to
farmers that most influence is obtained. In this respect a viewpoint longer
than the short term needs to be taken." Allan Frazer to 1976 MIRINZ conference.*

In 1976, when Allan Frazer was posted to the Board's London Office as
the UK director, microwave ovens were just starting to appear in the kitchen,
and freezers were now commonplace. On the shelves in supermarkets, which
now had a much more dominant share of the retail business, was lots of
inexpensive poultry meat. With more and more women joining the
workforce, the food industry was in rapid transition. Changing retail trends,
subsidised local production, and the huge growth in poultry sales were giving British consumers much more 'protein shopping' choice.

Allan Frazer could see New Zealand lamb needed to redefine its place in
a market where consumers, wanting lean meat, attractively presented to
catch the eye, would put a premium on convenient, smaller cuts which could
be cooked quickly. He had already been involved in promoting moves
towards leaner lamb production, and he returned from the UK as one of the
strongest advocates for change to the national flock.

This message was repeated by everyone from visiting experts to Nuffield
Scholarship winners who had peered into freezers overseas. Improved quality
– specifically a larger and leaner product – was the way for New Zealand
lamb to retain its appeal. A bigger carcass was a better proposition for
cutting, with lower costs per kg.

Some went on to urge that the further processing to prepare such cuts
should be done in New Zealand. Others, including Board economist Jack
White, were more equivocal about the costs versus benefits of moving away
from the carcass trade, and more cautious in their optimism about whether
the world was really waiting to pay extra for prettily packed frozen chops.

However, the developing trends were sufficiently clear and so were the
implications. The New Zealand sheep flock literally didn't measure up to
the needs of newly developing markets or for the directions in which the
traditional UK one was moving, with a weakening in the influence of the
traditional high street butcher.

With containerised shipping there were strong economic arguments not
to ship bones or fat which the customer would discard: one container would
hold more than twice as much boneless cuts (15 tonnes) than carcasses (7
tonnes), and 12 tonnes of bone-in cuts.

The Middle East wanted lighter lambs. The British wanted heavier ones.
Compared to the current production, both wanted a much leaner animal.

*The Board's Allan Frazer,
long-time campaigner for
larger, leaner lambs.*

Customers like those in the HRI (catering/food service) business wanted portions that weighed the same to be the same shape. Meanwhile, some farmers were producing lean but leggy lambs, which delivered the right weight but the wrong conformation. Heavy lambs tended to have a heavy covering of fat, but little lean meat in areas like the eye muscle of chops. Almost half the lambs produced in 1971-72 had up to 18mm fat cover, on an average carcass weight of 13.5 kg.

Over the next 25 years, the national flock was to be reshaped, with an emphasis on larger, leaner lambs. Fat was literally trimmed off lambs in response to signals sent to farmers – most directly, through processing company killing sheets which detailed the classification or grading of, and therefore payment for, all stock sent for slaughter. But the initial push towards leaner production came from the Board.

The Meat Export Control Act of 1922 had established the Meat Board as the authority with statutory responsibility for grading, so the Board's team of production supervisors was the frontline force in ensuring standards were consistent and fair across the country. Almost universally respected for the way they did their job, they were masters of resolving problems in a non-confrontational way, although they did have the power to prevent product being exported if standards were being compromised.

The grade allocated when the dressed carcass was weighed underpinned the way farmer suppliers were paid for their stock through the schedule and other payment mechanisms, and how overseas buyers of carcasses specified their purchase. A combination of weight and fat cover was used to classify both beef and sheepmeat. More recently the additional element of muscling or conformation has been included in beef classification.

An efficient classification system takes on a life of its own as a marketing tool, as the US so effectively demonstrated when one of its three beef export grades, USDA Choice, became the virtual gold standard of beef quality in Asia. In a more modest and more objective way, the New Zealand lamb classification system achieved definitive status in Europe where it was relied on to describe the product in a totally consistent way.

But back home, because it was integrally linked to the payment system in a way unique to New Zealand, classification bore the weight of a number of conflicting objectives and aspirations.

There were farmer requirements to be more fairly rewarded, including recognition for yield and quality, as well as weight, conformation and fat cover, with an undercurrent of wanting maximum return for what had been produced, whether or not it was heading in the right direction – especially if there was grass aplenty. In the common company saying: "The most dangerous animal is a farmer with grass in front of him."

With a weight/payment system structured in steps, those with carcasses close to the cut-off points between grades were likely to feel disadvantaged. Missing out on an extra dollar per kilogram quickly mounted up across a line of 100 sheep – or just one cattle beast.

Questions about grading or the schedule regularly raised the passions at Electoral Committee meetings and also found their way on to the agenda of the Board. A common refrain was the 'averaging' of payments without any recognition of superior performance or quality. At any given time, there was sure to be a review of either beef or lamb grading in progress, usually under the auspices of the Board's Grading or Production Committee but sometimes involving independent groups.

John Polson was chairman of the Grading Committee in 1973 when the Board set up the Meat Export Grades Investigation Committee to consider both beef and sheepmeat classification. Along with the future Minister of Agriculture (and Hawke's Bay farmer) Duncan McIntyre as chairman, the members were Alistair Nicol of Lincoln College, Northland farmer John Oldfield and Ted Sutch, formerly from the Department of Trade and Industry, as secretary.

The McIntyre Committee, like its 1965 predecessor the Smallfield Committee, looked deeply into the concept of classification and travelled overseas to see comparative systems in operation. But, according to the MEC annual report, it produced "little of value" for the cost of the exercise. The changes the McIntyre Committee recommended in its July 1974 report were, on the beef side, largely in response to producer pressure for better rewards. Both producer and market pressure can be traced to the changes made to sheepmeat classification.

Farmers were beginning to take beef production more seriously. While cattle were common on farms around the country, their role was regarded as secondary to sheep and mainly to keep pasture quality up. Now beef producers were making changes in response to market signals from the US about good prices for lean manufacturing beef as a component of hamburger formulations. With exotic breeds like the Charolais (introduced to New Zealand in 1965), South Devon and Santa Gertrudis (1969) and Simmental, Blonde d'Aquitaine and Limousin (1972) there was now a range of large-framed, fast-growing animals which rapidly and efficiently produced big yields of meat. Among the earliest properties to run exotics was Mount Peel where in the early 1970s, John and Mark Acland had 600 Angus cows inseminated with a variety of exotic breeds – a bold experiment by their head stockman at a time when no-one used artificial insemination in the beef industry and it was illegal to do it yourself on a dairy farm. Through the Gunn-Acland partnership, many of these exotic genetics

Vic Edgar, area supervisor for the Board, who later joined DEVCO as quality control officer.

Ernie Greville, chief supervising grader for the Board from 1958 to 1983.

were sold to Australia as well.

John Acland was keen to see a national beef recording and improvement system. There were high hopes for Beefplan to do this. Launched under the auspices of the National Beef Council in 1973, it was jointly supported by the Government (through MAF), the Board and the Dairy Board through its Livestock Improvement Association. Beefplan, the Board's 1973 annual report said, was designed to help farmers use performance recording and genetic information to "achieve rapid improvement in the production and profitability of their beef enterprise". Among the foundation members of Beefplan were Board member John Daniell and PPCS board member Robbie Burnside.

One of the most significant recommendations by the McIntyre Committee was for more objective measures and descriptions and a move away from vague and ambiguous descriptions such as 'Down' (not a downgrade but a preferred larger carcass, though prone to fatness) and 'Prime' for sheepmeat. Good Average Quality and Fair Average Quality were used for both beef and sheepmeat. With the leaner Y grades often referred to on company killing sheets as 'Seconds' there was an implicit preference for fatter carcasses.

The McIntyre Committee standardised a neutral cypher-based terminology where the first letter Y (lean) and P (prime) represented the fat cover and the second letter L (Light, from 8 –12.5kg), M (Medium – from 13 to 16. 5 kg) and H (Heavy – 17 kg and over) represented the weight ranges. This had an unintended but positive spinoff in the Middle East where many customers decided that YL stood for Young Lamb and YM for Young Mutton.) Descriptions also became more neutral : 'cutter' instead of 'reject' for instance.

The new classification was to immortalise the Board's chief supervisory grader Ernie Greville who introduced a new means to assess a carcass as overfat, the farmer receiving less because it could not be exported in whole carcass form.

Ernie Greville had earned the wrath of Southlanders and the nickname of the 'fat king' for rejecting as overfat up to 50% of certain farmers' lines. Through extensive trials he had established that a calibrated ruler, used on the total tissue depth over the point between the 11th and 12th rib, 11cm from the midline of a carcass, gave an accurate predictor of its overall fat content. This became known as the GR (Greville) measure.

Unfortunately the principle did not work as well for beef animals, in part because fat cover could be damaged during hide removal. Beef classification remained dependent on visual assessment, with marginal carcasses quartered to get a better measure. More accurate classification for beef, especially of beef yield, was to remain an unreachable grail despite the high hopes for new technologies, which began with Brian Hennessey's first investigations into modifying an electronic probe used on pig carcasses in 1974.

From 1975 onwards, beef was classified in five fat covers from M (little or none and mostly Manufacturing Cow) to G (too much), with two conformation classes for the L (light fat) category. There had been a strong argument for three classes to better single out the best prime carcasses. Bull was a separate class. Half way through the season, as farmers hung on to stock waiting for higher guaranteed prices, a new E (Ernie) grade was introduced for grossly overfat beasts.

With sheepmeat, the GR measure was first used only to make a firm ruling whether or not carcasses came into the 'overfat' category. Other fat depth measurements continued to be made by visual assessment. The 1973-74 standard set by the Board for overfats was more than 18mm of fat at the GR site.

In 1974, after a very good year for grass, 17% of the lamb kill graded F (overfat) but the Board persisted with the leanness message by reducing the cut-off point to 16mm. Crichton Wright, now chairing the Grading Committee, also repeated the refrain of more strict policing. In 1975, the Board's own schedule put a premium on Y grades. In 1977, it was announced that the GR limit for L and M grades would be 15 mm the following year, with the ultimate aim of 10 mm for the PL grade.

The GR measure, used to indicate the fat depth component of classification. The large meat area at top is the eye muscle. Most end-users prefer a large eye muscle.

This was resetting the standards with a vengeance. Overfats, and the subgrade now required to be cut before export or at point of entry, the leggy Omega (O) grade, remained the focus of farmer controversy and protest. A meeting in Yaldhurst in December 1975 called for the grading goalposts to be moved back the other way to reduce the incidence of Omega grades, and for the right to export them through owners' account. In response the Board set up marketing trials under the supervision of a farmer committee. It was chaired by central Canterbury farmer Mervyn Barnett, who had been outspoken in arguing that, as research by Alan Kirton at Ruakura showed Omega grades yielded the same amount of meat as P grades, companies should pay farmers the same amount for them.

The Board sent Mervyn Barnett to see for himself the product in the market. The result was a finding that, as Board chairman Charles Hilgendorf put it, the UK trade "regards the O-type carcasses as second-best" so in the absence of any alternative markets, "those choosing to continue the breeding and management programmes which produced them would have to accept lower returns". Mervyn Barnett, shortly to become a member of the Board (and later to chair the Grading Committee), was thereafter a strong supporter of the national grading system and worked to reduce the number of Omegas and eliminate the need for an Omega grade.

While new genetics had been brought in for beef, sheepmeat producers were working with essentially the same breeding stock and management systems they had used for over two decades, resulting in static productivity for both meat and wool. Now the Board promoted breeding and management advice to encourage a reshaping of the national flock, especially in a leaner direction.

At times they swam against a tide of objections, and tiptoed through the minefield of breed society sensibilities. Overfatness, in both beef and sheepmeat, was another area where Federated Farmers persistently questioned the cut-off points or the consistency of the Board's grading standards, sometimes, as in 1981, supported by the Electoral Committee. After all, the more simplistic local market grading tolerated higher fat levels.

Allan Kirton, whose research backed many of the management changes that led to a leaner national sheep flock.

As assistant general manager, production, Allan Frazer put his energies into the leaner lamb message, both before and after his term at the London Office. He was a member of the unfortunately named Over Fat Working Party which brought together a wide range of interest groups to advance this aim and determine the most effective means of producing leaner sheepmeat under New Zealand conditions. Backed by the Board, the DSIR, government's research arm, was already investigating electronic means of assessing fat in live sheep and carcasses.

"There was wonderful support from people throughout New Zealand, meat companies and everyone else," Allan Frazer recalls. "We were just into ultrasonics then, but we had people at DSIR Grasslands looking at the impact of different grass species, we had a geneticist group come out… people really got the message that this major market was saying the product is far too fat. …We were trying to work on tenderness at the same time, so I guess quality was my theme. My reflections from the market were that we were no longer in tune with the customer's requirements. And lean poultry was, I suppose, the thing that triggered that as much as anything."

Some of the most persuasive information came from research by Alan Kirton at Ruakura. He told the *Meat Producer* on his retirement in 1998 that he rated proof there was no taste or quality downgrade from leaving ram lambs entire as one of the most important production-shaping changes for the New Zealand national flock. Rams (like bulls) naturally produce leaner meat and grow faster; non-castration was therefore "a bonus for doing nothing". Other strategies recommended by Alan Kirton were early weaning, early drafting, and increasing the stocking rate. Another Ruakura scientist, Clive Dalton, promoted rotational grazing, production on hill country, and an increase in twinning. As well as rams, cryptorchids, where the testicles are prevented from descending, became more popular.

There were also stirrings about making changes through breed selection, with promotion of performance information through the recording scheme Sheeplan, and suggestions that more use should be made of larger maturing sheep such as Southdowns or Suffolks. In 1979, the Sheep Breeds Committee was formed to look for meatier types of lamb.

The same year an extra subdivision PHH was put into the P grade to separate lambs weighing between 20 and 20.5 kg and with up to 17mm GR. (PX was up to 15 mm GR and PH between 15 and 17 mm. Both described the weight range between 16.5kg and 19.5 kg, and the majority, 75%, graded the leaner PX.)

Another comprehensive review of export sheepmeat grading, including a carcass measurement survey, took place from 1981 to 1983. The screws continued to turn on sheepmeat fat with adjustments to the classification system again in 1983 when the P grade was further subdivided into two leanness categories, the fatter category comprising carcasses with a GR exceeding 12 mm and designated the T (trimmer) grade. From 1983-84 the GR measure became the official indicator of lean content for all classification, not just to determine the overfats. The grading probe demonstrated by Brian Hennessey was used on a trial basis but was still not regarded as accurate enough on sheep or beef, besides being more expensive and slower

Waitaki Waitrose specification display at the Timaru field day 1977.

than human graders.

Each change was accompanied by a reminder that it was moving the product in the direction of "meeting consumer demand". In 1983 Allan Frazer pointed out that a 14 kg YM grade lamb of light fat content would return nearly $1 a head more than the equivalent weight PM.

Producer heat went on to the beef classification system after the Board introduced its price smoothing scheme in 1976 following the collapse of beef prices in 1974. Initially the Board used P1 Steer and M (Manufacturing) Cow grades as the benchmarks to calculate support payments.

Bull was added as a benchmark from August 1979 following protests by bull producers. It was one of the relatively rare occasions, according to Richard Johnstone, then an Electoral Committee member, that the very sheep-focussed and South Island-dominated Board of the time had to take notice of them. The prevailing view of beef cattle was 'they're only there to clean up scrub'.

Dr Tony Kempster was brought out from Britain in 1982 to promote the heavier weight lean lamb message. British customers, like Colin Cullimore, managing director of the Dewhurst butchery chain, said: "We need a consistent guaranteed supply of lean, heavier lambs that can be well-butchered, boned out and rolled, to sell as an easy-carve roast. The breast and flaps can go into manufacturing, the loins boned and rolled for roasting and slicing...Lamb could be sold as a branded grocery item, which allays the cook's feelings of guilt at using a convenience food."

Waikato farmers Peter Levin and Frank Peacocke, pioneers of the bull beef business, claimed that they should be recompensed for the lower support payments they had received under the previous benchmark system. They pursued their case against the Board to the High Court where it was dismissed.

Beefplan had been struggling to make headway, suffering administrative problems despite the valiant efforts of Beef Industry Council chairman Graham Everitt and Massey production expert Bob Barton. In 1977 it was reconstituted, with the Board taking over administrative responsibility and Michael Kight the chair. Initially under Rowland Woods, and later Paul Harper, as executive officer, the Council set about developing a co-ordinated computer-based beef recording system.

With the advent of SMPs in 1978 – payment for quantity – it was at first more difficult to keep the momentum for new quality initiatives. And as production numbers went up, average lamb carcass weights came down – from 12.93 kg in the 1980-81 season to 11.55 kg in 1981-82.

The Board brought British animal production scientist Tony Kempster to New Zealand in June 1982 to help campaign for leaner, heavier lamb production. He criticised the export classification and schedule for putting more emphasis on discouraging fatness than encouraging lean production. His suggestion was that producers should focus on production practices to achieve profitable "target areas". Selection seemed to be focussed on fat thickness and differentials between grades, he said. Instead it should be on the primary objective of growth of lean meat.

He said: "Those responsible for setting price differentials should consider whether in the long term interests of the industry it would not be prudent to pay rather more than the current market will bear for leaner carcasses, to encourage producers to begin to move in the desired direction."

The opportunity for this, along with a number of other quality initiatives, came with Board ownership in October 1982.

A Final Authority?
1976-80

"We wanted competition and to hell with any umbrella structure that might do this or do that in a planned way." John Foster.

"A Meat Industry Authority should be established, to act as a licensing authority and to plan the overall logical development and rationalisation of killing and processing facilities on a national basis."

This was one of the principal recommendations of the Nordmeyer Commission, and it was to have a significant influence on the various new plant proposals and ownership machinations of the industry through the latter half of the 1970s. The Authority was a bit like the Titanic – it started in a blaze of glory but it hit the Hawke's Bay iceberg and sank under a flood of calls for a competitive industry.

The idea of a Meat Industry Authority was put forward by the FCA in its original submission to the Nordmeyer Commission. At the request of the Commission it commented further, particularly on the composition and responsibilities of the proposed Authority.

MAF also supported the establishment of an Authority in its submission, as did a number of other organisations. The Board and Federated Farmers opposed it on the grounds that no radical changes were required and that the prevailing licensing system was basically sound.

MAF proposed Authority members should be independent and not directly involved in the industry or have any financial interest in it. It then sought the impossible by requiring them also to have a good background knowledge of the industry.

The submissions from the FCA and MAF formed the basis of a number of follow-on recommendations from the Commission, including an independent chairman with two other members nominated by the Board and FCA respectively who were not directly involved in the industry. However, the Authority should have the power to co-opt additional members to sit during hearings involving specific issues.

Other recommendations suggested the Authority have powers of decision – which could be appealed – on the issue, renewal, surrender or revocation of slaughterhouse and abattoir licences, and power to impose limitations on those licences.

The proposed Authority was designed to limit the politicking that surrounded any move to change the ownership or structure of the processing sector. Following the flurry of new works early in the century and a spate of closures and ownership changes in the thirties and forties, only three new export plants had been built in the 30 years to 1972 – Alliance's Lorneville at Invercargill in 1960, Hellaby Northland at Whangarei in 1969, and Pacific Beef at Hastings in 1972. As well, three local abattoirs had been converted to export – AFFCO's Rangiuru in the Bay of Plenty in 1969, T H Walkers at Hawera in association with Dawn Meats in 1970 and Crown Meats' Aotearoa plant at Cambridge in

Malcolm Wallace, persistent promoter of a meat plant for the West Coast, pictured on the day the Phoenix plant at Kokiri was officially opened. At left is Joe Ryan, also a foundation board member. Photo: Damer Farrell.

1971.

As stock numbers grew so did the calls for more killing capacity and larger works to meet the peak kill demands from farmers. Farmer and co-operative owners put significant pressure on the Board to get companies to comply with their 'open door' obligations. Mick Calder, who as secretary of the Board from 1978 generally fielded the correspondence relating to the interpretation of the legislation, recalls that, while the marketing co-operatives insisted on their rights to space, freezing company management was well versed in the art of explaining why all available killing space was committed to their own clients.

While the biggest ownership battles had been raging in the South Island there was some manoeuvring in the North Island as well. Hellabys were seeking approval to build a new plant at Taumarunui, where the Gear application had lapsed. Hawke's Bay Farmers' Meat Company (HBFMC) and Pacific Freezing had both applied to build new sheep and lamb plants in Hawke's Bay.

Pacific had already tilted at the licensing windmill with the struggles of its two shareholding companies – Dawn and Richmond – to establish its Pacific Beef processing facility. This had continued after the granting of the licence which provided for a kill of only 250 animals per day, half its built capacity and a limit which waved like a toreador's cape for Graeme Lowe. In typical style he had lobbied every politician who would listen to him, and had also pushed the licence restriction to the limit by increasing the throughput for local kill.

He continued to protest that Pacific was the only plant subject to a restriction on the kill and succeeded in getting the limit raised steadily from the daily rate to weekly limits of 1250, then 1375. His persistence eventually paid off when the restriction was removed in June 1976. Clearly the bid for a licence to build a sheep and lamb plant at Oringi, in the face of a competing bid from HBFMC to build at Takapau, was more grist to his mill.

The Board had made a point of commissioning research into aspects of the meat processing industry so it could make informed decisions, for instance the 1971 report by Morrison Cooper and Partners which concluded there were cost advantages in siting packing houses or cutting rooms at plants. Now with four proposals for new plants in the North Island, and complaints from farmers about difficulties in getting stock killed, the Board sought an objective assessment of killing and processing requirements.

It established a committee chaired by Ivan Thomas, a former general manager of New Zealand Railways, to study likely killing requirements in the North Island. The committee reported there was already excess capacity and stock numbers were not increasing sufficiently rapidly to justify the construction of completely new facilities, although it did favour the Hellaby application. There was a case for some replacement of facilities and some rationalisation of ownership.

The Board accepted these findings, but decided to monitor the rate of increase in sheep numbers. However, as the Meat Industry Authority was imminent, it kicked for touch on all the plant applications before it.

Charles Hilgendorf commented: "For the Board to make far-reaching decisions before the Authority was set up might well prejudice its likelihood of success." The Board now supported the establishment of the independent licensing authority; an about-face since the Nordmeyer Commission.

Hawke's Bay Farmers Takapau, a three-chain sheepmeat processing plant. Built over three years at a cost of $33 million. The 'Rolls Royce' plant compared to the 'Model T' at Oringi.

The cynical would say it was easier for the Board to deliver a hospital pass to the Authority than to deliberate on each of the politically sensitive issues and, whatever its decisions, suffer the inevitable backlash. Not surprisingly, this is what faced the Authority.

The Meat Industry Authority came into being when the Government passed the Meat Amendment Act 1976. As the title implies, the Act amended the 1964 legislation, and in doing so preserved much of the old order.

New plant applicants were still required to prove economic necessity almost to the extent of showing that their proposal would not be detrimental to existing operators.

The Act formalised the xenophobic attitude towards overseas ownership that had come through in some submissions and in the Nordmeyer Commission report. The Authority should not issue a new licence, or renew or transfer any existing licence, to any non-resident, without the prior consent of the Minister.

Despite these provisions the UK-owned Borthwicks, managed by the New Zealander Peter Norman, made some rapid moves in the ownership stakes. In 1975 it had indicated an interest in a new plant in the Wairarapa, but this had not proceeded.

Early in 1977 Borthwicks reached agreement with the Co-operative Wholesale Society (CWS) to form a joint company for slaughter and processing of stock, leaving the procurement and marketing activities independent. The aim was to rationalise the use of both companies' plants in the lower half of the North Island, CWS at Longburn and Borthwicks at Waingawa and Feilding.

Then during the first hearing of the Authority in 1977 on the applications from HBFMC and Pacific Freezing for their respective plants in Hawke's Bay, Borthwicks dropped a bombshell by putting in a bid for Gear in Petone.

Ivan Thomas chaired the Authority. Other members were Tom McNab, the farmer representative, Trevor Kelly for the unions, and FCA chairman Ted Roberts, formerly of Swifts, representing the companies, with Gilbert Boyd from MAF as the secretary.

The Authority sat for 24 days hearing the Hawke's Bay applications and finally rejected them all early in 1978. The time taken probably reflects the guerrilla tactics of some of the players as much as the complexities of the issues involved. It also indicated that any hearing of the Authority was likely to become a media circus as well as an opportunity for extended submissions and politicisation of the issues. Further, it provided a telling display of the conflicting and contradictory motives of industry participants.

Not only had Borthwicks bid for Gear, but they and other companies put in counter-claims for Hawke's Bay processing capacity. John Foster sums up the Borthwicks/CWS position: "We oppose the grounds for an additional licence; there's plenty of capacity here. But if the Authority was persuaded otherwise then we have got the best credentials for having the extra capacity."

In addition each of the interested companies and various branches of Federated Farmers put in submissions and attended to present them. The Board did not make specific representations to the Authority but provided copies of relevant reports.

The Board's 1977 annual report states that "the arguments and debates that followed the announcement of Borthwicks offer to Gear became animated and, at times, emotional", and the whole issue was further complicated by the involvement of Brierley Investments, the corporate which had made its entry into the meat industry with the purchase of bacon and ham company Huttons.

Brierley and HBFMC then made a joint approach for shares in Gear. "After due consideration and discussion with the companies concerned and with Federated Farmers", the Board recommended in favour of this joint bid, and the Minister accepted it.

John Foster was a little more emphatic. "Suddenly, in the middle of the first hearing, Borthwicks announced a takeover bid for Gear, and you can imagine what happened. Brierley was in boots and all buying Gear shares in a big way, and then Brierley shunted those through Selwyn Cushing into a joint venture, which finally HBFMC took over. So Hawke's Bay Farmers had control of Gear."

And Borthwicks was literally out in the cold, a fact the *Dominion* unkindly rubbed in with the headline 'Borthwicks Bungles Bid'. According to Peter Norman the original plan developed in the early seventies was for Borthwicks to buy Gear, but that was turned down by the Board. The next move was a proposal for Borthwicks to join HBFMC to form a new company, the Wairarapa Meat Co, which would buy Gear and close the Petone plant, once again in the interests of rationalising capacity.

"It had the backing of Brierley, Selwyn Cushing was our financial adviser. We had actually moved into the Gear Company's offices when permission was refused again. We were ousted. Hawke's Bay Farmers bought Gear and (in 1981) closed it, transferring one of its chains to the new Takapau plant, and Brierley got the benefit of any residuals of Gear for Huttons."

The Authority's eventual decision to decline a licence to any of the Hawke's Bay applicants was a serious disappointment to many producers who were convinced of the need for more competition in the processing sector, if not more capacity. Some even called for the Authority to be abolished and for the industry to be delicensed. In this they were aided and abetted by Graeme Lowe and John Foster of Dawn – but not by the Board. Lowe reports that about that time the Board was "discussing the merits and demerits of delicensing the meat freezing industry. A paper… was circulated among members of the Board, its tendency being to advise against delicensing".

The Board's view was that the freezing industry was too important to farmers and to the New Zealand economy as a whole to be left entirely uncontrolled. It did consider that new licences should be issued more readily, but within the scope of a rational plan for the efficient development of the industry. The best way to achieve that would be through the broadening of the criteria under which the Meat Industry Authority was required to act.

The Hawke's Bay applicants were not to be deterred and Pacific submitted a further application for a three-chain plant at Oringi in July 1978. They cited evidence of poor performance in the industry and the impact of increasing stock numbers. HBFMC also lodged an application for a three-chain plant at Takapau.

The Authority set the hearing for October but this time the other main overseas-owned company, W & R Fletcher, objected and the hearing was delayed until December. In the interim Borthwicks/CWS applied to extend the Longburn works. The tactics were apparently to delay and obfuscate the hearings as much as possible.

The second hearing concluded in February 1979 after another marathon session of 24 days, with HBFMC being granted a licence, while Pacific lost out again.

According to the Board's 1979 annual report the HBFMC licence was for a three-chain sheep and lamb plant. John Foster suggests: "They wanted to build three chains but they got the message from the first nil decision and they cut back from three chains to two. Then apparently they agreed one chain with one coming from Gear Meat so it fitted in perfectly with Ivan Thomas's idea of rationalisation. The third chain came as the result of de-licensing."

The tenacious principals of Pacific Freezing applied again in June of 1979. They also lobbied Federated Farmers to apply pressure to the Authority, the Board and the Government to abolish the licensing system. Graeme Lowe kept up his contacts with the Prime Minister and the Minister of Agriculture as well as local politicians. He and John Foster also went to the Board on the basis that they had tried the system and had been shut out.

As Foster recalls they told the Board: "We have gone through the system and we have failed. We think there is only one solution, to delicense the industry and let competition come in and we'll build and take our chances. I'll never forget the reply by Charlie (Hilgendorf), it was so out of character. He told us to go back to Whakatu (HBFMC) and ask for some space. All his doctrine and philosophy subsequent to that was for more and more competition and private enterprise and freedom and market forces."

John Foster thinks that the Board was more influenced by overseas companies in those days than by New Zealand companies. "The other balance was that there were more overseas companies in the North Island than the South Island so it was a sort of a conspiracy. Whether that holds up or not, it was one of the theories."

Certainly Peter Norman would not agree with that idea of a cosy relationship with the Board. He was of the view that the overseas companies were refused because they were owned overseas and they had such a dominance in the meat business at the time.

In its short existence the Meat Industry Authority actually did consent to some applications. Early in 1977 it granted meat export slaughterhouse licences to Hellaby's at Taumarunui and for a regional abattoir with a meat packinghouse licence at Kokiri on the West Coast.

Mick Calder recalls that the latter decision set off a round of discussions on the provision of financial assistance from the Reserve Account with the irrepressible Malcolm Wallace who was the persistent promoter of the West Coast abattoir proposal.

Initially the Board and later the Prime Minister and Minister Finance (Robert Muldoon) and Minister of Agriculture (Duncan McIntyre) were sceptical that a meat plant on the Coast would be viable. The Wallace persistence finally paid off in 1980 when the Board and the Government agreed to the use of Reserve Account monies to finance a scheme to enable producers to take up shares in the co-operative Phoenix Meat Company and build an export beef processing

The official opening of Oringi. Prime Minister Robert Muldoon, Pahiatua MP Falloon (obscured) and Graeme Lowe. Photo: Graeme Lowe.

plant. The scepticism was also unfounded as the loan was repaid before it was due and the company has prospered.

In the meantime the Board had been involved in other moves that were changing the face of the industry. As Charles Hilgendorf reported in 1979: "It may be seen that in these times of accelerating change the Board is prepared to take whatever steps are necessary to protect the interests of producers, the people who make this vital industry possible. In the discharge of that responsibility the Board is clearly becoming more involved in different elements of the industry, most often as the initiating or catalytic agent making such projects possible." The idea of the Board acting as a catalyst to get changes in structures and ownership in the industry was to be developed during the eighties.

Arising from the earlier takeover battles in the South Island the Board had started negotiations in 1978 with Waitaki/NZR and CFM for NCF Kaiapoi to be acquired by a farmer-owned company, in line with the Board's desire to see key farmer-owned works in each region. The aim was to establish the financial arrangements and conditions of sale with the owners of the works. The farmers in the region would be required to contribute a proportion of the cost.

The negotiations on price were completed but Robert Muldoon and Duncan McIntyre thought that it was too high and would not consent to a Board application for a loan from the Reserve Account. A sticking-point was the capital expenditure required to bring the plant up to EC standards and extend the facilities to enable further processing of lamb.

A consultant's report reassessed the levels of expenditure for hygiene and further processing and another loan application was made in May 1979. This was turned down because the establishment of a farmer-owned key works was considered "not to be in the best interests of the industry". The proposal was revised after discussions with farmers and further protracted negotiations with the Ministry of Agriculture and the Ministers of Agriculture and Finance.

The new concept was to use the Reserve Account funds to acquire the company and convert it to a co-operative with 80% owned by farmers, and 20% by C S Stevens Ltd. Farmers would be required to pay 20% of their part of the purchase price with the remaining 80% to be taken from retained supplier rebates.

"New works boost industry capacity" proclaimed the Board's 1981 annual report, with pictures of Hellaby Taumarunui, Oringi and Takapau, and Phoenix. The pride of the West Coast – the Phoenix Meat Plant at Kokiri, (pictured) opened in 1980, and another new-style construction. Graeme Lowe advised long-time West Coast lobbyist Malcolm Wallace on his approach to gaining a licence and also how the plant could be built for much less than the $25 million originally discussed; he also was a foundation shareholder.

This finally gained ministerial approval in October 1979, and the Board established a company called Freesia Meats Ltd to receive the loan and acquire the shares in NCF Kaiapoi. The first directors of Freesia were chosen from outside the Board to preserve a degree of separation, and much to their surprise they were also nominated to be the original shareholders of the company.

They were John S B Brown a solicitor from Stone & Co, the Board's legal advisers, Rob Thompson of Coopers & Lybrand, and Rob McLagan, CEO of Federated Farmers who was the chairman.

The sale of the shares to farmers was promoted by Mervyn Barnett, elected to the Board in 1979, as the local member, plus Ted Turrell and George Rennie from the Canterbury Meat & Wool Section of Federated Farmers. The conversion to a co-operative was completed in 1980 with the sale of some 72 % of the shares to farmers and the balance to Stevens.

The low percentage taken up by the farmers was a serious disappointment to the promoters, who had assured the Board and the Government that farmers were keen to support the key works concept. Freesia Meats Ltd then went into virtual hibernation until it was resurrected as the Board's investment arm in late 1985.

Other projects involving the use of Reserve Account funds outside the core meat industry included loans to East Coast Farmers Fertiliser Co Ltd, Southland Co-op Phosphate Co Ltd, Federated Farmers to part-finance the acquisition of an office block in Wellington, and the Farmers Mutual Group. Funds were also invested in Dairy Industry Development Bonds.

There was also a short-term loan to the aerial topdressing company, Fieldair, to assist it to convert to a farmer owned co-operative. David Frith as a representative of Auckland Federated Farmers was one of the promoters of the company's case and, after one meeting, Kemp Stone advanced the view that here was a potential future chairman of the Meat Board.

The other big action involving the Board and the Reserve Account was the reorganisation of the fertiliser industry ownership, which started in July 1977. The final outcome was that the Board arranged for a loan to the Ravensdown Supply Co-operative to enable it to acquire the fertiliser assets of Kempthorne Prosser (KP) and a further loan to Fertiliser Holdings Ltd to acquire 3.3 million shares in NZ Farmers Fertiliser Co which had been previously held by KP.

The myriad machinations of these deals, in which the ubiquitous Brierley Investments also had a hand, are detailed in *The Gumboot Takeover - The Story of the Ravensdown Fertiliser Company* by Bryan James. Sir Peter Elworthy was heavily involved and recalls that "the role of the Meat Board and Charles Hilgendorf in particular was significant and pivotal".

Licensed to Kill
1979-81

"The producer, and the country as a whole, are paying a high price for a licensing system which actively militates against innovation, adaptation, relocation and plain, old-fashioned competition within the meat processing industry." Charles Hilgendorf.

As time went by, even the Board was changing its position on meat industry licensing. After the first Hawke's Bay hearing Charles Hilgendorf commented, "Events in the processing industry in the past year… have strengthened the Board's belief that there should be much freer access to licences than has been the case in the past." The second marathon Hawke's Bay hearing of the Meat Industry Authority in February 1979, reinforced the need for a review.

The Pacific Freezing brigade was keeping the issue alive. Graeme Lowe kept up a constant barrage of letters and contacts with the Meat Board and with the Government via both the Prime Minister and the Minister of Agriculture, while John Foster lobbied other interests.

The Prime Minister was eventually persuaded to call a conference on the meat industry in March 1979. The FCA put forward papers on slaughtering and processing charges, which were still under price control, licensing in the industry, the reliability of statistical livestock information, spread of kill, hygiene and livestock buying schedules. The Board submitted similar papers on price controls and licensing in the industry.

The conference discussed the views of both organisations that there had been a lack of success of the Stabilisation of Prices Regulations in holding down K & F charges.

The Board's view was that the regulations had failed "resoundingly to hold killing and processing charges at reasonable levels, and that in effect producers had been subjected to nothing less than a cost-plus pricing system." It advocated allowing charges to be determined by market forces.

"A return to a competitive free enterprise system might blow some invigor-

Tomoana on fire, September 1979. A spectacular event remembered in Hawke's Bay. W & R Fletcher spent some $40 million building a new six-chain sheepmeat operation, but little thought was given to readying the plant for future demands by adding cold storage or space for increased further processing. On the point of commissioning, the new plant was destroyed by fire, and then rapidly rebuilt after what was the largest insurance claim of the time. Photo: Graeme Lowe.

Harry Davis, general manager of Waitaki and chairman of the FCA from 1978-80, who was critical of the lack of support from government for the industry when inflation was surging along at double figures.

ating air through the boardrooms of the freezing industry, resulting in action to restrain cost increases through greater efficiencies in the companies' use of capital and labour." One of the outcomes of the conference was that K & F charges were removed from price controls, releasing pent-up pressure so that charges rose by a staggering 25% in the 1979-80 season and continued to rise in subsequent seasons.

On licensing, the Board proposed modifications to the system to enable new processing licences to be granted more readily, "provided they come within the scope of an overall plan for the rational and efficient development of the industry".

The Board still believed that the Authority should have responsibility for guiding the development of the whole industry including the local processing aspects. It reported later that, "While there was some pressure for complete delicensing the Board considered that a licensing system was necessary to retain the 'open door' provisions of the Act." A rather lame reason for persisting with the system and the Authority.

Taking a position it would later reverse, the FCA at the same time put out a statement opposing any idea of delicensing. As Harry Davis, chairman of FCA said in his 1978-79 report, "Our views on this matter have been expressed many times and I can only repeat that we believe that licensing of our industry is appropriate at this stage." It was a cast-iron means of limiting the aspirations of any new competitors, and of antagonising Lowe and Foster.

At the Meat & Wool Section of Federated Farmers annual meeting in May 1979, Richard Johnstone, who was a delegate and also an Electoral Committee member, gave a speech in which he pointed out that he considered John Foster was on the right track and farmers ought to get rid of this licensing business.

At the next meeting of the Electoral Committee he introduced the remit on delicensing of the meat industry. Johnstone says: "We were killing cattle in Auckland and they were getting four cents more per kg in the Hawke's Bay, so we started carrying our cattle to Hawke's Bay to be killed at Pacific. I discussed this with Charlie Hilgendorf at Ruakura and suggested delicensing (as a means of improving competition) and he didn't say yes or no. But he didn't rule it out.

"So I had a discussion with (Board member) Warren Martin as to how I should introduce this remit. I said 'Would it be "That the Board investigate?" and he said 'Hell, no! Always go for the jugular. They'll water it down. You put it as strongly as you can.'

"So I took his advice and introduced the remit that the meat industry should be delicensed. We had four meat company directors sitting around the table as Electoral Committee members – Selwyn Lloyd and Brian Wills from AFFCO, Thomas Crosse from Richmond and Pacific, and Mel Falconer from Alliance. As chairman I called on them in turn and they got up and spoke against it. It was really hilarious.

"I reserved my right of reply. During my summing up I said, 'I was going to mention that those who spoke against the remit were directors of freezing companies and then I decided that I wouldn't.' In the end the remit was watered down and they decided that the Board should do an investigation."

Both Lowe and Foster recall an Agricultural Economists' Association conference in Blenheim in July 1979 at which the latter gave an address on aspects of the industry including the case for delicensing. John Falloon MP and Ruth Richardson (legal adviser to Federated Farmers and future MP and Minister of Finance) were in attendance. Ruth Richardson thought the licensing system could be tidied up by government with a halfway house, and indicated that the caucus agricultural committee was looking at introducing efficiency and competition as additional criteria for a licence.

John Foster said to her: "Jeepers, Ruth, we would never get out of court! We were 24 days arguing just economic need and justification and stock numbers. Add two nebulous things like competition and efficiency and we would never get out. The barrier to entry would be huge."

Ruth Richardson then went to Alan Wright, president of Federated Farmers, and persuaded him it was time for delicensing. In August 1979 an Amendment Bill was introduced into Parliament. This proposed the repeal of some of the economic criteria before the Authority when considering applications for a licence, reducing the functions of the Authority, and transferring consideration of industry mergers and takeovers to the Commerce Commission.

The Board's submission generally supported the amendments but argued there was little point in having the Authority if its functions were to be reduced. Consideration of the bill was even more protracted than the hearings of the Authority.

John Foster recalls one meeting with Robert Muldoon after he, Graeme Lowe and Hamilton Logan, then chairman of Richmond, had broken all speed limits to get to Wellington by car after the airport was closed by a storm. They had been summoned by John Falloon who said, "The old boy has gone cold on this thing, you had better come down."

At the meeting, which started 20 minutes late because he was caught in the same storm, Muldoon expressed concern that if the legislation passed significant works were going to close, people were going to be thrown out of work and the Government was going to be blamed. "What can you say to help?" he asked.

They began to put their case to an impatient Prime Minister. John Foster recalls: "You can imagine – Piggy (Muldoon) 20 minutes late; he wasn't going to waste time. Graeme was stammering along and Muldoon said to him 'Stop! You have changed the tense and lost the subject'.

"I came in and said: 'The real problem is that the industry can't kill the stock numbers they claim they can kill.'

" 'And who would you be to criticise anyone who is not here to defend themselves? I've heard these stories before,' said Muldoon. 'I would have thought that the Meat Industry Authority would have sorted that out'."

The Pacific team then said that they had proof that, at the height of the season, the maximum throughput through the combined works was 70% of their rated capacity. Stock numbers were rising and the available capacity would be inadequate to handle the kill.

"We had the MAF's new estimate of stock numbers and he could see that they were moving up. He grabbed those numbers and asked 'Has MAF seen these?' 'Yes,' we said. And so he put those aside."

"We also said that it would take us two years to build a plant and a year to

Boning mutton carcasses at the new Takapau works in 1983.

commission it, so we were three years away. Anyone who was planning on the basis of getting a licence was obviously thinking of doing it anyway. And there were plenty of old places that should close. He got those points and thanked us. We were there for 15 or 20 minutes. And Falloon rang us the next day and said we were back on track, it would go through."

The amendment to the Meat Act eventually went through in April 1981. The final version proposed the dissolution of the Authority and the transfer of responsibility for licensing of slaughtering and processing plants to the Director-General of Agriculture. The criteria for the granting of a licence related principally to meeting the technical specifications and conditions required for such processing plants, specifically the meat hygiene requirements.

The 'open door' provisions that obliged licensees to accept stock for slaughter as offered by or on behalf of owners, were retained, though this condition became increasingly difficult as competition in the industry heated up and companies endeavoured to avoid providing any assistance to their competitors. The producer co-operative marketing companies still relied heavily on the Board and the Minister to get companies to meet their obligations.

The legislation also transferred control over the issuing of meat export licences from the Minister of Agriculture to the Board. It also set out the matters to be considered for granting such licences. These included consultation with the MEC on both the issue or cancellation of a licence and on conditions including quantities, classes and forms that could be exported, and the applicable countries.

So the short but active life of the Authority was terminated, the processing sector of the meat industry was delicensed and Pacific went on to build its plant at Oringi, starting construction 18 months behind HBFMC at Takapau.

Oringi opened in November 1981, three months after Takapau, and the ceremony was said to have been Robert Muldoon's largest political meeting before he successfully contested the general election later in the month. Four thousand people turned up and Muldoon later complained to the Broadcasting Corporation that his speech was not covered on television. Apparently the Corporation considered the ceremony was too political so close to the election.

The old order was gone but the floodgates did not immediately swing open. There were still considerable economic barriers to closing old plants and industrial problems in opening new ones.

Pacific Freezing's Oringi, a three-chain sheepmeat processing plant. Once again built with 'foil, polystyrene and four by two' it was constructed within a year and for only $24 million.

Smoothing Prices or Seizing Product 1975-79

"The Board will continue its policy of market intervention, regardless of the level of prices, if it considers the exporters' schedules are unrealistic or if feels it could improve the market returns thereby. Profits (and losses) on such intervention (trading) operations could be recorded against an account established from funds at present in the Meat Industry Reserve Account." Annual Report 1975.

Despite frequent utterances that it still considered private enterprise provided the best and most efficient means of processing and marketing New Zealand's meat for export, the Board was moving or being moved inexorably towards greater participation in the export business.

During the middle and late seventies the economic and trade impacts of the first oil shock began to show and price support or intervention in one form or another was practically the norm. Price-smoothing arrangements introduced in the Meat Export Prices Act of 1976 were being refined as the cost/price squeeze took hold, meat company financial results wavered, and schedule prices fluctuated in the wake of disruptions to increasingly sensitive markets.

In addition, the Board had strengthened its view that intervention, rather than supplementation, was an essential aspect of price support for sheepmeats and it was honing its own schedule-setting skills and the management of market interventions on behalf of the producers.

Darcy Freeman joined the Board as the marketing services manager in February 1975. He had spent most of his working career in the Borthwicks organisation and brought with him a wealth of industry knowledge and experience, which some commentators considered was then sadly lacking at the Board. He and Graeme Harrison formed the team that negotiated with the industry on costings and yields. As Harrison tells it, "I used to prepare the bullet from our side and negotiate it; and Darcy was the nice guy".

In addition, Monte Waller from CWS was persuaded to come out of retirement to help the Board sell the mutton it acquired during its intervention in 1974-75. Sales were negotiated mainly to Japan/South Korea, the USSR, the UK, and some to the development market in Peru, with the meat companies acting as the Board's agents. Again, Waller had industry experience and credibility, some of which rubbed off on to the other members of the staff.

The Board had also moved to strengthen the commercial side of its operations overseas. Derek Dickinson from Swifts had joined the London office in 1973, as the UK marketing officer. So the Board not only had the legislative authority to intervene in the marketplace, but also had started building up the necessary staff to manage such interventions on both sides of the world. In doing so it was, in part, adjusting to the political climate,

Cattle numbers kept increasing steadily throughout the 1970s.

which favoured economic intervention, but it was also setting the scene for a period of rivalry and argument with the major companies and their associations.

In this context, the elected members invariably represented the Board at meetings with the FCA which was represented by chief executives of the companies, and not their directors. Therefore, it was farmer politicians arguing against meat company executives who had generally cut their teeth on wrangles with the unions.

As Ian McKellar, former chairman of CFM pointed out, "We (company directors) were kept out of it a fair bit, and I think it was probably a jolly good job because there was so much politics and you had to remember every facet of it. I got quite good at it in the end… but, oh dear, it was convoluted."

The impact of the various government incentive schemes introduced during the early seventies was beginning to show through in substantial increases in sheep numbers and production. The impact of these policies is detailed in *Farming without Subsidies* compiled by Ron Sandrey and Russell Reynolds. In that publication Tony Rayner points out: "In due course, the toll that the protection of domestic industry had on agriculture was implicitly recognised by government and various forms of compensation for these costs were introduced. While assistance had long been provided for agricultural activities popularly considered in the 'public good' at the time – research, extension, market development and marketing boards – it was not until the 1960s that there was significant subsidisation at the farm level.

"However, from then until 1984 there was a gradual acceleration in production grants and subsidies… loans at below market interest rates became increasingly valuable as market rates increased. Instead of allowing international market prices to force a shift towards diversification, domestic policy became increasingly concerned with sheltering the traditional pastoral industries from the realities of the overseas market place. The Livestock Incentive Scheme of 1976 was designed to boost stock numbers at a time when they were, appropriately, falling. Land Development Encouragement Loans were likewise aimed to increase production, particularly on marginal land."

Sheep numbers had been rising in the late sixties but had dropped back to 55 million in 1973 and hovered around that level through to 1976. Then the subsidies and other assistance measures kicked in and sheep numbers surged to reach 69 million by 1980. Lamb production and export receipts at fob increased commensurately. Despite the setback to beef returns in the early seventies, cattle numbers kept increasing steadily through the decade assisted by expressions of confidence from the Board and support by way of supplements, firstly under the price support scheme in 1974-75 and then the new Price Smoothing Scheme in the 1975-76 season.

But increased fob returns did not translate to improved returns at the farm gate. One of the major reasons was industrial disputes, which always occurred at the most inopportune time, when the unions could exert the most leverage. The Government was closely involved in the industrial relations scene, too closely for some in the industry when Robert Muldoon intervened with his three-way split to settle the 1978 impasse.

Harry Davis, the general manager of meat operations of Waitaki, commented in his 1978-79 annual report as chairman of the FCA: "The freezing industry is a very public industry. When it is necessary to increase killing and processing charges, farmers are quick to react. Wages are a very significant part of processing costs. Present trends in wage movements therefore, whether by government policy or by negotiation are not encouraging. Freezing companies cannot absorb major wage movements. This means that farmers' costs increase and unfortunately we are at a stage where further significant moves will not only reduce farmers' incomes but also their ability to reinvest and increase stock numbers."

The FCA engaged Mr (later Sir) Lewis Ross to make an independent analysis of processing income and costs over a five year period. His survey showed only two-thirds of freezing companies made a profit from processing in the period 1974-77 and in 1978 this declined to 50%. Harry Davis concluded, "The meat processing industry does not make excessive profits and during the period of price control we have been restricted in the recovery of many costs."

Much of the blame for this state of affairs was sheeted home to the need for more labour to meet the requirements of the hygiene regulations introduced by the US and the EC. The Board thought there was also room to improve processing efficiency and labour productivity.

The processing industry also argued for its fair share of the handouts from the Government during the latter part of the seventies. Particularly, it sought equality in the application of the export incentives available to other sectors of the economy.

The Export Performance for Qualifying Goods taxation incentive scheme had been introduced as an extension to the Increased Exports of Goods Incentive scheme under the provisions of the Income Tax Act 1976 to encourage the growth of export sales values. Initially meat products were excluded, but after some intense lobbying by the FCA and MEC, meat was added as a 'qualifying product' in 1978 but only in specific forms within the principle of 'net domestic value added'.

The main product category was defined as: "Chilled or frozen retail consumer packs principally comprising edible meat portions, which have been processed beyond the primal cut stage, have a minimum packing standard of clipped, tied or sealed wrapping and which are sold for retail consumption without further processing or packaging." Other definitions also relied on the phrase "sold for consumption without further processing or packaging".

In his 1979-80 annual report Harry Davis said the industry considered this too restrictive, and the FCA contended alternative means of further processing could add as much domestic value as further cutting of the product. In particular, it cited the increasing demand for chilled beef and lamb from supermarkets and the food service sector (hotels, restaurants and institutions or HRI) overseas.

"Modern technology has allowed the export of an extremely high quality product that is able to compete directly with the market's domestically

Meat diplomacy. Hellaby's sausages were always a hit at New Zealand diplomatic functions in Washington. The Board therefore decided to develop sausages specifically for sale at retail in the US market. The all-beef 'Bangers' were developed by Craig Hickson, then the Board's product development manager. The project suffered from delayed approval from the USDA and technical requirements which made it impossible to reproduce the usual flavour of NZ sausages. Pictured sampling the Bangers are, from left, Rod, later Sir Rod Weir of the Combined Producers Boards, then on the A and P Board; Board deputy chairman Charles Hilgendorf, another A and P representative and Craig Hickson. The sausages, made by Kowhai Meats Ltd of Feilding, failed to capture the US consumer.

produced fresh product. In addition such product requires investment in specialised equipment, there is an increased risk involved but employment opportunities are enhanced and export value is being added to the product. Often, to cut this product further incurs a cost that cannot be recovered in the marketplace," Harry Davis said.

Further submissions to the Government brought some improvement in eligibility, but the scheme was to prove expensive as other countries increasingly focussed on the incentives, as well as the other agricultural support measures, as grounds for countervailing duty action.

The Meat Export Prices Act of 1976 introduced the new Price Smoothing Scheme, which from the Government's standpoint was aimed at providing some stabilisation of sheepfarmers' incomes, as an important element in general economic welfare.

The scheme also encompassed the new Meat Income Stabilisation Account (MISA) first operated in 1975.

The Price Smoothing Scheme endorsed by government was largely what had been developed by the Board in 1974-75. It operated with minimum and trigger prices, allowing market prices to fluctuate within the band between. At the lower end prices were supplemented and at the trigger point a graduated levy drew off funds to separate self-balancing buffer accounts for beef and sheepmeats. Minimum prices were set to reflect market realisations rather than some measure of income adequacy.

The minimum pricing formula worked on the basis of a rolling two-year historical average of market related returns plus a one year forward projection but with a discretionary 15% movement around the arithmetic average; trigger prices were set at a predetermined percentage above the minimum.

The minimum and trigger prices were set on the same basis as the companies' schedules 'at the scale' rather than the previous system that set prices at fob.

The self-balancing element of the Stabilisation Account was important to the Board as it relieved the Reserve Account (MIRA) of the price support role and allowed funds to provide more direct support when the Board considered it necessary. The Board had made sure that the scheme gave it the authority to intervene at the minimum price if it considered that action was appropriate, rather than just pay supplements.

Quite separately, the Board retained the ability, under the Meat Export Control Act, to offer its own schedule and to intervene in the market if it considered that prices were too low, even if they were above the minimum prices, and to use the Reserve Account to fund such interventions. The Reserve Account funds could still be invested in projects considered beneficial for the industry.

The Board was given responsibility for the management of the Price Smoothing Scheme and some of the wrinkles were still not sorted out when it first came into play in the 1976-77 season.

The Board reasoned that by intervening (for sheepmeats) at the minimum price farmers would receive the equivalent of the schedule offered by the exporters plus any supplement to bring the amount up to the minimum. However, any increased product value over the original schedule price could be used to offset funds required to raise the price to the minimum.

In this respect the Board had an advantage over the companies in that the funds used for any minimum price intervention came from the Stabilisation Account. There was the added benefit that, subject to the approval of the Minister, it could be accommodated by way of Reserve Bank overdraft.

The New Zealand meat rosette. The 'brand value' of the rosette, built up over the years it was used in a number of international markets, was estimated at hundreds of thousands of dollars, though the greatest recognition of it was for lamb and in the UK market.

Initially, the interest rate for the overdraft facility had been debated. The Government view was that a nominal rate would be inappropriate while the Board held investments in government stock, via the Reserve Account, which earned higher rates. Officials proposed that a nominal rate of 1% should apply only when the overdraft exceeded the nominal value of these investments, then about $56 million.

The Board protested that the two accounts were unrelated and in April 1977 Finance Minister Muldoon agreed interest would be charged on the Stabilisation Account at the rate of 1% per annum. So the Board had the advantage, so long as the Minister was willing to provide support, of much cheaper finance than the companies could negotiate through their bankers.

While still professing support for the private enterprise system, the Board was signalling that statutory intervention was an increasing prospect. The 1976 annual report explained: "The Board's philosophy on marketing essentially favours a private enterprise approach qualified by the need to protect the producer from the more severe market fluctuations and also ensuring that market operations lead to maximum returns both in the short and longer term."

The view was that it was desirable to leave the marketing of beef cuts as much as possible in the hands of the exporters. With a simpler product such as mutton, where markets were limited, there was a considered advantage in intervening and acquiring the product.

The annual report went on to note that the Board also considered that with the price smoothing arrangements and the experience it had gained with both price supplementation and purchase of the product, it was well situated "to protect the producers and at the same time retain those elements of private enterprise which make for efficient marketing".

In 1975-76 beef producers received the minimum prices set by the Meat Export Prices Committee in the early part of the season until prices improved in overseas markets in February. But the market for beef in the US was weak and chicken and turkey products were starting to challenge beef for the 'centre of the plate'. In Canada, there was strong price competition which led to informal price fixing arrangements with the Australians and later the introduction of quotas. The beef market collapsed and prices were supplemented again from the end of 1975-76 to the early months of the 1976-77 season.

The Board's interventions in the mutton market in both 1974-75 and 1975-76 had raised the question of taking over the marketing of mutton permanently as it was a commodity product used for 'manufacturing' purposes and sold to limited numbers of buyers. In August 1976, at the mid-year meeting of the Electoral Committee, Charles Hilgendorf discussed the merits of such a proposal.

"Don't let there be any mistake; the Board strongly believes that meat that can be truly marketed (and this applies particularly to lamb and table beef) is best handled by the individual private trader rather than by any monolithic monster whether it be Board, Commission or Government. But much mutton is not truly marketed. It is mostly sold as bulk raw material for manufacturing.

"It is sold to a small number of countries – often, virtually to only one, and to a small number of traders in that country. The Board has probably been able during the past two seasons to sell at better overall prices than would have been possible if it had not been in the market." It would be hard to tell if this would always be the case, however, and under existing legislation, the Board could not take ownership of all mutton on a continuing basis.

A committee of the Board had investigated the merits of taking over mutton. The advantages included: the elimination of weak sales because of storage and cash flow pressures; more stable longer term marketing arrangements with buyers, particularly in Japan; a more consistent schedule of prices to producers; facilitation of product improvement and market development.

In addition the Board could ensure a more efficient marketing administration and staffing if it was permanently involved. There were also disadvantages such as the possible difficulty of arranging killing space with companies reluctant to process for the Board; problems in arranging private storage at certain times in the season, requiring the Board to provide additional high cost storage; the producer co-operatives would have no access to mutton. There was also the view that while intervention at low prices may have strengthened the market it was possible that Board ownership might lower overall prices when demand was strong.

Charles Hilgendorf concluded that the Board would not be making a hasty decision but would discuss the matter with farmers, the Government and exporters. He noted that the latter had already expressed their total opposition to the Board taking over mutton marketing. "Just how strong this opposition is we have yet to determine in view of the speed with which some companies hand over their mutton to the Board when the going gets tough."

This statement departed from the Board's usual stance that marketing was best left to private enterprise and it would only intervene when it could see benefit for producers. The differentiation between consumer-related products, which the private companies were well equipped to handle, and the possibility of more centralised marketing of commodity products where there were limited sales outlets, was to develop especially as the trade with the Middle East picked up. The prospect of the Board taking over marketing in one form or another was given a frequent airing from then on.

This changing attitude was perhaps more starkly emphasised in the 1976-77 season when the Board took the unprecedented step of intervening in the marketing of New Zealand lamb in the UK. Some would aver that the change occurred because Graeme Harrison had been transferred to the Board's London office.

Schedule prices for lamb and mutton in New Zealand were more than satisfactory in the early part of the season and buffer levies totalling $7.2 million were collected. However the state of the lamb market in the UK was of particular concern. Prices for New Zealand lamb fell by seven pence per pound within two weeks in early February.

The market had opened with a shortage of New Zealand lamb during January following a loadout ban in processing plants here, but as the season progressed shipments started arriving thick and fast. Allan Frazer, the Board's UK director, described the situation at the end of February 1977 as "the biggest drop in New Zealand lamb prices that has ever occurred".

He went on: "In our view a fall of this nature in such a short period cannot be justified, particularly when all the signs point to prices for meat tending upwards as the year proceeds. Certainly, a fall from the 'scarcity' values being recorded in December and early January was inescapable, but such a rapid fall cannot allow for any assessment of consumer response."

Adam Begg greets Richard Butler, president of the National Farmers' Union in the UK. The NFU was supportive of the actions taken by the Board to prop up lamb prices in the UK.

Wholesalers had over-reacted to the varying short-term supply situation and had not given sufficient regard to the prospect of the prices firming later. A loss of confidence was the only logical explanation for the fall and the Board decided some action was needed to rectify the situation.

It bought a shelf company called 'SodaWren' from its solicitors in London, renamed it Meatmark Ltd and set it up to buy and sell New Zealand lamb. Graeme Harrison recalled: "This was real radical stuff. It all came down to trying to schedule vessels." The pressures of the new killing season following the loadout dispute meant the shipping arrival programme, which was planned to synchronise the flow of product onto the market to match expected offtakes, was severely disrupted.

A plan was developed, accepted by the Board and the company was established on 21 February 1977. It is a date that Graeme Harrison remembers well. He came back to the office from a meeting and was advised that the company papers were ready to go and, "Oh, by the way, your wife has just gone to the maternity home".

The Board saw Meatmark as a move to assist the private enterprise system by acting to stabilise prices in a difficult marketing situation and not a move to set up in competition with the established wholesalers. It offered to buy PM grade lambs delivered to store in the UK at 40.5 pence per pound, with appropriate relativities for other grades.

The market did firm to some extent before Meatmark bought any product. The move reflected the developing attitude at the Board that it could intervene using the backing of the funds in the Meat Industry Reserve Account and act as a 'strong' seller to correct short term price fluctuations.

The *Meat Producer* for March 1977 reported that support for the Board's intervention had come from the sheepfarmers of the UK. An article in *Big Farm Weekly* stated that a threat to UK sheepfarmers' returns had receded as a result of the move. "The price shakeout, which occurred mainly as a result of bunching of supplies following a strike in New Zealand late last year, did not affect prices for home-killed produce. But the National Farmers Union (NFU) obviously feared that, if the weaknesses continued, British producers would suffer. So Agriculture House (NFU Headquarters) has welcomed the board's plan to set up a company, Meatmark."

The report went on: "The move, however caused a rather nervous reaction in Whitehall and was met with outright hostility from the retail meat trade. Eyebrows were also apparently raised in Brussels, but there the dominant reaction was probably one of approval."

The Board set its buying price. "Then over the next few weeks there was a stand-off. Everyone sold under the price, and the New Zealand companies were the worst," Graeme Harrison recalls. "They didn't want it to be known that they were the weak sellers, because the whole thing came down to who was going to hold their product. But they had cashflow problems. Then the British companies decided to start selling and because the gap between our prices became too great, we started buying.

"We finished up with product in 20-odd cold stores and we took whatever shipping weights were delivered so we were absolutely screwed on the product weights. And then came the big lull. We had all this product in store and I was the fall guy. Allan was the European director but everyone said 'That bloody Harrison caused this'. So if it failed I was gone. Then in June we started to get nibbles.

"So we started to sell and we had given an undertaking to sell back through the industry, through the UK importers. And then Charlie Hilgendorf came across and we were selling quite well. We had to go to meet a Commonwealth supportive group within the House of Commons. Afterwards old Charlie pulled me aside and said, 'Whatever you do, young fella, don't make too much money'. What it really came down to was that the Board did not want to face up to the structural problem in the industry. Meatmark made £20,000, and it was the most glorious result for the Meat Board. It didn't make too much money, so therefore the farmers of New Zealand were satisfied."

In setting up Meatmark the Board had emphasised the aim was to provide short-term assistance to private enterprise in a very difficult but temporary marketing situation and the company would continue only until the market had stabilised at the retail level.

Hilgendorf stated that Meatmark should not be regarded as the thin end of the wedge for either a permanent or wider Board marketing policy in the UK. It was anxious to get out of buying as soon as possible, but had no intention of disbanding Meatmark, keeping it as a backstop if price instability occurred again.

The chairman of the MEC, Bill Leonard, was not convinced the Board's action was necessary and may even have been harmful because, in his view, the market was stabilising of its own accord. He also claimed that the Board should disclose its policy on the 'disposal' of Meatmark's stocks as "exporters did not want the Board to panic and start dumping lambs in October because that would bring down the price for the new season".

Charles Hilgendorf roundly rejected this. "The facts show that the price of New Zealand lamb was plunging at 3p per lb per week and some importers were predicting that prices would drop even further before the market reached rock bottom.

"Far from showing any sign of stabilising, the market scene on the eve of the Board's intervention was one of the trade lacking confidence and gripped by near panic." Meatmark would release stock onto the market in its own time and in a manner that would not disrupt or harm the market in any way. "The Board had no need, nor was it under any compulsion, to be a weak seller," he said.

Bill Leonard, chairman of the MEC, who was critical of the Board's actions.

The Board's actions also attracted the attention of Aubrey Begg, a former Labour MP from Southland, and the party's spokesman on agriculture, who was later to become a member of the Meat and Wool Boards' Electoral Committee. He had expressed the view that "the Board was hellbent on socialising meat marketing".

This contrasted with the views of Bruce Barclay, Labour's then shadow Minister of Agriculture who had berated the Board for not getting into marketing. Charles Hilgendorf again reiterated that the Board was not interested in acquiring and marketing meat except as an occasional safeguard operation, even though its interventions were becoming more frequent.

The market intervention operations continued to feature with mutton in the 1977-78 season mainly influenced by the changes in buying policies in the USSR. The previous season the Soviet Union had made large purchases, resulting in prices for mutton moving above their trigger levels. But in 1977-78 the USSR buyers stayed away. Prices dropped to the minimum level of 30 cents per kg in April and in May six companies decided that the market would not even sustain that price. The Board then exercised its option for the third time in four seasons to take over the product and market it on its own behalf. It eventually assumed ownership of 25% of the season's mutton kill.

This time the Board explained that it considered it was better placed than some companies to finance the storage of product and to hold out for a better price, particularly for mutton. Of course, it relieved the companies of the marketing risk.

It also restated in the 1978 annual report that the intervention of a strong seller could stabilise a weak market situation. In that particular instance its belief proved to be almost correct. The returns did improve but a substantial depreciation of the US dollar against other world currencies eroded the benefits of the higher prices that had been achieved.

The major 1978 development in the price support arena came from government rather than the Board. It was the budget announcement by Prime Minister and Finance Minister Muldoon that Supplementary Minimum Prices (SMPs)

NEWS FLASH: Mr Hilgendorf likened the sheep meat situation between the Prime Minister and the board to that of an orchestra, where Mr. Muldoon was playing the big bassoon and the board was playing a minor instrument giving forth quieter sounds which were more acceptable to some ears.

Trying to establish harmony between the conflicting national and international demands of the meat industry. Cartoon by Ian Stimson.

would be introduced for each of the main farm exports to restore farmer confidence and to act as further financial incentives to expand agricultural production.

SMPs had their origin in the Zanetti Committee's idea of supplementary payments, which had appeal to the incoming National Government in November 1975, and particularly Robert Muldoon.

The scheme would involve the establishment of a series of minimum prices to provide a supplement to the price smoothing arrangements operated by the Boards. The SMP scheme was to be an interim measure to assist farming for two years, but it would be rolled forward until 1985.

The introduction of the scheme, and its eventual demolition, probably caused more long-term damage to the industry than the benefits it was designed to provide. It encouraged the further expansion of already rising stock numbers, with consequent expansion of capacity by meat companies; severe strains were imposed on the marketing or disposal activities with new untried markets having to be developed; and the termination of the scheme required that much of the infrastructure was dismantled or 'rationalised'.

The Board did not embrace the concept of SMPs with any enthusiasm and expressed its disapproval of the scheme and concerns about the effects.

These concerns were heightened by the fact that the SMP prices were well above the existing price smoothing minimum prices. In the case of cow beef the SMP minimum was also above the trigger price for that grade, which technically meant that some of the Government's supplement would have to be taken back as a buffer levy.

The introduction of the SMPs meant that the price support mechanisms could no longer be considered self-balancing. The element of government subsidy was likely to be large and there were concerns that the level of subsidisation could reinforce the inflationary trends in New Zealand and be unsustainable as it did not bear any relation to market returns. Other countries could claim subsidised exports from New Zealand were unfair or injurious and might apply countervailing import duties.

Charles Hilgendorf summarised the Board's view that through the SMP scheme "the Government is seeking to establish a firmer base for farm development and investment decisions. This is a sound objective and evidence of the Government's willingness to make resources available to farming.

"The Board believes, however, that ultimately, we must find the means of achieving the same result without the risk, inherent in the present scheme, of compromising our belief in enterprise and competition and the entire philosophy on which our meat and wool industries have been developed," he said. "Producers have fought hard and long to achieve a degree of independence in the running of their industry's affairs. They should think equally hard and long before yielding this independence to either the mandarins in government departments or to the politicians – no matter how well-intentioned or enticing their blandishments."

The Board's concerns fell on deaf political ears. The popular opinion was there were so many government policies supporting other sectors of the economy that the SMP scheme was needed to provide a balance. Inflation was still rampant, interest rates were high and rising, the value of the New Zealand dollar was artificially high. Some means of providing farmers with relief was politically desirable, and Robert Muldoon was just the man to provide it. It was also election year.

Despite its criticisms the Board agreed to act as the Government's agent to administer the SMP scheme alongside the Price Smoothing Scheme, but with separate identification and accounting procedures. In detailing the arrangements it noted: "The Board will arrange for supplementation only. It does not have the option of purchase and marketing, but this possibility will continue to be available under its own scheme." This apparent lack of an option to intervene was going to become a bone of contention.

The irony was that during the 1978-79 season producer prices improved to the extent that neither the price support scheme nor SMPs were required. Even so the Board again took action in the market place – this time with the co-operation of the MEC.

The Storage-Under-Board-Control (SUBC) scheme was introduced to hold agreed quantities of New Zealand lamb off the UK market as a means of stabilising a short term drop in prices. Prices had crashed in November 1978 as a significant volume of NZ lambs, which had originally been held for sale to Iran, were diverted to the UK market when payment problems were experienced with the Iran contract.

Supermarkets increased their buying power rapidly through the 1980s.

Then as the new season's shipments began to arrive in quantity, a three-week nation-wide strike of UK lorry drivers halted the clearance of vessels and distribution. This, plus the bargaining strength of the major bulk buyers – the supermarkets, multiple butcher chains and secondary wholesalers buying direct ex ship – put severe pressure on prices when deliveries started.

The Board had considered reactivating Meatmark but SUBC prevailed. The scheme enabled prices to be held but did not succeed in raising them as anticipated. This move did, however, cause a further MEC and Board review of shipping programmes and storage arrangements with the aim of devising better ways to control the flow of lamb onto the UK market.

The chairman of the MEC, Ron Cushen, reported on the project in 1980: "The principal factors in the new system are, determining the market requirements, formulating a shipping programme to match, and adhering to the programme – despite the temptation to utilise spare shipping space or alleviate New Zealand storage problems. This has been a major step forward and the objective is to market that product in the best interests of the New Zealand economy."

The price support arrangements were required again in 1980 when a collapse in the beef prices in the US caught everyone by surprise. Prices for imported beef dropped from 139 US cents per lb in January to 110 cents in March as a result of competition from ample supplies of pork and poultry and a slowing of the US economy. Also, interest rates in New Zealand increased from 15 to 21% in the first three months.

Arrangements were discussed with the MEC and a supplementary payments scheme came into effect in April 1980. The support action lasted for 10 weeks and cost some $9.75 million.

Similarly in 1980-81, after a promising beginning, prices, particularly for beef, fell well short and price support for beef producer returns was required for much of the season.

In addition, while no intervention or support was necessary, the schedule price for lamb hovered just above the initial SMP minimum price of 110 cents. When the Meat Export Prices Committee reviewed prices to take account of reduced EC import tariffs, exporters moved their schedules up to match. They were anxious to avoid Board intervention.

The exporters only lifted the schedule by more than two cents above the minimum price in August 1981 when the bulk of the kill was over.

At the end of the 1980-81 season the Board reviewed its price support and intervention operations over the previous seven years. It noted it had intervened in the market for lamb in 1974-75 and in the market for mutton in both 1974-75 and 1976-77.

The sheepmeat account had a credit balance of $7.4 million which would be necessary to assist in financing the expected downturns in market opportunities as sheep numbers and the production potential of the industry expanded.

The beef portion of the Stabilisation Account had reflected the cyclical nature of the beef market over the previous seven years. It had been $15.5 million in credit at the start of the 1980-81 season, as buffer levies had more than compensated for the supplements paid out, but drawings of a record $23.4 million during the 1980-81 season resulted in a deficit of $7.8 million. So the overall balance of both accounts stood with a deficit of just $400,000 at the beginning of 1981-82. It was never going to be enough.

The Government changed the whole concept of price suppport for the 1981-82 season. In March 1981 – another election year – it had announced the minimum SMP prices for the following season. It was usual to reveal the prices in the July budget. The new season's SMP scheme prices were for the most part 20-30% above those ruling in the current season and even above the existing schedule prices for all categories of export meat, except mutton.

The architects of the SMP scheme had detached it from the realities of the market and played the political card.

The Prices Committee, on the other hand, was bound to the principle of operating a scheme funded by a self balancing account so the prices that it set for the 1981-82 season reflected the assessed market trends.

As a result, for the first time since the introduction of the SMP scheme, the Committee prices were below the SMP levels for all benchmark grades. The Board's representatives on the Prices Committee were convinced that the arguments put forward by the Government representatives on the Committee were designed to push its prices as close to the SMP levels as possible.

Consequently, a large proportion of the funding that was expected for price support would come from the Stabilisation Account, to lessen the funds required for the Government-inspired portion of the arrangement. This intention has not been denied subsequently. The push for the Prices Committee to agree to higher levels of minimum prices would persist for the next three years.

Walking the Trade Tightrope 1972-83

"As with anything that's had too much attention from the government, farm policy is a mess and a tangle, an immense dog's breakfast of programmes, laws and regulations… But farm policy although it's complex, can be explained. What it can't be is believed. No cheating spouse, no teen with a wrecked family car, no mayor of Washington, DC, videotaped in flagrante delicto, has ever come up with anything as far-fetched as US farm policy". P J O'Rourke, 'Parliament of Whores'.

Early in September 1982, the United States called for 'voluntary' restraints on beef imports from third country suppliers for the rest of the calendar year, using, for the first time, provisions of the Meat Import Law of 1979.

On almost the same day, at the Four Nations Beef Conference in the US, cattlemen from the United States, Canada, New Zealand and Australia were discussing problems facing the world trade in beef.

As the October issue of the *Meat Producer* reported: "Discussion focussed on the restrictive access policies of Japan, and the highly disruptive beef trade policies pursued by the European Economic Community (EC) over recent years."

Welcome to the world of trade policy and market access, where contradictory positions are commonplace.

Market access is seldom negotiated between equals; hence the popularity of the mechanism known as the 'voluntary restraint' whereby an exporting country agrees to abide by volume restrictions under threat that worse will otherwise be imposed by a powerful customer country.

In these high-stakes games small countries never negotiate from a position of power. It is an environment where incremental gains can take years to achieve, and even holding your ground counts as a victory. The fact that the New Zealand meat industry emerged with significant wins from the biggest agricultural trade negotiation of all, the GATT Uruguay Round, is a tribute to its years of lobbying and support for the New Zealand case. And to the Kiwi style.

It could be argued that New Zealand achieved most where there was most to lose – in access for sheepmeat to the EC.

With Britain's entry to the EC, agreed late in 1971 and a reality from January 1973, the New Zealand meat industry moved into a new strategic approach to trade policy and market access.

While the processing sector tackled the realities of non-tariff trade barriers by implementing the hygiene requirements of the US and the EC, the Board took a leading role, in partnership with successive governments, in the quasi-diplomatic activities which challenged protectionist policies. According to the particular customer country, these were expressed through a range of barriers including tariffs and bureaucratic fine print.

"Lamb is the Calf of the Sheep" says the sign. Lamb played so little a part in the German diet that the Board had to invent the word 'Lamm' to differentiate it from sheep and sheepmeat. The sign is on one of the 'Tastewagons' used to cook and serve the product in what proved a very effective promotion.

This more subtle role, unlike market development and other commercial activities, was not one where results could be clearly seen, or easily appreciated by the levy-payers back home. But the issues of maintaining an equitable and predictable level of access for lamb to the EC, for beef and lamb to the US, and later for beef to new Asian markets, became a significant part of the Board's activities.

New Zealand celebrated Britain's winning of an agreement for continued access for New Zealand sheepmeat as part of the price of its admission to Europe. It was a notable victory for the courteous but tough-minded diplomacy spearheaded by Overseas Trade Minister 'Gentleman' Jack Marshall, supported, in his own style, by Prime Minister Keith Holyoake. It contrasted with the empty hands that rewarded the greater bluster and bluntness of the Australians, led by 'Black Jack' McEwen.

But it was also the end of the golden weather, a welcome to the real world for the dominant sheepmeat industry. New Zealand's historically open access for its sheepmeat to Britain had been an anomaly in a generally tightly protected agricultural trade environment.

In the 1970s in the US, New Zealand faced barriers to access for beef and an active, but so far unsuccessful, lamb producer lobby. Some form of import control in the name of 'supply management' was always likely from Canada, a potential source of indirect shipments to the US. Though it varied dramatically in form and application, each move by the US was followed by one from Canada.

Government purchasing agencies controlled many of the other import markets such as the new diversification prospects of Iran and other Middle Eastern countries. Japan, the world's biggest food importer, had closed its doors to beef imports in 1974. Its Livestock Industry Promotion Corporation (LIPC) and in Korea the Livestock Products Marketing Organisation (LPMO) set annual quotas as well as purchasing all imports.

These countries managed their markets in the interests of their producers rather than consumers. Their influence was such that Jock Mills, as Asian director for the Board, told the *Meat Producer* in 1977, the LIPC must be the safest meat business investment in Japan. Such were the differences between its procurement and selling prices the LIPC could not help but make money. Its 1976 trading profit was $US100 million of which $US65 million came from the beef trade. These funds were used to assist domestic production.

Len Keen, Board secretary until 1978, who for several years proposed a toast to General de Gaulle at the Association of Economists annual conference dinner. He appreciated the General's continued 'non' to British entry to the EC, realising the delay gave New Zealand more time to diversify its export marketing strategies and present its case for continued access and special treatment. Len Keen's toast was always honoured with the consumption of copious quantities of the appropriate liquid.

Imports of beef, veal and mutton to the US, a market equally dominant for New Zealand product, were subject to the 1964 Meat Import Law. Since 1968 New Zealand had each year 'voluntarily' restricted its exports in line with the 'trigger level' which allowed access quota to rise in tandem with domestic production.

Australia was the world's biggest exporter of beef, with Argentina, Brazil and Uruguay largely restricted to a second-tier price market by protocols surrounding their endemic Foot and Mouth Disease. New Zealand was the world's biggest exporter of sheepmeat. Within Europe, countries such as Britain were significant traders of beef, and Britain and Ireland of sheepmeat. The US exported relatively little red meat, especially outside the North

American continent.

The General Agreement on Tariffs and Trade (GATT), the international agreement that established a set of world trade rules, treated agricultural protectionism more leniently than industrial trade. For instance it tolerated agricultural quotas and export subsidies.

In Europe and Asia, the spectre of wartime food shortages still loomed large in governmental minds. The special position of farmers in the economy was given greater point by concern that the population explosion would result in demand for protein outstripping supply. Accordingly, food security and support for farmers' incomes were foundation stones of the agricultural policies of most countries. This found expression, for instance, in Article 39 of the Treaty of Rome, the founding document of the EC.

Throughout the seventies protection was respectable. Many controls had the dual aim of ensuring the survival of domestic food producers while making sure their supplies would be topped up whenever there was a sign of shortage. As in New Zealand, it was a given that support for farmers was good for a country and its whole economy.

Support systems in the apparently more market-oriented US had flourished since the 1930s. Well-established paths to political influence were already laid out, and following these, much of the frontline work in arguing the New Zealand meat industry's case for access to the US had been done through professional lobbyists. At the same time, the Government, Meat Board members and other industry representatives played their part.

With access for sheepmeat to Europe, the situation was different. The EC was still a relatively new entity, its Common Agricultural Policy (CAP) still in transition phase. France, one of its foundation members, was fiercely protective of its own sheepmeat industry, as was Ireland, which joined at the same time as the UK.

Once Britain was part of the EC, issues relating to New Zealand

Bromhead's view of the French attitude to access for New Zealand products to the EC. Auckland Star, 17 May, 1980. NZ Cartoon Archive.

sheepmeat would be negotiated with a multi-layered bureaucracy struggling to reconcile vastly different attitudes, currencies and consumption. Equally important, decisions would be made against the background of a beef regime that encouraged over-production and was rapidly developing into a market monstrosity.

From being the second largest meat importer in the world (after the US), the EC soon became the second largest meat exporter, at subsidised prices.

Government negotiators had walked a delicate tightrope during and after the agreement for Britain to enter the EC. The compelling arguments of their campaign centred on New Zealand's agricultural efficiency and the dependence of its economy on livestock industries. They also tugged much more skilfully than their Australian counterparts at the sentimental heartstrings of British decision-makers, never letting wartime support and other past commitments be forgotten.

In 1973, however, there was still no common sheepmeat policy. Unlike butter and cheese, covered by Protocol 18, there was nothing binding in writing. Nonetheless, it was acknowledged by the foundation six members that New Zealand was very dependent on its sheepmeat trade. In a White Paper, Britain had made a commitment to continuing advocacy for New Zealand sheepmeat.

Despite recently boosted efforts to diversify, dependence on this traditional market was still huge. In 1970-71 New Zealand had sent 87% or 287,000 tonnes of its lamb to the UK. Also the biggest mutton buyer, Britain accounted for 70% of New Zealand sheepmeat exports. It was also a valuable (14,000 tonnes) secondary market for its beef and offals (41,000 tonnes). The British Government advised it could only agree to special arrangements for one or two priority trades with its EC counterparts. New Zealand chose its most critical and vulnerable exports, butter and cheese, for special treatment – and sheepmeat for commitments of ongoing support from the British Government. The beef trade disappeared overnight.

New Zealand Government and meat industry leaders knew it was virtually inevitable that a common sheepmeat policy would be imposed, if only for symmetry with other branches of European agriculture. The concern was how closely it would resemble the established regime for beef – unmanageable, distortionary, and necessitating tight restrictions on imports from third countries. Beef import levies varied from week to week, playing havoc with any price setting. The internal price support system relied on intervention with the prospect of large stockpiles.

The aim for sheepmeat, therefore, was to advocate a system that separated imports from any internal support measures and avoided any intervention and storage arrangements.

From the EC side, there was a fear that price-competitive imports from the Southern Hemisphere, particularly New Zealand, would drive down domestic prices and further inflate the CAP's ballooning support budget.

The Board's aim was to ensure the rules for the sheepmeat regime, when written, would safeguard access to the UK and maximise development potential within the EC. New Zealand had its eyes on markets new to it such as France, where lamb, seen as a luxury, was priced well above UK levels,

EC Commissioner for Agriculture Poul Dalsager meeting with Darcy Freeman, and deputy Secretary of Trade and Industry Ted Woodfield, all of whom played a prominent role in the EC sheepmeat negotiations.

or Germany, where average annual per head consumption was under a kilogram.

Working closely with the Government, Charles Hilgendorf led a vastly increased lobbying effort, targetting not only the political and farmer group allies in the UK but also the decision-makers of the EC. These included DGVI, the division of the European Commission devoted to Agriculture, the Agricultural Council and its various Agriculture Minister members, and producer groups. The mechanism was information, the facts and figures of the New Zealand situation, always emphasising the aim to be a complementary, not competing supplier; with a record as a responsible and orderly marketer of sheepmeat.

Rowland Woods, the Board's Brussels representative in the run-up to the EC Sheepmeat Regulation.

Having conceded at the time of Britain's entry to the EC that beef access was not a priority, New Zealand was left to compete with other beef exporting countries (notably those from South America, also with historical claims on sentiment) for a small part of reduced-levy quotas for manufacturing beef. Some manufacturing beef could be imported under the 'jumelage' (twinning) system which required the importer to buy a proportion of meat from the intervention stockpile, where quality was often not up to scratch. Jumelage was eventually replaced by the third country 'manufacturing beef' quota, where the European Commission provided importers with licences to import manufacturing beef at reduced levy rates. Only following the 1979 Tokyo Round of GATT did New Zealand achieve token recognition of its interest in the European beef market with the allocation of a country-specific quota for 300 tonnes of high quality 'Hilton Beef'.

By 1972 the Board had opened an office in Brussels, headed by Rowland Woods. The Board was the first producer organisation from a non-member country to be represented in the bureaucratic capital of the EC and the decision reflected the awareness that to an increasing extent Brussels would influence decisions affecting the UK market. Mick Calder, posted to join Don Martin and Derek Fechney at the London office, was one of a group of bright young recruits to the Board, with economic expertise, who found themselves contributing to the New Zealand case. Back in Wellington were Allan Frazer and Graeme Harrison, and later Laurie Bryant and Paul Spackman.

Rowland Woods, who had previously worked for MAF in Wellington and as an agricultural policy adviser in the New Zealand High Commission in London, faced the daunting task of establishing and nurturing working relationships with the Brussels 'Eurocrats', and with producer and farming organisations. These included the Confederation of Agricultural Producer Organisations (COPA) and its constituent bodies in actual and potential markets.

It was hoped to acquire a better understanding of the structure and functions of the meat industry in Europe and to discern the expectations of the various interested parties regarding the development of the CAP in the enlarged group. It was also to demonstrate that New Zealand producers were just as interested in getting the maximum return and in the orderly development of markets. They were not out to sell at any price and wreck the market.

UK meat retailer Clive Godden pictured with New Zealand deputy Prime Minister and Minister of Overseas Trade Brian Talboys. Maintaining relationships with end users was an important part of the New Zealand preparation for the EC Sheepmeat Regulation.

Much of the New Zealand meat industry's influence and impact in market access stems back to effective contact with the people making the decisions, but also those preparing the information the decisions would be based on. It was a hearts-and-minds campaign which took place officially overseas and informally in New Zealand homes where key people were welcomed when they visited the country.

Mick Calder, as economics research officer in London at the time, recalls commuting once a month to Brussels to assist in building up the database of information necessary to understand the workings of the officials in Brussels. The database was also designed to be used as a basis for the New Zealand input to the negotiations on the sheepmeats regime and to establish a strategy for managing the New Zealand sheepmeats trade when the proposals were finally introduced.

In 1976 Allan Frazer and Graeme Harrison took over in London and the same year put the New Zealand case to a sympathetic hearing at committees of the House of Commons and House of Lords. By then it was apparent that agreement on a sheepmeat regime would be a long drawn-out process and that Britain and France would almost never find themselves on the same side of any agricultural argument.

It was not until April 1978 that a draft regime finally went to the Council of Ministers. In the meantime France, already causing rage by selective closures of its market to imports, particularly from Britain, had further inflamed matters by allowing the levy-free import of fresh and chilled 'select' lamb carcasses from Ireland. By now the full impact of the 20% Common Customs Tariff on profitability, along with rising diversification, had reduced New Zealand lamb exports to the UK to just over 200,000 tonnes, around two-thirds of 1971 levels.

Following National's return to the Treasury benches in 1975, Southland farmer turned politician Brian Talboys led, as Minister of Overseas Trade, a strong campaign by government and Board to persuade the British and other European governments of the justice of New Zealand's case for unimpeded access. They emphasised the solid foundations for concerns at the likely negative consequences of a common sheepmeat regime. As Sir John Marshall had before him, Brian Talboys earned respect for his courteous persuasiveness, mastery of his case, and persistence. Others to lobby strongly in support included the British meat companies such as Vesteys and Borthwicks, and shipping lines including P & O, OCL, and Blue Port ACT.

The Board's two publications *A Cause for Concern: The Draft EC Sheepmeat Regulation* and *A Commonsense Approach to the EC Sheepmeat Market*, were widely distributed in 1978-79. The books argued strongly for support payments to be structured in a way which, unlike the beef regime, didn't encourage excess production or the building and filling of storage.

The Sheepmeats Regulation was finally agreed in 1980. Typically, agreement came after a marathon session of talks in Luxembourg, and in what the *Meat Producer* described as a "classic EC package deal", a collective compromise which also resolved disputes about Britain's budgetary contributions, lamb access to France and community farm prices. There would be free intra-country trade in sheepmeat within the EC; producers' incomes were guaranteed through deficiency payments or intervention.

In what, on balance, was substantial success for the negotiators, New Zealand was guaranteed access for its sheepmeat, at a bound tariff of 10%. Though its exports, like those from all third countries, were for the first time limited under a 'Voluntary Restraint Agreement' (VRA), New Zealand had gained the lion's share of imports. Its 245,500 tonnes (for the Community of 10 after Greece joined in January 1981) represented 81% of available third country access.

There was no formal restriction on chilled sendings – the first chilled lamb shipment prepared to a detailed customer specification was from Borthwicks to Marks and Spencers and barely preceded the establishment of the sheepmeat regime. But the EC fired a warning shot by insisting that there would be consultation should the traditional style of New Zealand's sheepmeat sendings be subject to any change (for instance, by increasing the proportion of further processed or chilled cuts).

The biggest concern was the impact of seasonally adjusted variable premium payments which were certain to encourage UK farmers to increase production, teamed with a 'clawback' system for these payments if sheepmeat was exported. As Wellington-based Board economist Paul Spackman predicted in the October 1980 *Meat Producer* there would be more and more domestic lamb on the UK market, timed and priced in a way that would make it very difficult for New Zealand to maintain its orderly exports.

The new sheepmeat regime brought crucial new responsibilities for the Meat Board. Under the VRA, signed by EC Agriculture Commissioner Finn Gundelach with the New Zealand Government in July 1980, it was charged with managing the licensing of exporters and of quota allocation through the issue of VRA certificates. The Board was designated by the Government as the authority for monitoring shipments. Under the VRA, it was also required to monitor the 'sensitive markets' in France and Ireland. The Irish market was so sensitive that no shipments were permitted, other than those informally crossing the border from Northern Ireland – and this was a trade the Irish expected the Board to prevent. So the Board was drawn further into the planning and control of shipments and marketing in the major market in the UK, and in Europe.

Trade policy staff, by now headed in Wellington by Laurie Bryant, and represented in London by Bill Joyce and Paul Spackman, and in Brussels by Sven Larsen, moved almost immediately to prepare for the scheduled review of negotiations in October 1983.

For the beef industry, the seventies had started with an access honeymoon. As the Board's New York office reported in the January 1973 *Meat Producer*, US President Nixon in 1973 and 1974 lifted all quotas on imported beef so the "US could win an increased share of the beef now so eagerly sought in many parts of the world... a clear acknowledgement of a world-wide shortage of beef".

But protectionist muscle was soon flexed again, as world and domestic supplies increased. The beef VRA was re-imposed in 1975, then the US Emergency Farm Bill introduced a 90-day import embargo. In a move which was to have major impact on the dynamics of the global beef business, the US Meat Export Federation (USMEF) was formed in 1976. By 1978 US beef exports showed their first significant growth.

Cattlemen had lobbied Presidents Ford and Carter for a countercyclical

The newly elected Board of the Meat Importers Council of America (MICA) in 1975. From left they are, standing: Edward J Henderson, A J Mills & Co Inc, J B Heywood, Thos Borthwick & Sons (US) Ltd, Herbert Pearl, A J Cunningham Packing Corp, Avery A Shapiro, Capri Importers Inc, James Canfield, Austracan (US) Inc, Kenneth Roberson, MICA, Stuart M Polevoy, Global Distributors, Inc.
Seated: Al Leifer, Peirce Trading Corp; John E Ward, Tupman Thurlow Co, Inc, chairman William O'Reilly, John Thallon & Co Inc, treasurer Moritz Velleman, Ovimpex Inc, George C Patterson of Canada Packers, division of Wm Davies & Co. MICA represented the traders who used imported lean beef for their manufacturing formulations. They lobbied strongly against import restrictions such as the Meat Import Law.
William O'Reilly visited New Zealand during his term as chairman, and a number of MICA members established long-lasting friendships with their New Zealand export partners.

quota on imports. They invoked the International Trade Commission (ITC) to assess whether beef imports caused 'injury' to the domestic beef industry, and ignored the ruling that they did not. Meat Board deputy chairman Adam Begg appeared before the ITC in August 1977, and the Meat Importers Council of America (MICA), under its director James Canfield, lobbied intensely against the proposed law, publishing the book *Meat Facts* which argued that lean beef imports were essential for sustaining US hamburger production. After at first defying the cattlemen by increasing imports, President Carter signed the new countercyclical Meat Import Law at the end of December 1979.

This law reversed the previous situation where imports increased in tandem with domestic production. Now imports of 'fresh/frozen' beef (but not cooked or canned beef) from foreign suppliers to the US would be reduced when levels of local production rose. At the same time Canada proposed supply management measures likely to have similar effect. For New Zealand this meant that the only prediction about the quantities which could be sent to its biggest beef market was that the total was likely to be less than the year before.

As in the EC, the Board made sure it kept in contact with key associated and producer organisations. It was a regular participant in the Four Nations Beef Conferences, an Australian initiative which first met in Bermuda in 1976. The Board and the industry also provided political support for the MICA, as well as some financial assistance via a very circuitous funding route involving W & R Fletcher in New Zealand and Tupman Thurlow in the US. It was not considered appropriate for MICA to be seen to get funds directly from the exporting countries.

American sheep producers were also clamouring for protections to be applied to what was a promising diversification market for New Zealand lamb. This was despite the fact that the domestic sheepmeat industry was small and shrinking, and the Board was giving significant funding ($200,000 for one two-year period) to the LPCC (Lamb Promotion Co-ordination Committee) which had been set up by New Zealand, Australian and US producer organisations in 1971. The LPCC did not have any political power, or ability to control imports or influence prices or markets, but it did provide a means to communicate, to monitor trends and to observe other production methods and practices.

Graeme Harrison's thesis *Political Restraints on the Marketing of New Zealand Agricultural Commodities in the United States* describes how US sheep producer representatives "found it very difficult to get anyone in Washington excited over the fact that... lamb imports had increased considerably" when the first Meat Import Law was being formulated. Once again, and also thanks to New Zealand's lobbying, lamb was excluded from the 1979 Meat Import Law, which covered veal, mutton and goatmeat as well as beef.

Meat Board North American director Brian Jeffries addressing the 1979 annual meeting of the American Lamb Council in Denver, Colorado.

Despite praise for the Board's policy of "having a sounding board for discussion by three different countries" expressed by Howard Derrick of the American National Lamb Feeders Association, who was chairman of the LPCC in 1979, US sheep producers turned to a new and more threatening approach. In 1981, they petitioned their government to impose an additional duty on lamb imports from New Zealand, to countervail the subsidies offered by the New Zealand Government to sheep producers. The seriousness of this approach was that, in a countervailing case, it is only necessary for the petitioners to demonstrate that the subsidised imports cause or threaten injury to domestic producers. It does not have to be *serious* injury, in which case safeguard action can be taken.

"Countervailing duties might harm New Zealand, but did nobody any good. The real need is to increase consumer demand for lamb," the *Meat Producer* reported Board chairman Adam Begg speaking at a 1981 meeting with the National Wool Growers Association (NWGA) and National Lamb Feeders Association (NLFA) in Los Angeles. This played a significant part in persuading the producer groups to withdraw their petition, while New Zealand's defence connections, including the good relationship Board member Fred Dobbs had with the aviation industry, helped dissuade the US Government from action.

Adam Begg's argument was greatly assisted by being able to say, with hand on heart, that New Zealand, having signed the subsidies code at the conclusion of the Tokyo Round, would be phasing out export incentives by 1985. However, it's unlikely he realised just how wholesale the lifting of subsidies in New Zealand would shortly become.

More intense lobbying by the Board's North American representative Brian Jeffries and others, went into the drafting of the 1981 Farm Bill. As proposed, along with the usual substantial provisions for farmer support, it included a protectionist clause that meat exports to the US must be produced using only chemicals and animal remedies used in the United States. In the event, the Bill passed in the closest ever vote in the history of the House – without the offending amendment which could have been used to wipe out a trade worth $400 million to New Zealand.

The more immediate issue for New Zealand was the EC sheepmeat review. As Adam Begg told the Board's Electoral Committee, it was clear that British production and slaughter patterns were developing to the detriment of New Zealand. Production had jumped from 238,000 tonnes in the late 70s to an estimated 291,000 tonnes in 1984; variable premium payments had climbed to £172 million in 1983. Low prices and erratic exports to the Continent made it hard for New Zealand to be a responsible marketer.

The new socialist government in France regarded the New Zealand voluntary restraint level as too high, and was pressing for an early review. The European Commission was determined to negotiate lamb and butter as one package, and there were warnings of 'enormous pressure' to come on New Zealand to reduce its lamb quota. The Commission came up with the concept of 'Minimum Import Prices'. It was an attempt to set the prices for imported lamb above local ones which, as Adam Begg pointed out to the Electoral Committee, had the hallmarks of a bureaucratic and cost nightmare.

New Zealand's approach was to highlight its own moderate and responsible behaviour, and expose the excesses of the CAP scheme. Brian Jeffries, by now the UK director, emphasised that lamb would be carefully phased onto the market. On the offensive, the book *New Zealand and the European Community: the Current Issues,* published by the Ministry of Foreign Affairs and Department of Trade and Industry, and circulated in EC government, commercial and agricultural circles highlighted how the CAP had distorted trade.

Once again, after the review, continuing sheepmeat access seemed sufficiently secure for the Board to feel comfortable about closing its Brussels office. Almost immediately, however, worrying signs emerged when Prime Minister Muldoon, to achieve improved medium term access for butter under the 'special arrangement', was prepared to consider linkage to the sensitive market arrangements for lamb. This did not produce problems for lamb at the time, but it foreshadowed more difficult negotiations at a later date.

In the meantime, no change had been made to the quota limits, even though actual tonnages shipped to Europe were falling below these levels, in part as more and more was diverted to Iran. With hindsight, these were dangerous signals to send.

The Minimum Import Price scheme was 'not progressed'. Though sensitive market status for France and Ireland was extended, there was now a figure – 10% – put on allowable growth for New Zealand exports to France. And, as the Board's annual report coyly puts it, "also included was clarification of access provisions for chilled product".

Chilled lamb was to become the topic calling for the most delicate of tiptoeing along the trade policy tightrope. New packaging technology could deliver it, shipped by sea, in condition so perfectly fresh it posed a head-on challenge to locally produced product – most sensitively, in France. This was the product with the greatest potential to increase returns to New Zealand producers, or unleash the most hostile political lobbying by European producers. It had the power to derail access negotiations – and in 1989 it almost did.

Planned Marketing
1975-80

"There is considerable dissatisfaction with the present system of marketing New Zealand meat – demonstrated by the multitude of papers and speeches on the subject in recent months and the various moves by the Board and industry to endeavour to paper over some of the larger cracks. Unfortunately, in my view there was either too little glue on the paper or too many paperhangers and the cracks are still appearing." Mick Calder, speech to the NZ Society of Farm Management, July 1982.

The whole pattern of New Zealand's export meat trade changed from the mid seventies on as supplies increased and markets became less accessible. The sheepmeat marketing (or disposal) imperatives were increasing as production volumes rose, costs increased, access conditions tightened and price instability developed in the major markets. Lamb always received much more of the attention because of the significant growth in production and the developments in Europe.

But beef was also in the limelight especially after the second oil shock in 1978-79 which destabilised the major markets. Both the US Meat Import Law and the EC's beef regime had widespread international impact.

Controls on access to the major markets for New Zealand beef prompted the development of new outlets. One of these was the USSR, which became a more regular buyer during the seventies and gradually increased the volume and value of its purchases from New Zealand. In the sixties and early seventies purchases had been spasmodic and mainly concentrated on carcass mutton and some quarter beef. By the mid seventies the Soviets were buying significant tonnages of boneless beef, but later this trade diminished as alternative markets

Advertising which appeared in Time Magazine *designed to reinforce awareness of New Zealand Lamb among influential members of governments and official bodies in the run-up to the first EC Sheepmeats Regulation.*

Lord Vestey, chairman of the parent company of W & R Fletcher, shows Board chairman Charles Hilgendorf some Weddel frozen products at the Anuga Trade Fair in Cologne in 1977.

Senior Board area officer Len Wood jokes that he travelled so much while demonstrating how to handle New Zealand meat that Thomas Cook used to send him a Christmas card. "Only a few countries knew how to handle frozen meat, so we had to show them," he recalled in an interview with Meat Industry *on his retirement in 1984. He developed and refined techniques of breaking down frozen carcasses with high-speed band saws.*

proved more attractive to New Zealand exporters.

The UK was still the largest market for New Zealand lamb and was the benchmark price-setter for sales to other countries, so there were perceived benefits from endeavours to influence UK supply and demand factors and thus the prices for New Zealand meat.

Some companies had the long-held view that London agents did not always market New Zealand meat at the best of times or to the best advantage of New Zealand sellers, and had set up their own UK operations. In September 1975 the three big co-operative freezing companies – AFFCO, Alliance and HBFMC – formed Associated New Zealand Farmers (ANZF) to operate on their behalf in the UK. The company was established in association with McPherson Train & Co Ltd, an old-established British meat importer and marketer.

Originally McPherson Train held 25% of the company. ANZF also purchased two other marketing and distribution companies owned by McPherson Train, Michie & White and Fred Curzon & Son. So, with the local connections of the British companies such as Borthwicks and Weddel (Vestey), and newer links like Richmond's with Dalgety Lonsdale, the New Zealand meat industry was well represented in the UK and could exert some influence. This became increasingly important as the UK and its EC partners moved slowly but surely towards the introduction of a common sheepmeat regime.

The Board was anxious to demonstrate that the New Zealand meat industry could be a responsible supplier within any scheme. It promoted its ability to control the export industry (demonstrated by the introduction of the lamb market diversification scheme), its ability to intervene in the market both in New Zealand and in the UK, and its influence on shipping arrangements, particularly to Europe. The strength of this last argument was somewhat dented by the Waitaki challenge to the exclusivity of the conference lines in 1979.

The Board's office in London was the centrepoint for operations in the UK and Europe. At the instigation of Lionel Godsland, an extensive UK network of area representatives was set up. Len Wood, Tom Christmas, Arthur Abrams, Eric Marston, Vic Prow, and Roy Hicks dealt with the trade while Angus Hardy and Colin Knight were responsible for shipping matters.

Len Wood was probably the longest serving member of the team. He had joined the Board in 1959 as an area representative in the Midlands, extending the network of retailers and wholesalers using New Zealand lamb and sorting out any problems. His area was extended in the seventies when the Board was encouraging the trade to develop markets for lamb in Europe.

The Board also had on-the-ground representation in Europe. In addition to the Brussels office, Jan van de Ven was based in the Netherlands and covered Northern Europe; Renato Alquati covered Italy; Nondas Karabas was responsible for Greece and Cyprus; and later Eckhardt Hubl was appointed to cover Germany, with assistance from Franz Laufenberg. In other areas the Board also used the services of local public relations agencies to operate as New Zealand Lamb Information Bureaux.

These and the area representatives gave the Board close links to the meat industry and consumers throughout Europe and were a steady source of commercial intelligence. They also liaised with New Zealand Government posts, assisted in gaining access for the Board to political opinion leaders, contributed to promotion programmes and provided useful market feedback.

They were also expected to help sort out the inevitable problems that occur from time to time in the meat trade. The Board had greater market coverage and was probably better informed than any of the companies. It had its own people in the field and also had unique access to most of the companies' own UK offices and European agents.

The Board had a well-established promotional programme for New Zealand lamb in the UK . Brian McCarthy worked for the Board in London for 18 years until 1997, for the last 10 years as UK advertising and promotions manager. He believes the Board pioneered a great deal and led some radical excursions in marketing. "The Board was at its most influential during the late seventies and early eighties, a time when sales promotion was in its infancy and virtually non-existent in anything other than grocery products. It was also a time when the newly-developed supermarkets bore very little resemblance to the huge influential complexes of the nineties," Brian McCarthy recalls.

An outline of advertising and sales promotions planned for 1979.

The Board introduced partnership promotions to the meat departments of the supermarkets at a time when they would only listen to 'meat men' and treated their own marketing gurus with some disdain.

Shipping and retail changes each brought a degree of price instability. As Graeme Harrison pointed out in the May 1979 *Meat Producer* : "Since the beginning of the 1970s, supermarkets and butcher chains have handled a growing share of retail sales, and there has been an increasing trend by UK importers to sell lamb directly on an ex-ship basis. At the same time depot and central market sales have declined significantly. As a result the market is becoming more susceptible to supply changes."

Container shipping meant that volumes arriving were larger and discharge was much faster than with the conventional vessels, so importers had less time to arrange the sale of product, leading to more ex-ship selling. The supermarkets and large multiple butchery chains had the muscle to exercise market leverage by playing sellers off against each other and adjusting their purchasing to the expected pattern of seasonal arrivals from New Zealand, again leading to considerable short term price fluctuations.

Graeme Harrison summed up the situation in 1979: "During the past three years, the late January to March period has seen something of a crisis of confidence in the New Zealand lamb wholesale trade in the United Kingdom.

"On each occasion there has been a difference of opinion between importers and the New Zealand Meat Producers Board as to the causes of the crisis. Importers have regarded sharp falls in wholesale prices at this time as a normal adjustment by the trade to changes in supply and demand.

"The Board, for its part, has considered that importers have over-reacted to the situation by allowing wholesale prices to fall to levels which were difficult to justify given the prices of alternative meats, particularly beef and domestic lamb."

The Board's German merchandising officer Franz Laufenberg taking New Zealand lamb to the new consumers of Northern Europe. Tasting was always a very important part of the promotion. Pictured is a demonstration of cuts in the German language.

UK sheepmeat production patterns were also changing as a result of adjustments to their agricultural policy in the lead-up to the introduction of the EC Sheepmeats Regulation.

Internally, the focus was support of an increase in sheep numbers and extension of the production season to take advantage of the anticipated freer ac-

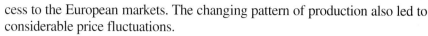

Popular British TV chef Glynn Christian, born in New Zealand, promoting NZ Lamb and the rosette which identified it. At left is Roy Hicks, who set up the Board's UK catering advisory service to work more closely with the HRI (food service) sector.

cess to the European markets. The changing pattern of production also led to considerable price fluctuations.

The companies, via the MEC and the Board, had endeavoured to counter some of these supply and demand changes by planned shipping programmes, and the later storage and release programmes, to control the flow of New Zealand product onto the market.

The aim was to manage the supply of New Zealand lamb in relation both to expected demand and to supplies of competing products. However there were production factors to take into account, such as the early season throughput and storage, as well as cash flow considerations at the New Zealand end. In a production-oriented industry these were often dominant with increasing pressure to ship the product no matter what the market conditions were like.

The obverse of this was that delays in the planned programme, due to ship delays or slippages and more particularly industrial action, would eventually lead to bunching of arrivals and subsequent price weakness. The bunching of arrivals had been the reason for the Meatmark action.

This attention to joint action to control the flow of product on to the UK market intensified following the SUBC decision in 1979. Charles Hilgendorf pointed to its importance in his chairman's message in the 1979 annual report. "The United Kingdom is still by far our most important lamb market and long will it remain so, because there is no country or group of countries capable of absorbing the 200,000 tonnes or so of New Zealand lamb the British eat annually.

"That is why the Board, along with the Government, has worked so hard to ensure that a common sheepmeats regime in the EC doesn't brutalise our trade. That is also why the Board continues to invest the majority of its manpower and promotion expenditure in Britain, and why through tighter programming of ships and possibly further storage schemes, it is endeavouring to maintain a smooth flow of product on to the UK market and prevent oversupply at critical times."

As further preparation for the introduction of a common sheepmeats regime the Board had moved in 1976 to establish a degree of control over the development of sales of lamb into North European markets.

Firstly it determined that, while Germany was a relatively small market, unaccustomed to handling frozen lamb, there was considerable potential to increase sales at profitable prices. The Board used its new licensing powers under the 1976 amendment to the Meat Export Control Act to "ensure that this market is developed in an orderly and efficient manner". It issued criteria relating to processing, distribution and market servicing to be met before operating in Germany. Originally only five exporters were licensed for the German market.

The other application of the licensing provisions was in France where the twin aims were to promote the orderly development of the market and to foster relations with the French sheepfarmers' organisation – Federation Nationale Ovine (FNO). The French were regarded as the most likely to inhibit the development of a practical sheepmeats regime favourable to exporters like New Zealand.

Consequently Rowland Woods, the European adviser at the Brussels office

"Raewyn Blade, the New Zealand housewife" as described in a Lamb Information Bureau press release from the 1970s, was for several years the voice and face of New Zealand lamb with a very successful promotion campaign starting on commercial radio in Britain.

promoted moves to establish an organisation in partnership with the FNO to market New Zealand sheepmeat in France. In effect that meant all sheepmeat sales to France were under the control of the Board.

The organisation was called Francais et Nouvelle Zealande Importations des Moutons (FRANZIM). While this was part of the Board's push for co-ordinated marketing it also aimed to demonstrate to the French that the Board could exercise control over export sales of sheepmeats to specific markets.

Sven Larsen, who took over as manager of the Brussels office in 1977 reported: "French producers are reconciled to the need for increased imports. Their long-standing objection to imports from New Zealand stems from their belief that we want to sell too cheaply.

"Through FRANZIM we are proving that our own producers in New Zealand and our exporters, want the best possible prices... and we do have the discipline to work with local producers in developing the French sheepmeat market to the benefit of all concerned; that is to say, the French producer, the French consumer, and – hopefully – the New Zealand producers."

The co-operative venture faced some difficulties during its five years of operation. In the initial years imports of frozen sheepmeat were subject to French-imposed quota restrictions. As a result of these restrictions the market was developed under a 'cuts only' policy to maximise the returns from the restricted quantity that could be supplied.

There was some reluctance on the part of the French to ease or change their import regulations for frozen sheepmeat while the common sheepmeat regulation was being negotiated. Low priced imports from South America were also a limiting factor in the development of sales. FRANZIM was wound up in 1980-81 when the EC Sheepmeats Regulation was introduced.

However, these and other actions had demonstrated that New Zealand could act responsibly and, more importantly, that the Board had the power to exercise control over exports from New Zealand.

When Allan Frazer took over as UK director, Derek Fechney returned to New Zealand as assistant general manager of the Board. The responsibility for the marketing and promotion activities of the Board in Europe, which had been a bone of contention between Fechney in London and Woods in Brussels, passed back to the UK when Woods returned to New Zealand in 1977.

The aim of the Board was to develop a co-ordinated marketing and promotion policy for the whole of Europe as part of the lead up to the sheepmeats regime. But because of a degree of French intransigence, and some Irish tinkering, the agreement was not finalised until late in 1980.

Charles Hilgendorf retired from the Board in March 1980, and was knighted the following year. True to character, as he bowed out of this phase of his industry career, he had some philosophical advice for the Board and the meat producers of New Zealand. During one of his retirement speeches he recalled that the Board was set up to look after the interests of meat producers and to advise the Government. Over 60 years of existence its role had not changed much, though its independence and authority had increased greatly. "I see no reason why this tendency should not continue and I hope it will. A strong Board is an invaluable insurance against the inherent tendency of all governments to increase their interference in the industry. However there is no doubt that the

Heidi-Marie Zimmer demonstrating the type of lean lamb demanded by German consumers at the Cologne Cold Store of West German importing company Martin Lund. In the background is the Board's merchandising officer in West Germany, Franz Laufenberg. Heidi Zimmer would shortly set up her own company with Gunter Bagowski, selling New Zealand lamb cut to exacting specifications under the Weida brand. In 1990 she was awarded the QSM for her services to New Zealand meat.

New Zealand Lamb promoted as a value for money dish.

more influential the Board becomes the more vulnerable it also becomes."

The Board derived most of its powers from Acts of Parliament, which also could be revoked or drastically changed. There were three factors of which the Board and those elected to it needed to be continuously conscious, Hilgendorf said.

"Firstly, the Board should not directly flout government policy. Remember that our founding Act says 'the public economic welfare will be promoted by the establishment of the Board'. If necessary fight measures we do not like hard and long but stop short of getting too close to that last ditch from which there is no retreat.

"Secondly the Board must be able to collaborate closely with the processing and more particularly the marketing side of the industry. For this to be possible the FCA and the MEC must be strong organisations and it is in the Board's interests they should be so. I believe the foundation and strengthening of the MEC during the last 10 years has been one of the most important developments in the meat industry," he said. The Board worked closely, and for the most part amicably, with the rest of the industry: if it did not the arguments for a Board with quite a different constitution would be very strong.

"Thirdly, the Board in exercising its powers, must do so fairly and must be seen to do so. Continuing failure to do this would, I think, be extremely dangerous for the Board: and yet it is not always easy. This is why the Board has never wished to keep an equity interest in any of the enterprises in which it has helped farmers (fertiliser works, freezing works) and why it prefers to see loans repaid as quickly as possible. Any direct financial interest by the Board makes it difficult for it to act impartially. I am sure it is wise for the Board to aim as far as possible to use its powers indirectly."

In view of later developments these words seem prophetic.

Sampling lamb in Denmark.

The Merchant Adventurers 1972-80

"Within the independents there was the belief that apart from the first ship-ment of beef into the States and lamb and mutton to the UK pretty well every other diversification had been achieved by an independent member… Amal-gamated Marketing, R C McDonald, Dalgety, Stevens, … Dawn, Mathias, Evans, Hartnell, Meatex." John Foster.

A framed cheque for $1.4 million on the wall of Gray Mathias' Auckland office records the first sale of New Zealand meat to Bulgaria in 1977.

Blue Star Line staff, who retrieved the cheque from the bank and presented it to Mathias in recognition of the nerve-wracking but ultimately profitable transaction, were among the many people associated with the meat industry who helped him complete the deal.

In many ways the story was symbolic of the experience of the independent exporters who led the way in almost all the newer markets for New Zealand meat – Japan, South America, Russia and Eastern Europe, and the Middle East. Most were businesses of modest size and capitalisation – literally kitchen table operations. Nonetheless, they took some huge financial risks to close impor-tant deals, often cementing relationships which last to this day.

They boldly went where few had been before and where they were unlikely to speak more than a few basic words of the language. Unlike official delega-tions, they usually went alone – and did their own laundry.

They were the supreme risk-takers both in personal safety and financial security. While some found themselves staring down the barrel of a gun (or, perhaps more appropriately for the industry, being threatened with a knife), the greatest danger they faced was business insolvency or bank-ruptcy. The attrition rate was at least as high as for the major processing companies.

As Ross Finlayson, who had a lengthy career with Amalgamated Market-ing, says: "They used to refer to us as brokers, but I made them change that name to traders, because we were taking a financial risk. We were buying the product and selling it at whatever margin we could make. I used to tease meat company people like Phil Mansell and Monte Waller and Ron McKinlay and say we're twice as good as you, because we have to buy it AND sell it. All you have to do is sell the bloody stuff. We have to buy it, and sell it, and make a margin in the middle, which justifies our existence, and we bloody well did. We made a huge amount of money."

Gray Mathias was typical of many independent exporters in that he had worked for one of the big companies, in his case Hellabys. He set up business in 1974, backed by Ian Jenkinson, also formerly of Hellabys.

Motivated by the call for increased diversification, and associated penalties, he researched government purchasing agencies around the world then "sent off some information which made us out to be a much grander organisation than we really were". At the time the two men and two women conducted all business from one table using a lazy susan to share equipment.

The Bulgarian sale began with a phone call to Gray Mathias while he was in Amsterdam, following up his initial approach. Madam Garkova of the Bulgarian purchasing agency had a request for 1000 tonnes of boneless manufacturing beef and was offering a price close to the premium US market.

Within three days agreement was reached and Mathias was on his way back to source the product. A Who's Who of the meat business contributed to the supply: Richmond, HBFMC, Kowhai Meats of Feilding, Evans Export, Alliance, Dawn Meats.

The most notable absentees were the British companies, Borthwicks and Vesteys. The latter soon became involved because, under the terms of the conference agreement, Mathias had to give first cargo option to the Vestey-owned Blue Star Line. Shipment was arranged on the *Auckland Star*. One of the largest refrigerated ships in the world at the time, it was already bound for the Black Sea port of Odessa.

As Gray Mathias recalls: "They agreed to take the cargo. Everything worked very smoothly. We loaded it in the South Island first, got the Alliance product on, and Alliance got paid for it. Then we had one of our group in a light plane going around the North Island, diving in and picking up documents from the bank for each supplier, at the same time drawing the cheques."

But on the point of departure finance for the shipment fell through. Mathias couldn't get the certification the bank required to give him a letter of credit.

"Blue Star stepped in to enforce some of the fine print in their agreement. They needed certification that the product had been carried at minus 12°C. I think they saw it as a way that they could stick it up me, just letting a small player know his place. Because I couldn't get the certification I couldn't pay for the meat – the freight cheque bounced."

The rest of the New Zealand meat industry rallied to his rescue, albeit some unwillingly and even though many, like John Foster, thought, "Mathias will never emerge from this".

"Graeme Lowe was quite sick at the time, but he was really good in terms of advice to me on how to deal with it… he acted to calm a number of people and in the background got a lot of support. Gordon Glaister of Amalgamated, without even talking to me provided a reference," Gray Mathias says. Graeme Lowe had a very good understanding of the lengths it might be necessary to go to, having once taken Concorde to the US to collect payment as his export beef arrived.

Even the Meat Board was involved in the ultimate $1 million credit agreement, because Mathias Meats was half owned by PPCS which at that stage had its funding lines guaranteed by the Board.

By this point a number of people were jumpy. "Afterwards there was a rumour that my house was being watched to make sure that I didn't pick up the $1 million and run off with it, " says Mathias.

The sale had been made on the basis that the product would arrive in good condition, and though the cargo was frozen, Mathias was keen to avoid any delays which might detract from the image of good quality.

He had organised for the meat to be unloaded at the port of Burgas and, after working his way through the rigmarole of Bulgarian MAF regulations,

Gray Mathias (standing) and John Upton of Mathias and Horizon Meats.

was called to a meeting at 10 am to confirm things were 'all set'. Two hours, two bottles of Bulgarian brandy and two large flasks of red wine and very little food later, there was nothing left to do but wait for the ship to dock later in the day. He filled in the time at the beach where he fell asleep, awaking just in time to avoid being groomed by a giant machine along with the surrounding sand.

The next morning he heard that the ship had been refused entry to Burgas because its draft exceeded regulations and was being diverted to Varna. Chasing it along the coast by hydrofoil he was once again frustrated in his attempts to see the ship unload. A tanker had caught fire triggering a major emergency and the *Auckland Star* had turned away to safety, adding another day to the delivery date.

"All this delay worried me that the Bulgarians would be concerned about the length of time the meat had been in storage, even though it was frozen. As soon as the ship finally came in, I went to the skipper, Sandy Kinghorn. I knew the Bulgarians would want to see the ship's records and anything else that could prove that the product had been stored properly.

"I'd already seen the official who would be doing the inspection, a lady wearing a light cotton sunfrock. We also knew the meat was in the coldest part of the vessel. So we did six or seven temperature probes and picked the two cartons of meat registering the lowest. Then we revved up the coldness of the hold, and positioned those cartons so they would be the first tested, and she would not see they'd already been looked at.

"Just as we thought – she did a couple of temperature tests, and was out of there as fast as possible."

The Bulgarians had a state-of-the-art refrigerated railway wagon waiting on the wharf.

"They agreed they would pay me the money. We agreed to start unloading the ship. I was anxiously seeking transfer of the funds but they said they wanted to eat some of the product first.

"The whole deal depended on the edibility of this manufacturing cow meat, and I couldn't find any of the steak cuts. They cooked it and we ate it. I was so worried… but they enjoyed it, they were happy with the taste of a bit of boner cow chuck that someone grilled from frozen in a hotel oven!"

The story ended happily, with the Bulgarians handing over the funds on the spot. Mathias paid all the suppliers – with interest – "and made some friends for life – and I made a profit". Bulgaria has remained a good customer for Mathias Meats, and Gray Mathias, looking back says: "It was the best thing that could have happened to me. Knowing I had the ability to get around all the difficulties put any other problems I've had since into perspective."

Relatively few new frontiers remained for the New Zealand meat industry to conquer by 1970. Most were in the Middle East, Eastern Europe, Africa or South America, but only the Middle East held the promise of any high returns.

The US beef market had started with trial shipments by Borthwicks of quarter beef needed to fill a shortage of hamburger beef in the 1950s. The first McDonald's opened near Los Angeles in 1955. The US emerged as a major market for New Zealand after the post-war supply agreement with the UK ended in 1960, the start of what industry commentator Graeme Goodsir calls a golden decade for everyone in the cattle and beef business, worldwide. Coinci-

Ces Stevens carving New Zealand lamb, assisted by Mrs J Van den Berg, the wife of the C S Stevens Ltd's Belgian agent.

dentally, it was a time when drought had cut back the US cattle herd while fast food outlets were proliferating and the potential for beef consumption seemed limitless – despite the problems, such as Amalgamated Marketing and Hellabys sending a shipment that took so long to arrive the crew had to resort to eating some of the beef.

C S Stevens and Dalgetys led the way into Japan, where the first sheepmeat exports were sent in 1958. They were followed by the Top Trading Consortium of AFFCO, Alliance, HBFMC, SFM and Waitaki. The product breakthrough for the Japanese market was developed in 1965 – the boneless rolled shoulder, which could be sliced for traditional-style cooking.

Borthwicks representatives like Wayne Geary moved into Korea before the post-war days of curfew had ended. Amongst the earliest to market to the Pacific was Graham Ashley of Tara Exports, also in the sixties.

Bruce Ryan, who chaired the Board's Shipping Committee at the time, recalls that Borthwicks had the original deal to export beef to Russia, with quarter beef.

"I went with the first shipment. We were trying to beat the Australians to a contract, and we had negotiated a better freight price than them, but we had to guarantee demurrage, if the vessel stayed more than three weeks in port. So I was sent over to make sure that it stayed less than three weeks. That vessel was the *Majestic* and it was the first the New Zealand Shipping Corporation bought. It was renamed the *Aorangi* and I followed that ship around for years."

Amalgamated Marketing began what was to prove another very successful relationship when it sold 18,000 tonnes of lamb and mutton to Russia in 1970. The company, with strong links to the dairy industry, had been importing potash from Russia. As Ross Finlayson recalls, despite immense political and economic upheaval, the Russians have bought some quantity of meat every calendar year since then.

"I used to have my dining room table covered with papers, trying to work out the shipping schedules," Ross Finlayson says. "When I first started doing the business with Russia I used to have one and a half pages of lined foolscap with different suppliers, each with 7 or 8 tonnes, to the total of 500 tonnes or whatever. Today – you'd be lucky to have five."

In 1971 Jordanian businessman Maurice Khalaf asked the Board in London to name five companies he could buy lamb from for the Jordanian Army. He telexed the five, all processing companies, without any reply. "So he went back to the Board and said 'You've obviously given me the five big companies (which I suspect included Borthwicks and Weddel and NZR), can you now give me five of the next rung of companies if they exist' – he knew nothing about New Zealand," Ross Finlayson remembers.

"He got no reply from any of them either. So he went back for the third time and said, 'You've got to give me the name of some trading companies. Amalgamated was one of those – and the only one to reply to him."

It was the beginning of another relationship that continues to this day, with New Zealand succeeding nearly every year in securing the valuable supply contract for chilled lamb for the Jordanian Armed Forces.

Amalgamated was also allocated exclusive rights to develop Chile as a market in 1972, its links with the Australian arm of the giant US Continental Grain Company, already trading in South America, undoubtedly a factor in the decision. This business, developing a niche market for lamb during Allende's socialist experiment, came to an abrupt halt with his overthrow and the rapid revaluation of the escudo which, under Allende, had been so low you could dine sumptuously for $US1 a head.

Bruce Ryan was involved in early negotiations with Chile, which was buying lamb and quarter beef. "Allende had hired as Minister of Finance Fidel Castro's chief finance man, and he was the guy we negotiated with. I remember we were presenting knives and steels with the Board insignia, and they were frightened to accept them… in Peru you could bribe anybody but in Chile they were frightened of accepting even a small token.

"Strangely, Chile was absolutely full of meat and dairy produce but the whole distribution system had fallen down, so they found it easier to import from us than get it elsewhere in town. It was a crazy situation."

Peru was the other South American market designated for development in 1972, and the rights for this went to Dalgetys. Eric Miller, and later Warwick Wilson, had the job of negotiating with the colonels who were buying mutton.

The Pacific market, while not offering the highest returns, had the attraction of no access restrictions and no need to challenge larger competitors for quota allocations. The Pacific was always regarded as a 'grocery' trade, wanting a bit of everything, other frozen goods as well as meat. The icon of New Zealand exports to the Pacific was canned corned beef – Hellabys and Vesteys.

The independent exporters took the opportunities the big companies were not flexible enough or sufficiently interested enough to develop. Yet ultimately the work done by the people who island-hopped through the Pacific and ended up drinking kava in Fiji and attending chiefly weddings in Papua New Guinea contributed to the viability of the major companies.

Before the Pacific was developed there was a major problem with selling lamb and mutton breasts and flaps. People like Graham Ashley, and Athol McQuilkin (originally with Tara and now with Harrier Exports), Don Claassen of Fresha Exports and Gray Mathias and John Upton worked the contacts throughout the Pacific. They added markets like the US territories of Guam and Saipan to the list of export markets as well as Western Samoa, Fiji, Tonga, and the very significant market of Papua New Guinea, which for a number of years rated the fourth most important market by volume for New Zealand sheepmeat.

Much of this meat went to its final destination balanced on the bars of a bicycle or on the head of a hill tribesman – one of whom was stabbed by his wife when he wouldn't hand it over for cooking. Though the value per tonne may have been low it was highly valued by the customers, including the Samoan villagers who indignantly rejected the $7 a kg legs of lamb that had been dispatched in error instead of the expected $1 a kg flaps.

Exporters to the Pacific would often have to travel in a tiny plane or coastal ship to get to a high class tourist hotel to deal with the needs of a fastidious French chef. For a long time the top market for New Zealand chilled beef – by volume and by value – was Tahiti (developed by AFFCO), with other tourist destinations also figuring and the buyers as discriminating as anywhere else.

The Independent Meat Exporters' Association, IMEA, had been established

A poster developed for Papua New Guinea which became a large importer of New Zealand lamb because of the demand for breasts and flaps. It also became a political football when protectionist forces claimed that New Zealand was foisting off fatty food to the detriment of local health.

in the late 1950s. Famously, it held its annual conference at Wairakei – scene, according to Gray Mathias, of "serious golf and serious partying" and, John Foster remembers, of heated debates sometimes cooled by involuntary plunges in the pool.

At the outset, members of the IMEA did not, by definition, own processing facilities, and the open door policy of the Meat Act guaranteed them access to a processing service. Relationships were enormously important to the smaller exporters who needed a guarantee of continuity of supply. Though many worked in harmony with large companies for most of the time, few were left in any doubt about who wielded the ultimate power. John Buxton recalls how the independents were frustrated "out of their minds" when Peter Norman of Borthwicks chaired the North Island Freezing Companies Association during 1972. "There was hellish trouble getting an understanding of freight negotia- tions, specifically with Crusader Line for mutton to Japan. Independents had to leave the room when it was being discussed. The companies refused to invite us into their holy environment."

Colin Henderson's experience of the squeeze put on his Benmore company is also typical. For a number of years the beef export business he had been developing through southeast Asia and the Pacific had been supplied through Hellabys in Whangarei. Within a week of the plant being taken over by Weddel in 1986, there was an attempt to cut off supply. Though he suceeded in reinstat- ing it through an injunction, the message was clear – that security of supply means owning the processing facilities. This helped to hasten more formal relationships with Auckland City Council and its abattoir.

By the time the IMEA and the MEC merged with the FCA to form the Meat Industry Association in 1985 the distinction between independents and others was seriously blurred. The larger and more ambitious independents – notably Graeme Lowe and John Foster of Dawn Meats and Graeme Thompson of Fortex – had already invested in bricks and mortar. Gray Mathias was also actively planning to establish his own chain of satellite plants, though later this was scaled back to a shareholding through his marketing arm, Horizon Meats, in the new processing plants, Blue Sky Meats in Invercargill and Waitotara near Wanganui.

Taking delivery of Alliance frozen lamb and mutton in Papua New Guinea during the 1980s.

The Middle East Safety Valve
1972-82

"Nobody in New Zealand could kill Halal. The industry at the beginning rejected it on the ground that the labour unions wouldn't have it. That is when I decided to take Blue Kennedy to Teheran. I had heard that he was quite a revolutionary himself. I arranged for revolutionary guards to come and give him a guard of honour at the airport, and he was escorted all the way down-town. He was invited to lunch with all the union bosses in Teheran, who gave him a very welcoming speech. They sat on the ground, and they said we have now broken bread with each other, we are brothers in arms. And they offered him a sub-machine gun as a souvenir, which he politely declined, he said the New Zealand Government would take it from him...

"I think the two turning points were Adam Begg's visit to the Ayatollah Khomeini and Blue Kennedy's visit to the Iranian unions." Hassan Shaida.

In the early seventies, with growing concern about the need for sales of greater volumes to match the expected growth in lamb and mutton production, the Board, the companies and later the MEC focused on the Middle East. Its markets were attractive because of their tradition of sheepmeat consumption, and the boost to their economies from the rise in oil prices following the oil shock of 1972.

Eric Cammell recalls an unsuccessful trip to Yugoslavia in 1970 to try to sell mutton, which was something of an embarrassment to the New Zealand industry at that stage. "I came back through every country in the Middle East, because the shipping lines had said they were going to start a direct service to the region."

Lionel Godsland from the London office had reviewed the Middle East markets for the Board in the late sixties. This was followed by a further market study in 1972 by Jack White, the Board's chief economist, who considered there was good potential for sheepmeat sales, particularly in Iran. He recom-mended arranging regular reports on the state of Iran's economy and market.

At that time the demand was for live sheep and New Zealand was at a disadvantage to Australia in freight rates and time taken for shipments to the Middle East. Australia's sheep production system, with its greater emphasis on wool, also meant that it could supply large numbers of 18-month-old male sheep (wethers), the preferred animals for the trade.

Further, the live sheep trade from New Zealand struggled to get under way due to a government ban on live exports arising from concerns about feeding and distance to the markets. The ban was lifted in 1975 but there were tight controls on the numbers exported each year and on stock conditions.

From the outset, the New Zealand representatives put the case for importing frozen meat instead of live sheep. Minister of Agriculture Colin Moyle remem-bers leading a team to Iran in 1975 to negotiate a contract where six frozen carcasses would be taken for every live sheep supplied – then finding, as calcu-lations were by weight, they could supply 12 carcasses. At that stage the frozen

Board member Crichton Wright, part of the first combined industry delegation to Iran.

product was generally mutton because it was cheaper, but the Board and industry representatives suggested the Iranians should take lamb, as it would better suit their requirements.

The Board moved to implement Jack White's recommendation. Hassan Shaida, a journalist, who was banned from working in the political sphere during the Shah's regime, had turned to writing on economic subjects. He remembers: "I was approached by someone who said that the New Zealand Meat Board was interested in a monthly report on the economy, and that's how I became involved. From time to time the Board would let me know about people visiting Teheran, and I made a point of meeting everyone."

Such a meeting occurred during a visit by one of the managers from Borthwicks UK, possibly Norman Hunt, accompanied by his Middle East agent Rashid Fares. The visitor asked why he was advocating the supply of frozen meat when all other advice was that "live sheep is the future". Hassan Shaida stuck to his opinion and when asked about the potential size of the trade, he replied, "Within 10 years we could sell 100,000". The visitor asked, "Kilos or tonnes?" and Shaida replied "Tonnes".

There was considerable merriment and Rashid Fares asked the usual meat industry question, "How many kilos of meat have you sold in your life?" Hassan Shaida's response that he had never sold any added to the merriment. However Shaida was proven right, even though the live sheep trade from Australia persisted and developed slowly from New Zealand after a number of animal welfare and political glitches.

Hassan Shaida's resolve to meet everyone brought him into contact with the Board/MEC delegation, which made an extensive visit to the Middle East region in 1974. The group included Crichton Wright, John Polson and Graeme Harrison of the Board and Ron Cushen and Ross Finlayson representing the MEC.

They concluded there was considerable potential for sales of New Zealand sheepmeats especially in Iran, Iraq, Jordan and some of the Gulf States but it was inhibited by the lack of regular shipping services to the area. There was some follow-up to an inquiry from Iran and eventually Borthwicks sold a considerable tonnage later in 1974.

Later that year a second delegation including a MIRINZ representative visited and agreed to provide technical assistance to the Iranian Government on the handling, storage and thawing of New Zealand frozen lamb. Again, the aim was to persuade the Iranians that frozen product, particularly lamb, was more suited to their requirements.

As part of his vision for an independent New Zealand, with its own secure oil supplies, Prime Minister Norman Kirk invited the Shah of Iran on a state visit. He came in September 1974 with his wife, the Shahbanou. As Bruce Ryan recalls: "Norman Kirk said, 'I want him to see some farming in New Zealand'. The big thing at the time was farm development in the Te Anau basin and he decided that the Board should arrange it. Charlie Hilgendorf – who Ryan suggests had quite a bit to do with instigating the visit – said, 'He won't use the same toilet as she does and how many farms in Te Anau have two toilets?'"

The vast MacGregor station at Mount Linton at Ohai in Southland did, and

The official lunch at Mount Linton for the Shah of Iran. From left:Prime Minister Bill Rowling, Mrs Rosemary Hilgendorf, the Shah, the Shahbanou, Charles Hilgendorf, Mrs Glen Rowling.

it was there that the Shah and his entourage were entertained. The official party, treated to a menu including roast baby lamb garni, crown roast lamb in aspic, lamb medallions madelon, roast leg of lamb (and beef, Otautau turkey, chicken and ham) included the new Prime Minister Bill Rowling, following the sudden death of Norman Kirk.

Despite the huge potential for cultural and protocol misunderstandings, and understandable nervousness – Jean Begg who was delegated to hand the Shahbanou her coat remembers a moment of panic when confronted with several minks – the occasion was a success with photographers recording genuine smiles. When the royal party discovered they had mistakenly assumed that Peter Norman was a Muslim slaughterman – a story told in *The Meat in the Sandwich* – there was laughter all round.

It was in a relaxed atmosphere therefore that a member of the Shah's entourage made contact with Board member Crichton Wright, and indicated that he had authority to discuss the purchase of meat. Subsequent discussions were held to determine what the Iranians wanted and how much, relative to the ability to supply.

Brian Freeman, who was then head of Borthwicks' sales department took over the negotiations in association with his shipping colleague, Tony Fawcett. The Board also decided there was a need for more formal representation. Early in 1975 it opened an office in Teheran and appointed Hassan Shaida as its Iranian representative.

A second combined Board/MEC Middle East delegation in 1976 further investigated potential demand, particularly in Iran. This delegation included Mick Calder and Hassan Shaida from the Board, and Roger Bews from Alliance representing the MEC. Peter Freeth from the *New Zealand Herald* accompanied them.

The Middle East was brimming with oil money and attracting countless entrepreneurs and others with ideas on how the money should be spent. Hotel rooms were scarcer than caviar and almost as expensive, especially after the necessary payment to actually occupy a room already confirmed by telex. "In one place the four of us slept in one room designed for two singles. Another time we had to wait until after midnight and the previous occupants had left to catch their plane and the room was serviced – the warm bed policy," recalls Mick Calder.

The delegation again confirmed the huge potential for sales of lamb to Iran, which they estimated at around 50,000 tonnes per year, despite Hassan Shaida's firm contention that it could grow to 100,000 tonnes.

Borthwicks did not have the field to themselves as other companies competed for sales both into Iran and other markets in the Middle East. Eric Cammell says a lot of meat was sold in these early years, using private Iranian traders initially to assist in dealing with the Iran Meat Organisation (IMO), which was the state trading entity controlling meat imports. The IMO, then headed by Dr Oloumi, bought the meat and distributed it through depots to retailers in the larger urban areas at subsidised prices.

There was considerable interest in supplying the Middle East contracts as the demand was invariably for frozen carcasses supplied in bulk – a commodity trader's dream come true. The IMO became very skilled at negotiating with the competing and eager suppliers from New Zealand.

Their technique was to take a suite at the James Cook Hotel in Wellington and invite suppliers to a series of consecutive meetings to negotiate for the contract. The company representatives would enter through one door and be shown out another, so they could not see the next team waiting. The IMO would play succeeding companies off against preceding offers and eventually settle for the lowest price. However the IMO was usually seeking a tonnage that was far greater than a single company could supply and some aggregation was required. The companies caught on to the extortion when they sought to make up the volume and compared notes on pricing. Their strategies to counter it included putting in blind bids to ensure that a nominated supplier got the contract, to which all of the colluding parties then contributed. Similar techniques sometimes had to be used with other single buyer markets.

The Board monitored the Middle Eastern markets closely to ensure they were developed in "an orderly and efficient manner" and consulted frequently with the MEC. There were also unsuccessful attempts by the Board and government to establish joint ventures with Iranian interests in stockbreeding and meat processing to further the development of the trade.

Hassan Shaida reported that one of the difficulties in developing Iranian contacts and sales was a closed shop situation with import regulations created for the benefit of a number of third country middlemen, who traded in live sheep and owned most of the specialist ships. Another was the shipping congestion resulting from the oil price hike, which brought an upsurge in imports of general cargo. Ships awaiting discharge could be delayed by up to three months. The situation got so desperate that some meat shipments were discharged at Hamburg and transhipped by road to Teheran, risking long delays clearing Iranian customs at the border.

The Board and the MEC continued the strategy to persuade the Iranian authorities of the advantages of buying frozen lamb directly from New Zealand, rather than buying live sheep. It was argued that frozen lamb could be supplied at a lower cost and better, more reliable, quality. It was also suggested that with the high costs of transport the live trade would eventually become uneconomic. These arguments had limited success although carcass sales increased to over 25,000 tonnes by 1977. But, as Hassan Shaida noted, most of this was indirectly via middlemen.

The dynamics of the Iranian market changed completely following the revolution that overthrew the Shah and established the Islamic Republic. The whole trade was disrupted and sales plummeted in 1978-79. Hassan Shaida remembers: "The Khomeini regime banned all frozen meat, not only on religious grounds, but also because the slaughter had not been supervised by a Moslem and therefore wasn't Halal."

Urgent action was required. This involved highjacking an Iranian Islamic delegation of religious leaders, government officials and slaughtermen during an official visit to Australia. Hassan Shaida went to Sydney to meet the leader, Hojatol Islam Mohammed Sharif Mahdavi and, on behalf of the Board, the Government and the MEC, invited the delegation to visit New Zealand as well.

The aim was to show the Iranians how New Zealand meat processing plants operated and the extent to which they complied with Muslim slaughter requirements. The ploy succeeded and Hojatol Mahdavi, who was the personal envoy of Ayatollah Khomeini, was to spend the next four years in New Zealand as the supervisor of Muslim slaughter for the Iran market.

Arising from the visit, the Board, in consultation with the MEC, declared Iran a development market in June 1979. The Board would be the prime contractor for sales to the IMO. Individual exporters could still negotiate sales but the price and other conditions had to be confirmed with the Board and the MEC.

At the same time the Board was invited by the IMO to discuss a possible contract. The delegation comprised Adam Begg, deputy chairman of the Board, Ron Cushen, chairman of the MEC, John Stoddart, the Board's marketing services manager, and Brian Freeman of Borthwicks. Chris Beeby, the New Zealand Ambassador, and Hassan Shaida joined the delegation in Teheran.

The IMO was anxious to acquire as much meat as possible to build up stocks depleted during the revolution. It also sought a contract backed by the New Zealand Government. The delegation did not believe it could commit the next season's production without consultation with the industry so no contract was finalised during the visit. However, the delegation went to the highest level to convince the Iranians New Zealand could guarantee Halal meat. Through

The New Zealand delegation during a "historically unique" audience with the Ayatollah Khomeini. From left: Ron Cushen, Adam Begg, John Stoddart, Chris Beeby, Hassan Shaida, Mohammad Nakhai Menhaj, Ayatollah Khomeini. Photo from Jean Begg.

Members of the delegation which met the Ayatollah, at a debrief on their return to New Zealand. From left: Board deputy chairman Adam Begg, John Stoddart, Ron Cushen and Brian Freeman.

the auspices of Hojatol Mahdavi the delegation was granted an audience with Ayatollah Khomeini in Qum, 150 km from Teheran. Both Ron Cushen and Hassan Shaida note it was the only audience the Ayatollah granted to any Western delegation.

There were formal speeches from Ambassador Beeby and the Ayatollah. "The Ayatollah looked frail and tired, but his eyes had great power," John Stoddart noted. "He said that countries that were far away could still share the same ideals and moral standards. He hoped that New Zealand would realise that the Islamic Republic of Iran had been created to introduce justice and morality. He sent greetings to the people of New Zealand.

"The audience lasted no more than 15 minutes, but according to Mahdavi was considerably longer than most, a sign of the regard in which the Ayatollah held New Zealand."

The delegation then had a 'photo opportunity' with gun bristling revolutionaries before taking the the hazardous journey back from Qum. John Stoddart recalled: "The driving heightened the prospect of premature death. Cars, lorries, and buses overtook each other with suicidal aggression… Wreckage littered the road testifying grimly to the frequent outcome of this reckless driving… Perhaps it was the divine nature of the journey that saved us from anything worse than gooseflesh." They negotiated 15 roadblocks manned by heavily armed forces before finally reaching their hotel, where they celebrated survival with Coca-Cola.

It took two more delegations to Teheran, and a further visit by an Iranian religious authority to approve the alteration of plants so that the slaughterboard faced Mecca, and the Halal method used in New Zealand, before a contract was finalised in October 1979. It was signed by the Board, as the prime contractor on behalf of the industry, to supply 200,000 tonnes of lamb over a four-year period with a firm order for 45,000 tonnes for the 1979-80 season. The order included an option for New Zealand to supply up to 10% more than the 45,000 tonnes. In practice the annual tonnage of the contract went way beyond the figures originally envisaged, with 64,000 tonnes being shipped in the first year.

The Board appointed Borthwicks as the managing agent and the day to day responsibility was in the hands of the old firm of Brian Freeman and Tony Fawcett. But ultimately, everything involving the Iran contract had to be done in the name of the Board.

"The Board was a statutory body and a government agency, and the Iranians think that anybody who represents the Government is more ethical than commercial companies who will cut corners to make more money," says Hassan Shaida. He believes the post-revolution trade with Iran would never have grown to the extent it did without the existence of the Board. As well as status in the eyes of the Iranians, it had the representation and the contacts to achieve things no company could have accomplished.

Apart from the audience with the Ayatollah, which Hassan Shaida says was "unique in history", the Board was able to negotiate a specific discharge wharf for New Zealand meat during the height of the Iran/Iraq war when all other shipping had to wait its turn.

Shaida sees the signing of the contract as the result of a concerted effort by the Board, the MEC and the New Zealand Government to overcome a chicken-and-egg situation. "If New Zealand was to have continued access to Iran, and indeed any other Muslim market, it had no choice but to extend Halal slaughter in its freezing industry. New freezing works could not supply the large-scale Halal kill without a firm long-term contract, while Iran would grant no such contract in advance."

The delegations' visits broke that deadlock. The relationships cemented by all that travel – Adam Begg who visited Iran five times went through seven passports – also provided the industry with an easy outlet for disposing of the ever-increasing tonnage of lamb that was being produced.

The Board's Iran representative Hassan Shaida (right) explains grading procedures at W & R Fletcher's Westfield plant to the leader of an Iranian delegation Mohammad Nakhai Menhaj, and Iranian slaughtermen's representative Haj Gholam Mashhadi Mohammadi.

"Khomeini's blessing was pivotal, and it came after Adam made the commitment to Halal slaughter," Jean Begg recalls. The decision was almost immediately tested from an unusual quarter – she says fundamentalist Christians saw this as mocking God and blamed the delegation for the "impossibly bad winter" that year in Southland.

Setting up for Halal slaughter at times involved considerable expense and negotiations between union and management. Blue Kennedy had a major job of persuasion on his return from Teheran. First, there was the basic requirement to have the animal facing Mecca when slaughtered. Then there was the need to have practicing Muslims make the first cut while reciting from the Koran. It was the Board which brought in the first group of Iranian slaughtermen but in 1982 the role of recruiting appropriate people and maintaining some supervision of their welfare became one for the FCA.

One of the major long-term pay-offs from the investment in Halal slaughter was the refinement of electrical stunning techniques, with the methods devised by the MIRINZ team putting New Zealand at the forefront of humane animal handling.

Good prices were a more immediate advantage. As the sales volumes to Iran were determined in advance, the Board was taking the risk (backed by an understanding with the Government) and the prices for the Iranian contract were virtually as good as those in older established markets.

However, as Graeme Harrison pointed out, addressing the 1982 MIRINZ Conference: "Had it not been for the gratuitous emergence of Iran and other Middle East markets as major buyers… the extent of problems in the New Zealand lamb marketing system would have been sheeted home several years ago. The conclusion of the contracts in 1979 and 1980 masked the real situation. Iran became the industry safety valve as production increased and import constraints developed, particularly in the UK." The commodity trading approach to the Middle East markets had negated any stimulus to further processing so the industry did not have the range of cuts that would have assisted in developing sales in other more sophisticated markets, he said.

The Board was still not convinced that the markets were stable and it continued to push for a more co-ordinated marketing strategy for New Zealand meat. Adam Begg raised the issue in his chairman's message in the 1979-80 annual report. "If natural market forces are allowed to operate… it is conceivable that in a few years the Middle East could become our single biggest regional customer. That, of course, raises the question as to what is the right balance of international distribution, the right balance of risk. Following a best-price-of-the-day policy might make commercial sense in the short term but it could also undermine New Zealand's position in markets like North America and Japan which have been developed over a period of years at considerable effort and expense."

To better balance risk, both the Board and MEC "must become more involved in market allocation and the issue of licences (as with sheepmeats in the EC) and possibly establish procedures to maintain and develop markets that initially may not pay world prices," he said.

He noted that outside pressures had forged a much closer, more effective and amicable relationship between the Board and the MEC. In addition, he pointed out that the record performance of the industry over the previous two years, aided by the Iran contract and despite the disruptions of its war with Iraq, had cast the industry and the Government in an optimistic frame of mind. However he cautioned that New Zealand was still reliant on two or three big customers. Possible disruption from the implementation of the EC sheepmeats regime and upheavals in the Middle East could devastate that fragile optimism.

The long-term contract signed by the Board with the IMO started well with sales of 64,000 tonnes in 1980 and the industry anticipated an expansion in volume the following year. It was expected that 107,000 tonnes of carcass lamb worth in excess of $250 million would be delivered during 1981, a valuation that gave an internationally competitive price of $2300 per tonne. It was likely similar quantities would be contracted the following year. Hassan Shaida's prediction of Iranian sales of 100,000 tonnes per annum had become a reality.

Sales to Iraq were also looking good with a contract for 33,000 tonnes of lamb in 1981. Contracted sales to these two countries accounted for over a quarter of the New Zealand lamb production in the 1980-81 season with prices comparable to traditional markets. The Board reported: "The contracts were an important boost to early season exporter confidence."

The importance of the Middle East as a market outlet was again recognised in 1981 when a Board/MEC mission visited Algeria, Morocco, Jordan, Syria, Egypt, Tunisia, and Nigeria. The common elements of these markets were the growing demand for meat and the use of central buying agencies for food imports. Algeria was the first country to react to the mission and a buying delegation visited New Zealand later and negotiated a contract for 2000 tonnes of lamb. Other contracts with Syria, Jordan and Egypt followed. As part of the strategy to exploit their potential, in early 1982 the Board declared Egypt, Iraq, Jordan, Syria, Libya, Morocco and Tunisia development markets.

However, increasing dependence on negotiated sales to single buyer markets in the Middle East was a two-edged sword for both the industry and the Board. As Eric Cammell admitted: "I guess we took an interest in the region to get the volume away. It didn't become really apparent that the volume produced was too great until 1979-81. And the companies thought keeping their plants full and getting maximum throughput was more important than getting a price for it overseas."

Sales were moving the product, but with the requirement for large volumes of frozen carcasses shipped in traditional refrigerated vessels, the trade brought reductions in the use of the new container terminal facilities. Also the emphasis was reverting to the commodity business. Companies concentrated on through-

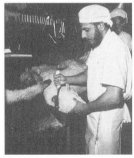

Halal slaughter. From October 1979, when the import of non-Halal meat was banned, meeting Muslim religious requirements was essential. The Board, had until 1997, the responsibility for administering the Halal certification which accompanied every consignment of meat, while the MIA recruited the slaughtermen. Iran provided its own certifying authorities; but as trade grew with other Muslim countries certification was carried out by the Federation of Islamic Associations of New Zealand Ltd (FIANZ) and the New Zealand Islamic Meat Management Ltd (NZIMM).

put rather than meeting the diverse requirements of the markets that had been developed, or marketing to gain the best return.

Adam Begg had pointed out that there were dangers of internal conflict in Iran which could result in the temporary cessation of exports, and similar comments could be made about other countries in the region. The military conflict that developed between Iran and Iraq in 1981 increased the risks to shipping with the result that the discharge port for Iranian lamb shipments had to be changed from Bandar Khomeini to Bandar Abbas, further down the Gulf and away from the war zone. It also led to major delays in berthage due to port congestion, increased ship turnaround times, and additional internal distribution difficulties in Iran.

To add to these problems there was the incident with the *Chion Trader*, in which a cargo of some 3000 tonnes of carcasses was found to be somewhat less than frozen when it arrived for discharge in Iran. The refrigeration equipment had failed because of a valve blockage; the Iranians noted the temperature was above the required level, but did not reject the cargo. However, the master of the vessel decided to take the ship to Bahrain to unload and refreeze the meat before delivery in Iran.

Unfortunately the Iranian port authorities then considered the meat had been transhipped in Bahrain and the cargo was refused entry on return. This resulted in a sequence of negotiations over the liability and ownership of the meat, as well as the seemingly inevitable delays in payment from the marine insurers.

The vessel was one of the Blue Star Port Line fleet and insurance had been internally arranged within Union International, so the industry and the Board were at loggerheads with the Vestey organisation. Unfortunately, those carcasses were taken over by the insurers' agents and then set free on the international market to sell at best prices. "They tried to give them away," said Hassan Shaida.

In the latter part of 1981, what the Board's annual report called "payment procedural problems" developed towards the end of the contract leading to delays in the delivery of the last 15,000 tonnes. These problems compounded in the 1981-82 season when completion of the contract was delayed due to a continuing shortage of foreign exchange in Iran because of the conflict with Iraq. Supply talks started in October for the 1981-82 season with the New Zealand negotiators requiring settlement on the previous year's contract before moving to the new one.

One way out of the payment dilemma was to arrange for the exchange of New Zealand lamb for the equivalent value of Iranian oil, with the New Zealand team undertaking to find a customer for the oil and arranging for it to be delivered out of the war zone. It sounded a simple solution but it was fraught with difficulties.

"We weren't supposed to be exposed to any risk," says Norman McRae, who, as the Iranians wanted to deal with the Board, headed the delegation which found buyers for the oil. "But if we delivered the meat before the oil was delivered, and before the money was paid into the escrow account in New York, we ran the risk the Iranians could default and funds from the delivery of oil wouldn't get released. Obviously, we couldn't get insurance. But the pressures were such that we had no option but to carry on. Again Muldoon said, 'Do it,

A team of Iranian inspectors passes some Halal slaughtered sheep while visiting the Tomoana works.

the Government will underwrite it if it goes wrong'."

The lamb contract was negotiated with the Government Trading Company (GTC) on behalf of the IMO and was linked back-to-back with the oil contract. As Hassan Shaida points out: "We had product which was rapidly approaching its expiry date, 90 days after slaughter. On the other hand, Iran had oil which nobody wanted. So we had two problems. In the first year we had not a clue how to sell oil. We went through London and met oil traders who wanted to take us for a ride. We went all over the place trying to sell oil, and we didn't succeed because the amount of discounting offered would have wiped out every penny we would have made. So I went to my friends in the National Iranian Oil Company and the Government and said 'I can't find a customer who will leave us some money'. They introduced us to a small Swiss-based Spanish oil company called Euravia, and then we had a reasonable discount."

It was a matter of getting all the ducks in a row and being satisfied the risks had been minimised. Although the oil buyers reputedly took the risk on the oil contract, it was reflected in price discount. However, the oil deal did provide for payment in US dollars through a revolving credit facility, which was topped up as each shipment was delivered. This enabled the GTC to open letters of credit for the lamb, so the supply arrangements were back in place much to the relief of the industry. But the opening of the initial letters of credit also took some time to sort out. "The banks were not used to the Iranian bureaucracy. They and the companies expected things to happen tomorrow. They don't happen just like that in Iran," says Hassan Shaida.

In June Dick Burrows, the New Zealand Trade Commissioner in Teheran finally signed the 1982 contract on behalf of the Board. It had required the Board/MEC team to visit Teheran four times and there was no intention of going back to sign the final document. This happened nine months after the start of a season in which the companies had been anticipating shipments of over 100,000 tonnes spread throughout the whole period. There were serious marketing implications.

The late signing of the contract, and the Iranian stipulation of a maximum 90 days between slaughter and delivery, meant that the volume was limited to 60,000 tonnes – with the usual provision of plus or minus 10% – to be shipped between July and December 1982. It was reported that the contract would provide a boost of confidence for the industry by relieving storage problems and financing commitments, but the predicted, or hoped for, firming of prices in other markets did not eventuate.

The delay in signing the contract led Norman McRae to point out, in the July 1982 *Meat Producer,* New Zealand's vulnerability to becoming too dependent on one major market. "Iran will remain an important market but the industry must continue its efforts to broaden its base in the Middle East as well as other parts of the world."

Weak Selling and Deteriorating Markets 1980-82

"Almost overnight the Board had to adapt to the most dramatic change in its history. While we had been involved in selling lamb and mutton for periods in the past we had to change from being basically a non-commercial operation, into a fully commercial one dealing with New Zealand's biggest business." Darcy Freeman.

In 1982 the industry celebrated the centenary of the first shipment of frozen meat on the *SS Dunedin* to London. The occasion was marked in New Zealand with a ceremony at the North Otago estate where the shipment was prepared, and in England with a number of events, several involving the Royal Family, including a visit by the Queen Mother to the historic Smithfield market. These were organised by Board member Mervyn Barnett, who went on to become a centenary expert, involved in celebrations for Christchurch Boys' High School and the New Zealand Rugby Union.

For the meat industry, it was also a memorable time for developments in ownership and control. Peter Norman, as chairman of the MEC, described 1981 as a year "filled with challenge, change, achievement and disappointments". The dominant topic of discussion was marketing and how the industry should meet the demands of the 1980s. "There are times when even retaining the free enterprise system is a struggle," he said.

These comments related to the continuing discussions between the MEC and the Board about marketing the massively increasing volume of sheepmeats against a background of restrictions in traditional markets, developing higher-risk new markets, rising intervening costs and static or falling market-related returns to producers. The airing of both industry and Board views on these issues also involved frequent treks 'up the hill' to ensure that the Ministers of Agriculture and Finance, Duncan McIntyre and Robert Muldoon, were fully informed. The debate was further entangled with issues relating to the operations of the Board's Price Smoothing Scheme and the Government's SMP arrangements.

The major challenges alluded to by Peter Norman largely concerned selling sheepmeat. Export lamb slaughterings rose to over 31 million head in the 1980-81 and 1981-82 seasons and then jumped to 35 million in 1982-83. Export returns for meat and associated products exceeded $2 billion to June 1981. This was a major achievement in the face of slow economic conditions in the UK and US and the disruptions caused by the introduction of the Sheepmeats Regulation in Europe.

In his MEC report to June 1982, Peter Norman claimed exporters had performed well under persistently trying circumstances, which included interest rates of up to 22%. He pointed out the companies had continued to sell lambs at average prices comparable to the previous year. Acknowledging disappointment with the marketplace returns, he said this endorsed the

Mervyn and Mavis Barnett present a gift to one of the patients at the Queen Elizabeth Hospital for Children in London. The Board gave a tonne of lamb to the hospital to mark the centenary of the export of frozen meat from New Zealand to the UK.

need for such measures as SMPs. "However, we cannot be held responsible for the fact that raging inflation has increased processing, transport and freight charges, any more than fiscal policies that have increased the cost of money supply, a vital factor in the operation of a seasonal type enterprise such as meat exporting."

The change and achievements of the MEC in the early eighties came from the switch from traditional European markets for sheepmeats to the emerging Middle East ones. The industry's disappointments in 1980-81 centred on the poor performance of the UK market. This was the case again in 1981-82, particularly in terms of prices received, and was attributed initially to the impact of the EC Sheepmeats Regulation.

As expected by New Zealand analysts, the higher guaranteed payments to the UK producer encouraged production increases there and insulated production decisions from the market. Farmers tended to slaughter lambs for income or cash flow, regardless of demand. Also as predicted, the amount of UK lamb competing on the market with New Zealand lamb was further increased because support premiums were 'clawed back' if product was exported, and this discouraged UK sales to previously developed markets in France and Germany.

This put pressure on New Zealand lamb. The uncertainties resulted in severe price fluctuations, exacerbated by a seaman's strike in January-February 1981 that disrupted the shipping programme, and later by the April announcement of the sale of another 25,000 tonnes to Iran. Prices, which had been languishing at around 55 pence per pound, surged up to record levels of around 70 pence in May before falling back to 55 pence as domestic supplies flooded onto the market. As a consequence of these uncertainties, the level of New Zealand lamb shipments to the UK was reduced to 163,000 tonnes in 1980-81 – the lowest for many years.

Peter Norman confirmed the need for a range of markets to realise the best return for the New Zealand farmer, ensure a profit for the exporter, and keep all market doors open. "I doubt whether there has been any other period during which the MEC and the Board… have worked harder to strike a balance in our global lamb marketing than over the past twelve months," he said.

The other major disappointment for exporters was the continuing requirement for price support and the increasing government support via SMPs. The Government's decision in March 1981 to announce prices for 1981-82 and the assurance that 1982-83 prices would not be less than those announced caused concern for the MEC, as detailed in its annual report: "Not for the reasons for which (supplements) exist, that is to provide the farmer with a guaranteed minimum income, but because of the threat they imply to product ownership by meat exporters". The MEC emphasised the importance of the exporters retaining ownership and marketing of the product even if – as seemed very likely from the market situation – their export schedule prices could not match SMPs.

For the Board, acting on behalf of the Government, the announcement required it to focus more attention on its schedule monitoring activities and on the administration of the SMP scheme, as it was clear that significant payments would be necessary.

At a time when there were wide differences of opinion, all sectors of the industry worked together to prepare the gift of lamb carcasses which was, as this waybill shows, transported free of charge by the conference lines from Port Chalmers to Tilbury.

Initially it was agreed to operate a system involving the Board, the MEC and government officials, whereby the necessary supplements arising from any shortfall between market prices and the Government's minimum prices would be determined. The Board would continue to operate its Price Smoothing Scheme and would use the schedule monitoring system to determine the level of supplements under the Government scheme.

The Board was now grappling for an appropriate method of operating two schemes with differing goals, the Government's for income adequacy through SMPs, and the Price Smoothing Scheme that was broadly related to the market. At the same time, the Board had a firmly established policy of intervening in the market for sheepmeat rather than supplementing prices under the Price Smoothing Scheme, and it maintained the right to intervene with its own schedule at or above the smoothing scheme minimum prices.

The Board's moves to increase co-ordination of marketing, which included extending the range of development markets under its control and tightening the licence conditions for the supply of lamb to markets in Europe, were making the industry uneasy. In 1979, the Board had also negotiated with the companies to buy 50% of DEVCO, with its exclusive licences to market New Zealand lamb in the US and Canada.

As it was then reluctant to own shares directly, the Board had arranged for them to be held through a new Meat Industry Research Trust. The objects of the Trust were to use any funds it derived from its investments for educational and research purposes in the New Zealand meat industry.

The major concern of the industry was that the Board would move to a statutory takeover of marketing in the style of the Dairy Board's single selling operation. The Board itself was at pains to dispel such fears.

In the May 1981 *Meat Producer* Adam Begg commented on the "totally incorrect reports coming from Southland that the Board is proposing some form of compulsory acquisition for meat". He stated: "The Board has no such plans and has frequently reaffirmed its support for private enterprise in the meat industry." Talks with the MEC about changes to marketing were aimed at strengthening the present system, not weakening it. "We are discussing how the Board can most effectively use its statutory powers to complement the marketing knowledge and expertise of the exporters."

Mervyn Barnett told the Lincoln College Farmers' Conference, the same month, how factors such as international trade protectionism and changing consumer requirements were rapidly reshaping the industry and changing the nature of the Board's involvement.

In Barnett's view the Board had been forced into greater involvement in marketing because of its historic claim to industry leadership through the Meat Export Control Act, which rested on the principle of producer control. The Board was directly responsible to the people who made the industry possible, the producers. The Board had the ability to look beyond short-term commercial expediency to longer-term objectives. It had the responsibility to do so in the producers', and in New Zealand's, best interests.

Barnett pointed out that the Board and MEC were considering a unified approach in a number of areas including development of non-traditional markets, and supervision of important lamb contracts. New Zealand was fortunate that the Middle East had emerged as a major market, he said. "Rather than rely on lucky breaks in the future, I think we must do more to create our own opportunities... mainly through a partnership of the Board and the MEC. This would not be a single marketing organisation, a monolith. But it would have authority in specific regions whose collective volume in future could account for 40% of New Zealand's lamb sales.

"This way the private enterprise system would be given the chance of robust survival in a world where crisis situations are leading more and more to government intervention and takeovers."

Barnett also called for greater discipline in UK lamb marketing. "New Zealand is let down at times by consignment sellers... whose cashflow situations occasionally make them weak sellers. These are not necessarily small companies... I see a continuing role for the Board in the close monitoring of markets, elimination of weaknesses where possible and protective moves in times of crisis. (But) to intervene massively in the UK would, in my view, lead us straight into a global single-selling organisation."

The Board considered weak selling a symptom of a fragmented marketing system. The sin was to sell at prices that were below the level considered to be reasonable given the market's conditions of supply and demand. The excuse was usually selling in anticipation of a perceived downturn in the market, never to relieve a tight stock position or to improve cash flow. In the Board's eyes dropping prices, for whatever reason, was a self-fulfilling act leading others to lower prices to maintain market share. It thus caused a downturn, which the original sinner could point to with justification.

Academics argued that no company would persistently operate as a weak seller since continually selling below the market would soon put it out of business. The counter was that if the particular company was always first to lower its prices a little then it could sell more volume and profit from it. The followers would generally have to take a lower price to regain their share.

Weak selling would become a fruitful source of friction between the Board and the exporters. The Board threw down the gauntlet in another area by challenging the MEC to propose a better marketing plan for meat, including contingency provisions for dealing with adverse events like the sudden loss or downturn of a major market.

The MEC's first response was a general invitation to the Board to join with it. As Peter Norman explained in his 1981 annual report: "The proposal encompasses all aspects of marketing such as shipping, promotion, production estimates, market intelligence, market planning, as well as the facility to deal with single buyer markets. It is intended to combine the benefits of private enterprise marketing expertise with the statutory powers of the Board."

This fell well short of what the Board had in mind to move the industry away from traditional methods of commodity trading with inherent price fluctuations to a more disciplined marketing approach. The Board indicated there were four main areas of marketing that needed to be addressed.

First, there was the UK lamb market where a market supply and a pricing mechanism operated from New Zealand was necessary. Single-buyer

The crowd at the centenary celebrations. Included in the front ranks are FCA chairman Trevor Gibson and Ashburton MP Rob Talbot.

markets such as Iran, which would be supplied by a nominated single-seller controlled by the Board or a joint Board/MEC body, were the second group.

Then came markets that could be developed only by the application of differential pricing procedures. These split into premium price markets such as Germany, France and Denmark, and discount markets like those in the developing areas of North Africa.

Finally, there were the speciality markets which required particular entrepreneurial skills to develop. The prime example was the Beta lamb market in Italy that had been profitably developed by Fort Export, but crashed the following year when it was inundated by product from other companies trying to muscle in.

In his report to the August 1981 meeting of the Electoral Committee, Adam Begg stated again it was not the Board's intention to move to a single marketing authority which would cause the companies to lose their independence. However, the Board was concerned that "the meat exporting companies will not be able to survive in this dramatically changing marketing scene unless there is a co-ordinated approach. The danger is that an unco-ordinated or fragmented industry might, in failing to cope with changing circumstances, give way to a single-seller organisation."

Reviewing the recent price volatility in the UK market, Adam Begg said the Board put it down to the "financial frailties of one importing company or another, which might be under liquidity pressure and was taking the easy way out by undercutting lamb prices. There have been too many examples to believe otherwise. The nervousness of one affected others and there was sometimes a needless rush for the lifeboats."

The spectre of 'weak selling' had been raised again.

The Board's staff was asked to formally respond to the MEC proposals and detail how the Board's basic objectives could be achieved. In fact, staff had been reviewing marketing options for some considerable time in view of the increasing instability of prices and the frequency of the Board being obliged to intervene. Their general view was it was more 'when' rather than 'if' it would be required to take further action.

The culmination of the discussions and debates was the formation of the Joint Meat Export Marketing Council (JMEMC) in September 1981. The Council comprised five members each from the Board and the MEC. Its aim was to provide closer co-ordination and planning in export marketing, including shipping, storage and distribution, to maximise the return to New Zealand for all meat exports, by whatever steps considered necessary. It also sought to preserve the independence and virility of the export meat industry.

The JMC had little time to settle down before being confronted with major decisions, including a contingency plan for lamb marketing. It was the scene of major debates over pricing in the marketplace. It initially concentrated on planning the marketing of the 1981-82 season's lamb, focussing first on the UK to avoid "unnecessary price swings". The Council also decided to ask exporters for regular reports on prices and quantities of sales to all destinations to ensure they were keeping up with market trends.

As the 1981-82 season began the exporters' schedules for mutton were

Robert Baldey, who took over from Peter Norman as head of Borthwicks in 1982.

Peter Johnston of W & R Fletcher at the time of the establishment of the JMEMC.

not up to the Meat Export Price Committee minimum and support was required. The Board kept to its policy of intervening in the market rather than paying supplements. It therefore offered to pay the minimum price and market mutton on its own behalf.

Three exporters decided to match the Board's minimum and retain ownership. But the remainder passed ownership to the Board which purchased more than 100,000 tonnes during the season. The lamb market was also weak to the extent that SMP supplements were required, but exporters maintained prices above the Board's minimum until late March 1982.

Delays in signing the Iran lamb-for-oil contract and further price slides in the UK put pressure on schedules despite the efforts of the industry and Board, working through the JMEMC or Joint Meat Council (JMC), as it soon became, to stabilise the market. This included voluntary price guides for sales to various markets and storage and market release programmes. It then had announced the policy of establishing minimum prices at which product could be sold in various markets as a means of maximising returns to New Zealand.

Peter Norman commented: "While it might be a fine ideal in principle, in reality it certainly has drawbacks unless it is administered with great finesse. MEC members argued vigorously that achieving a satisfactory price must be balanced with moving volume into consumption. It is of little benefit to hold out for an extra $100 per tonne and finish up at the end of the season with unsold product in store." This rehearsed again one side of the continuing weak seller arguments.

Various alternative proposals regarding ownership and control of product and levels of supplementation when the exporters' prices fell below the Board's minimum had also been considered.

This prospect was becoming more evident during February 1982 when schedule prices fell from 137 cents per kg to 120 cents while exporters were suggesting that 96 cents would be more realistic. The MEC was worried about the risks its members faced in owning and financing an estimated 85,000 tonnes of the season's remaining product that did not have a market because there was still no Iran contract.

The Board, for its part, considered the exporters were being unduly pessimistic and it also advised it would maintain its longstanding policy not to use producers' funds to supplement lamb prices, intervening in the marketplace instead.

Adam Begg later told the May-June *Meat Producer:* "That policy has been firmly vindicated by the events in March and April which proved again that supplementation without the backup of a buying policy clearly affects prices in the marketplace." In the Board's view, with the Government making up the difference between the exporter's price and the SMP level, the exporter had less incentive to make the best price. "He can just take the money and run, leaving the Government to compensate for the poor return from the market." This comment was the first shot in the debate that took place later in the year.

At the end of March a compromise was reached. The Board would purchase all lamb at its minimum and then sell back to the exporters 54% of the product destined for the "traditional low risk markets" mainly in the UK and Europe. This would be sold at guideline prices determined by the JMC. The Board would be responsible for the remaining 46% of higher risk product classed as uncommitted to any market, including that destined for the delayed Iran contract, and accept all the risks.

The prices for product repurchased by the exporters were equated to a PM grade schedule of 121 cents per kg while product retained by the Board would have a nominal value of 109 cents to give an average of approximately 116 cents which was the Price Committee minimum for the benchmark PM grade.

The aim was to relieve exporters of their marketing risks, while maintaining prices to the producers. It was not long before the wheels began to fall off the scheme. Market prices showed no improvement and exporters sold at prices below the agreed JMC guidelines.

The Board also had evidence of a number of devices or scams to get around the JMC prices as a means of promoting sales. These included deferred payment terms, pre-recognition of reductions in the JMC prices, contributions to promotions, automatic acceptance of agreed product claims and price offsetting or averaging against other items such as offals. While these were well-known ploys, they were very difficult to prove with substantive evidence. Buyers were reluctant to dob the players in or to act as a dummy buyer for the Board.

In mid-April the MEC advised the Board that its members could only sustain a price of 105 cents for repurchases for the 'safe' lamb destined for the 'low risk' markets. That would have meant a supplement of 11 cents on the Board's buying in price of 116 cents (the Price Committee minimum) as well as leaving it to realise a return of 131 cents per kg on the high risk product to break even.

The Board decided on 30 April that it was obliged to stand in the market for all lamb at the price of 116 cents for the benchmark PM grade. Exporters had the option of matching that price or passing control of their product to the Board. They could also repurchase the uncommitted product the Board had stored on their behalf since the end of March.

The Board was surprised that, after having made such dire predictions about the state of the market, all but nine exporters were optimistic enough to retain ownership of their product. Also most of them wanted to repurchase the product retained by the Board.

This reaction brought forth the cynical inquiry from the Board: "There was still no Iranian contract, so what spurred this sudden renewed confidence in the market?" Anthony Hubbard of the *Dominion* later reported (14 July 1982) that this sudden about-face had severely damaged the exporters' credibility, the Council replying to the Board's charges with a mild complaint about "negative statements" and focussing on 100 years of achievement. "Given the seriousness of the Board's charges this sounded a bit like the man, accused of beating his wife, who replied that most of the time he treated her well," Hubbard commented.

The other surprise was the two notable exceptions to the decision to retain product. The British-owned companies, Borthwicks and Vesteys, de-

To cash in on the popularity of home freezers, the Iceland supermarket chain asked for a special pack of lamb to go into the freezer, as displayed by Chris Arnold, the Board's promotion officer in London.

cided to hand their product to the Board.

The Board's decision to intervene brought a flurry of activity to get the appropriate systems in place and to finance the operations. It had been advised by government that it should fund the intervention operations from commercial sources rather than rely as previously on overdraft facilities at the Reserve Bank.

Mick Calder recalls a discussion around the Board table which provisionally estimated the required funding at about $US100 million. "Adam Begg turned to me and said that I, as secretary of the Board, would be responsible for raising the funds. It came as a bit of a shock as I had never contemplated dealing with that amount of money before. I found it became easier if you forgot about the zeroes."

A three-year loan facility of $US125 million was arranged through Banque Indosuez New Zealand Ltd, a French merchant bank that had recently opened for business in New Zealand. It was settled on 'very fine terms' reflecting that the Board, as a statutory organisation, was considered near enough to a sovereign risk. In fact the terms were better than those for a government loan arranged two weeks earlier.

The market in the UK continued to deteriorate and in late April the MEC, in an about-face from its previous stance against market intervention, recommended to the Board that Meatmark should be reactivated. Graeme Harrison advised strongly against acceding to this as it was too late in the season to expect a market upturn. Also the price importers were seeking from Meatmark was too high, so there was no advantage in taking over the product. Nevertheless, the Board agreed to the MEC request when it was repeated three weeks later.

Peter Norman commented that this action injected some stability into the meat trade in the UK. However the Board felt it was a short-term palliative that did not address the underlying problems. Meatmark operated until mid July and suffered a loss eventually recorded at $12.5 million; the obverse being that the companies were that much better off.

Price-cutting continued in the UK market with some companies selling

At the meat industry centenary celebrations at the Brydone Estate near Oamaru, where sheep were assembled for the first shipment of frozen meat to the UK in 1881. From left are: prime ministerial private secretary Harold Hewitt, Mervyn Barnett (obscured), Jean Begg, Board chairman Adam Begg, Prime Minister Rob Muldoon, Thea Muldoon, Board member Michael Kight, Minister of Agriculture Duncan McIntyre, shipping representative Bob Whyte and Mrs McIntyre.

below the Meatmark/JMC agreed price. The Board felt obliged to publicly criticise the trade. "Exporting companies have again shown that they cannot present a united front in the marketplace, even when the country's interests demand it. Short term profit is the name of the exporters' game, but when this leads to price cutting which threatens to depress market returns to an unrealistic level the Board has an obligation to producers and the country to right the situation."

The weak selling fracas continued.

The Board's intervention sparked off a round of public and private debates on the future marketing of export sheepmeats. The exporters focussed on what they considered to be cumbersome constraints that were not working. However, their attention was directed principally to the UK and European markets, with the balance of the 'homeless' product being left to the Board.

In June 1982, John Buxton of Towers presented a paper to the Meat & Wool Section of Federated Farmers, which concentrated wholly on Europe and advocated that marketing policies be formulated in New Zealand. The marketing would be done by a group of approved European distributors, controlled from the market place and working to JMC-monitored and agreed target market prices. This proposal did not receive any support, though elements of it appeared later.

The Agricultural Economics Research Unit at Lincoln College (Bruce Ross, Ron Sheppard and Tony Zwart) surveyed the senior management of 20 meat companies to identify problems and propose a new marketing system. Once again, the major problem highlighted was the instability of the price-setting UK market. Other issues were the inability of exporters to recoup market development costs in the newer markets, and the vertical integration by processors into marketing because the meat was available and by marketers back into processing to secure access to product.

The researchers warned against reduction of specialisation in processing and marketing. They proposed a carcass market in New Zealand which would ensure all potential exporters had access to product in a competitive market situation. This proposal did not gain any real support either.

The Meat & Wool Section passed a remit seeking a study of the merits of a single-seller Meat Board after hearing the Dairy Board's John Parker on the single-seller system. At the same time Peter Norman was expounding seven principal virtues of private trading based on competitive choice and freedom from controls.

Anthony Hubbard reported, in the *Dominion,* that Adam Begg rejected the single-seller notion on pragmatic grounds. Ideology was not relevant, what mattered was what worked. Nevertheless, Begg was still extremely critical of the activities of some exporters in the marketplace.

In attempting to meet the Board's requirements for a more orderly system, the MEC sought suggestions from members which ranged from a "single procurement/multiple seller system" to the free enterprise system with "no controls other than schedule monitoring and the isolation of emerging market/surplus situations". In other words, a free market with the risks removed.

The 'laughing lamb' was devised by Board Middle East director Bill Joyce to let consumers into the secret of the excellent quality of New Zealand lamb.

The MEC proposed first that the JMC should be strengthened through the provision of its own legislative powers. Secondly, the procurement of lamb should be under a two tier pricing system so farmers could choose to receive the Exporters Realistic Market Assessment (ERMA) or a pooling arrangement with farmers receiving a predetermined percentage of ERMA to be supplemented by actual market realisations. Supplements under the Board's Price Smoothing Scheme or SMPs would be additional and ownership of the product would remain with the exporters. Thirdly, the world markets for lamb would be divided into three strategic groups: the UK where there should be a restricted number of primary importers; established 'free markets' with some JMC control; and, single buyer markets as defined by the JMC, with a reconstructed New Zealand Meat Marketing Corporation being responsible for negotiation and implementation of all sales. The MMC had been established in 1975 as a means to achieve orderly marketing in the Middle East, though it was not compulsory to use it.

The Board proposed a National Lamb Pooling arrangement. Darcy Freeman had authored a paper advocating that the good features of the present system should be retained with urgent action taken to eliminate the main weaknesses. These were: the absence of any co-ordinated pricing policy to prevent unwarranted price slides in the market; continuing price competition among New Zealand exporters to maintain market share, particularly in the UK; the absence of a suitable vehicle to develop new markets; and the discouraging of entrepreneurial effort in product and market development because of the inability to recoup development costs.

Freeman noted the MEC would have no way of enforcing its policies and the only way to formulate and direct New Zealand's marketing policies was to vest central control of the industry in some agency working in close collaboration with the JMC. He concluded that the most effective and convenient body to control marketing was the Board.

The National Pool would be controlled by the Board working closely with the JMC. All lamb products would pass to the Pool at the time of slaughter. The Board would take control of the product; it would issue processing instructions and be the only exporter. The Board would sell the product through agents in accordance with agreed marketing strategies. It would also be responsible for the operation of any price support operations.

The proposal jolted the exporters into realising the Board was serious about essential changes to lamb marketing for the new season and the possibility of a central control agency. They put forward a counter-proposal, including a more formal structure for the JMC with specific reference to pricing controls. The whole plan, which presumed that product ownership would remain with the companies, would become known by the name of one element: a jointly-owned marketing company Meat Industry Trading Organisation (MITO, pronounced meat-oh) to handle 'at-risk' product.

Middle East director Don Harwood introduced the plaque to guarantee that New Zealand meat is Halal slaughtered. Middle Eastern customers look for this assurance and its integrity is essential.

Orderly Disposal
1982

"When the Board took over it was doomed to failure from the start. I mean absolutely doomed to failure because everybody stuck their knives into the Board before they could turn round." Ian McKellar.

On 5 October 1982, the marketing issues came to a head. With adverse marketing conditions and advice from exporters that they could not offer a meaningful procurement schedule, the Board and the MEC agreed on the Board's intervention in the sheepmeats market. They jointly announced that the Board would buy all lamb and mutton production for the following two seasons at the Government's SMP price levels, then market the product.

The conspiracy theorists in the meat companies reckon that the Board's intervention was a 'jack-up' between Robert Muldoon and Adam Begg, with Jim Bremner as the chief executive-designate throwing his spanner in the works for good measure. They also argue the Board's staff had been angling for a chance to implement its impractical co-ordinated marketing theories. The Board people say no, market circumstances for sheepmeats were so forlorn the Board was obliged to take the action, to implement its firmly held intervention policy.

The decision did, however, mean the Board and its staff finally had a mandate for market intervention for a defined period rather than the spasmodic short-term interventions of the previous 10 years. And, with a Board-imposed constraint on increasing staff numbers and other resources the task was going to be enormous.

Certainly the announcement exposed some of the divisions behind the public utterances. Also, despite the philosophical pain expressed by the free marketers in the industry, the companies managed to ignore their discomfort sufficiently to exploit the system and maximise the opportunities for profit. While the Board owned the product, the companies owned much of the essential information.

Robert Muldoon, Prime Minister and Minister of Finance, had a long-term involvement in the decision-making process with his hands-on management of the SMP scheme, so the possibility of some political contrivance cannot be ruled out entirely. He had already engineered a change in thinking regarding the prospects of intervention by the Board in a letter to Adam Begg 12 months earlier about the administration of the SMP scheme. At that stage there was the expectation of significant SMP support during the 1981-82 season.

In the letter dated 11 September 1981 the Prime Minister pointed out that one of the essential features of both SMPs and the statutory scheme operated by the Board was that the schedule system should fairly reflect market realisations. He commented that the Board could intervene and purchase meat itself if it considered the schedule did not do this. He then stated: "The relevant Acts impose no limitations on the price at which the Board may intervene and the Board has indicated that it will be ready to do so even when this may not be necessary under the Board's minimum price scheme.

"I recognise that the satisfactory operation of the SMP scheme may ultimately rest on this undertaking. I do not wish to underestimate the difficulties
involved and I am appreciative of the Board's efforts in dealing with these. The
Board is of course free to approach the Government again whenever potential
or actual problems arise. I am hopeful however that the arrangements that have
been discussed will go a long way to assisting the Board in the administration
of the scheme."

So Muldoon had explored the possibility of the Board intervening at prices
higher than its minimum price level as a means of forcing exporters to put up
schedules that were market-related. Some Board cynics considered it could
also be seen as a means of limiting the level of supplements paid under the
SMP scheme, even if the wording of his letter was more enigmatic than his
usual abrupt style.

There is some evidence to suggest an element of government coercion. One
version comes from Norman McRae who recalls that at one stage he and Adam
Begg went to see Muldoon to advise him the SMP scheme would not work as
the prices were too high.

Robert Muldoon's response was: "My advisers tell me that you should be
able to get those prices out of the marketplace." Norman McRae says: "Then
he said if we didn't do it, he'd legislate to make us do it."

Federated Farmers was also hinting at the possibility of Board intervention.
Tim Plummer, as chairman of the Meat & Wool Section, had noted in his annual address in August 1982 that there was a need to firm up marketing strategies. He suggested that the marketing policies of the larger companies were
hidden by the schedule structure and the schedule was pessimistically set to
account for possible contingencies, rather than to portray optimistic marketing
prospects. "I go further to suggest that the business acumen of some has been
to judge what return will satisfy their clients and then set the schedule accordingly."

*HM Queen Elizabeth the
Queen Mother with Board UK
director Harry Douglas at
Smithfield as part of the meat
centenary celebrations, 22
April 1982. The Queen Mother
had an honorary role with
Butchers' Charitable Institute
and made an annual visit to
Smithfield.*

In Plummer's view, if exporters did not show a responsible attitude, farmers must support the Board and seek new marketing policies. The farming sector might have to "look to those with the statutory power to direct product flow, price and presentation", he warned.

The other development leading to the decision in October 1982 was the increasing complexity of administering the price support schemes, particularly whether or not the levels of supplements being paid could be justified in relation to the exporters' schedules.

The Muldoon letter had been followed by correspondence from Duncan McIntyre, Minister of Agriculture, setting out the agreed system of administering the scheme, and emphasising the need for the Board to be "diligent in seeking to establish a soundly based exporters' schedule on which to assess supplements payable". His letter went on to say that the Board was at liberty to intervene at its discretion and financial risk, where it considered the exporters' schedule was unduly pessimistic, with the Board's schedule then being used to determine the level of SMP supplement.

The Government further tinkered with the administration of the scheme following the announcement of the SMP levels for the 1982-83 season. It advised a change to the use of weighted average killing and freezing charges for the determination of a weighted average 'minimum' price. This conflicted with the statutory requirements for the Meat Export Prices Committee scheme.

Subsequently Graeme Harrison, the Board's assistant general manager-marketing, prepared a paper dated 3 August 1982, highlighting the complexities of assessing market returns, particularly for mutton and lamb, which compounded the difficulties of operating a satisfactory SMP payments system. Part of the problem was convincing the Government Auditor about the suitability of the schemes and the level of funds being distributed.

The systems for determining SMP payments for beef were generally satisfactory but those for lamb and mutton were questionable. In the case of lamb, Graeme Harrison pointed out that changes in market prices in the period between procurement and eventual sale affected returns to the companies. He commented: "The industry would seek to base supplementary payments on current market factors rather than the forward market."

He also described the arguments that had developed between the Board and the MEC over forward price estimates and the level of supplement that would apply. Numerous proposals were put forward in an attempt to overcome these problems. One was the introduction of a voluntary price-reporting system by the MEC. It suffered the usual fate of voluntary schemes with not all the companies participating, the reported prices could not be verified and not all sales were reported.

The MEC had even proposed that the Board step aside and "the industry be left to establish its own schedules" and determine its own level of supplements. The Board had responsibility to administer the schemes using government funds so this was judged to be ridiculous and unacceptable.

The Board also considered that, because exporters immediately sought increased supplements whenever there was a downturn in market realisations, the use of supplementation to support prices took the pressure off exporters and did not contribute to selling strength in the market place. The Board's bargaining power was limited when the market prices being debated were above its minimum level but lower than the SMP minimum: the only real lever it had was to intervene at its own risk.

Graeme Harrison concluded: "Even if it were possible to devise acceptable procedures for lamb and mutton, the sums involved, due to unexpected market price change, can be enormous.

"Every 1p per lb change in the United Kingdom lamb market realisations is equivalent to nearly five cents per kilogram in producer returns. A change of 10% in global lamb realisations represents about $120 million in producer incomes over a season's national export production.

"This places a tremendous responsibility on the Board and unfortunately, in carrying out these duties related to minimum price arrangements, it has found itself in an increasingly adversarial position with the industry. This is particularly unsatisfactory in circumstances where the Board is administering SMP arrangements in which it has had no role in setting the minimum prices."

As it turned out government support via the SMP scheme in the 1981-82 season amounted to $156 million. Of this, $94 million was used to boost lamb prices, $9 million for other sheepmeats and $53 million for beef.

It would be wrong, however, to assume the Board was averse to exploiting the SMP situation to establish itself as the central marketing organisation for sheepmeats. The concerns regarding 'orderly marketing' were well established and the complexities of administering a price support scheme were acknowledged.

In the lead-up to the intervention decision the Board had agreed, albeit rather reluctantly, to support the MEC's plans, referred to as the MITO proposals, for the future of export meat marketing.

The MITO scheme's implementation assumed that, if the Board was satisfied the controls and pricing procedures were effective, it would not implement its longstanding policy of automatically assuming ownership or control at the minimum prices under the price support scheme. This was, in effect, a way of achieving the MEC's aim of retaining ownership of product by getting the Board's agreement to shift from intervention at the minimum prices for sheepmeats to a supplementary payments arrangement. The companies for their part wanted to retain ownership of the product but did not want to take responsibility when it was risky or difficult to sell.

The Meat Board 1983. Standing, from left: Jim Bremner, general manager, Reg Rusk, government appointee, David Frith, producer representative, Roger Marshall, producer representative, Brian Mooney, Dairy Board representative. In front: Mervyn Barnett, producer representative, Adam Begg, chairman and producer rep, Fred Dobbs, government appointee, Michael Kight, producer representative, Norman McRae, producer representative.

For the MEC the essence of the MITO proposal was "to isolate uncommitted product at the beginning of the season and take it out of contention". MITO was to handle the uncommitted or 'homeless' product, single-buyer markets, single-seller markets and product for market development. Any operating losses incurred by MITO would be met partly by funds made available by the Government from the Meat Income Stabilisation Account with the balance to be funded equally by the Board and the meat exporters.

The Board discussed the MITO proposals at a special meeting on 15 September 1982. The minutes of that meeting record that Federated Farmers had supported the proposed scheme and the Board considered exporters were obligated to make it work.

However, the minutes also record that, with uncontrolled pricing of New Zealand lamb occurring in the UK and on the Continent, the Board considered the proposal would be under pressure from the start. Even so there was a need to give it a chance to work. It was also noted that the opening schedule could be well under the Price Smoothing Scheme minimum.

So despite their misgivings, the Board resolved "that the MEC proposals on lamb marketing be confirmed and that the Board should co-operate with the MEC in taking action to implement these proposals." The meeting went on to express some reservations about carrying out pricing audits of importing companies and the commercial viability of the MITO structure and operations.

Following that special meeting the Board and MEC worked on aspects of the scheme including drafting the Articles of Association of MITO, administration, funding arrangements, and even the tax consequences for the companies, particularly the co-operatives.

The Board was advised that its powers were not sufficient to ensure that audit checks could be carried out on the books of UK importers of New Zealand meat. This meant that only limited or voluntary controls could be applied to maintain pricing guidelines once ownership of the product passed to the importers. To say there was disquiet in the minds of Board members and staff about the efficacy of the MITO plan would be an understatement.

As evidenced by the Harrison paper, the Board staff had been working on alternative marketing options, on the assumption that the established policy of intervention at the Board's minimum prices would be implemented, particularly when it became evident the trade was unlikely to meet the Price Smoothing Scheme's minimum schedule of 114 cents per kilo. Supplementation at the anticipated high rates would not be acceptable to the Board under those circumstances. As well, the Government's SMP minimum price had been set at 146 cents per kilo for PM grade lambs so any SMP payment would be about 32 cents per kilo or $4.65 per carcass.

The JMC met on 5 October 1982 to put the MITO proposals into place, and nearly two decades later there are as many versions of the events as there were people involved. The variety of interpretations tends to reflect the side they were supporting and the information available, along with some speculative leaps to fill in the gaps.

The minutes of the JMC meeting show that after receiving a report on the lamb marketing situation and production estimates for the coming season the Council reviewed prospects for dealing with the carryover stocks from the 1981-

Loads of lamb, from CFM's Canterbury plant at Belfast. Part of the carryover stocks which built up as production increased rapidly, fuelled by SMPs, and the Iran contract negotiations were delayed.

82 season which were to be acquired by MITO. These were nearly 100,000 tonnes or approximately 70,000 tonnes above normal levels. Adam Begg then commented that with the high level of stocks, the forecast increase in production, the restrictions on markets and the general level of market uncertainty, it would be extremely difficult, if not impossible, for the exporters to set a schedule for 1982-83.

He added that the Board would also find it impossible to set a schedule to determine levels of supplementation. As he saw it the industry was faced with a two-year problem to get rid of excess stocks. This view was endorsed by the chairman of the MEC, Eric Cammell, who advised that his members had agreed the previous day there would be difficulties trying to set a schedule for the coming season.

Adam Begg reported that he had spoken to Prime Minister Muldoon and asked if the Government would assist in a buy-in situation by the Board and been advised that the request would be considered. It was agreed to follow up with a joint Board/MEC approach to the Government.

The minutes then record: "The view was expressed that for the 1982-83 season the Meat Producers Board, subject to Government concurrence, should offer a schedule equivalent to the Government SMP of 146 cents per kilo for a PM lamb with regional variation. Finance arrangements for this to be determined in consultation with Government."

It was noted later in the meeting that the MEC representatives would need the agreement of the other members not on the JMC, as would the Board members. Eric Cammell offered all possible assistance from the industry, particularly with the secondment of staff to assist the Board with their tasks, although this offer was never taken up. It was agreed to issue a press statement confirming the joint agreement on the Board's intervention at the Government SMP level.

Eric Cammell reported in the 1983 MEC annual report that the decision to hand over ownership was made jointly and that, while some members disagreed, those directors on the JMC saw no feasible alternative under the circumstances – or in the foreseeable future.

He noted several significant factors surrounding the JMC's decision. These were the absence of a contract with Iran for the new season (although negotiations were under way); the large stocks of unsold old season lamb both in New Zealand and in the UK; the expected export lamb kill two million higher than the previous year; and the problems and costs of storage and holding stocks as the season progressed.

In his retirement speech, 'Reflections', John Foster commented there were clear signals from the Board that unless exporters put up a schedule equivalent to the guaranteed minimum the Board would own all the sheepmeats and market them as a single-seller.

"The MEC came up with a worst case scenario of 76 cents per kilo and a best case of 95 cents for PM lambs." This was well short of the 114 cents under the guaranteed farm income-smoothing scheme. "Over the following three and a quarter years of Meat Board ownership almost $1 billion of losses were incurred, which were funded from drawings from the Reserve Bank."

Board members and staff will contend to their dying breath that the figure of $1 billion was not a 'loss' but rather the cost of operating the scheme to support producer returns in almost hopeless circumstances.

But there is an almost complete divide between Board and industry in the interpretation of what followed. Gray Mathias, then representing the exporters says: "That was the start of the biggest ever waste of money. You would have to be real smart, wouldn't you, to lose a million dollars a day, which is what happened. One of my real regrets is that there were some real deals going at that time and I didn't make the most of them."

Eric Cammell said in his 1983 report: "Perhaps the most important factor of all was the Meat Board's refusal to supplement exporters if the schedule was lower than the Board's Price Smoothing Scheme minimum.

"Exporters' expectations of a schedule were considerably lower than the 114 cents demanded by the Board. A further complicating and extremely vital factor was the New Zealand taxpayer interest, through SMPs on lamb, which had been pitched too high in relation to market realisation. Thus the Government was apparently keen to see the Board more deeply involved in the selling of sheepmeats.

"Those were the circumstances in which the Board ownership decision was taken. There was indeed no viable alternative. The shame of it all, however, is that we were unable to persuade the Board to proceed with our MITO proposals. This would have meant Board co-ordination in traditional markets, but would also have created a properly constituted body containing the expertise and drive needed to develop new markets."

In a recent interview he confirms his view that there was more to the arrangement than just a Board/MEC/JMC decision. "Adam Begg definitely had made a deal with Robert Muldoon, which to my way of thinking didn't solve the problems at all. There's no doubt that between them they were going to set up a meat marketing operation. They wanted to do it and they had Bremner there as another advocate, and that's what happened.

"I went up to the Prime Minister's office and the deal had been struck before we even got there. Muldoon said, 'What are you here for, Cammell?' and I said, 'To tell you sir, we cannot carry on under the circumstances'. He turned to Adam and he said, 'Right, you're going to take over, Begg'. And that was it."

In Eric Cammell's view, Jim Bremner was against any form of company involvement and was to blame for the Board's rejection of his offer of industry assistance.

Cammell recalls he was under the impression during dinner with Adam Begg, Jim Bremner and Darcy Freeman after the meeting with Muldoon that they had agreed it would be best if the marketing was handled on a co-operative basis. "They didn't have the organisation to handle it, and I said 'We've got the people in the industry that can handle this, they are there if you want them'. And Adam and Darcy agreed with me."

However, the next morning the message was that the Board did not require the assistance of the companies. Cammell believes this decision was made after Begg and Freeman had consulted with Jim Bremner as the chief executive-designate. "Jim Bremner was determined that nobody from the industry was going to be involved in any way, shape or form."

This is how Gray Mathias remembers it too. "I remember thinking at the time, this is a historic occasion. There's no question a few of Adam Begg's

Jim Bremner, suspected of engineering the Board takeover of product in 1982 – while he was still chief executive-designate.

buttons were being pushed by Jim Bremner – I can see the body language right now. It was fairly straightforward. The Meat Board wanted the schedule of $1.12 or $1.15. We were offering 92c. I think the industry went back with 98c. There was no way we were going to meet."

Darcy Freeman dismisses the recollections as "nonsense" and does not recall any undertaking to use the assistance of the companies. The suspicions about Jim Bremner were that, because he had come from a single-selling organisation, the Apple and Pear Board, he would be pushing for a similar structure for the meat industry. His appointment as chief executive-designate had been announced in April 1982. Although he was to take over from Darcy Freeman in March 1983, many in the industry considered he had a significant influence on the Board's thinking well before that.

The Board met the following day, 6 October, and Adam Begg reported on his discussions with the Government on possible Board intervention and the background to the proposal. He then advised that, at the JMC meeting the previous day, the exporters had consented to the Board's move to intervene in the lamb and mutton markets, at the SMP level. Intervention above the Prices Committee level was not related to a view of the market and was therefore a departure from the established policy. The fact that it was to be at the SMP level tends to confirm that Muldoon had exerted some pressure, or as the conspiracy theorists would have it, that the Board had been determined to take over the marketing.

Subsequently there was a concerted effort by the exporting companies to persuade the Board and the Government that they should be allowed to retain ownership of the product and they put forward various suggestions about how this might be achieved, including a revision of the MITO type arrangements.

At the JMC meeting on 15 October it was reported that some companies had applied to the Minister of Agriculture to retain ownership of the product at the Prices Committee minimum of 114 cents per kilo and to receive the SMP supplement. But not all companies supported that level of prices. These proposals got no support and the MITO arrangement was put 'on ice', to form the basis for the resumption of private enterprise marketing when the problem of the excess stocks had been resolved and the Board intervention ceased. The presumption was that this would take two years.

Robbie Burnside, who had become chairman of PPCS in 1980, recalls that his directors and management were concerned that if the Board took over, their purely marketing company would have no business. "When the Meat Board came in and said, 'We're going to take over all the marketing', it appeared as though PPCS had nothing to do; we were history."

They were also of the view that "there was a group of people on the Meat Board who saw their role as progressing towards becoming a central marketing group". PPCS put the proposition to Adam Begg (Burnside's brother-in-law) that they should be able to offer the 114 cents per kg Prices Committee minimum to the farmers and still get the SMP component.

"Adam got onto Muldoon and he came back and said, 'No, you won't be able to do that because the Government is only going to pay the SMP factor through the Meat Board'."

Robbie Burnside believed that Begg or the Board had decided and then discussed with Muldoon the proposition that the SMP and the Prices Committee minimums all be incorporated into the one intervention price schedule so the companies would have to pay the SMP price levels to gain ownership of the product.

PPCS considered the proposition impossible but, according to Burnside, "Adam had made it very clear that he was going to stop us in our tracks". And further: "We (PPCS) went to see Muldoon about it, but we didn't get anywhere with him."

So the answer for PPCS (and the other companies) was to propose the Board pay the companies a commission for them to market the product on behalf of the Board. The Board had already indicated that it would ensure as little disruption to the companies' business as possible and would use their services in established markets. So this proposal was accepted, conditionally.

"We did very well out of that and it meant that PPCS had access to more product than we'd had before," recalls Burnside. It also enabled them to retain contact with their customers and to strengthen the marketing network. In contrast, other companies with processing plants saw their role as making money more by pushing up the throughput of their plants.

While the Board now owned all the new season's product, it was not in a position to completely co-ordinate the selling of lamb. The 100,000 tonnes of carryover stocks – 25% of total production – held by the companies was a concern. The Board considered using Section 10 of the Meat Export Control Act to acquire or take control of the carryover stocks and market them along with the new season's product and, in fact, had drawn up a Section 10 resolution. In the event, after further consultation with the MEC, the Board decided to leave the carryover stocks to the companies to sell directly.

Also in the interests of stability, the Board held back new season's product in some established markets so the companies could sell ahead of them to reduce their stocks. This altruistic move probably increased the amount of support recorded for that year. In Adam Begg's view, if the Board had "supplemented the exporters down to whatever prices they could have earned in the marketplace, chaos would have resulted. There would have been a rush to sell product quickly and prices would have collapsed in traditional markets like the UK. There would have been serious implications for access to the EC and for major markets like Iran, which look to the British market when negotiating prices. While this was going on the Board would have in effect been forced to write out blank cheques to the exporters and the Stabilisation Account would in all probability have ended up with an even bigger deficit."

The Stabilisation Account financial statements for 1982-83 show $219 million of support for lamb and $69 million for mutton. In addition there was SMP support of a further $146 million for lamb and $17 million for mutton.

The way these figures were bandied around became a sore point for the Board and its staff. The industry and other denigrators always referred to the deficit as the "loss on Board trading", while the Board considered it was the cost of supporting producer returns to the level determined by the Prices Committee applying its three year moving average formula.

Everyone knew that supply was ahead of demand and market prices were

Derek Dickinson, the Board's UK marketing officer.

Eric Cammell, chairman of the Meat Exporters Council for most of the period of Board ownership.

below minimum levels. Fred Dobbs, in his third term as a government appointee on the Board, recalled the initial stages of the intervention as "a fire sale period. There's nothing worse than the buyer knowing you've got more product than you or they can really handle".

The Board intervention was predicated on the view that it would take only two years for the problems to be resolved and marketing handed back to the exporters. Its system had to be set up with no substantial increase in resources, particularly staff numbers, unless absolutely necessary.

Even so, by the end of the 1982-83 season, staff in the Wellington office had increased from 35 to 55, with new executive and clerical staff required to handle the load. A number of marketing and accounting staff were recruited from the meat companies themselves, some of them admitting they thought the intervention was going to continue for longer than just the two years originally announced.

The marketing or selling system put in place was designed to maintain existing operators wherever possible, but the Board was never entirely happy with it. Adam Begg stated in the Nov-Dec 1982 issue of the *Meat Producer*: "The marketing arrangements for this season contain a degree of compromise between the most cost-effective way of handling the product and the need to retain the financial and administrative structures of the companies so that they can again assume ownership in the future."

The prime aim was to get stocks down to reasonable levels within two seasons. The Board decided the process should be accelerated and by the end of 1983 stocks were reported to be "generally normal", apart from the UK where they were still higher than desirable.

The marketing arrangements were spelled out in an 11-page document issued on 29 October, and immediately criticised by the Independent Meat Exporters' Association. In the *National Business Review* of 8 November 1982, IMEA secretary John Foster described it as an essentially unproductive bureaucratic effort, and "bound to frustrate some of the innovative independent exporters who have expanded in recent years". He was supported by his Pacific Freezing partner Graeme Lowe who, in commenting on the level of Board control, reportedly questioned the extent to which the Board and the Government were working hand in glove. He asked why SMPs couldn't just be paid to exporters.

Other exporters such as W & R Fletcher and Producer Meats were reported to be less concerned and having no trouble keeping their marketing operations going. This view was echoed by Peter Blomfield, executive director of the FCA, and by Eric Cammell who said that the individual marketing teams should be able to operate "if they have got anything to them".

The document was the first of many to detail arrangements continually being negotiated with the companies via the MEC. In part the continuing revisions were to cover new circumstances, but they were also because Board staff became aware of some of the ploys being used to benefit the companies at the expense of the price support scheme.

Companies continued to purchase stock on behalf of the Board, paying the SMP price. For this they were paid a buying and administration fee of 75 cents per head, which the Board considered more than generous. John Foster said that it was "inadequate to motivate companies in a sustained effort", but the fee was subsequently reduced by agreement. Companies were also paid processing and storage fees for the stock they processed.

Exporters were appointed to act as the Board's agents on a commission basis but they had to work through approved sub-agents, each restricted to marketing within a defined region. The commissions were paid on gross sale value and varied according to services provided. This resulted in the formal approval of a staggering number of 32 exporters acting as the Board's agents for sales to the UK market servicing 18 sub-agents operating in the market itself.

There were over 40 selling agents authorised to cover Western Europe. The Board received 33 responses for Japan, including three joint proposals. Costly duplications of such magnitude were unavoidable considering the undertaking not to disrupt existing arrangements.

The Board took the role as prime contractor for the single-buyer markets, particularly those in the Middle East declared as development markets, with appointed exporters acting as managing agents to administer contracts negotiated under Board auspices. Some sales to overseas markets were conducted directly by the Board through agents in the offshore markets.

The barrage of paper generated to put these structures in place was necessary to ensure everyone was informed of the Board's decisions and knew what was expected of them.

Adam Begg noted that the financing and administration of such an operation, and the setting up of buying and selling agency arrangements, was a mammoth task for an organisation previously geared to a totally different and much more limited role. "I am proud of the way our staff have responded and what they have achieved in six months," he said.

In the initial stages it meant some staff put in up to 15 hours a day to hold it all together, but it was an exciting and enjoyable challenge. It melded the staff into a team but contributed to a 'them and us' attitude between the Board and some of the companies. In many cases the Board requested feedback on options being considered but there was only modest response. There were, however, accusations that the Board was operating by bureaucratic edicts.

These circumstances also conspired to create a tightly knit and purposeful group at the Board table. Adam Begg's Board was a more diverse group than Hilgendorf's. For one thing, there were more North Islanders. The Board included producer representative Norman McRae as deputy, Michael Kight, Mervyn Barnett, John Daniell and Roger Marshall (who had upset the order of things by beating Warren Martin). David Frith, who had risen quickly through the ranks in Auckland Federated Farmers, also took the fast track from the Electoral Committee where he served for one year, 1982, to stand successfully on his second attempt for the Board, ousting John Daniell in 1983. The Government appointees for most of the ownership period were Fred Dobbs and Reg Rusk, and Bernie Ebbett followed by Brian Mooney represented the Dairy Board.

This Board was run in a much more consultative manner, with complete commitment and more formal contributions required from all members. It is generally agreed that Begg, known for his tough argumentative skills and re-

Darcy Freeman, the Board's general manager until March 1983.

fusal to back down, was less skilled than his predecessor at building consensus or a strong personal power base. But events conspired to make his Board, during the period of ownership, united in its purpose and against the many outside forces.

---

28 September 1982
The Chairman
The New Zealand Meat Producers Board
P O Box 121
WELLINGTON

Dear Sir
As at the end of September 1982 our company had 3959 tonnes of lamb which is uncommitted to any market at this point of time. The following grades are included in the tonnage:

1 700 tonnes of YL's
1 359 tonnes of PM's
600 tonnes of YM's
300 tonnes of PX's
3 959

Average f.o.b. cost (excluding storage and interest) from slaughter varies from 204.57 cents per kg for PM's to 199.87 cent per kg for YM's.

It is imperative that this unsold product is disposed of in an orderly manner and to ensure that this does occur we offer the above product to the New Zealand Meat Producers Board at the actual cost when purchased from the farmer.

In deciding as from March 29 to retain ownership of lamb, this company has purchased lamb at schedule from your farmers. We have supplied lamb to the Iran contract on a completely uncommercial basis because as a supplier, we were not privy to the changes and the detail of the contract. We have abided by the minimum prices scheme for all markets when controls have applied. In the United Kingdom in May we were part of the industry who asked for Meatmark to be introduced, but we were bitterly disappointed to have it withdrawn in mid-July and to note the resultant consequences in the United Kingdom for our product.

Those who have "played the game" appear to be carrying far too much of the responsibility of lamb ownership and marketing which must only be to the detriment of our shareholders.

We would like also to point out that unless we receive all funds due under the Iran contract by 11 October, plus liquidation of our unsold stock in New Zealand, our Company will not purchase new season's lamb at schedule, but will kill lambs on behalf of farmers and debit the farmer with all the charges.

Yours sincerely

A R Hutton
Managing Director
Waitaki NZ Refrigerating Ltd

Supply and demand. A letter from Athol Hutton of Waitaki to the Board in late 1982 puts responsibility for payment of higher schedule prices firmly on the Board.

All Care and No Responsibility!
1982-85

"There were ships tied up around the coast and every ship was full of meat. We didn't know whether to ship it or not because the Iranians hadn't paid. And all the cold stores were full to overflowing. Animals could only be slaughtered when the meat was loaded onto a ship; then they could slaughter some more to fill a gap in the freezer. But it worked; and that's what a lot of people don't realise." Norman McRae.

As the Board's star was rising with the exercise of its ownership powers, the meat processing and exporting industry was also undergoing a significant injection of new blood and energy.

'The industry' at the start of the Board intervention in October 1982 included 17 freezing companies, two marketing co-operatives (PPCS and PML) and 40 members of the Independent Meat Exporters' Association. Included in the latter group were some names soon to come to greater prominence: Advanced Meat Ltd, Fort Export Ltd, and W Richmond Ltd.

In 1982 Peter Norman's UK masters replaced him as general manager of Borthwicks, bringing in Royston Hine and then Robert Baldey. Ron Cushen, the group general manager of SFM who had chaired the MEC in 1978-79 and followed Ian Cameron of HBFMC as chair of the FCA in 1982-83, retired in 1983. He was replaced until mid-1985 by Owen Poole and then by Terry Cooke. Peter Norman chaired the MEC until May 1983, when Eric Cammell took over, and John Dotchin became deputy.

Both Ron Cushen and Peter Norman had, when acting as company or industry representatives, worked with the Board as much as they had taken stands opposed to it. Peter Norman, particularly, had spent a large amount of time in consultation with the Board. He had a very good working relationship with Charlie Hilgendorf.

New people were becoming vocal within the MEC and FCA, including Athol Hutton, who had joined Waitaki from Hawke's Bay Farmers Co-operative in 1981 and John Drayton who replaced Derek Morten at CFM the same year. In 1983, FCA and MEC secretary Tim Ritchie moved to London as the general manager of Towers, and was replaced by Bob Diprose. The membership mix was to change further when Alliance's Jim Barnes died suddenly in May 1984 and Sandy Murdoch was recruited from Waitaki. The 'older guard' was represented by Peter Johnston of W & R Fletcher, a diminutive but distinctive figure driving his yellow Jaguar 'Butterball'.

The Pacific Freezing/Dawn Meats duo of Graeme Lowe and John Foster had confirmed their status as industry trend-setters with their success in opening the Oringi plant. John Buxton had returned from the UK to be chief executive of the Christchurch-based New Zealand Farmers Co-operative. Though the business was almost immediately taken over by Bruce Judge, John Buxton successfully proposed developing a specialist meat business at its plant at Riverlands in Blenheim.

Owen Poole, chief executive of Southland Frozen Meat from 1983-85 and of Alliance since 1995.

Another newcomer which was to become significant had entered the industry almost by default in 1982. Fletcher Challenge took ownership of DMBA, the Dunedin Master Butchers-owned plant, when it was not paid for the export upgrade construction it had completed, and went on to develop a state-of-the-art further processing facility there. As the *Meat Producer* Nov-Dec 1982 reported: "Fletcher Challenge is interested in further processing both for local and export markets, and may move further into meat marketing in the future, said Mr Ian Donald, chief executive of the corporation's rural and trading sector."

Fletcher Challenge suggested to the Vestey organisation that it should give up the W & R Fletcher name under which it had been trading in the New Zealand meat industry for at least 70 years, and was rebuffed. But the British company's own merger soon led to a name change, to Weddel Crown.

By 1983 Fletcher Challenge had a 20% shareholding in SFM, which owned plants at Mataura and Makarewa, and had been invited by CFM to play the white knight against impending takeover by PPCS.

PPCS made more than a full recovery from its initial concern over Board ownership. It profited not only from the way it was able to operate, but also from shrewd ownership moves. It had acquired a 20% shareholding in CFM by anticipating Borthwicks would be forced to sell some of its assets after the unsuccessful share float of the late 1970s. Typically wily, Ian Jenkinson pre-empted CFM opposition to PPCS bidding for the shares. "I went round all the insurance companies and major banks in New Zealand, and said: 'In the next few months you're going to be offered shares in CFM by Borthwicks. I will give you fifty cents a share above the price you pay if you just transfer them straight to PPCS'. They fell into our hands like rotten bloody bananas."

While the returns were not great they had picked up assets "that you could do something with, because they were written down, not at all over-valued".

PPCS briefly held shares in SFM in 1983 before selling out – at a profit and with a dividend. As Ian Jenkinson recalls, "We owned those shares for a fortnight; in that time they paid their dividend, so we got $100,000 odd in dividend. It was accidental. Just bloody marvellous."

This windfall was at the expense of Fletcher Challenge, which held 20% of the company. The same year, Fletcher Challenge engaged in a brief skirmish with Waitaki (with some sniping interference from PPCS) for control of CFM. This they won after the Examiner of Commercial Practices gave them (and PPCS) the nod rather than Waitaki.

Fletcher Challenge and PPCS took over a company that was a bastion of the Canterbury establishment, and unceremoniously ousted Ian McKellar as CFM chairman. John Acland, the PPCS director who took over the CFM chair, recalls how John Neilson told him a local paper had described the audacity of Waitaki's earlier attempt as trying to take over the Cathedral: "Now you have even thrown out the bishop!"

Fletcher Challenge subsequently took control of the 103-year old SFM in 1984 and renamed it Challenge Meats. It was to be the beginning of their vision of the meat industry based on branded consumer-ready products, such as the Pastons brand in the UK.

The processing companies found life under the Board intervention arrange-

Building an export trade in live sheep was seriously considered when production was expanding rapidly. The ban which prevented the trade was lifted in 1975 and at its peak over 200,000 sheep a year were shipped, mainly to Saudi Arabia. New Zealanders were always uncomfortable about the animal welfare implications of the trade and as sheep numbers fell it dwindled to almost nothing.

ments was remarkably stress free. The Board and/or the Government took all the financing and commercial risks and the companies were paid their fees on a regular basis.

As David Spence of CFM recalls: "Life was easy under Board control and salary reviews were a breeze." There were also opportunities to rip the Board off in all directions. Ian McKellar says the companies were at work as soon as the Board took over.

There were instances of claims for product processed in pounds weight instead of kilos and charging for storage on product already loaded out. They withdrew meat from stores for further processing without advising the Board so that on occasions it was selling a non-existent product, paying storage, and then having to scramble to cover its commitments. All to the delight of the companies.

John Foster relates: "We fleeced the Board on storage rates, as much as anything. Because cold stores were expensive items used for a very short period of time, the rates for storing meat were set on a seasonal basis. So stock that was in store for two, three or four months had to cover the capital outlay for a year. We had those storage rates for 12 months, and that was a huge profit bonanza. I thought the Board would have called tenders for differing lengths of time."

Although the Board had arrangements to handle the sale of carcass and further processed product to the traditional markets, finding markets for the 'homeless' product was still a real problem. Amalgamated Marketing arranged for the sale of over 100,000 tonnes of mutton and lamb to the USSR between 1982 and 1985, and the *New Zealand Herald* dubbed Ross Finlayson "the Kissinger of the meat industry" for his frequent negotiating trips.

An Iranian contract had been signed in December 1982 for the supply of 120,000 tonnes in the period to March 1984 again, as with the previous contract, on the basis of a back-to-back oil deal. Including a provision for an additional 32,000 tonnes, the volume was too great for Euravia so a new oil buyer had to be found.

By now the Meat Marketing Corporation (MMC), had been re-established

Five vessels loading meat cargoes for a variety of markets at the Port of Napier. From left to right: the Mikolaj Rej *for PNG/Singapore; the* Winter Water *(USSR); the* Winter Sun *(USSR) next to the* Attica Reefer, *Saudi Arabia; the* Belgian Reefer, *Japan and Korea.*
Some 30 shiploads were required just to transport the massive meat order – between 13 and 14 million carcasses – negotiated with the USSR by Ross Finlayson of Amalgamated Marketing. The order took over two years to complete, and as Finlayson remembers: "The last ship was going up through the Bosphorus, and we got a telex to say that some of the meat on board the ship, according to its documents which were correct, was over 18 months old. The buyer refused to take it. I jumped on the plane, and we did a deal for the meat at a quarter of the original price. That got everybody off the hook." Apparently the meat was fed to prisoners.

Carcasses of lamb being unloaded in Iran. Because Iran took such huge quantities of meat any hold-up in the export had disastrous repercussions. ACT New Zealand leader Richard Prebble, then a Labour cabinet minister, remembers being rung by a Treasury official at home during Christmas 1984. "He advised that all the freezing works' freezers were full and that the nation's kill was going to have to be stopped in a few days. There was an order to sell all of the unsold meat that had been carried over from the previous season to Iran. But the brokers required a personal guarantee from the New Zealand Government. From memory, the total amount was about $800 million. I asked where the Minister of Finance was and we discovered that Roger Douglas had put down as his address over the summer holidays as RD Coromandel. You couldn't put a request over the radio to find the Minister of Finance, that would shake the country's confidence. I was looking at the issue for about a day and I decided that I had no choice but to sign. I did so without being able to consult with another Member of Parliament and fortunately the Iranians paid. That among other things made me decide that we just had to reform the meat industry."

specifically to act as the Board's agent to handle sales to single buyer markets. In deference to the Iranian desire to deal with government agencies, the MMC had a Meat Board logo on its letterhead.

The National Iranian Oil Co (NIOC) introduced the Board/MMC team to Toyomenka, big Japanese oil traders, and left the negotiations to the interested parties. As usual the oil traders wanted too much, but Hassan Shaida managed to get the Iranian deputy Minister of Oil involved to tell Toyomenka they were asking for too big a discount and they could modify the contract – which they did. The Board reported the contract proceeded very smoothly largely because of the co-operation and assistance of the Iranian authorities.

Regular meetings of the JMC reviewed progress and by March 1983 there was still concern about the estimated 100,000 tonnes of unplaced product. Production estimates of the volume of lamb for the 1982-83 season were put at 436,000 tonnes and mutton at 141,000 tonnes for a combined total 38% higher than the previous season. The Board representatives indicated a worst case scenario of 94,000 tonnes and a best case one of 41,000 tonnes, uncommitted and in store at the end of the season.

Adam Begg commented in the *Meat Producer* of May-June 1983 that placing an additional 38% of product profitably at a time when world trade was not buoyant would be a challenge. "That such an increase should coincide with widespread depression in almost all international commodity trades and a war between two major customers (Iran and Iraq) makes the task more than doubly difficult."

The high level of unsold stocks at that time of the year was because the Board and industry had concentrated initially on moving the tonnage carried over from the previous season. In addition, the peak of the kill had put strains on storage capacity particularly when companies introduced Saturday morning kills to satisfy the demands of their farmer clients. The Board suggested companies desist to avert future storage problems but they did not consider it their concern. The companies were paid regularly for their processing and freezing charges so production and throughput were their main concern to ensure their bread and butter, while the Board/Government provided the jam.

Payments to producers at the SMP price levels were unchanging throughout the year, so producers were intent on maximising their returns in accordance with production considerations and requirements. There was no incentive to adjust to changing market returns. The other concern facing the Board was that the government-inflated SMP levels were encouraging even more production than could be handled comfortably in the existing market circumstances. It was a no-win situation.

It got to the stage where 'storage relief vessels' were brought in to hold product going to Iran and relieve the pressures on the companies' cold storage. Naturally, all expenses were to the Board's account. Despite payment 'complications' with the Iranian contract, the Board decided to keep accepting product for shipment to Iran to reduce the pressure.

As Norman McRae says: "It really was an appalling mess when you look back. But I'm sure we dealt with it the best way. It was a joint effort by the industry and the Board. The Board had the 'mana' to be able to go in untainted with commercialism. It was seen as a government organisation, which is what the Iranians wanted at that stage."

In accordance with previously announced government policy, the SMP prices for 1983-84 were maintained at the level for the previous season. In contrast, the minimum and trigger prices determined by the Meat Export Prices Committee were adjusted according to the changing status of the markets for sheepmeats and beef. The minimum price for lamb was dropped by 15 cents per kg to 99 cents while mutton prices were slashed by 30 cents to 12 cents per kg. As a result the SMP prices exceeded the Board's minimum prices for lamb and mutton by 47 cents and 39 cents per kg respectively. Beef prices were increased.

The lower Prices Committee prices for sheepmeats were closer to the companies' market expectations, which led some companies to challenge the Board's acquisition of lamb under the terms of the Meat Export Prices Act in an attempt to win back some or all marketing control.

In the face of these continuing attacks, the Board had resolved in November 1983 to use the powers under Section 10 of the Meat Export Control Act 1922 to exercise control of sheepmeats intended for export, until such time as the decision was rescinded.

Ian Jenkinson saw this as: "the Board forcing us not to beat the system. We (PPCS) were profitable enough to meet the (Price Committee) price and just keep things going. I knew things were going to come right, and if it didn't it was going to be the end anyway."

Slaughter levels for lamb and mutton in 1983-84 were expected to ease from the peaks of 36 million and 9.3 million respectively recorded the previous season, but this did not necessarily reduce the pressure to find markets.

Every effort was made to find a sale for the homeless stocks and as Graeme Harrison reported in the *Meat Producer* of September 1983, these efforts were largely successful despite reduced tonnages sent to the UK and to North America due to the carryover stock situation.

The Board implemented a differential pricing policy to promote sales to newer markets at attractive prices. A greater volume of product, particularly mutton, was further processed as a means of improving its marketability both for retail and manufacturing purposes and reducing pressure on storage space. Some 7.5 million lamb carcasses were further processed, an increase of 50% on volume recorded the previous year. Mutton further processing increased fourfold and in 1983 over 40% – 3.2 million mutton carcasses – was boned out.

There were record sales of lamb to Iran, Saudi Arabia, and the Arabian Gulf countries, and the Jordanian army contract was regained. Sales were made to Peru, Egypt, Russia, and the Caribbean, and prospects were explored in virtually every country in the world by the Board's marketing team.

The team was led by Graeme Harrison and included Wayne Geary (ex Borthwicks), Don Harwood and Ian Singleton (ex Waitaki) and Paul Phillips. In addition, Trevor Stewart from PPCS had been appointed Middle East director of the Board's new office in Bahrain, later assisted by Ross Montgomery. Countries investigated included Mexico, Philippines, South Africa, and Gambia, Ghana, Guinea-Bissau and Senegal in West Africa.

The Government was involved with the investigation of the use of some of the sheepmeats in a reciprocal trade deal on railway rolling stock being pur-

A team of 23 worked on mutton further processing at Waitaki's Pukeuri plant in 1983. Such was the volume of product coming through that the lamb cutting team also trained to work with mutton.

chased from Hungary. In addition, the prospects of bilateral trade deals involving everything from mining and engineering equipment to containers and fishing vessels were explored with Poland and other Eastern Bloc countries by Baden Roberts (ex the Watties subsidiary Neill Cropper & Co Ltd) with assistance from Don Harwood and the Government trade representatives.

One of the most far-reaching market developments resulted from a delegation comprising Board members Michael Kight and Reg Rusk, plus Graeme Harrison, that reviewed the marketing of New Zealand sheepmeats in Japan. The delegation concluded that the New Zealand meat industry had largely failed to develop the market for lamb and that Board ownership and control of the product through to the marketplace was necessary to establish a firm and expanding market for lamb in Japan. This would lead to the establishment of ANZCO and Janmark.

The Board investigated the prospects for salting mutton for export to countries, including Chad, without a cold store infrastructure.

One suggestion was to increase sales on the local market, but local market suppliers opposed the move. Further, the denial of the exporters' request for the Government to waive the requirement for them to repay the SMP element, which related only to exports, sealed the fate of the suggestion. An early proposal to render some of the less saleable carcasses was also unacceptable at the time.

Despite all these efforts the stocks in store at the end of the 1983 financial year were still too high for comfort, particularly in the UK. The Board's accounts show that stocks held were valued at $480 million, or around 60,000 tonnes.

The Board was becoming increasingly dissatisfied with marketing arrangements that had been cobbled together with the exporters in a rush at the beginning of the 1982-83 season. Adam Begg recalled later, in the February-March 1984 issue of the *Meat Producer:* "It was essentially a stopgap selling arrangement we came to with the exporters and proved unsuited to long term marketing strategies. It could best be described as an orderly disposal operation." But not a fire sale.

The Board was reluctant to publicise the continuing and resource-sapping squabbles with exporters over all aspects of the processing and selling arrangements, but particularly pricing. Frequently it was called on by Duncan McIntyre to explain its position. The Board's concerns were exemplified by the number of sub-agents appointed in the UK who were "all competing against one another for the available business and putting intense pressure on prices", according to new Board general manager Jim Bremner in a report on his visit to Europe in April 1983. Bremner also stressed the need to improve the effectiveness of the distribution system to meet changing retailing patterns and distribution economics.

Arising from that visit Jim Bremner developed a discussion paper, 'A Strategy for the Future of Sheepmeat Marketing' with the emphasis on marketing and distribution and based on the premise of central ownership to achieve the objectives. The industry had been suspicious of Jim Bremner as a single-desk marketer and he was proving them right.

In the Board's view the market had changed dramatically in a short period

Erik Trautmann, who came from Danish Bacon to be the Board's European director.

of time and this required a new approach. "Quotas, voluntary restraint agreements, single-buyer markets, volatile political and economic conditions and fierce competition from pork and poultry are facts of life, which will be with us for the foreseeable future," said Adam Begg at the time.

Bremner's paper was largely endorsed by the Board. Begg considered the circumstances and the paper sufficiently important to seek written comments from each Board member, all of which generally supported the principal elements. In addition, there were positive comments and some consideration of the operational requirements from some of the senior staff members. Bremner's paper was to be the basis of the Board proposal for ownership and orderly marketing of the product through a centrally operated National Pool for export lamb procurement, which it intended to discuss with producers, the industry and Government. But the Government stepped in first.

Some industry leaders and others wanted a complete review. In the *Press* of 19 April 1983, Athol Hutton called for an independent commission to return the industry to international competitiveness. He felt efficiency could be improved in areas including type of meat produced, transport of exports, and procuring export meat, and joined several illustrious predecessors in calling for the number of processing companies to be reduced to three or four.

He also said that, for marketing purposes, ownership of the meat should stay with the farmer through the Meat Board or a meat commission. These organisations would provide limited marketing rights to companies with the financial and distribution resources on the world's free markets.

National MP, Derek Quigley commented, in a paper 'The New Zealand Meat Industry' dated March 1983, that the overall marketing policy for New Zealand lamb in the UK prior to the Board's acquisition "appears also to have been a problem". It was a concern as that market was a reference point for lamb prices in other countries.

However he considered that the difficulty "should now be overcome by the New Zealand Meat Board's involvement". He also commented on deficiencies in processing, shipping and distribution and urged consideration of a new strategy.

These and other calls resulted in an announcement from the Minister of Agriculture, Duncan McIntyre, in June 1983 that he was setting up a Meat Industry Task Force (MITF). Adam Begg was to chair the task force. Other

The Meat Industry Task Force. From left: Peter Egan, Ron Cushen, John Asquith (secretary), Malcolm Cameron, Brian Chamberlin, Adam Begg, Ian Jenkinson, Fred Dobbs.

members, who were appointed for their expertise and not as representatives of their organisations, were Malcolm Cameron (MAF), Brian Chamberlin (Federated Farmers), Ian Jenkinson (PPCS), Board member Fred Dobbs, Peter Egan (Advanced Meats), Ron Cushen (SFM), with John Asquith (MAF) as the secretary.

The MITF was to examine New Zealand's present meat marketing and develop a new strategy. It set a tight reporting timeframe so any recommendations could be implemented by the start of the 1983-84 season.

The Board's submission was based on the National Pool paper developed for discussion with industry stakeholders, and concentrated on the export marketing of sheepmeats which was described as "dominated by a production-oriented, commodity disposal attitude" which had not responded to changing conditions. It outlined perceived weaknesses of the system that the Board had attempted to rectify with interventions of increasing frequency, and followed the Board's now familiar line of 'controlled private enterprise' and 'co-ordinated marketing'.

The aim of the National Pool was for the Board to "ensure that there is co-ordination, discipline and control in meat marketing without sacrificing flexibility and capacity to respond to changes in the market situation." It was also promoted as the basis for a comprehensive longer-term strategy to develop lamb from a commodity to a branded product image. The proposal advocated a separation of production and processing operations, which related to farmer needs, from marketing (including further processing), storage and distribution functions, which should respond to market requirements.

The Board was at pains to point out to producers that Board members valued the principles of private enterprise but also accepted the benefits of collective strength and stressed the vulnerability of fragmented industry marketing. "We are not advocating single-desk selling." But to some people it looked remarkably like a single-desk proposal.

Submissions from other parties generally supported some form of central control. The MEC conceded it was inevitable that a central authority would be responsible for marketing policy and strategy, but advocated that it should be representative of the industry rather than producer-controlled.

MAF discussed two alternative systems with either a selective interventionist agency, which would facilitate the activities of private exporters and set boundaries, or a central marketing agency for price stabilisation, trade access negotiations and commercial trading and market development. Federated Farmers were a little more ambivalent, calling for further exploration of marketing structures, but the Meat & Wool Section proposed alternatives similar to MAF's.

The Task Force met for two weeks in the MAF offices in the old Dominion Farmers Building at 110 Featherston Street. "There was a two-bar heater, and I wore my overcoat. At 10 o'clock, the typical government morning tea wagon came in with huge pots of tea and coffee," Fred Dobbs reflects.

The Task Force report concentrated mainly on sheepmeats marketing because of the self-imposed deadline. It analysed the international environment, industry strengths and weaknesses, and recommended a structure and operational procedure aimed at maximising returns to New Zealand. It was just another meat industry review, as Fred Dobbs commented: "You're only polish-

Fred Dobbs.

ing the past. It's like polishing hubcaps. Seeing your face in them does you a lot of good but it doesn't make the car go any better."

The report recommended the Board continue as the central statutory organisation and control a National Pool for the marketing of sheepmeats. Farmers would be paid the minimum price or a set percentage (90%) of the estimated market return with the prospect of an end of season payout.

The Board would act as the primary exporter of carcasses and primal cuts, particularly to single buyer markets. Private exporters would be licensed to acquire carcasses and primal cuts from the Pool for further processing and for export, in accordance with an overall marketing plan.

It also proposed a statutory Meat Industry Council be formed to work with the Board in formulating strategic plans and to monitor marketing plans. This would have an independent chairman, two members from the Board, a meat processor and a meat exporter representative, the Director General of Agriculture, and two members selected for their commercial expertise. There were also recommendations on quality assurance, research and development, transportation and liaison with the unions.

Ian Jenkinson had reservations about the recommended central structure and the lamb marketing proposals. "I considered, rightly or wrongly, that Adam Begg was trying to turn the Meat Board into a sort of Dairy Board, and I wasn't going to have a bar of it. I went back to the office, got hold of my secretary, plus Stewart Barnett and a few others and told them that we were going to produce a second, minority report… I felt strongly that what the Board was trying to do was very wrong, so I produced the report. I don't think I did my relations with Adam any good."

But it did raise his stocks with his suppliers. "You've got to realise that part of this is psychology. Farmers love an underdog, and if you could pretend you were fighting the Government and fighting the Meat Board, the farmers thought you were bloody Christmas. And so part of it was an act."

Jenkinson argued for the existing system of procurement based on the schedule price for product destined for the 'traditional markets', with meat for the development or single-buyer or seller markets, and uncommitted product, handled by a new separate organisation. It was basically a rerun of MITO.

Ian Jenkinson said the Board should delegate most of its statutory 'trading-related' responsibilities to a Meat Industry Council as proposed by the Task Force, which would be responsible for overseeing all marketing and trading activities and the operations of a MITO pool. The Board as a central organisation should not be involved in selling meat. It would operate all "subsidy and skim- off schemes" on behalf of the Government and producers but would not intervene.

The release of the Task Force recommendations and the minority report roused an immediate and widespread debate on the merits of private enterprise versus central control. The Board was quick to criticise the minority report and "totally rejected the wholesale delegation of its powers" to an organisation on which it would have minority representation.

Fred Dobbs recalls the report was received, read, and never implemented. "We saw our faults, we confessed, we pledged better behaviour, with religious fervour… but we continued doing exactly as before because there was no gov-

110 Featherston Street, then known as Seabridge House, where the Meat Industry Task Force met. The building was built in 1916 by Fletchers as the Dominion Farmers Institute, and was the venue for the meeting which led to the establishment of the New Zealand Meat Producers Board in 1922.
From 1987 to 1997, the Board was located at 110 Featherston Street. Seabridge was the name of a grouping of container lines shipping to the UK and Europe, which was disestablished in 1995.
Photo: Trans Tasman Properties.

ernment endorsement, no minister to bang heads together."

Some meat companies (Hawkes Bay Farmers' was one) and the MEC – contrary to their submission – took out full-page advertisements in the major daily newspapers opposing the recommendations which they dubbed 'Meat Acquisition' by a central monopoly. They pointed out the loss of "free choice to maximise your returns" and decried the apparent haste that required an early decision on such an important matter. Farmers believed what they read.

The Meat & Wool Section of Federated Farmers was due to vote on the matter about six weeks after the report was released. Tim Plummer, who was section chairman (and later stood for the Board), changed his tune and issued a personal statement pointing out that a National Pool would divorce farmers from market signals and reduce competition on which they could judge performance. He urged farmers to think through the proposals before deciding. Others in Hawke's Bay echoed this. Southlander Aubrey Begg reported on a meeting in Oamaru opposed to the National Pool and called for a national referendum of farmers.

The main grounds for opposition were that the Pool concept restricted producers' freedom of choice when marketing livestock and that solutions to meat industry problems did not rest with more restrictions and controls. However farmers did support a Meat Industry Council to "formulate the structures and functions of a competitive private enterprise marketing system that gives the producer freedom of choice when selling".

The Board spent a lot of time at meetings to discuss the Task Force report and Jim Bremner reported that these highlighted farmer confusion about how the Pool would work. The Board pointed out that private enterprise selling channels would be used except in single-buyer markets. Federated Farmers eventually backed the proposals but noted some concern about operational aspects of the National Pool.

The MEC and the Independent Meat Exporters Association continued to oppose the scheme and advised they would submit alternative proposals to the Government. Some 'independent' meat exporters (Ross Finlayson of Amalgamated Marketing, Graeme Lowe of Dawn, Ian Cameron of Hawke's Bay Farmers', Gray Mathias of Mathias Meats, Bill Leonard of PML and Bob Trounce of C S Stevens) met Minister of Agriculture Duncan McIntyre and tabled a paper 'Regarding Future Sheepmeat Marketing'.

This noted the problems facing the industry were outside the control of the exporters and said the private enterprise system had been constantly "fiddled with". It also accused the Board of mismanagement of marketing during the 1982-83 season, an accusation subsequently refuted.

The 'independents' criticised the Task Force recommendations, claiming that, if implemented, they would curtail the activities of the industry's leading marketers and result in a loss of talented people. They supported an alternative proposal being developed by the MEC to establish a meat industry authority to plan and co-ordinate a private enterprise marketing system.

Paul Spackman, economics research officer for the Board until 1984, when he was posted to London.

Ironically, at the same time as they were criticising the Board's intervention, some other companies were writing to the Board seeking protection for individual market positions. A rift was beginning to develop in the previously stable relations between the Board and the industry.

At the Peak of the Kill
1984-85

"On the one hand it would seem the Government's approach is to move to a more market economy with fewer subsidies and other distortions, while on the other it is clear the new administration wishes to actively support the rapid development of industries with export earning and import saving capacity, which are also labour intensive. If followed consistently, these policies will have major implications for the meat industry which in recent years has been encouraged to produce more regardless of market signals." Adam Begg – address to mid-year meeting of Meat & Wool Section of Federated Farmers, 1984.

Notwithstanding the controversy raised by Ian Jenkinson's minority report, the Government accepted in modified form some of the general recommendations of the Meat Industry Task Force. It confirmed the Board as the central marketing authority for export sheepmeats and implemented the main recommendation for the establishment of the Meat Industry Council.

The structure was put in place early in 1984 with Reid Jackson as the chairman. Jackson was an entrepreneurial accountant from Dunedin whose introduction to the meat industry had come two years previously when appointed to the board of Alliance as a Meat Board appointee – a condition of the Board's original 1956 loan to assist the establishment of the company.

He held a number of other directorships, was involved in several private companies and admitted in an interview that working was his hobby. He was a man in a hurry and had impressed the farmers on the Alliance board with his somewhat forthright views on the need to focus on efficiency and profitability in the meat industry.

He hoped that the MIC would be the catalyst for "a major rationalisation which probably has to take place in the meat industry".

Jackson was an enthusiastic advocate for increasing the amount of further processing done in New Zealand: "The concept of selling our lamb as a commodity in carcass form is something which has been with us for 100 years, and which all companies have been trying to address in various ways. I think there's going to have to be a co-ordinated approach and this may mean some works simply become killers, others become processors, while others become further processors. We should be trying to take advantage of longer runs and specialisation."

He was totally opposed to setting up a bureaucracy under the MIC. "I would prefer to get an expert in each field to give me reports."

Both the MEC and the Board had supported the establishment of the MIC but the MEC was shifting ground and its attitude against the Board's continuing involvement in marketing was hardening. The MEC considered the Board was actively moving to establish a single marketing body, which had Eric Cammell avowing that a monopoly industry structure would not be in the best interests of the industry or the country.

The MIC first met on 21 February 1984 under the terms of a letter from the

Board member Roger Marshall continued the lean lamb crusade during the ownership years.

Minister of Agriculture to the chairman of the Meat Board, which formally notified the Board of the Government's decisions on the recommendations of the MITF.

The Council operated initially under the statutory authority of the Board and was funded by agreement between the Board and the industry. The aim was to get it up and running rather than wait for legislation, still being drafted, that would give it a funding base as well as the Government's sanction and authority.

Other members of the MIC were: Mervyn Barnett and Norman McRae representing the Board; Ian Cameron of Hawkes Bay Farmers' representing the FCA; Alan Clark of Meatex from the MEC; and Malcolm Cameron of MAF, with MAF's Pat McCabe as acting secretary. The secretary's role was taken over later by Terry O'Brien.

Two other members were to be appointed for their commercial experience. The Council had considerable difficulty finding suitable candidates and only Gary Paykel of Fisher & Paykel was appointed as an independent commercial member. The other member was Ron Cushen, a director of SFM following his retirement as CEO of that company. This appointment swung the balance of power on the MIC towards the industry.

The Council's role was to "examine, comment on and approve the strategies and plans …which are developed jointly by the industry and the Meat Board; and to monitor industry and Board performances in the execution of strategies and marketing plans and to report annually to the Minister of Agriculture and the industry."

The MEC expressed some relief that the MIC had been established with considerably more independence than recommended by the Task Force. Instead of accepting the MITF recommendation for the Board to be the sole importer of carcasses and primals to the UK, the Minister had determined that a limited number of exporters should be appointed as primary importers. Ministerial interventions were to become a familiar feature of MIC activities.

Both the MEC and FCA saw the MIC as a means of resolving some of the contentious issues that had blown up during the Board's ownership. These related to the Board's edicts on marketing, the arrangements to encourage further processing, and a means of settling disputes between the Board and the companies. The MIC was seen as a body that might eventually take over the functions and powers from the Board and operate as an independent industry control authority. Another one!

The MIC's first move was to call for comments from the Board and the industry on the outstanding issues. The tone of the responses set the scene for the remainder of the MIC's short but confrontational life. Later Reid Jackson was to comment: "There was sheer animosity evident in the FCA/MEC papers towards the Meat Board."

Jim Bremner noted that "a minority of companies would like to see the Board fall on its face and marketing to return to the old situation. Companies must now adjust to a new set of rules." As Norman McRae later recalled, "There were a lot of barneys in the MIC meetings."

The industry response to the MIC was to accuse the Board of inefficiency, citing delays in establishing prices, political interference in decision-making, and a rigid and non-consultative stance. The MEC statement contended: "A continuance of the present system could finally result in a single-selling system of lamb commodities with the New Zealand Meat Producers Board as the principal, and a continuance of surpluses from year to year. This being the case, we believe that importing countries will take further action to protect their producers against our suppliers."

The Board, for its part, reported on the current market situation, and then detailed its marketing plans in the short and medium terms in relation to developing a brand image and a professional distribution system. It also noted the 'market reforms' implemented, including reducing the numbers of importers/agents in major markets and the establishment of development and single-seller markets.

The Board had in 1983 commissioned a report from business consultants Glendinning and Associates on the distribution system for New Zealand lamb in the UK, with recommendations for a suitable alternative structure. The report noted that the market had changed in the UK, particularly as a result of the growth of large buyers such as the supermarkets and butchery chains. There was a need to co-ordinate prices and volumes. The findings were similar to those of the Task Force and recommended more controlled meat imports and distribution, with a limited number of agents operating. This was all grist to the Board's mill both in promoting more orderly marketing and the development of further processed and packaged lamb sales.

As a result the Board reduced the numbers of importer/agents from around 30 in 1982 to eight for the 1983-84 season and ruffled a few feathers in the process. The importer/agents were: Associated New Zealand Farmers Ltd (AFFCO, Alliance and Hawke's Bay Farmers'); Thomas Borthwick & Sons Ltd; Co-operative Wholesale Society Ltd; Dalgety Lonsdale Ltd (Richmond); Defiance Meats Ltd (PPCS); Swift & Co Ltd; Towers & Co Ltd (Waitaki NZR, SFM and Farm Exports Ltd); and W Weddel & Co (W & R Fletcher).

In 1982-83 these companies had collectively handled 80% of New Zealand lamb imported into the UK. The Board caused further upset to the companies when it reduced the number of agents in Europe "by selecting those companies that have a commitment to New Zealand lamb and have the distribution capability to effectively penetrate the market".

The way the Board had selected those agents, based on volumes handled and facilities available, was the cause of further criticism from the companies, particularly those excluded. One of these was the North Island producer-owned marketing co-operative, Producer Meats (PML), which contended that its UK operations and future trading were in jeopardy. This was to be another bone of contention for the MIC.

In 1983-84, Eric Cammell reported, the MEC had had to "grapple with what must have seemed to many of its councillors problems of daunting proportions". The main areas of contention included the establishment of the MIC, the new marketing procedures and Halal certification.

However if the MEC's problems were daunting, those facing the Board were almost overwhelming. In addition to managing the sale of an over-abundance of product it was trying to promote its views and future strategies against hostile opposition from the companies and continuous pressure for concessions under the intervention arrangements.

Eric Cammell, marketing manager of AFFCO and chair of the MEC from 1983-85.

Farmer and government attitudes were beginning to swing away from interventionist policies towards a more competitive market-based economy and that message was being delivered via the MIC. The Board was convinced that controlled orderly marketing was the only way to cope with the volume of product, and it should continue to take ownership and determine appropriate marketing. Its staff had almost begun to believe their efforts to structure the centralised marketing system would succeed and in the longer term provide a better return than a fragmented private enterprise system.

The short-term stock position had been tidied up and returns were improving, but production volumes were still a problem. The meat companies were concerned that the Board's intervention was continuing far longer than originally planned and they were still promoting modified versions of the MITO proposal as a means of wresting back some of the marketing control.

The Board still did not regard MITO as a serious proposition since it only dealt with the 'marketable' proportion of export sheepmeats with pricing arrangements for the 'low risk' UK and other established markets. As it had told the Task Force in its June 1983 submission, the whole proposal relied on "controls that could not be enforced, decisions being made by a number of committees with consequent inflexibility, a plethora of paper pushing for ineffective monitoring, and the establishment of a lame duck marketing organisation taking unplaced product while private enterprise took the cream of the markets." It was regarded by the Board as a last-ditch attempt by the industry to persuade it not to intervene but rather to pay supplements to support farmer returns.

The Board's revamp of the UK market had also introduced 'market disciplines' designed to provide more price stability and to achieve 'more realistic' pricing levels. This involved the Board selling carcasses and primals direct to importer agents to onsell to depots, major chains and multiple butchers within an overall agreed marketing plan.

In a move designed to complement this and strengthen the Board's UK and European management, it appointed Erik Trautmann as European director in January 1984. The February/March 1984 *Meat Producer* described his "hard commercial experience" – 28 years with the Danish Bacon Company, the last 12 as its managing director.

Pictured with boneless mutton packed for ANZCO's North Asian markets from left: ANZCO's South Island quality control officer Ken Botherway, with Terry Cooke, general manager DMBA, and Ralph Chen, assistant sales manager with Weddel Far East Ltd, ANZCO's agent in Taiwan.

Also in January 1984, the Board invested $350,000 from the Meat Industry Reserve Account to set up the marketing company, the Asian New Zealand Meat Company (ANZCO). This was in response to the findings of the previous year's delegation to Japan, and a subsequent visit by Graeme Harrison. The reports had painted a dismal picture of a market where a fragmented New Zealand selling system was being picked off by a small group of Japanese importers. Sales of mutton were reasonably regular, lamb was spasmodic and dependent on the state of demand in other markets, particularly the UK.

Harrison recommended development of a Board-owned commercial structure to undertake trading activities on its behalf in Japan. Initially, Freesia Meats Ltd was to be taken down from the shelf, where it had languished since the NCF Kaiapoi deal, to be renamed Freesia Meats Japan Ltd. Ultimately, an entirely new company, ANZCO, was established for the carcass trade.

The delegation report also led to the Board decision to declare North Asia (Japan, Korea, Taiwan and Hong Kong) a development market, with ANZCO licensed as the sole exporter of sheepmeats. Later in 1984 the Japan New Zealand Lamb Marketing Co Ltd (Janmark) – a joint venture between the Board, C S Stevens & Co, Top Trading Ltd and Waitaki NZR Ltd – was established to market further processed products. The market was expected to grow significantly and the structure aimed to combine the skills of companies and the Board in developing more stable pricing and supply arrangements.

The Board regarded the National Pool procurement system, aligned with private enterprise selling in the major markets, as a foundation for the development of a stable long term and integrated export marketing strategy. An integrated marketing system was required to match the concentrated buying power of the major retailers in Europe, to provide a greater degree of stability against price fluctuations and to comply with the requirements of the EC regime.

Packing saddles of lamb for the German market at C S Stevens Ashley plant in Christchurch (slaughtered at Kaiapoi and cut at Ashley plant, now Hellers Smallgoods). The European markets became increasingly selective and quality-conscious as supermarkets became more powerful as purchasers.

At the same time it had to provide for sales to single-buyer markets such as Iran, be capable of applying differential prices to separate markets for market development purposes and to make use of 'disposal markets' as and when necessary. The whole system was to be overlaid with provisions for price support including SMPs. Simple enough in theory but difficult to put into practice.

As part of the arrangement the Board wanted to change the basis of producer payments from the existing 'net delivered port works' schedule to an ex-scales payment with all amounts relating to further processing, freezing, storage, handling, distribution and marketing of product being charged to the Pool account.

The aim was to separate livestock procurement, slaughter and processing costs from those relating to marketing and further processing. The Board considered the system would enable producers to "identify the more efficient buying and processing organisations without the confusion of sometimes spurious claims of marketing efficiency".

This tilt towards disclosure of more information about the industry's costs and charges was part of the ongoing campaign for increased productivity and cost reduction in the industry waged almost continually by the Board at the behest of producers.

However, despite a fair measure of agreement between the Board and the FCA on most matters relating to the Pool, the companies rejected the Board's idea of splitting the killing charges from freezing and other costs at the scales. They also reneged on supplying specific details on charges and credits for by-products and for wool and pelt payments. The companies argued that they were offering an integrated service with charges based on total operating costs. As a result the Board was forced to concede that the scheme would operate on an ex-works basis for the 1984-85 season.

At the same time the companies' 'marketing choice' message was beginning to get through to farmers. While the Board endeavoured to promote its views on competitive procurement and processing, the message was effectively countered by the companies using their most potent public relations weapon – their drafters and stock buyers.

The Board's new communications manager Barrie Saunders could organise farmer meetings and put out press releases but company drafters and buyers could deliver the message on a one-to-one basis. The message was generally to highlight any Board mistakes or problems, including the increasing size of the deficit on price support, which was conveniently labelled the Board's loss. They also promoted the argument that Board intervention was limiting the producers' choice of livestock marketing channels.

As well, there was growing concern among farmers about the parlous state of the New Zealand economy and calls for more competition as a means of controlling inflation. These concerns were detailed in *Farming and Subsidies – Debunking the Myths* by Brian Chamberlin. The result was a clamour from farmers for a greater diversity of marketing channels for their stock.

The National Government's specific primary sector response to these calls for greater competitiveness and enterprise was to advise in June 1984 that the SMP scheme was going to be dismantled. SMPs for meat would cease on 30 September 1984 to be replaced by a lump sum payment arrangement for the 1984-85 season. The lump sum would be paid to the Board in two instalments estimated to equal the amount involved had the SMP scheme continued for that season.

A letter from Duncan McIntyre dated 21 June 1984 stated that the lump sum payment was made on the understanding that the Board would disburse it "in such a way as to ensure that producers of meat or meat products for export receive payments broadly in line with current SMP levels". At the end of the 1984-85 season all payments would cease.

By the end of the 1983-84 season the SMP scheme for meat had cost the Government (or the taxpayer) $595 million, with some 75% used to support the lamb prices. The lump sum arrangement would add a further $130 million to the bill. At the same time the deficit in the Meat Income Stabilisation Account had reached $495 million.

As part of the package agreed with the Government the deficit in the Stabilisation Account was to be converted to a subordinated 30-year loan at the Reserve Bank at an interest rate of 1% per annum with a 5-year moratorium on interest and principal repayments.

For the following seasons the Government authorised two new Meat Income Stabilisation Accounts for sheepmeats and beef to be established, with an interest rate of 10% per annum applying to the account both when in credit and debit. The rate was to be reviewed in line with movements in Government stock rates.

While this was happening, Prime Minister Muldoon somewhat imprudently

New Zealand's associate Minister of Finance, John Falloon, visited the Meat Board's European director, Erik Trautmann, in London in 1984 to discuss the new marketing system for lamb and mutton in the UK. From left: John Falloon, Erik Trautmann, NZ High Commissioner Bill Young, and Treasury external economics director Richard Shallcross.

called a snap election, and Labour took over from National in a landslide on 14 July. After a scuffle about the timing of the handover of power there was an immediate 20% devaluation, then the dollar was floated.

This and the announcement that the SMP scheme was to be dismantled threw a seriously large spanner into planning for the 1984-85 season. The immediate assumption was that the sheep and lamb kill would increase, with farmers heeding Muldoon's advice to "take the subsidies and run".

The Board had been working on a projected lamb kill of some 35.5 million head which would compound the marketing and/or disposal difficulties of the previous seasons. They now expected a surge of 2 to 3 million more in the kill, which was going to exacerbate those problems. As it turned out, the lamb kill rose to an unprecedented and unexpected 39 million head and the sheep kill to 10.8 million, causing the Board to scramble to find ways and means of dealing with the volumes.

By August 1984 the Board had determined that the market had still not stabilised to its satisfaction and the Section 10 decision to control sheepmeats intended for export, first made in November 1983, was reconfirmed.

There were barter deals with Poland with sheepmeats traded for mining struts and shipping containers. Sales were made to virtually every country in the Middle East as well as new markets in North and West Africa, the considerable financial risk with some deals believed to be worth taking in the circumstances.

The Board promoted the establishment of the Advanced Foods plant at Waipukurau to manufacture Lamb Roasts for Bernard Matthews plc from the lower value carcass grades, and New Zealand Processed Meats – a joint venture company with Watties – was set up to manufacture meat products from boneless mutton.

Some 90,000 tonnes of mutton was 'homeless' after the USSR did not come into the market. Jim Bremner had already advised the MIC in April 1984 that the Board was actively pursuing alternative disposal options which included: new market opportunities for carcass and boneless product; canning, both within New Zealand and offshore; rendering both within existing works or in stand-alone rendering plants; slaughter in non-registered plants for pet food and feed for fitches (the latest 'get rich quick' scheme).

Barry Brill and Ron Hassett from Watties and Mick Calder from the Board visited China to explore the prospects of setting up joint venture mutton canning operations. The mission decided that China would be a tough nut to crack; the Chinese had their own supplies and their own unique methods of costing their operations.

There was still a surplus of product, particularly of lightweight lamb and mutton carcasses that had not been slaughtered according to Halal requirements and could not be sold to the Middle East or North Africa, so were worth almost nothing. The only answer to save on the cost of storage and finance was to render them for whatever returns that achieved. This move caused a great deal of criticism about economic waste at a time when some people in New Zealand were reportedly on the poverty line. There were calls for the Board to supply food banks, which it did initially, but the logistics of the exercise were too time consuming in relation to the size of the disposal problem.

Buyback and Quality Push
1982-85

"It must be recognised that New Zealand lamb is not in a position to dictate to its customers. The task before New Zealand lamb is to persuade retailers, and through them their customers, that New Zealand lamb is worthy of their attention by virtue of its quality, attractiveness in use, and its value for money." Glendinning Report 1983.

No matter the logic behind the decision to render carcasses, or how much ultimate saving to the farmer, had there been any realisation of the long-lasting negative capital that would be made out of it, a safer if more costly option may well have been chosen. But with the freezers full, there was really no choice.

Unfortunately, that powerful image of waste served to obscure what was a period of enormous achievement against the odds, a time when the meat industry jumped or was pushed into a number of more modern practices, and when real cutbacks were made in what had been a relentless escalation of costs. It was all the more remarkable that these initiatives occurred while there was a growing volume of price supported product, and continued when the withdrawal of SMPs threatened to swamp the system.

During the period of ownership many of the aspirations of the Board and its staff for further processing, product development, orderly marketing, market development and co-ordinated promotion were implemented as part of the overall marketing programme.

The kick-start to value-adding and product diversification, along with a number of associated quality initiatives and developments in areas such as chilled meat and packaging technology came during this hectic time. One of the major incentives was the Buyback scheme, or the 'Lamb Carcass Purchase Agreement For Further Processing' (LCPAFFP) as it was officially known.

Despite the many messages about further processing to add value and meet consumer needs, and the introduction of export incentives to do so from 1976, by September 1980 only 16% of total lamb production was further processed, compared with 13.5% in the 1974-75 season; processed mutton output was around only 8%. Companies pointed out that labour rates were prohibitive and such costs limited further processing in New Zealand, when it could be done cheaper in the marketplace.

Beef production was different as the main market was boneless product for hamburger manufacture in North America and the upmarket chilled trade around the Pacific Rim. Therefore most was further processed and only around 3% of export beef remained in bone-in form.

Despite the slow physical change to further processing, the industry had recognised the trend to an increasing diversity of market requirements by introducing Standpack, under the guidance of David Heynes, in 1976. This set out standard product codes and specifications for all meats.

Standpack was the first comprehensive list of meat cut and pack specifications. David Heynes from Borthwicks, who was later tragically killed in a car accident, masterminded the project as adviser to the FCA.

The Buyback scheme was introduced to increase the volume of further processed lamb. Under Buyback, exporters could buy carcasses back from the Board at a favourable price, to encourage the production of very sophisticated lamb cuts for particular markets. Processing needed to go beyond the primal cuts stage as defined by the Government's Export Incentive scheme. Exporters could sell the product on their own behalf direct to retailers in specific markets designated in advance, subject to some Board constraints.

Promoting the concept, which was also part of the National Pool system recommended by the Task Force, the Board's chief executive Jim Bremner noted the need to reposition New Zealand lamb to achieve premium prices. He saw Buyback as creating a marketing environment in which a successful branded product image could be developed with a "dynamic interface between the New Zealand processor and the distributor", including a comprehensive marketing plan and appropriate support in the marketplace.

In his view: "Previous efforts… have been aborted by the inability of New Zealand processing companies to impose the necessary disciplines in the marketplace which are required for successful branded product marketing." This statement may have helped ensure that the definition, value and application of branding would develop into a perpetual point of difference between the Board and the industry.

Buyback presented an offer no profit-focussed company could refuse. Though there were costs and difficulties negotiating new work processes with the unions, there were also the tempting spin-offs of a longer season and greater job security. And cushions such as the Board agreement to take back any residual cuts not fitting into company marketing plans undoubtedly weighed heavily in the scheme's favour.

Suddenly, everyone was doing it. New companies and new facilities were being built. By 1984-85 100,000 tonnes of lamb were being processed under Buyback, although the parameters of the proposal were continually refined in response to pressure from the companies. There were continual negotiations about the value of the carcasses to be bought back, another area for fruitful exploitation, and a source of complaint from the companies and criticism about them from the Board in the first responses to the MIC.

The Board did concede there had been some delays in determining the Buyback prices but this was largely due to the wide disparity between the agreed carcass formula and prices being offered by the companies. It noted the companies were endeavouring to recoup their full processing rates even though they were receiving export incentives of $1.60-$1.70 per carcass. In addition they were seeking discounts of 10-15% on the carcass price to cover their reputed additional market development costs.

The Board's view was that further processed product could and should be sold at a premium over the equivalent carcass return once the market was developed. However, the companies persistently argued that it was not possible to achieve premiums for further processed lamb cuts.

They claimed this was especially the case in markets where primal cuts were being sold for less than the carcass equivalent price for corresponding further processed cuts. They argued that the formula for Buyback should be

Stewart Pope, manager of the catering advisory service in UK and Europe.

calculated on the lower of either the carcass equivalent price of the cuts or the primal cuts price.

As a result of pressure from the companies, while not accepting the thrust of their arguments about the lack of premiums, the Board reluctantly agreed to examine the relative prices. It would even consider the prospects of withdrawing primal cuts from those markets where Buyback cuts were making significant progress.

Even though some progress was being made with the benefit of export incentives, the companies also argued that there were additional costs in developing the markets for further processed cuts, in the newer markets and in Europe in particular. Again the Board yielded to the pressure and agreed to sell carcasses at a discount of up to 15% to the carcass equivalent realisations, to be phased out over a period of two years.

In addition the Board agreed to continue to take back 'residual' cuts that companies were unable to sell in the target markets. So the whole Buyback scheme was tilted heavily in favour of the processing companies, and added to the costs the Board was already facing in the support of prices to producers.

By May of 1984 a workable solution had been thrashed out between the Board and the companies. Even so, the whole operation was a continuing source of frustration to the Board's staff, particularly Paul Phillips, who had to implement the arrangements, and Don Harwood, who had taken over as group manager, marketing.

Phillips pointed out a year later that, while some progress had been made in the three years the scheme had operated, the companies had still not developed a marketing mentality. "We have not been sufficiently market-led in our arrangements; we have tended to allow extraneous political factors to colour our judgement and have tried to impose on the market a convoluted structure reflecting the many disparate factions of the New Zealand meat industry."

So while the MEC and the Board consulted frequently and many of the discussions achieved satisfactory outcomes, there were also numerous and sometimes rather acrimonious debates between the parties at a staff technical level before agreement on some of the more contentious issues.

The Board was convinced that further processing was one of the keys for the future. While the main thrust was to get product development through the Buyback system, the Board also promoted cutting in its own right. The MIRINZ Processed Meats Centre was opened and its director Brian Chrystall charged with assisting the development of lamb products.

Further processing enabled a degree of flexibility in matching products to markets and it provided some relief when pressure came on for storage space. So companies were encouraged to undertake further processing by way of contract cutting and boning to standard specifications.

However, these good intentions also gave rise to some sharp practices and at least one good story about them. In the most popular, told by more than one company executive, a Board staff member rings the company to tell them: "Your cutting charges are too low; they are lower than the bottom of the range on the Board's computer system". The exceptionally bright,

Brian Chrystall, first director of the MIRINZ Processed Meats Centre.

(usually young female) clerical worker then reportedly offers to resolve the problem by raising their company's charges to fit the Board's system. This is allegedly accepted by the (usually young male and relatively dumb) Board representative. It has been suggested that a number of young female clerks in meat companies were given a rise in salary for their negotiating prowess and proficiency in increasing processing returns for their organisations, at the Board's expense.

Janmark was set up in 1984 with the objective of increasing export sales of further processed lamb to Japan to 50,000 tonnes annually. Ces Stevens was chairman of Janmark. He had been associated with the Board as chief executive of DEVCO in the early sixties, but had subsequently set up his own company pioneering the entry of New Zealand mutton and lamb to Japan. His innovative technique had been to use small refrigerated ships diverted from the Japanese whaling fleet. He admitted the target for lamb cuts sales could prove to be optimistic but: "We are going to give it a try because it's such an important objective, not only for the industry, but for New Zealand."

The Board put more money into promoting new cuts for the UK catering market, through the advisory section started by Roy Hicks and later run by Stewart Pope; it also pushed convenience foods such as 'Meal Makers'.

Graeme Thompson of Fort Export praised Board ownership in the April-May 1984 issue of *Meat Producer* for giving his company "the ability to draw on specific grades of lamb, and theoretically in unlimited quantities". He said his company was further processing 50% of production compared to an industry average of 26%. Alliance's Sandy Murdoch was similarly complimentary of the Board when he showcased his company's specialist range of freeze dried and cured meats.

One company which particularly revelled in Buyback was DEVCO, a pioneer of marketing further processed lamb. Previously it had struggled with the supplier requirement that it should take and sell complete carcasses when operating in a market that preferred racks, racks and more racks – a configuration more like a Dachshund dog than the New Zealand lamb. Under Buyback DEVCO could order cuts more in proportion with market requirements. But it got carried away and over-ordered which, together with other factors, would later leave it precariously positioned.

The meat industry gained another enthusiastic booster with the new Labour Government in 1984. Mike Moore, the Minister of Overseas Trade, put a lot of energy behind many promotion initiatives and became synonymous with the Lamburger (actually a Richmond invention).

Sue Suckling became one of the best known females in the meat industry when, with great publicity, she launched the 'Zealambi' range of lamb and mutton products in Asia, a joint venture between Waitaki and H Noelke of Germany. It was set up in 1983 and established Pacific Foods in 1985 at the Waitaki plant in Nelson. The company aimed to produce up-market convenience foods (meat balls, dumplings and satays) using a combination of further processing, high technology and added value.

The story of the Advanced Foods plant at Waipukurau sums up the hectic pace, dramatic ups and downs, and determination to win through, that

Mike Moore eating lamburger at Heretaunga CIT, August 1983.

Bernard Matthews, the Turkey king outside No 10 Downing Street.

characterised the years of Board ownership. Similarly the subsequent treatment of its carcass supply requirements sums up the industry attitude to anything connected with the Board.

During the 1970s Peter Egan had carved out a profitable niche in boneless mutton. As one of the designated mutton processors after the Board took ownership, the Egan family's Advanced Meats plant at Awapuni in Gisborne, upgraded for export in 1981, stood out for the efficiency of its operation and the high yields achieved in its boning room.

In mid-1984 Advanced Meats presented the Board with 'absolute proof' (the documentation from a container of Waitaki boneless mutton) that its major competitor was undercutting prices in the UK market. Peter Egan also gave Adam Begg and Jim Bremner a written proposal to take over all New Zealand's mutton marketing on a global basis.

Travelling on to Australia, he was called back urgently. Egan recalls: "In some excitement, I came to Wellington only to be told that they were going to turn down my mutton proposal. However, would I like to evaluate the feasibility of using the Bernard Matthews turkey technology to further process lamb? At that time, lighter weight lambs were being rendered, there was just no market. How soon could I get to the UK?"

A week later he had looked round the plants and was sitting opposite Matthews, who insisted that Egan tell him what was wrong with his factory to prove he understood what he was looking at. "So I counted off the 10 most obvious faults in a fairly blunt manner. He turned to his managing director and said, 'Has Mr Egan signed a confidentiality agreement?' And I said, 'No I have not, but if you say what I've seen is confidential then it shall remain so'." He went on to tell a disbelieving Matthews that, if the Board decided to go ahead, they could have a plant up and running well within a year.

Jim Bremner met Peter Egan at the airport on his return. "He said 'Well, is it on, or isn't it?', and I said I thought it was, having done some elementary costings. We then did a full feasibility study. I came to Wellington for a Railways Corporation board meeting, and prior to it I dropped four copies of the report into Jim Bremner. At 12 o'clock that day New Zealand devalued by 20%.

"We re-costed it. We weren't into computers in those days, so it was all hand done. It still showed that the Board should do it. Rather wearily I put in a handwritten note to Jim Bremner saying if the Board wished to proceed with this, Advanced Meats would be interested in taking a 50% equity and designing, building, and commissioning the plant." To his surprise – he would have accepted 10% – the Board agreed to 50%. The Advanced Foods plant was built at Waipukurau, the central Hawke's Bay site being the most promising for meeting Matthews' requirements for year round supply.

For every successful innovation, several fell flat, among them most of the 'reformed' products. Waitaki's 'Zealambi' products looked great but consumers in the target markets in South East Asia failed to appreciate their attractions.

The Task Force had also made recommendations on product quality. This was another area where PPCS and Ian Jenkinson begged to differ,

Mrs Joan Egan launching the lamb roast with David Joll, Bernard Matthews' managing director, and Colin Moyle.

maintaining what was to be a consistent stand against setting industry-wide standards which would, by default, become industry-wide minimum standards, continually being ratcheted up.

The report recommended that the Board should operate a national quality assurance programme including the registration of all grades, specifications and packaging. It said that meeting those standards should be the responsibility of the processors and exporters, with the Board monitoring them.

This was a time when concepts of 'quality' including Total Quality Management were beginning to be talked about. Meat Industry Council chairman Reid Jackson was a strong advocate for increasing the overall quality of New Zealand meat exports.

The Glendinning Report of 1983 had said New Zealand lamb was the "worst presented and least attractive commodity available in the supermarket... New products properly developed, packaged and presented are critical to giving New Zealand lamb the best chance of getting the highest market return under future market conditions."

Overseeing the quality initiatives became an additional role for the Board's production supervisors. Strict cutting and packaging guidelines were laid down for product processed under the Buyback scheme, for example. New photographic standards for dressing were introduced. Suggestions promoted by the Board's administration officer for production, David Wright, included chemical fat testing for mutton and an online sampling scheme for individually wrapped lamb and mutton cuts.

Chris Newton, formerly at Waitaki's Pukeuri, took over as chief production supervisor on Ernie Greville's retirement in 1983. When he moved on to work with ANZCO at the end of 1985, the Board's central regional supervisor Mick Wilkin became the new chief. At management level, Peter Gianotti, formerly with Alliance as works superintendent, joined the Board as group manager, operations in 1984. Newton remembers "an incredible, crazy three years" of ownership. And half way through, changes were also made to the beef and lamb grading system. It was a seven-day a week worka-

The production supervisors during the period of Board ownership, when Chris Newton was the chief.
Back row, from left: Graeme Clent, Jim Hastings, Adrian Waterhouse, Ray Adams, Jim Sutherland, Graham Switalla, Charlie Mildon, Giller, Jim Gladney
Centre: John Cartney, Wayne Adams, Ray Taylor, Gordon Alexander, Tom Christmas, Dean O'Keefe, Lou Caudron, Russell Copp, Tom Baillie Brian Barbour, Norman Lake, Frank Butt, Mick Wilkin, Neville Morgan, Morrie Heap
Front row: Eric Bell, Stan Sutherland, Ted Geayley, Chris Newton, Keith McDiarmid, Colin Manning.

holic time, exhausting but exhilarating for the new opportunities and experience which could not have been gained elsewhere. "Everyone could put forward new ideas, especially after Jim Bremner became CEO", Chris Newton says.

Another quality initiative pushed by the Board, especially Allan Frazer, during ownership, was the widespread introduction of guaranteed tenderness in lamb. But this would not be accepted until several years later and some powerful customers made their feelings plain.

Tenderness in meat relates to a variety of factors which begin with ensuring that the animal is as free from stress as possible during transport and before slaughter. But most important is preventing 'cold shortening' which occurs if a carcass is exposed to temperatures of below 6° C before the muscle has had time to 'condition' or dissipate its reserves of energy.

Conditioning can happen naturally, but this would cause holdups in a large scale processing plant. Accelerated conditioning speeds up the process by applying electrical stimulation to carcasses just after slaughter. Aging is a further tenderisation of meat caused by its natural enzymes.

Dr Ron Locker of MIRINZ had made the early discoveries about the nature of the post-mortem behaviour of muscle. Conditioning was then introduced using climate-controlled holding rooms before freezing. Apart from making considerable extra demands on storage space, and controls of temperature and humidity, the tenderness outcome was still variable.

Early in his term as MIRINZ director, Dr Lester Davey and a colleague travelled to the US and Britain to evaluate the tenderness of lamb sold there. Buying DEVCO frozen lamb from supermarket displays, Lester Davey cooked his way across the US in a variety of makeshift kitchens, following the methods used by the US housewife – putting a frozen leg into the oven. The resultant roasts, tough and oozing unappetising juices, would have been unappealing even to a nation not already 'turned off' sheepmeat by wartime experiences with mutton.

It was a timely discovery. Lester Davey's report led to a requirement by DEVCO that all lamb for the US market should have been through the accelerated conditioning and aging (AC & A) process.

"There was less of a problem in Britain, because most of the lamb at the time was being bought by High Street butchers who cut the carcass themselves and in doing so allowed it time to thaw naturally," Davey says.

MIRINZ scientist Bruce Marsh was beginning to investigate how electrical stimulation might avert cold shortening when he left for a new job in the US. The technician working with him, Bill Carse, continued the investigations and, despite having little formal training, had by the early 1970s developed electrical accelerated conditioning into an industrial process which could be used to produce repeatable levels of tenderness. Extensive trials were conducted by MIRINZ with the co-operation of AFFCO at Horotiu. The Board made a $5000 award to Bill Carse for his work in 1983.

Lester Davey's research also showed that to deliver a repeatable level of acceptable tenderness, accelerated conditioning should be used with the natural tenderising process of aging. He discovered that following electrical stimulation, and with the correct temperature, the aging process could

Lamb going through the conditioning tunnel, the first stage in the tenderness protocol.

be concluded within 24 hours. The storage saving implications of being able to shorten the naturally lengthy process were enormous.

Despite the firm scientific backing for the procedures involved, and considerable variation in the tenderness of product being produced, especially as huge quantities were being processed, many companies were reluctant to introduce AC & A. They argued it was not needed for the major UK market, and resisted a Board move to promote AC & A product in the UK because any premiums earned would be shortlived while the discount effect on non-AC & A product would be long-lasting.

The quality push was also assisted by the investment in cleaner production processes during the previous decade. In the US New Zealand now routinely scored among the lowest rejection rates for meat quality – around .04% compared to 3% plus from Costa Rica and some EC countries.

The *Meat Producer* reported that Temple Grandin, on a visit in 1982, called local meat plants "the cleanest I have ever visited" and estimated only 10-20% of plants in the US would pass a New Zealand export works inspection. The magazine also noted that David Lange, confronted by open-air meat handling at Smithfield in 1981, questioned "what the EC is on about" with its third country hygiene demands.

Hygienic processes paved the way for the growth in chilled meat exports, another quality area where MIRINZ made significant strides, and one which depended on high levels of microbiological cleanness as well as temperature controls.

The chilled meat trade – much of it expensively air-freighted – was still very minor in 1982, with 5869 tonnes of chilled beef exported (2200 tonnes of it by Graeme Lowe's Dawn Meat Co to the Middle East, with much of the rest going to the Pacific and South East Asia) and only 1137 tonnes of chilled lamb.

The Middle East had been targeted early as a market for chilled meat because of the high number of expatriates working there with a taste for and ability to pay for luxury product.

Careful control over the 'cold chain', making sure that meat was held at safe storage temperatures throughout transport and transhipment, was absolutely essential when ambient temperatures could be over 40° C. MIRINZ microbiologists led by Colin Gill and Peter Nottingham introduced a number of innovations in temperature monitoring and control and highlighted the important relationship of consistent temperature to meat quality. In 1983 the Board subsidiary Management Information Resources (MIR) developed a data logger which monitored the temperature within a container throughout its shipment.

The real breakthrough was in packaging which extended the shelf life of chilled meat. Controlled Atmosphere Packaging or Captech has been said by some to be as important for the New Zealand meat industry as the introduction of refrigerated shipping 100 years earlier. It was developed in a joint venture between MIRINZ (with Colin Gill heading the microbiology section) and UEB. Launched for commercial use in 1988 after nearly three years of development, it superseded vacuum packaging as a means of extending the shelf life for chilled meat to the point where it could be safely

Captech, the packaging breakthrough which extended the shelf life of chilled meat. By withdrawing all the oxygen and replacing it with carbon dioxide the CapTech foil pack provides a controlled atmosphere in which lamb will maintain a fresh condition – while continuing to age and become more tender – for at least 16 weeks.

Graham Bell, awarded the first MIRINZ fellowship for his work which included lengthy periods in Saudi Arabia.

transported by sea.

Knowing the potential of the new packaging, a Chilled Lamb Working Party was convened in 1985 with members including David Wright and Paul Spackman from the Board and Wayne Geary and John Miller from the meat processing industry. By 1986 Borthwicks and Waitaki were sea-freighting chilled lamb to Marks and Spencer. Securing the valuable contract was quite a coup, and it continues, through AFFCO, to this day.

The New Zealand delegation to the Gulf States in 1982 noted in their report that Saudi Arabia and other countries had become very standards-conscious after being treated as a dumping ground for "inferior and misrepresented foods" in the first heady days of their oil wealth. Among the things they wanted to avoid was "hormone residues".

They were very anxious to establish effective food import regulations, but were hampered by the lack of trained people. Other problems included lack of familiarity with frozen meat. This led to problems with shelf-life regulations. Saudi regulations said that frozen meat had to enter the Kingdom within 40 days of slaughter and set an expiry date of 90 days after slaughter; possible but difficult for New Zealand to meet with irregular shipping and seasonal production, especially compared to Western Australia. For chilled meat, expiry dates from three to five days after slaughter would be hard to meet even with air-freight.

These requirements were far more stringent than for many other countries. More to the point, MIRINZ had ample evidence that, stored correctly, frozen meat maintained its quality for 24 months. More recent work on controlled atmosphere packaging showed chilled lamb would remain wholesome and even improve in quality for at least eight weeks.

But the customer must also feel comfortable about the science. The 1982 delegation recommended New Zealand enlarge its studies on the storage and shelf life of chilled and frozen meat, and establish a working relationship with the Saudi Arabian Standards Organisation (SASO). Following a visit by Saudi officials to see New Zealand storage and processing facilities the shelf life limit was lifted to 120 days, just sufficient to allow New Zealand frozen meat to enter the market.

Despite the enthusiastic support of Trade Minister Mike Moore, it wasn't until 1986 that the joint research project with SASO got fully underway and Dr Graham Bell from MIRINZ made his first visit to Riyadh. It was the start of a relationship that continues to this day.

Flexibility and Muscle
1982-85

"Labour costs are something that companies can control. They may not have control over the exchange rate or where the market's going, but they can manage labour costs… From 1984 when the wage freeze lifted, you can see that wage increases to the meat industry were always 2-3% below the going average." Anne Knowles.

In 1981 AFFCO's Southdown Freezing Works closed after 75 years. The Gear Meat Company at Petone shut its doors for good not long after, in its 98th year, and in 1982 W & R Fletcher closed the 92-year-old Patea works.

Southdown, just off the Great South Road in Auckland, had been through a very militant spell. At Gear, on the waterfront at Petone, a union vote was directly involved in the decision to close. Roger Middlemass remembers the shed meeting, where management had asked the 700 workers to take wage cuts to allow much-needed capital investment: "I said… the company wants 20% wage cuts or they will close your plant. You will lose your jobs forever. But if you take 20% wage cuts you are setting a precedent for other freezing workers right down the industry. My advice is tell them to close the bloody plant. They had a secret ballot, and said close it. And they did! I saw (Gear general manager) Barney Sundstrum 18 months later and said you were going to close it anyway, weren't you. He said, yeah."

As chairman Mick Groome put it at the time: "It is apparent that the union hierarchy will not accept pay rates or dispute procedures necessary to ensure

"Management's finally getting together with the union."

"It's too late, it's all over, it's gone." Ron Shardlow remembers how HBFMC general manager Ian Cameron walked into a workers' meeting and signalled the closure of the Gear Meat Company plant at Petone. After beating off Borthwicks to take control of the plant in 1977 HBFMC wanted to redevelop it but could not negotiate the necessary agreements with the union. The union claimed the company was "incompetent and incapable of managing the plant efficiently" and was just using Gear as a temporary facility while their new works at Takapau was being built.
Nevile Lodge, Evening Post, *16 November 1981.*

the viability of the plant."

Closure was always on the cards for plants like Gear and Southdown. So close to a major city, they were in the wrong place for everything from stock procurement to effluent disposal. Gear's kill was quickly absorbed at Hawke's Bay Farmers' other plants at Whakatu and the newly opened Takapau.

Patea's closure, which had a much more devastating effect on its local community, also had an inevitability about it. Costs were totally out of kilter with comparable operations. Confronting the Patea figures was one of the first tasks for John Prendergast, appointed chief financial officer of W & R Fletcher in 1979. Formerly with cement manufacturer Cemac, he was one of the first high-level appointments by the parent Vestey organisation not to have been groomed by working in their plants in Australia and England.

Patea, a multi-species plant, had struggled for some time, John Prendergast says. "Basically it was very old and tired and didn't have a great industrial record. You could say that was a company fault or a union fault, and it was probably a bit of each. It had quite a large Maori workforce and there were various tribes and factions who did not pull together."

Former CFM general manager Derek Morten carried out a 'Continuation Study' at the request of the union-convened Patea Action Committee, but his conclusions brought no joy.

For instance: "I suspect a deliberate overmanning to cover absenteeism, which the FCA assures me is bad… The manning shows 9 beef butchers and 41 labourers… if they are all in the beef house proper, it gives a productivity of about 7.2 bodies per day per man employed. We would expect double that at Belfast; Graeme Lowe at Pacific claims better than 16 although I have not seen it working: even the worst laid-out ones average about $9^{1}/_{2}$ to 11… Why do they need a float of 32 men, plus a tradesman labour float of 8, plus drawing on lamb-cuts men, if… absenteeism is not a great problem?"

The report concluded: "If there is any chance of making Patea succeed, it

New Zealand meat scientists and meat companies developed an impressive range of world-leading mechanical dressing technology, for both sheepmeat and beef. The diagram shows the mechanised processes developed by the MIRINZ engineering project team led by Graeme Longdell and Gus Robertson.

In the late 1970s developments at MIRINZ literally turned lamb dressing upside down. By inverting carcasses and suspending them 'head up' both manual and mechanical pelt removal became much easier, as did avoiding carcass contamination. This change paved the way for a series of machines to perform various dressing tasks. By 1987, it was calculated the new procedures saved $1 a carcass. The MIRINZ work completed various trial procedures by individual companies including W& R Fletcher, CFM, AFFCO and Borthwicks which introduced inverted dressing at its Waingawa plant in the late 1970s.

MIRINZ photographs.

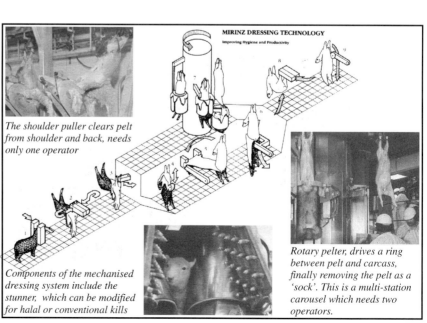

MIRINZ DRESSING TECHNOLOGY
Improving Hygiene and Productivity

The shoulder puller clears pelt from shoulder and back, needs only one operator

Components of the mechanised dressing system include the stunner, which can be modified for halal or conventional kills

Rotary pelter, drives a ring between pelt and carcass, finally removing the pelt as a 'sock'. This is a multi-station carousel which needs two operators.

will need top class management, and where will they get this for a plant with Patea's record?" It had been making "gross losses" on procurement which were likely to continue. "To be successful Patea needs a combination of interest-free capital of at least $5.5 million for the first three years… plus a relatively trouble-free industrial climate, plus reduced overall mannings… We saw no opportunity for producing these conditions, and hence the only alternative was closure."

"I think the rumours had been around for a long time and it wasn't a great shock to people," John Prendergast said. "But when reality struck, it was the death of the town."

None of the industrial relations issues such as demarcation and payment for mutton slaughtermen, which had dogged the industry through the turbulent 1970s, were resolved as the new decade began. But Peter Blomfield and the employers in the FCA began a new strategic approach to introduce different ways of working and redress some of the balance of power which had clearly swung the union way.

Automated dressing, firstly in the form of the pelt-pulling machine, was well on the way to becoming a reality and with it came the threat of job losses. Associated systems included trotter removers, a brisket cutter and the frame boner, loin boner, neck-breaking and head-splitting equipment, brain removal machine, and devices for brisket cutting, belly opening and viscera removal – ultimately all incorporated into the revolutionary inverted dressing system.

Anne Knowles points out that it was the biggest technological change since the move from single slaughter to the chain method, which occurred in the 1950s. "Everybody was on strike because they didn't want to do it, and the companies simply changed the system and put in the chains and said if you come back to work then you have to do it that way. We thought we could take a different and better approach with automated dressing."

The strategy was to give the unions an appreciation of the wider issues forcing companies to focus on cutting labour costs. It began with a multi-sector working party. Many of the members of this were in a group which travelled to Canada in 1981 led by Industrial Conciliator Len 'Blue' Fortune.

"We were… trying to persuade the unions that the introduction of technology would really be a good thing and they shouldn't be threatened by it," Peter Blomfield says. "They met with the Canadian unions and the equivalent of our Labour Department, Canada Labour. They visited a number of sites including one of the big General Motors plants, and a big paper-making place, and saw a lot of things."

Frank Barnard from the Auckland and Tomoana Union was in the group. As well, there were Engineers' and Electrical Workers Union members, and national meatworkers' secretary Blue Kennedy who was "a bit reserved about it, because he was concerned about what the other people were going to say", Peter Blomfield recalls. "Middlemass… wouldn't go because he was not going to be indoctrinated by the employers, but it wasn't the employers who were doing the indoctrination. It was the other union people, or government servants. They saw a lot of examples of how technology had been introduced. And the unions in Canada talked to them about why they shouldn't be threatened by it."

Included on the employer and company side were Max Willyams from Waitaki, Borthwicks' Bill Gordon and Barney Sundstrum from Gear. As intended, there was the positive spinoff of allowing some natural adversaries to see different sides of each other.

The Canada trip was followed up by a demonstration of changing land use within New Zealand.

Anne Knowles said: "We flew over the Bay of Plenty… in those days Rangiuru (at Te Puke) was one of the main meat-producing areas and the change to kiwifruit was really dramatic."

The group also went to Waitaki's Stoke plant in Nelson to hear about the manning implications of the automated pelting machine. Company representatives also talked about the change in marketing focus.

Then a questionnaire was sent to each of the industry's 26,000 employees, pointing out that there were going to be changes and asking for ideas about how new jobs could be created or things done better or differently in their particular area.

As hoped, some constructive responses came through. As a final step the employers drew up an agreement taking all current employees into the future. It focussed on retraining, relocation, strategies such as 'grandfathering' wages (continuing to pay someone who moved into a lower-paying job at their previous rates) and, as a final step, redundancy.

This was a sticking point at the last minute with the national union reluctant to be seen to agree to redundancy. But the communication campaign eventually paid off. The pelt-pulling machines were introduced with minimum disruption, and wage rates moved up less than the national average at the end of the wage freeze.

The wage freeze years, from 1982 to 1984, were noteworthy for innovative union strategies to source extra money. There were claims for cold money, smell money, and double time for contact with faecal matter. Anne Knowles was on the working party which devoted much time to inspecting a "wide variety of totally awful areas" to make rulings on this.

She recalls a foreman's ingenious demonstration of the cleanness of Islington's new state-of-the-art rendering plant, for which the Engineers and Meat Workers were claiming an extra 'smell' allowance. "He wore the clothes he had been wearing at work to the movies at night. His wife didn't say 'My God, you stink' and nobody around him got up and moved away." The evidence helped win the MIA case against making an extra payment.

There were also disputes over more flexible patterns of work. To meet the calls for greater added value and increased international competitiveness, employers were keen to introduce some form of shift work for better utilisation of plants.

As the new plants were being built at Oringi and Takapau, Borthwicks' Longburn manager Bill Gordon and Roger Middlemass of the union had developed a proposal to introduce an 'eight circle': two teams each working four 10-hour days on, four days off.

But company general manager Peter Norman's attempts to promote it ended, as he recalls, in "fiasco". Summoned to Parliament along with Peter Blomfield by a 10 pm phone call, he was first harangued by ministers Peter Gordon, Jim

Bolger (then the associate Labour Minister) and Duncan McIntyre. "Then in came Muldoon, and he said: 'You're not going to do it.' And I said, 'But it's a wonderful idea, sir'.

" 'You are not going to do it,' he said. 'If you persist I shall go on the radio tomorrow morning and say that you have done it completely contrary to the views of the Government. It has been suggested by a British company, we are not going to permit it, and it's an intrusion into the rights of the workers.'

"Of course, we didn't do it. We were terrified." And they retreated, Peter Blomfield recalls, to Wellington's famous all-night eatery, The Green Parrot.

But the concept did not go away. In June 1981 Ken Findlay of the West Coast Union declared that "because of technical improvements four days work for five days pay is a fair compensation for loss of workers' jobs".

A workers' strike held up the opening of Takapau in October. Roger Middlemass circulated the pamphlet '4 for 5' subtitled 'The Workers' Response to Mechanisation and Automation in the Freezing Industry'. Almost immediately, Prime Minister Muldoon announced the Government would not countenance any 'four days work for five days pay' deal. Predictions of huge job losses came thick and fast.

National meatworkers union secretary Blue Kennedy in full oratorical flight at a meeting at Rugby Park, Invercargill. Photo: Southland Times

Against this background, discussions were taking place over the staffing of Oringi. The two protagonists could not have been more different. The entrepreneurial capitalist determined to make his ideas of a cost-efficient workforce a reality, Graeme Lowe, negotiated with Roger Middlemass, the dogmatic socialist bargaining from the perspective that workers had an ownership in the plant as of right.

At some stage, all the branches of the Meat Workers' unions were involved. If it had been possible to rewrite the rules, Graeme Lowe would have preferred to bypass the West Coast branch and affiliate directly with Blue Kennedy's national union. Knowing that Pacific intended to lower manning levels and to cut the cost of killing, mainly by introducing the new pelt-puller designed by Raph Engle, all parties realised the final decision would set a national precedent.

Before the plant opened, there was a tussle over who could be employed to test the new dressing systems. The 'four for five' argument emerged again. Pacific was keen to operate two shifts. As John Foster recalls: "They said if you can afford to build a works you can afford to pay five days, especially if only half the numbers are employed."

Recruitment was also an issue. Graeme Lowe's unpublished memoir notes that Pacific "decided that every effort to select workers with good records, unlikely to be trouble-makers, should be made". Lowe recruited workers with no meat industry history. The anti-union stand was solidly supported by the town of Dannevirke. Local MP John Falloon led a march of 'concerned citizens' through the main street, where every shop had a display in support of Lowe. Roger Middlemass warned his representative Ray Potroz to stay inside at night.

At the official opening of Oringi in November 1981 there was an unexpected addition to the lineup of speakers who addressed the 4000 people attending. Worker Miles Blake gave an impassioned speech. Three days earlier he had approached Graeme Lowe saying workers had voted for a plant-specific

Graeme Longdell, leader of the process engineering team at MIRINZ, went on to be its director from 1992-97.
Photo: MIRINZ

union with him as president, and asked if he could speak. Despite their original intention to keep labour politics right out of the occasion, Pacific's principals John Foster and Graeme Lowe gave him the go-ahead.

"He made this quite remarkable speech that had old Piggy (Muldoon) leaning forward," John Foster remembers. "He said: 'We don't want any outside interference. We'll have our disputes with management, but we hopefully will always work while we are discussing them. Mr Prime Minister, we want your assistance to give us the legislation to do that.'"

It was just what the Prime Minister, having lavishly praised Pacific Freezing and Graeme Lowe in particular, wanted to hear. But it acted as a red rag to the West Coast Union which had not been invited to the opening.

During the test of wills over the following weeks, union men Potroz and Middlemass were arrested after climbing the fence in a vain attempt to address a meeting. If Middlemass planned a meeting at 8 am, Graeme Lowe would hold one at 7.30. Lowe's innovation of a single lunchroom to cut across management/worker hierarchies was seen by Middlemass as a clever form of industrial espionage – as was the fact that Lowe's son Andy worked on one of the chains.

Trevor Arnold, who temporarily took over as manager of the plant while hostilities were at their height, recalls routinely going through a "union stockade of eggs and mudballs".

The power game was protracted and at one point extended to threats against Lowe's Hawera plant. By March 1982, however, Pacific instructed its staff to join the Wellington West Coast Branch, and Miles Blake faded from the scene. Raph Engle's mechanisation proved an expensive failure, downgrading an unacceptably high number of carcasses to 'cutters' and the inventor went bankrupt. But Oringi was up and running with 320 people working three chains, compared with up to 700 at Takapau, although shift work would not come in till later.

The focus of strife went back down south in 1984 with the long-running industrial disruption at Ocean Beach, the plant Alliance had bought from CWS in November 1981. One of the nastiest confrontations, the saga made the reputation of Alliance's industrial relations manager Tony Forde as a hard man. By standing his ground and refusing to be scared off he eventually broke the power of the union officials like Tony Taurima and Colin Manson.

These men were not only calling strikes at whim but, it emerged, fraudulently using their members' strike funds. As Clive Lind points out, it was the

Jack Scott, assistant secretary of the Meatworkers Union (left), leaving the Lorneville plant with Colin Manson and Tony Taurima.

greed and corruption of those officials which brought their downfall, and tested the loyalty of even the most devout union members.

The full story is told in *One Muff Too Tough* by Michael Turner. Amongst those embroiled at various stages were Blue Kennedy, who ingeniously escaped the serving of a summons by squeezing himself out of a toilet window and making a last-minute dash for the plane leaving Invercargill. At another critical point, the airport was closed by floods, so Anne Knowles arrived via Dunedin to find large numbers of people milling around in the foyer of the Ascot Park Hotel. A line of slaughtermen, distrusting their official union representatives, sat behind them throughout the meeting.

Jack Scott took over from Blue Kennedy as national secretary of the Meat Workers Union in 1985. Kennedy was viewed with suspicion in some sectors, which made use of arcane rules to cut him and the national office out of direct involvement in dispute resolution. But his easy relationship with Muldoon meant that other people had seen how they could work with him.

Alliance operations manager Tony Forde (left) and general manager Ian Graham, pictured at Alliance Lorneville plant.

Colin Moyle, once again Agriculture Minister after the 1984 election brought a Labour Government back to power, appointed Blue Kennedy to the Meat Board in 1985. On every count the teetotal fundamentalist Christian Kennedy was an outsider to what he saw as a "closed fraternity". Many of his Board contemporaries speak of him warmly, but Kennedy himself was in no doubt that he wasn't at its decision-making heart. And if his presence helped with the understanding of issues, it didn't stop them inflaming.

The FCA annual report records 1984-85 as a "traumatic year" for wage bargaining. Every single occupational group challenged wage freeze regulations, most taking strike action. The focus of discontent this time was shift work. It was a particularly pressing issue with the call for increased value-adding through further processing. Shift work in lamb cutting and boning areas was seen as essential to keep pace with carcass throughput. Shift work in cutting and boning rooms had been introduced at some of the NZR plants later acquired by Waitaki, in the 1970s, but the award had no provision for it. The shift issue came to a head in the major national strike at the height of the 1986 killing season. The longest strike in 30 years, it lasted eight weeks in Auckland and six weeks through the rest of the country.

The election of the Labour Government dramatically changed the industrial relations environment. Minister of Labour Stan Rodger was determined there was to be no involvement or interference by government.

"Jim Bolger who was Minister of Labour during the early 80s was virtually the chief mediator of the country any time there was a dispute," Anne Knowles recalls. "There would be committees of enquiry and commissions, and the calling together of the parties at the Minister's behest."

But, she said, with Labour's deliberate 'sideline' stance, "You couldn't go into a strike knowing in the back of your mind that the Government would allow this to happen for about a week, and then step in."

Waitaki's Joe Ryan, chairman of the MIA, supported by new Alliance chief executive Sandy Murdoch and chair of its industrial committee, was adamant that the industry had to keep together. The companies did, despite extreme pressure on them to break solidarity. But as the weeks passed they became worried about the impact on New Zealand's reputation in the market.

Alliance chief executive Jim Barnes and detective Tom Downey watching Alliance strikers in early 1984. Photo Southland Times

When things came to a head Stan Rodger was out of the country and Richard Prebble was acting Minister of Labour. He called union and management to a meeting in the Beehive – the first negotiation held there since Muldoon's three-way decision in 1978 – and he was prepared to "basically bang our heads together and see what sort of outcome could be achieved", according to Anne Knowles. Discussions, involving "a goodly crowd" from the union, took place in his Beehive office. On the employers' side, from the MIA, were Joe Ryan, Peter Blomfield and Anne Knowles.

It was the only time a concession was made to her being a woman. At the time she was six months pregnant. When negotiations stretched into the night, Richard Prebble sent his private secretary out for food. It was fish and chips for everyone except Anne Knowles, who couldn't stomach them and ate toasted sandwiches in splendid isolation.

The evening ended with an agreement that shift work could be introduced in lamb cutting plants. It did not cover shift work on the slaughterboard.

The torrid industrial climate of 1985-86 ensured that people like Pacific's John Foster and Graeme Lowe had sympathetic ears when they argued for urgent reform of industrial legislation. It was something the Labour Government had itself identified as very important and had canvassed through a green paper.

On one visit to Parliament to see Finance Minister Roger Douglas, Foster and Lowe were driven instead to his Thorndon home. "He had the flu but he had put us off twice before and wasn't going to put us off again. He met us in his dressing gown in the living room and said he was concerned about ACC and addressing the power of the unions.

"He said, 'I've got something, which I can't share with you. It's not what you want but it's a step in the right direction. You are going to have to be a bit more patient to get what you really want'."

'It' was the 1987 Labour Relations Act. This brought significant change, though not the move to full enterprise bargaining which other lobbyists like the Employers' Federation had been seeking. Intended to introduce greater flexibility, the new statute did, however, contain several clauses which were to have far-reaching impact on the meat industry pay fixing structure.

Most significantly, the Act required the terms and conditions of employment for groups of workers to be fixed by a single set of negotiations. There could only be one agreement at any one time covering any one worker. This had major implications for two-tier bargaining.

The Act provided for unions to cite companies out of the national award and register individual company agreements. It cut the options for groups like tradesmen to bring issues from other national groups into the negotiations, and made it a condition that agreements could only be registered after negotiations with a union.

The MIA annual report of 1987-88 provides lengthy detail of the new legislation. In just three lines it also records: "The first agreement for slaughtering on a shift basis in the meat industry was negotiated with the NZ Meatworkers Union by the Fortex Group for its Seafield Plant."

Fortex was a special case. The employers were determined to set the environment so that every company could establish agreements to suit their own circumstances.

Backlash and Bickering
1984-85

The Group marketing structure "is certainly a great improvement on competing with each other in the marketplace. It's a very positive step. In the next 12 months we will have to refine what has been set up and ensure that the roles of everyone are clearly defined." Peter Blomfield, Meat Producer, Jan-March 1985.

By late 1984 the Meat Industry Council had become frustrated with the lack of progress in the development of a joint strategy for the sheepmeat industry, largely because the parties were not getting together.

Reid Jackson commented that the MIC, which was charged with considering a jointly prepared strategy, found itself in an intolerable situation. "The Meat Board has been trying to address the problems as it sees them, but the industry hasn't done so."

As part of its five year strategic plan for product and market development the Board had announced plans to take over the marketing of carcasses and primal cuts in the Western European, Mediterranean and Gulf States markets, which had been done previously by the companies on a commission basis. The Board advised that it was taking this action because there were no structures established in these markets to co-ordinate the development of sales.

In order to head the Board off this idea, in the latter part of 1984 the companies, led by Athol Hutton, put together a compromise proposal for disciplined Group marketing arrangements. The MEC indicated that the proposal was aimed at "bringing more effectiveness to lamb marketing and maximising export earnings by curtailing excessive and unnecessary competition... The compromise assured the continued presence of the private sector in these markets."

Graeme Thompson says: "It came from a meeting with (Overseas Trade Minister) Mike Moore in Christchurch, an unofficial meeting with Athol Hutton and two or three other of the big company senior executives. Mike Moore told them the industry had to be seen to be getting its act together, or the Government would be doing something about it. He said: 'If you buggers are going to take this meat back over, I've got to see some structure'.

Pressure from the Minister also led to the establishment of the Meat Industry Association (MIA) as a single meat industry representative organisation. Gray Mathias of the Independent Meat Exporters Association recalls: "The FCA and the independents and the two co-operatives and the MEC all disbanded and became one group. This was imposed under the hand of Mike Moore. It was a conditional deal... we had to agree to speak with one voice." Agreement was reached at the end of 1984 and the new MIA came into existence in July 1985 with an executive of 16, headed by the former FCA chief executive Peter Blomfield. Joe Ryan, the general manager operations of Waitaki, was its chairman and John Drayton, the general manager of CFM, his deputy.

The gloves came off and meat industry critics had a field day when the Board announced plans to reorganise the meat industry, which included new marketing structures for Western Europe, the Mediterranean and the Middle East.

The Group marketing proposal was accepted with some alacrity by the MIC as a means of getting exporters and the Board working together. Reid Jackson commented: "We now have a situation with a Group structure where there is regular dialogue between Group leaders and the Board. That ought to be creating a good background for a forum that can get on and produce a strategy."

The Group scheme started out with five Marketing Groups set up to market lamb carcasses and primal cuts to the Board-designated markets of Continental Europe, the Mediterranean and the Gulf States. The aim was to limit the number of exporters to each market to a maximum of five, or one from each Group. It was intended to extend the Group scheme to other market areas like the Caribbean, South Pacific and South-East Asia as and when marketing plans were developed. The MIC indicated a preference for the Groups to be reduced to four by the 1985-86 season.

This particular issue set off a series of bitter exchanges between the Board and the MIA, which continued for the next nine months. The debate was stirred by increasingly frequent government involvement as the new Labour ministers got to grips with the situation and officials started pushing for a more open market system. The MIC pushed the Government line and acted as the reluctant mediator. Later, in the *New Zealand Farmer* of 12 September 1985, Marianne Kelly and Sharon Cuzens labelled the infighting during the 1984-85 season as "Posturing, politicking and pettiness".

The Board was strongly critical of the Group scheme, which it regarded as "selling by committee ... cumbersome and excessively costly" and unlikely to develop the New Zealand-owned, market-based, commercial structures that the Board considered necessary. Led by Jim Bremner, it adhered tenaciously to its alternative marketing plans. However, the MIA continued to develop its proposals based on the Group structure the MIC had endorsed.

By March 1985 the new Government had formed its preliminary view on the future of the industry and the role of the MIC. Agriculture Minister Colin Moyle said it had decided that "the MIC should guide and facilitate the evolution of the desirable structure for the marketing of New Zealand sheepmeat. Within this... the Council should create an environment that would progressively return meat marketing to the private sector as individual operators, and groups of operators, demonstrate the capacity to market meat."

The Government also indicated that it wished to end its involvement with industry stabilisation schemes at the end of the 1985-86 season. The funding of any future price smoothing arrangements would be on a commercial basis.

Scrapping over the marketing arrangements, particularly for Greece and the Gulf States, continued when the Board proposed the establishment of a consortium with meat companies to handle the sales of carcasses and primals. The idea did not get off the ground as none of the companies were attracted to the idea. As an alternative the Board then proposed to form its own company in the Middle East, with the view that once it was up and running other companies would be enticed to join it – the ANZCO/Janmark model. The Gulf States company was tentatively named Arabmark, but this idea also hit the sand.

The flurry of paper exchanges developed into a snowstorm in the second half of 1985. The MIA produced a paper, 'Future Structure of the New Zealand

Agriculture Minister Colin Moyle (right) with Don Harwood at the Board's London office. Don Harwood went to London as deputy to Erik Trautmann in 1984-85 then became the European director from 1986-89.

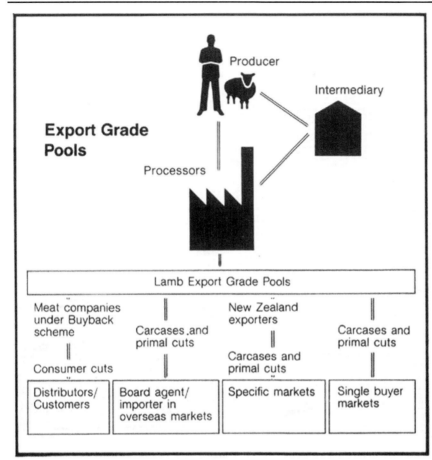

The proposed National Lamb Pool, as explained in the Meat Producer.

Sheepmeat Industry', which announced the industry's intention to take back ownership of all sheepmeat at the earliest opportunity, preferably by 1 October 1985. It echoed Ian Jenkinson's minority report to the MITF and was long on history but short on detail about how arrangements would work.

It proposed deregulation of the industry, with the MIA responsible for all matters beyond the farm gate and the Board relegated to look after on-farm issues such as livestock improvement and grading. However controls were still required to handle the single-buyer markets and the "production overhang that needs to be disposed of".

For this there would be a Sheepmeat Ad Hoc (SHOC) committee, which would buy surplus stock at nil value and find ways of disposing of it by the end of the following season by unexplained means that would not dislocate the industry's mainstream sales efforts. It was another version of the MITO proposal, which the Board rejected as "unworkable". The MIC politely asked for more detail about how the scheme would work.

Within a month the MIA had issued their second strategy document, 'Consumer to Producer: Producer to Consumer', but subsequently called 'Future Strategy – A Return to Private Sector Marketing' which commentators noted must have been written by someone else as the style and the approach were quite different.

This was a more refined version of the MITO scheme and proposed a com-

Exporter groups

Group A:
Leader: Athol Hutton, co-ordinator Bill Melhuish (both Waitaki)
Advanced Meats Ltd
Farm Export Ltd
Farmers Meat Export Ltd
Fletcher Challenge Ltd
Fresha Products Ltd
Oceanic Exports NZ Ltd
Riverlands Foods Ltd
Southland Frozen Meat Co Ltd
Waitaki NZ Refrigerating Ltd

Group B
Leader: Sandy Murdoch, Alliance.
Co-ordinator: Eric Cammell, AFFCO
Alliance Freezing Co
AFFCO
Hawke's Bay Farmers Meat Co Ltd

Group C
Group leader and co-ordinator: Stewart Barnett, PPCS
Canterbury Frozen Meat Co
Fort Export Ltd
R & W Hellaby Ltd
Meatex (NZ) Ltd
PPCS
Producers Meats Ltd

Group D
Group leader: Graeme Lowe, Dawn Meats
Co-ordinator: Bruce Bishop, W & R Fletcher
Aotearoa Meats Ltd
Columbia Exports Ltd
Dalgety Crown Ltd
Dawn Meat (NZ) Ltd
W & R Fletcher (NZ) Ltd
J W Hartnell LTd
R C Macdonald Ltd
Mathias Meats (NZ) Ltd
W Richmond Ltd

Group E
Leader: Bob Trounce, C S Stevens
Co-ordinator: Craig Boyce, Borthwicks
Thos Borthwick & Sons (NZ) Ltd
CWS (NZ Marketing) Ltd
Mair Foods Ltd
C S Stevens & Co Ltd
Tara Exports Ltd

bined Board/Group committee to manage a National Lamb Pool. The Groups and the Board would act as agents of the Pool for the sale of commodity items with each being responsible for its own funding. The Board would be responsible for the single-buyer markets and have joint responsibility with the Groups for disposing of the surplus, which it would also fund.

The Groups would sell in all other markets, and would phase in their involvement in development markets, once they had been established.

The Board's main concern with this proposal was that it was still left to finance the difficult-to-sell product with no opportunity to offset potential losses in the more profitable markets. Adam Begg commented: "Like so many industry papers the proposals were based on the needs of the companies in New Zealand rather than the marketplace. It also involved the companies taking what they wanted for the established markets and leaving the balance for the Board."

The Board countered by issuing its own strategic document proposing refinements on the system operating at the time. It announced it was opening up and simplifying the Buyback scheme using a standard price approach for each grade in conjunction with free access to markets other than North America and Japan. The arrangement was still based on central control, and the Board noted that not one company had advised that it favoured the immediate return to private enterprise.

The Board then lobbed in a hand grenade by reconfirming its plans to market carcasses and primals on a more direct basis to the three contentious regions of Western Europe, the Mediterranean and the Gulf States – through its offices in London, Athens (to be established) and Bahrain. It justified the decision on the need to control the commodity trade to maximise returns and ensure the transition to further processed and chilled product was well managed.

The Board followed this up with a bigger bombshell by advising all agents and distributors in those areas that the decision was to be implemented in three months time, from 1 October 1985. In a protest letter to the MIC, the MIA claimed that the Board had acted unilaterally and contrary to the undertakings given regarding discussions.

To get some clarification, the MIC asked MAF economist Dr Sid Durbin to evaluate existing sheepmeat marketing policies. An initial draft of the paper commented that the MIC had inherited a can of worms. Durbin noted that "one might interpret the present situation as exporters resenting the takeover of trading responsibilities by the Board and utilising a more favourable political climate to redress the issue."

His lengthy final analysis noted the criticisms of the more market approach to trading in sheepmeats but also suggested there were limitations with the centrally controlled marketing policy and alternatives needed to be investigated. In his view the issue came down to whether prices were set on an administrative basis as they were with the Board operations or by a market-oriented pricing mechanism in New Zealand. He tended to favour the latter but with appropriate arrangements for the management of the EC Voluntary Restraint Agreement (VRA) on sheepmeats, and servicing of the Board-negotiated contracts to the single buyer markets.

The MIC reiterated that it had been given the role of developing policies to progressively return marketing responsibility to the private sector, favouring a disciplined Group marketing system for sheepmeat rather than the Board's direct marketing proposals.

Even so, all sides presumed that the National Lamb Pool would still be part of the solution, at least in the short to medium term.

The Board moved quickly and notified the MIA that it was considering the MIC's position at its meeting in August 1985. On the advice of Barrie Saunders, the Board's public relations manager, Adam Begg wrote to Peter Blomfield noting the MIA's assertions that its members could handle marketing through a disciplined Group system. Therefore, the Board would be giving serious consideration to a total return of sheepmeats marketing to them for the coming season.

He asked how the MIA would structure operations, particularly the handling of the VRA and the Iran contracts. The MIA response wavered and suggested a progressive transfer would be more appropriate, with a system and infrastructure developed over the next 12 months and full implementation on 1 October 1986. It was also evident the MIA considered that a National Lamb Pool of some sort would be required in the foreseeable future.

Group A leader Athol Hutton (Waitaki).

Adam Begg reported this to the Electoral Committee in late August. He also indicated it was becoming clear to the Board that farmers did not want a build up of any further deficits in the Stabilisation Account and that a majority wanted to see a progressive return of sheepmeat ownership to the exporters.

However, he did not accept the MIC/MIA solution, which allowed for established profitable markets to be serviced by the exporters while producers were left to carry the costs of stockpiles and single-seller markets. "To ask our staff to continue with a system in which neither they nor the Board has confidence would not be acceptable."

He then looked into the future and restated the views of others that, over the next few years, the industry would be left with three to five major companies and some specialist operators. At least one of those companies should, he believed, be farmer-owned and controlled, and perhaps incorporated within the existing Board marketing structures. The Board could then return to its original role. This was the first airing of the proposal that was to be developed as Freesia Investments Ltd.

The Board now began considering the transition arrangements and its role. In a letter to Minister of Finance Roger Douglas, Adam Begg noted general agreement of the need for the industry to continue to move from trading in carcasses to marketing consumer-ready items, an effective and disciplined New Zealand presence in the market, the progressive transfer of ownership and commercial responsibility for sheepmeats to the companies, and the need to remove uncertainties about future structures which had caused some confusion in the marketplace.

He proposed that a statement should be made to set the scene for the next three years, allowing time for the Board's progressive withdrawal from direct involvement in trading. He suggested neither the Board nor the Government could responsibly extricate themselves from involvement inside of three years, without serious disruptions.

Group E leader Bob Trounce (CS Stevens).

The Board also wanted to sort out the extent of government support for its commercial funding of the National Pool and its price stabilisation scheme from 30 September 1986. Some form of government guarantee to underpin its commercial funding was considered necessary and there was a need to settle arrangements regarding the Stabilisation Account especially since a further deficit of an estimated $200 million was likely for the 1984-85 season. It was suggested that this deficit be merged with the $495 million subject to the 30 year subordinated loan arrangement.

The speed at which the deficit grew in 1985 was alarming, with Board members speculating each month on the increase since the previous meeting. Their estimates were always too optimistic.

One further development was that when the Meat Export Prices Committee met that year it determined very low minimum prices to avoid the build-up of deficits in the 1985-86 season.

Discussions with both the Government and the MIC assumed a continuation of the National Pools and the Board still clung to its proposals for controlling carcass and primal cuts marketing using some form of joint venture arrangement with the companies, or more specifically, with a group of them.

A new element was introduced when government officials put forward a proposal advocating the opening of the whole system to competitive forces. There was the possibility of a Board marketing company competing for supplies in similar fashion to an independent exporter, but a preference for a separation of the Board's marketing activities from its traditional regulatory functions.

The Government's views were conveyed in a letter from Colin Moyle, Minister of Agriculture, and Mike Moore, Minister of Overseas Trade and Marketing, to the MIC in mid-September. This suggested the progressive removal of restrictions on access to markets and to product, separation of the Board's statutory and commercial functions, and the development of an effective procurement market for sheepmeat in New Zealand.

Exporters would gain access to all markets other than Japan and North America for product forms other than carcasses and primals from 1 October 1985. The North American market was to be opened by 1 October 1986 and Japan no later than 1 October 1988. Also there was to be competitive access to EC and single-buyer markets once the Board's legally binding agency arrangements were terminated. The Board was asked to advise the MIC on proposals for servicing the European, Mediterranean and Gulf States areas for carcasses and primals, to meet immediate requirements without inhibiting the longer term freeing-up of those markets.

The MIC endorsed the arrangements. It added, however, that there was a need for a major integrated processing and marketing company owned by producers. It suggested an opportunity existed for the farmer-owned and operated companies to join forces in a major co-operative enterprise to acquire the trading activities of the Board. The companies were urged to consider this prospect, which they did, both before and after Freesia Investments was established.

The MIC also noted that, with the withdrawal of SMPs and lower level Price Committee support, there was some concern about returns to producers in the short term and the dislocation that might occur from a sharp reduction in stock numbers.

Group C leader Stewart Barnett (PPCS).

The Government also advised the Board separately that they would support the funding of a compulsory self-balancing National Pool for sheepmeats for 1985-86. Consideration would be given to extending the support for three years provided arrangements allowed companies to by-pass the Pool to buy stock direct from farmers to meet their requirements for further processed product including chilled. It was a somewhat unrealistic proposition, and strangely reminiscent of MITO. The companies could take the cream of the lamb crop and leave the Board with the 'at risk' product.

Group B leader Sandy Murdoch (Alliance).

Also the Board would have to demonstrate it had explicit plans to allow competitive access to all product by the 1987-88 season. The Government would guarantee refinancing of any financial obligation from the 1985-86 Pool provided the Board undertook to eliminate any liability within the following season, probably by a levy to cover any repayments.

The Board still considered the Government's policy was not viable. The main concern expressed by Jim Bremner was the return to a multiplicity of sellers and there were doubts about the ability of the companies to finance the risks relating to the single-buyer contracts.

Staff morale sank at the thought of progressively passing everything back over the three year period, so there was an element of trying to hold on to the activities the Board had particularly sweated over during the previous years. Many considered it would be irresponsible not to fight to the last ditch for the policy which the Board believed promised the producer the best return in the longer term.

Despite its misgivings the Board undertook to comply with these requirements, endorsed by the MIC, and started planning for the new season and for the operation of the National Pool for the following two seasons. The first task was to sort out the Mediterranean and Middle East marketing arrangements for carcasses and primals.

The MIA put forward modified Group structures for each region, with no specific marketing plans, and the Board stuck to its original proposal for the establishment of Board/industry consortium companies. Jim Bremner acknowledged that the MIA would be disappointed but he believed that some members would seek to join the proposed consortia. He was sadly in error as the companies consolidated their opposition to the arrangement.

The MIC's initial response was disappointment that the parties had been unable to reach agreement. It then changed tack and agreed the Board's proposals for handling these markets should be put into effect. The MIC also expected individual companies might consider joining the Board's companies in due course.

On the strength of that letter, the Board rather provocatively announced it would cease supplying product to companies operating in the Mediterranean and the Middle East. The companies turned to the Government in protest at this unilateral action.

The immediate reaction was a letter to the MIC from ministers Moore and Moyle, copied to the Board. They advised that both the MIC decision and the Board's actions "would be inconsistent with the Government's indicative policy and contrary to the process of freeing up these markets in the longer term". They asked the MIC to readdress the issue. They also said that while not want-

Group D leader Graeme Lowe (Dawn Meats).

ing to impose a solution, "the Government was disposed towards the concept of two consortia operating in competition over these markets, with the inclusion of the Board as a trading participant in one consortium."

So the whole issue was reopened. The debate continued as many of the leading participants travelled to Europe to attend the Anuga trade fair in Germany. The company executives were travelling with Mike Moore on a mission to the Middle East prior to arriving at Anuga. As luck would have it the Government plane was delayed en route by technical problems and the company men had plenty of time to bend his ear on the way up to Bahrain; and time to formulate a strategy once they got to Germany.

Once the company representatives arrived in Anuga there was a concerted effort to persuade Adam Begg to change the Board's decision. Mick Calder particularly recalls the cocktail party arranged by Ambassador Ted Farnon at the end of the fair. The New Zealand exporters would encircle Adam Begg to confront him with their case for a more liberal approach. Athol Hutton admits that the ploy was for him and Graeme Lowe as the tallest to tower over Begg from each side while the others (Eric Cammell, Stewart Barnett and Alan Clark) confronted him.

Unsuspecting European importers would see this group from New Zealand, go to meet them and walk blithely into the middle of a very heated debate. The formation would break up and the participants circle until another opportunity arose to bail Adam Begg up and the process would be repeated. Ted Farnon was nonplussed by the strange behaviour.

Typically, Begg stuck to his position. So the next move by the company representatives was to lobby Mike Moore for hours when they met up with him again in Bahrain. Moore is reported to have rung Colin Moyle in the middle of the night to get some action to have the Board's decision reversed. This gave rise to a terse exchange of letters between the Board and the Government.

Adam Begg issued a press statement from London reaffirming the Board's position and drawing attention to the fact that it was acting in line with the recent agreement with the Government. He noted in passing "Ministers Moore and Moyle publicly stated as recently as two weeks ago that more progress had been made in marketing New Zealand sheepmeat in the past three years of Board control than the previous 100."

The Board pointed out that its decision was part of an overall three year programme for the operation of the National Pool as agreed with the Government in September and the establishment of a separate commercial operation. The action taken on the disputed markets was in accordance with the understanding that, if the parties could not agree, then it was up to the MIC to decide. The MIC had supported the Board's proposal. The Board was disappointed to discover, though, that whenever the companies complained, the Government intervened and weakened the Board's position. It was therefore reluctant to reverse the decision that had been made.

Colin Moyle's response was short and sharp, advising that the decision on the Mediterranean and Gulf markets was to be reviewed by the MIC on 1 November. Until such time "it is the view of the MIC and the Government that all existing Groups are entitled to conduct business in those areas".

The MIC was cast into the role of siding with the Government rather than acting as an independent authority. The Board arranged to see the acting Prime Minister Geoffrey Palmer to put its case, but to no avail. He and two Hawke's Bay MPs, David Butcher and Bill Sutton, had already been lobbied by Graeme Lowe and his fellow Dawn Meats directors in August not only on returning marketing control to private enterprise but also on opening up the US lamb market.

Subsequently, on 24 October a letter from Palmer advised the Board its proposals for the Gulf States would not comply with the arrangements as agreed. The Government expected the Board would adhere to the general direction of the policy and previously agreed marketing arrangements would apply. Advice received suggested that the Government would consider withdrawing funding support unless the agreed arrangements were followed.

Following a session with the Meat & Wool Section of Federated Farmers, further meetings with the Government and advice from the MIA that they would prefer the transition to last one year rather than three, the matter was reviewed by the Board early in November 1985.

Chairman of the Meat Industry Council, Reid Jackson.

The Board was not prepared to agree to soft solutions to gain political peace and could not envisage continuing to run the Pools in a climate of uncertainty and disruption. It certainly was not going to manage a National Pool when its actions could be countermanded by government edict. It would be better to withdraw.

The decision was made to terminate the National Pools at the end of December. The Board undertook to work with the Government and the companies to manage the transition arrangements to transfer responsibility for marketing back to the companies. This included making special arrangement for the EC markets and the single-buyer contracts as well as trading out stocks held in the Board's name.

The Government agreed the Board would retain its traditional functions and Reserve Account funds would be available to establish commercial operations separate from its statutory functions. Then began a two-year wrangle with the Government over the liability for the deficit that had been built up in the Stabilisation Account as a result of the price support operations. The Board refuted the Government contention that it was liable for the deficit.

The other casualty was the MIC. Adam Begg told the Meat & Wool Section of Federated Farmers of his concern that the MIC had not been able to perform the functions it was originally established for. It had become bogged down in industry politics and there was still no legislation to formalise it after two years. Recent activities suggested the Council was in danger of becoming a tool of government policy and Begg saw little reason for the Board to continue to finance its activities. Subsequently, the plans to pass the carefully formulated legislation never got off the drafting board and the Council was wound up.

The Board could console itself that it had dealt with a record tonnage of sheepmeat production in circumstances where the companies had only been prepared to take responsibility for the low risk product. The prices paid to producers for lamb and sheep had been maintained at the levels ordained by the Government and farmers had been happy to receive the bounty. It had initiated the establishment of a structure and method of administering contracts for substantial tonnages of lamb to single-buyer markets even if the barter payment

*The unique characteristics of
the meat industry, as summed
up by Anita Busby, editor of
the* Meat Producer *from 1987-
89.*
*"Meat industry people don't
need to take advice or listen to
new ideas. They already have
all the answers. They strangle
new thoughts at conception. If
that fails, they discredit the
source. If you haven't been in
the meat industry for years,
you don't know what you are
talking about. If you have,
you're washed up...*
*Presenting any view on
restructuring for the meat
industry is akin to holding a
loaded gun at your head.
There will be a clamour to
pull the trigger. You pull it
yourself, then blame the Meat
Board! Someone will always
bring a bigger gun to the party
and it is likely to go off when
least expected."*

systems left something to be desired in terms of risks.

While the goal of complete co-ordination of marketing had eluded the Board, the companies had compromised their independent stances to the extent of developing the Group marketing system to handle the exports to the major UK market. At the same time the Board had established the basis for controlling the flow of product to quota markets such as the EC and the US. Last but not at all least, and despite the constant sniping about the pricing, it had promoted the development of further-processed lamb and mutton to levels that could never have been imagined in the 1970s.

There was a sense of achievement at these initiatives. There was also a feeling of loss at what might have been, or that the whole exercise had been an unfortunate waste of effort.

As the *Dominion* put it, in an editorial on 14 November 1985: "The Meat Board's decision to relinquish its monopoly on the sheepmeat trade is in one sense the end of an era for our major export industry. For three years the Board has had the thankless task of selling lamb on an oversupplied and highly unstable market. Now, it has decided to throw it back to private enterprise.

"Some will try to make political capital out of it and say the Board has shown itself to be a failure at marketing. The truth is far more complex. The meat industry still faces the most profound problems, and they are likely to persist at least for the next two to three years – perhaps much longer. Nobody should think that the switch back to private enterprise selling will automatically resolve those difficulties.

"The changeover occurs in peculiar and unsatisfactory circumstances. The Government, or at least those who have a final say over its economic policy, is ideologically uncomfortable with the notion of single desk selling by a producer board. At the same time, the meat companies have had a running battle with the Board over arrangements for 'buying back' lamb from the Board and for private enterprise participation in certain markets. Faced with an unenthusiastic, even hostile government, and a decidedly hostile group of companies, the Board decided it was no longer worth the trouble.

"This is an unsatisfactory situation for a number of reasons. The Board has some cause to feel that its effectiveness has been undermined by the Government. In a sense therefore the changeover is happening not for the reasons of commercial management but for political reasons...

"The onus is now firmly on the companies to show that they can do things better. Certainly the Board has made mistakes: in some instances its pricing policy does seem to have been too rigid; sometimes it showed a certain arrogance in assuming that it alone knew what was best. But nobody can pretend that the marketing problems will go away just because private enterprise is back."

Musical Shares
1986-87

"Money was a raw material, the same as water to a freezing works, the same as anything else. It amazed me the way some meat companies would take forward cover religiously every Thursday on the product they bought. In April 1986, I realised that sooner or later New Zealand was going to devalue its currency and so we brought no more funds back from overseas. And come July we had a 20% devaluation. We picked up tens of millions. That's nothing you could do beavering away with a pen and pencil, or with a shovel... these are the things that make money. Everybody should have known we were going to bloody devalue, whether we needed to or not." Ian Jenkinson.

The withdrawal of the SMP scheme and other direct agriculture support mechanisms caused a massive increase in the kill in 1985 and depletion of the nation's capital stock of sheep as farmers wrung every last drop out of the subsidies bucket and adjusted to the new realities of market-related prices. Sheep numbers started a steep decline from the 1984 peak of 70 million. By 1986-87 there were only 33.2 million lambs to kill, 24% fewer than the peak of 39.2 million two years previously. The corollary was overcapacity in the processing sector, and pressure on company financial viability.

Athol Hutton had promoted the introduction of the Group marketing system and been a leader in the bid to get marketing back into private hands. Now it was time to start on the processing side of the industry in New Zealand. He wanted to get the industry to think in terms of food production facilities concentrating on increased further processing rather than meat works producing commodities.

Ironically, given the arguments between the Board and the companies over the value of further processing and the pricing of carcasses for the Buyback scheme, he even commented: "Every time we move further away from the carcass we get a better return for the farmer and the provider of capital". Of course, comments like that just added salt to the wounds of the Board's staff – even if they came just before Waitaki's innovative 'Zealambi' project fell apart.

The problem of overcapacity of slaughter and processing facilities as well as the costs of exiting had been highlighted by the Pappas Carter Evans and Koop (PCEK) report commissioned by the MIC and released in March 1985. It had pointed to the low productivity levels in the industry compared with similar operations overseas and analysed the higher costs of retaining under-utilised plants. It recommended a reduction in capacity of 35-40%, estimating this would save the industry up to $150 million per year. In the South Island the hit list was shared around companies and included Islington, Burnside, Pareora, Ashley and Ocean Beach. In the North Island the logical closures were all Waitaki plants, but PCEK suggested it would be better to share the closures and the costs with others.

PCEK report – Reid Jackson, the chairman of MIC and Ralph Evans of consultants PCEK deliver the suggestion that up to nine plants should be closed to reduce processing capacity by 40%, and tradeable killing rights should be introduced.

PCEK concluded: "The New Zealand meat processing industry is a weak competitor internationally and is enmeshed in a web of anti-competitive forces in the domestic environment.

"Its position is not the fault of any particular group of people, but the result of long interaction of many factors: high barriers to exit; similar technologies and plant configurations; restrictive practices of companies, unions, the Meat Division of MAF and the Meat Producers Board; optimisation of farm economics to the farm gate but not beyond; and licensing and price controls, which are now lifted but still affect the character of the industry.

"All of these factors have contributed to an industry where the lower cost producers cannot drive the higher cost producers out. This in turn has led to a general lack of innovation and vigour in cost reduction and to uniformity in pricing – or using a well-known phrase, to the 'cost-plus mentality'."

The report noted the high barriers to exit in terms of the write-off of overvalued assets and the costs of labour redundancies. A rule of thumb put the cost of closure at $5 million per sheep or lamb chain, on top of the asset write-off. For many plants it was cheaper to keep running than to close. Market forces alone, the report concluded, could not save the industry.

PCEK recommended two principal courses of action. The first was establishment of a Tradeable Killing Rights scheme to stimulate the stronger competitors among New Zealand meat export processing plants to take up volume from the weaker or uneconomic plants, which would close. And secondly, phased abolition of averaging schemes in stock and meat transportation, and structural policy changes to reduce the cost of export meat inspection.

The Tradeable Killing Rights solution proposed that all plants be allocated a kill quota as a percentage of the kill, which companies could buy, sell or transfer via a central register. It was advocated as a scheme which would compensate for the closure of uneconomic capacity while promoting a strongly competitive structure for the operation of plants that remained in or entered the industry.

The PCEK report was damned with faint praise by the industry. MIA chairman, Trevor Gibson of AFFCO said it "did not give us anything new or profound. All companies concede the need for greater cost efficiency and productivity but the Association believes that the key to these problems will be found outside the consultant's solutions of Tradeable Killing Rights and 40% plant closures."

The industry decided to rely on its own negotiated arrangements to achieve the improvements considered feasible and practical rather than accept a controlled form of rationalisation. However market forces disrupted some of the carefully laid plans and negotiated arrangements tended to wind up on the rocks. In 12 months the whole industry went through a significant transformation.

Adam Begg described 1986 as "the worst season financially since 1960-61" for meat producers and a year of major upheaval for the meat industry.

Deregulation had removed almost all of the price support mechanisms so farmers were feeling the cool realities of the market. Adverse weather

FCA chairman Trevor Gibson felt the industry could sort itself out without consultants' help.

conditions, high and rising interest rates and other costs, and a 28% re-valuation of the dollar brought wild fluctuations in farmer returns. This put heavily indebted farmers in real difficulty and farm mortgagee sales became common.

Seeing themselves as being the first sector to bear the brunt of the new free market policies, farmers reacted strongly. Thousands marched on Parliament in May, hanging Prime Minister Lange in effigy from a tree while topdressing planes buzzed the Beehive with flour bombs. Adding to farmer pessimism was the national meatworkers' strike which, in places, lasted eight weeks.

A plethora of meat company ownership changes, which had been simmering in the background during the period of Board ownership, came to a head with a rush. It was the meat industry version of musical chairs (or shares) except that the music did not stop for long and the 'game' would drag on for a number of years.

With diminishing stock numbers, certainty of supply became crucial, and the companies unable to do their own processing were the most vulnerable.

Farmers march through Invercargill in 1986 to protest the loss of farm subsidies and the impact of government deregulation. As Christine McKenzie recalls: "At a stroke our incomes halved and our expenses doubled. Every newspaper seemed to bring new shocks. Closure of post offices, loss of local policemen, reform of the school system. It was the nearest thing, without physical violence, to a state of war or siege. We had to put away the chequebooks for several years. We grumbled and moaned and marched but we never lost spirit. We had gatherings where we passed on old skills from growing vegetables all year round to mending holey gumboots." For many Southlanders like her, the saviour was an organisation called Women in Agriculture which taught new skills and kept many farm families together.
Photo: Southland Times

Ian Farrant, company director and inspiration behind the Apex manoeuvres.

PPCS, assisted by astute Dunedin businessman Ian Farrant, had seen this coming, and began to position itself during the period of Board ownership. Flush with funds, PPCS sought investment advice from Paul Collins and Bruce Judge of Brierleys, and decided to float Apex Ltd, as a means of getting some of the money back to their co-operative shareholders. According to Ian Jenkinson, "The sharemarket was booming. As somebody said in those days you could float a rusty bucket." Its CFM shares were the PPCS contribution to the capital of the company and PPCS farmer shareholders were issued two 50 cent Apex shares for every PPCS share they held. All PPCS directors were also Apex directors.

Apex was used as a vehicle that saw PPCS eventually acquire the control of CFM from Fletcher Challenge (FCL) – which had been invited in by the directors of CFM to act as a white knight to attempt to stave off the move by PPCS – and the minority shareholders.

Apex also acquired a controlling interest in R & W Hellaby that was subsequently transferred to AFFCO in 1986. This deal was financed in part by the new Board company, Freesia Meats Ltd, later to become Freesia Investments Ltd (FIL).

Waitaki was also the focus of attention. During the period of Board ownership Goodman Fielder Wattie (GFW) had built up its shareholding in the company to around 40% for reasons that Joe Ryan saw as "mild megalomania". In 1986 it moved to increase its interest in the meat industry through several transactions which involved Peter Egan in one guise or another.

Advanced Meats Ltd, a company jointly owned by GFW and Egan family interests, made the first move. Following the Board's withdrawal from marketing, Peter Egan was concerned about the supply of carcasses to Advanced Foods Ltd for production of Bernard Matthews Lamb Roasts. Egan had sold his 50% shareholding in Advanced Foods to GFW but was still managing director. He came to the conclusion that the answer to securing supplies lay in Advanced Meats taking an equity shareholding in the Hawke's Bay Farmers' Meat Company.

Advanced Meats had already taken 50% of Gisborne Sheepfarmers, which operated a plant at Kaiti. Egan and GFW consulted Brian Johnston and his colleagues at Jarden & Co including Keith Taylor, who was later to become more closely involved in the meat industry through the ownership of Taylor Preston. On the basis of the advice, Advanced Meats mounted a surprise raid on HBFMC with the aim of acquiring shares or proxies covering a 25% shareholding. The HBFMC structure, some directors believed, made it immune to a takeover bid.

Peter Egan recalls he had arranged to see the general manager of HBFMC, Ian Cameron, at 8 am on the day that they stood in the market, as a courtesy to advise him of the bid. "The fact that he did not turn up for work until 8.10 am that day was somewhat embarrassing. I had only just finished telling him what our intentions were and he'd commented that we couldn't do it, when the phone went to tell him what was happening." Advanced Meats acquired the 25% it was seeking within three days, and Peter Egan got an agreement for carcass supply to Advanced Foods through Takapau.

The New Zealand division of Borthwicks had been the focus of several enquiries since the disastrous outcome of its float. Both PPCS and then GFW looked at buying all or part of the Borthwicks operations but withdrew because they could not make the figures work. Then Waitaki, via John Neilson, negotiated to buy the Borthwicks/CWS business and completed the transaction early in 1986 at a price the sale document puts at $67 million – higher, industry sources say, than GFW had considered.

The purchase bought Waitaki four plants built around the turn of the century – Waitara, Feilding, Longburn and Waingawa, the latter two notorious for industrial strife.

HBFMC general manager Ian Cameron, who was surprised by ownership changes in his company.

The Vestey organisation also got in on the act early in 1986 when Union International and Crown Corporation merged to form Weddel Crown. Crown Corporation was the result of a previous merger of the stock and station interests of Dalgety and Crown in 1983. The merger with Weddel brought together the operating company W & R Fletcher (NZ) Ltd and the Westfield Freezing Co Ltd (Westfield) and Nelsons (NZ) Ltd (Tomoana) plants with the Crown Meat Division plants, a newly upgraded former local trade abattoir at Cambridge (Aotearoa) and the much older and strife-torn site at Feilding. Later that year the company bought the former FME beef plant at Whangarei. Lord Samuel Vestey and Sir Roderick Weir both sat on the board of the new company, chaired by Peter Johnston and styled the second biggest meat exporter after Waitaki NZR.

It was a heady time for mergers and takeovers and there were even suggestions of a subsequent plan by the Crown Corporation to use its investments in the leveraged investment companies Rada and Prorada to take over Waitaki, but the web became too complex even for those days.

Rationalisation and restructuring were virtually the only games in town in the mid to late eighties – at least prior to the sharemarket crash in October 1987. It was the age of the corporation, high leveraging, grandiose ideas and company planes. The meat companies were not immune from the euphoria, but were constrained by the realities of the decline in stock numbers, the impact of the fluctuations in the exchange rate and tight market conditions overseas. Waitaki had a company plane, as did PPCS, but in typical style, chairman Robbie Burnside was the pilot.

Crown lost most of its money in the 1987 crash and Weddel Crown was 'demerged' in 1988 to become Weddel New Zealand Ltd.

Peter Egan, a close friend of GFW chairman Pat Goodman, as well as a squash opponent of Gordon Wattie, was well aware that procurement wars would make the competition between companies more deadly and lead to the demise of some of them. He wanted GFW to take action and achieve some rationalisation of the processing capacity they owned through Waitaki.

"By competing against each other for stock and paying the farmer more than the market price indicates should be paid, the processors are reducing their profit margin," he noted in an analysis prepared for GFW. "I believe if GFW asserts itself and GFW interests can be seen as a common factor in a number of works, rationalisation will be made a good deal easier."

Egan recalls telling the then managing director of GFW, John Howarth, that they should either "do something or get out of the meat industry". GFW

David Cullwick who described the events of 1986 as "merger mania".

decided to increase its shareholding in Waitaki to over 50% and to roll all of their meat interests into that company. In the process they bought the Egans out of Advanced Meats and moved that company and its shareholding in HBFMC into Waitaki. The end result was a massive company controlled by GFW with a 73% shareholding and owning 17 processing plants throughout the country.

David Cullwick, then Professor of Marketing at Victoria University, labelled the developments to early 1986 as "merger mania".

These mergers were part of the first stage of restructuring, to be followed by an 'unsettling' period of streamlining operations (rationalisation was the popular term) before consolidation and a reorganisation of product and marketing strategies.

The mergers had resulted in the emergence of three major groups: GFW/Waitaki, Weddel Crown and the farmer co-operatives (AFFCO, Alliance and PPCS). There was the medium-sized Fletcher Challenge group and then the smaller independents. The wild cards in the shakedown included the Brierley-owned J C Huttons, Richmond, Dawn and C S Stevens. David Cullwick suggested that the best of these would survive but the competition would be tough and some would end up being absorbed by the big three.

Waitaki turned to PCEK for advice on the future. The PCEK team built on previous advice for the MIC, tailoring it to their analysis of Waitaki and its particular requirements. In their report of September 1986 they estimated the earnings from GFW/Waitaki's investment in the 17 processing plants would represent a return of less than 6%, if they did not take decisive action. "By any reasonable yardstick, this is an unacceptable performance." And even this figure was fragile as falling stock numbers and new entrants could erode the company's 'kill day loadings'.

They advised a reduction in capacity at least in line with lower stock numbers and proposed "Waitaki should be looking to close 10 of its North Island chains" and "the only economic way of achieving capacity reductions is to close whole plants". The report also echoed the advice to the MIC, suggesting that while Waitaki could make unilateral closures in the North Island it would be desirable if its competitors matched its moves. Unilateral closures would not be economic in the South Island due to Waitaki's lower share of capacity and the higher margins available.

The report targeted the Longburn plant at Palmerston North, still an industrial nightmare in close proximity to three other Waitaki plants. It recommended mothballing Longburn until work practices could be improved or closing it.

The report gave priority to arranging the closure of six chains in the Hawke's Bay region. The options were: close the big HBFMC plant at Whakatu; purchase and close the recently built Pacific Freezing (Dawn/Richmond) plants at Oringi and Hastings and close Waitaki's own Takapau plant; or work completely 'in house' and close Takapau and Wairoa.

The choice would depend to some extent on the ability of Waitaki to retain access to stock and the willingness of other companies to negotiate or co-operate.

The report also suggested that marketing be given a higher strategic priority with a reallocation of funds from processing to market development. In the view of PCEK "the group has an opportunity for gaining sustainable competitive advantage in marketing, particularly given its leading position as a supplier of chilled product to the UK."

The Richmond chairman Hamilton Logan and his chief executive Rowan Ogg sought and received similar advice from merchant banker, Southpac Merchant Finance. At that time Southpac was headed by John Anderson (later Sir John), with a team including Andrew Meehan (later of Brierleys) and Jim McElwaine. All were to play their parts in the succession of transactions relating to ownership and rationalisation of the meat industry in the late 80s and 90s.

Alan Clark of Meatex, the MEC representative on the MIC.

Southpac had also been called in by Graeme Lowe and John Foster of Pacific Freezing/Dawn Meats to report on the state of the freezing industry, particularly the effect of the capacity problem on Pacific, and to suggest options that could be pursued.

Southpac was subsequently appointed to facilitate rationalisation plans for the industry in the lower half of the North Island. It recommended the closure of nine to 14 chains and, like PCEK, concluded it was more economic to close a whole plant than cut chains in different works.

The resulting negotiations took several twists and turns before they were finally settled. Part way through Richmond negotiated another very complicated arrangement to take over Dawn Meats and gain the Pacific Freezing plant in Hastings, Oringi at Dannevirke and the pelt processing operation at Shannon.

Graeme Lowe was a reluctant party to the final agreement. As his unpublished biography notes: "After considerable doubts, much harassment, late night meetings, last minute consultations, long toll calls, and argument Graeme submitted to what he personally did not consider to be inevitable."

The agreements for the sale of Dawn to Richmond plus the associated transactions were signed on 7 October 1986. They included a provision offering employment to John Foster in an executive position and assurances regarding the employment of other staff of Dawn.

John Prendergast recalls taking part in "grand discussions" between Waitaki, Richmond, advised by Southpac and John Anderson in particular, and Weddel Crown about North Island over-capacity, particularly on the east coast.

"There were a large number of clandestine sessions about solving the problem at the Southpac offices in Wellington. Throughout all these negotiations there were lots of heated discussions on market share and who was going to benefit and who was not going to benefit," he says. Those involved included Waitaki's Athol Hutton and, periodically, his chairman Jim Valentine. On the Weddel side were Prendergast, Spencer Hagen and Peter Johnston. From Richmond there was John Foster and his lawyer Andrew Morrison from Hawke's Bay. As advisers to Richmond and on the overall restructuring, Southpac had to manage a dual role and was seen to do it in an impartial way.

Peter Egan recalls that Richmond and Weddel were willing to contribute to any realistic rationalisation proposal to reduce capacity. By that stage Waitaki held 53% of HBFMC and the HBFMC plant at Whakatu (built in 1912 and now with six sheep chains and one beef) was the orphan in the line-up.

"It could be shut with some pain but, with the pain being shared across the parties, reasonably easily. It would be one of the toughest business decisions of

Sir Rod Weir of Dalgety Crown, who would later chair the Weir Committee on electoral reform.

my life," Egan says.

The result of the negotiations was the closure of Whakatu and the export side of Waitaki's Advanced Meats slaughtering operations in Gisborne, with Weddel Crown taking over the physical assets at both sites. The costs of the closure were shared among the three parties according to their livestock market shares in the lower North Island. As John Prendergast recalls: "Weddel Crown paid about $27 million, which was basically to cover redundancies and the write-off of Whakatu, and we obtained the Whakatu site, two orchards, a fire station, a village store, a number of houses and a very substantial amount of cold storage which was part of the attraction to us.

"I'd say Waitaki were the losers because they paid in excess of $50 million and essentially didn't get anything apart from the value of the shares they had in HBFMC. I would say Richmond was the winner, picking up the new Takapau plant for $10 million, and securing all the livestock buyers." In hindsight, Weddel realised the livestock buyers represented a lost opportunity.

The Whakatu closure decision was a severe jolt to the industry and outraged the farming community of the east coast and Hawke's Bay because the plant had been regarded as the flagship of the meat processing sector in that part of the world. Farmers saw the plant closure as an economic waste which would also severely limit the availability of killing space and competition for their stock. Hawke's Bay Farmers' continued on as a shell company, owned first by Waitaki and then Alliance.

As with the closures of Gear and Patea, the decision to shut Whakatu resulted in many redundancies, which seriously affected the local community and touched the national consciousness. At Whakatu, 2160 people lost their jobs, 1800 of them meatworkers.

The transaction also required approval under the terms of the Commerce Act 1986. Initially the Commerce Commission decided the agreement among Waitaki, Weddel Crown and Richmond on the closures of Whakatu and Ad-

The Whakatu plant was a central part of the Hawke's Bay community, to the point where people would gather each year to hear the freezing workers sing carols at the end of their Christmas Eve shift. Its closure was a logical move but rocked the region.

vanced Meats was in breach of the Act as it would reduce competition in the area. The companies were asked to prove it was not a restrictive trade practice. The closures were a fait accompli and eventually the deal was cleared, but the prospect of legal action had implications for any future negotiated closures.

In another move with far-reaching implications, Richmond took ownership of Takapau in exchange for a secret 25% Waitaki shareholding. They were labelled the 'Equus shares', and were held by Southpac, as it was considered unwise for Waitaki to be seen owning shares in a Hawke's Bay company. A much disputed condition of the sale was that Richmond would amend its articles to remove the restrictive voting conditions that applied and move to list the company's shares on the stock exchange.

The Bernard Matthews Lamb Roast. An innovative use of lamb in further processing. Security of supply for these products would be an ongoing problem for Advanced Foods.

The sale was a bitter disappointment to Peter Egan and Advanced Foods as they lost their carcass supply arrangement when Waitaki sold Takapau. Richmond had sneaked in ahead of them while Peter Egan was in Canada to assist with the ill-fated launch of Bernard Matthews Lamb Roasts in supermarkets there.

Peter Egan recalls: "As I understood it, part of that deal was that Waitaki was going to retain ownership of Takapau. On a verbal understanding with Athol Hutton, in the event he did not retain it, Advanced Foods would pay $15 million for the plant and secure its supply. I had a commitment to be in Canada with David Joll. I took off, and at about 2 o'clock one morning while I was sound asleep, Athol Hutton rang me to tell me the deal was done and announced, and they'd had to compromise with Richmond. This meant Waitaki rolling Takapau into Richmond for a secret 25% shareholding."

Waitaki did not now own any works in Hawke's Bay to honour their commitment to Advanced Foods. This set off a race for Peter Egan to tie down a sustainable carcass supply arrangement with Waitaki and its successors – or anyone else he could find. John Foster had considered the original Board involvement in the Advanced Foods plant and the supply arrangements were unfair to other local operators so there was little prospect of securing carcasses through Richmond.

There was probably some glee that Peter Egan's bulletproof supply arrangements, provided courtesy of the Board, had been sabotaged. It also served to demonstrate that the rules had changed and there would be less benefit in future from 'cosying up' to the Board.

Another person operating under new restrictions was Graeme Lowe. The Dawn/Richmond sale he had agreed to so reluctantly was coupled with a four year restraint of trade preventing him from operating east of the ranges from "Wellington to Wairoa inclusive", although he could establish and operate an office in the restricted area. Lowe proceeded to buy all the shares in T H Walker in Hawera, bought the upgraded Te Aroha abattoir in 1986 and built on an initial shareholding in Namron Meats in Paeroa by buying out Rex Fraser's 35% interest in March 1987, renaming the company Lowe Walker Paeroa. These were the foundation stones of the Lowe Walker empire, which was ultimately to grow to five beef plants and a shareholding in other sheep and beef businesses.

Freesia, or MIRAcles and MISAry 1985-88

"Our aim is to act as a catalyst for investment in the distribution and marketing of meat and meat-related products. The meat industry has traditionally had most of its investments in processing but we think there are considerable advantages in pushing money into the marketplace instead."
Mick Calder, Meat Producer, *July-Sept 1987.*

While all these frantic company transactions were being negotiated, the Board was developing its own commercial operations. As heralded by Adam Begg's statement to the Electoral Committee in August 1985, and as part of its strategic planning for the five years to 1989-90 for presentation to the MIC in 1985, the Board moved to set up a separate commercial arm.

Co-ordinated marketing objectives were to be maintained through ANZCO/Janmark, the marketing arrangements with Bernard Matthews via its half share in Advanced Foods, the possible revival of Meatmark in the UK, and DEVCO. The Meat Marketing Corporation was managing the single buyer contracts and acting as the Board's agent for the Iran contract.

On top of this, the intention was to establish a producer-owned company that would become a leader in rationalising processing facilities, reducing costs, encouraging product development and improving marketing operations. Perhaps an impossible dream? The aim was to get together with the farmer-owned co-operative companies to create a strong integrated producer-oriented operation of sufficient size and strength to exert a significant influence on the meat industry.

Initially, the Board would concentrate on the development of a strong marketing organisation with involvement in processing as a second priority. The Meat Industry Reserve Account monies were producer funds so, perhaps naively, the Board believed that investment on behalf of the producer would be appreciated.

While the Meat Income Stabilisation Account was seriously in the red as a result of the price support operations, the Reserve Account had been maintained separately with funds in excess of $200 million, though ownership and responsibility were a matter of hot dispute with the Government.

Ironically, perhaps, in light of later developments, Board secretary Mick Calder questioned the commercial proposal in an internal memo on 30 September 1985. "Little if any analysis has been carried out to show whether all of the intentions for the company are feasible, economically sound, or of real benefit to producers. Without such analysis the Board and government may be committing funds to an expensive disaster. It could be said that the Meat Industry Reserve Account funds are being used to pay for rationalisation, rather than company or Government funds… It is questionable whether the presence of a strong producer company, competing on a fully commercial basis would effect the marketing improvements that have been suggested."

Despite these cautionary remarks the Board went ahead with plans for its marketing activities post-ownership.

The Government endorsed the Board's proposals in a letter dated 15 November 1985 from Minister of Finance Roger Douglas and acting Minister of Agriculture Fraser Colman. This approved the Board investing Reserve Account funds in a company to carry out its future trading activities and noted the Board envisaged using over $100 million for the purpose.

The mechanism for the Board's commercial strategies was the company at first known as Freesia Meats and then as Freesia Investments Ltd. At the end of January 1986, Freesia, last seen when it facilitated the farmer purchase, then sale, of NCF Kaiapoi in 1980, was reactivated "to invest in the industry, provided any commercial venture operates on an arm's length basis and has no advantage over other companies because of its relationship with the Board".

As Freesia did not have any staff the Board administered its initial activities. Allan Frazer, manager of planning and development, had outlined an investment strategy for the Board in November 1985 and noted that action had been taken to assess potential on and offshore partners for the venture.

The initial thinking centred on a potential consortium involving the UK-owned Weddel and Alliance with a possible new investment from Bernard Matthews (Advanced Foods' partner), to provide access to product and marketing facilities in the UK and other countries. Alliance also wished to avoid the prospect of a takeover by proprietary companies although such action from another co-operative could not be ruled out.

Subsequent discussions with investment advisers Jardens suggested the focus should be on a grouping of the co-operatives, especially as PPCS/Apex were reportedly holding talks with a number of operators including FCL, Weddel and Alliance.

Freesia's initial directors were former MIC chairman Reid Jackson as chairman, Bernie Knowles (managing director of the Wool Board and ex CEO of the Dairy Board), Farquhar McKenzie (managing director of Alliance Textiles Ltd), John Holdsworth (consultant and company director), and Norman McRae, Mervyn Barnett, David Frith and chief executive Jim Bremner from the Board. The first formal meeting of Freesia took place on 7 February 1986. The Board had by then overcome earlier concerns about members serving on commercial companies with interests in the meat industry.   David Frith says his observations during the board ownership period had demonstrated how effectively innovation and effort could be focussed, where government or Board funds were available for commercial advantage. "Europe's Common Agricultural Policy is living proof of that. Total vertical integration is the best available structure."

The new company began its activities on the run. The impression was that the company would have up to 70% of the $200 million funds available from the Reserve Account.

Its guiding principle was to move towards co-ordinated marketing. Op-

Foundation Freesia board member David Frith. Like fellow board member Mervyn Barnett, he saw powerful potential for added value through producer ownership.

Independent consultant Brian Allison, who advised Freesia on its investment strategy.

tions included an indirect investment in Alliance via a trust to ward off takeover action and the formation of a consortium marketing group involving Alliance (along with the processing assets of CFM), AFFCO, and Associated New Zealand Farmers in the UK. Another permutation was to take up the Waitaki holding of HBFMC shares in ANZF. There was a possibility of some investment in the meat interests of the Wattie Group, and a possible shareholding in Bernard Matthews.

One of the first companies keen to receive assistance from Freesia was PPCS which was contemplating the sale of its Apex shares and the repurchase of the CFM shares from Apex. Although PPCS later backed off, it was proposed that Freesia assist in the repurchase with a $15 million convertible note. It was also suggested that Alliance should be encouraged to buy Southland Frozen Meats from Fletcher Challenge, again with assistance from Freesia.

The formation of a marketing company in the South Island involving Alliance, PPCS and Freesia, and provisionally named South Island Marketing Co (SIMCO), was also contemplated. There was some suspicion the companies had decided Freesia was an easy touch – a low cost banker to the industry. A number of options were considered but invariably the companies got cold feet about a Freesia input which carried the stigma of the Board, declaring they wanted to make their own marketing arrangements. The same liking for marketing independence limited any real prospects of proposed mergers involving just the companies.

The directors of Freesia, wanting to show their commitment to proposals for developing marketing in the longer term, had commissioned independent management consultant Brian Allison to investigate establishing a producer-oriented marketing and processing company with particular reference to a joint marketing operation. He concluded that such an operation would best be centred around Associated New Zealand Farmers (ANZF), then jointly owned by AFFCO, Alliance and HBFMC and recommended Freesia take a shareholding in the company as a first step.

There was also a case for Freesia arranging for the Board's investments in ANZCO/Janmark and DEVCO to be transferred into ANZF to extend its operations into the Asian and North American markets.

Allison noted it would be desirable to include Richmond and PPCS in the producer controlled group. However, he commented: "Unfortunately Richmond's involvement has been prejudiced at least in the short run by events surrounding the restructuring of ownership and processing capacity in the Hawke's Bay. Moreover it is understood that PPCS is committed to an independent strategy."

Freesia had its detractors among the companies and also some of the farmers. Ian Jenkinson of PPCS was one of the critics and said later that the company did a lot of harm. "It was a pathetic move on the part of the Board. But they were thrashing around trying to find a role for themselves and there's a lot of organisations in the political field that do that."

Still, that view did not prevent Jenkinson's company Apex from gaining further benefit from Freesia money. Freesia took over an undertaking from the Board to provide financial assistance for AFFCO to buy the Hellaby assets from Apex and subsequently close down the Shortland plant, and start rationalising its operations. Jenkinson suggests, though, that AFFCO paid more than was necessary.

The initial request from AFFCO to the Board and then to Freesia was for $25 million to fund part of the transaction with the balance from the Bank of New Zealand. In part, the request was prompted by government and advice from Rob Thompson of Coopers and Lybrand acting as the bank's adviser. Subsequently AFFCO's new chief executive, Max Toy, and Reg Bernie, its finance manager, raised the request to $35 million over the first half of 1986. Unfortunately for AFFCO the Board was negotiating settlement of the MISA deficit with the Government and this complicated financing arrangements.

Initially the Government had approved the use of $20 million from the Reserve Account to establish and fund Freesia with a shareholding of $10 million and a loan of $10 million. The understanding was that when Freesia required more funds the loan limit would be extended. However, the arrangement was complicated by the Stabilisation Account debate. Finance Minister Roger Douglas claimed that all MIRA funds should be used to offset the required write-off of the MISA deficit that had ballooned out to a billion dollars following the production surge of 1985 and the subsequent selldown of stock.

The Government had also suggested at one stage that rationalisation of the industry (or a reduction in capacity) was essential and that Freesia could use MIRA funds for redundancy payments to ease the financial strain on the companies. Freesia politely declined the proposal.

Negotiations went on for two years and were finally settled in March 1987 with the Board and Federated Farmers agreeing to the transfer of $100 million of the MIRA funds to the Government to offset some of the write-down of the MISA deficit. The balance of the MIRA – about $135 million plus a written-down investment in shipping containers – was to be transferred to the Board for its own purposes, including the funding of Freesia.

Strong support for the Board in these negotiations came from the chairman, Bruce Anderson, and deputy chairman, Snow Petersen, of Federated Farmers Meat & Wool Section. Any decision on the Reserve Account had to be made after consultation with 'the industry' – represented by the Board and Meat & Wool Section.

The length of the negotiations meant some fancy financing was needed for the commitment to AFFCO. This included partial funding from Freesia with the balance as a loan from the BNZ backed by a government guarantee.

Freesia also sought advice from Brian Allison on an appropriate investment strategy. In his view: "The main industry participants are still focussing largely on structural changes related to the costs of production and the costs of processing... A broader strategy is needed in order to speed up the international repositioning of the New Zealand industry while avoiding unnecessary erosion of the processing sector."

He recommended the total marketing effort of the industry be enhanced and strengthened and said Freesia would have a critical role in stimulating

Federated Farmers Meat & Wool Section chairman Bruce Anderson, who backed initiatives for all sectors of the industry to work more closely together.

the appropriate changes. He assessed that Freesia would need about \$315 million to achieve the goal. It would have to borrow, and he suggested the company should aim for 50% equity.

The directors of Freesia were confident that funds would be available from the Reserve Account so they entertained other proposals for investment. These included an early request from Richmond – which was declined – for funds to assist it to buy Dawn Meats as a continuation of the Southpac-inspired rationalisation of the North Island companies including a projected further step of combining Richmond and AFFCO.

Other petitions came from farmer groups in the Wairarapa seeking funds for the establishment of separate export slaughterhouses in the north and in the south of the region. A new plant was needed to compete with Waitaki's ex-Borthwicks plant at Waingawa, which was so plagued by industrial action that farmers considered it almost moribund.

However, despite frequent presentations of similar proposals involving a number of different parties Freesia was never inclined to make an investment in the Wairarapa. The northern group eventually formed the Heavy Lambs Trust and processed lamb through Progressive and subsequently Lean Meats to supply their own marketing operation started by John Atkins in San Francisco. The southerners, under the guidance of Cedric Percy and Rick Vallance, formed a supply management relationship with Weddel Ltd and called it Weddel Tararua.

Adam Begg resigned in March 1987 after over 18 years on the Board, the last seven as chairman. He had presided over one of the most turbulent periods of change in New Zealand's history and been a pivotal figure in a sector that bore the brunt of that change more than many others.

On his retirement Adam Begg was asked, in the *Meat Producer* (Jan-March 1987) what was the most frustrating part of the job. "I've been particularly disappointed at the lack of progress that the industry has made in marketing and in controlling processing costs. It's very frustrating being able to see what needs to be done and not having the means to put the idea into effect. For the last 10 years, industry leaders have been saying we must be market-led and yet still most of the effort is concentrated back at the slaughterboard. I don't believe the industry is going to become market-led until New Zealand companies invest more in terms of people and money in the marketplace."

Asked about the future of the Board he commented: "It is essential for producers to have a Board that remains strong and retains its regulatory powers. It has been said before that the Board is not a political lobbying body; it is a statutory body with statutory functions. It's therefore susceptible to changes in Government policy and farmers shouldn't believe they can be protected from political change. That's why, with changes taking place in the industry, I've thought for some years we needed a strong commercial operation which, in association with the Board (but separate from it), could best serve the farmers' interests in future. The regulatory function is still necessary to ensure that quality products get to the marketplace.

"In the current free market-forces environment, there's a tendency to discount the need for producer boards. Farmers should guard them jeal-

Jim Thomson, Board chief executive from 1987-91, a commercially-focussed operator charged with making Freesia a reality.

ously – they are envied by producers all over the world. If farmers waver in allegiance the effectiveness of the Boards will be diminished."

Adam Begg and his Board were aware farmers would perceive Freesia had used their money and would hold them accountable for the perceived or actual results. The Board needed to consider its position and look to an improved marketing structure through Freesia to produce the results.

Begg was confident about Freesia, which he saw as "a catalyst to bring about change in the marketing direction in the industry".

Freesia was an important part of the job description for Jim Thomson, who joined the Board as chief executive early in 1987, replacing Jim Bremner who had resigned. Apart from the Christian name, there was little similarity between the two men, with the more commercially-oriented Thomson, who came from Steel & Tube Holdings and had experience in the banking and computer fields, unlikely to ever be accused of wanting to bring back statutory single desk selling. In fact, he ventured quite a long way towards a 'co-ordinated marketing system' on commercial lines.

He recalls: "I would have a director type of role with regard to Freesia, on the basis that the investment in it was an investment of Meat Board funds, and I was ultimately responsible for those funds."

With new chairman David Frith, and deputy Mervyn Barnett, there was a formidable new team charting the Board's course. Both Frith and Barnett believed strongly in the concept of producer ownership. In Frith's view the Board needed to convince farmers they had to invest in and take responsibility for their industry. "There was an opportunity for the farmers to have a major influence on the industry commercially. In some cases they disappointed."

David Frith had served in the army and his training in tactics and the deployment of resources came to the fore. He saw his role as having to "go out and convince the troops that we were doing the right thing". Therefore it was better that his loyal lieutenant Mervyn Barnett focussed on Freesia, ANZCO and the commercial side.

The new Board team had to go forward without one vital member. Reid Jackson became ill and died early in 1987. He had played an important role in the industry from his time as a director of Alliance and as chairman of the Meat Industry Council, followed by his chairmanship of Freesia Investments. His drive and commercialism as well as his independent perspective had brought some much-needed cohesion to the industry, and some of that would be eroded following his death.

Peter Egan replaced Reid Jackson as chairman of Freesia in April 1987, just after the settlement had been reached between the Board and the Government on the MIRA/MISA funding. The AFFCO transaction was finally settled with Owen Pierce, a partner in Spicer and Oppenheim, and Bernie Knowles appointed to the Board to represent Freesia.

Finalisation of funding also allowed some tidying up of the Board's investments. Although the intention was to move all the Board's commercial interests to Freesia as a holding company, the shareholding in Advanced Foods and an associated loan were the only assets transferred at the time.

The Board did consider transferring the interests in DEVCO, and in

Peter Egan, who took over as chairman of Freesia after the death of Reid Jackson in 1987.

Fortex managing director Graeme Thompson.

ANZCO/Janmark. However the DEVCO shares involved pre-emptive rights in favour of the industry shareholders, and the company still had an exclusive licence to export lamb to Canada. The ANZCO/Janmark transfer was not considered appropriate either because of ANZCO's exclusive licence for the export of sheepmeats to North Asia. Exclusive licences were in conflict with the Board's undertaking to government that Freesia would not have advantages or disadvantages compared with any other meat company.

The final funding provided to AFFCO was $35 million, initially in the form of preference shares and subsequently as a loan with defined repayment terms. Not surprisingly the terms were changed several times over the years as AFFCO was involved in a number of restructuring moves. They had also made an undertaking to seriously consider a joint producer controlled marketing operation. However, as with other such undertakings, nothing eventuated.

One of the areas where free market competition came most quickly and savagely into play was in procurement. Procurement premiums were not a new phenomenon but the imbalance of processing capacity relative to the declining stock numbers increased the intensity of competition for throughput. Companies would publish their own schedules in the faint hope of fooling their competitors and then offer significant premiums to attract stock.

Farmers quickly learned to play the bidding game and would ring around the company stock buyers to elicit the best price on the day. Loyalty to a particular company now had a price, which was tested to the limits. A three-year cycle developed as companies built up courage in one year, splurged on procurement premiums in the next and suffered the financial consequences including pressure from the banks to show more restraint the following year. Of course, fluctuations in market prices overseas and climatic adversities did not help.

During 1987 the procurement battle heated up as companies offered higher prices for stock and some rationalisation continued. C S Stevens Ltd suffered a financial setback and the assets of the company, including the recently purchased NCF Kaiapoi plant, plus Sockburn and the Ashley cutting plant, were sold to Alliance. There was no Freesia involvement.

The other producer co-operative marketing company, PML, continued to rely on gaining access to killing space and suffered when processing companies began offering procurement premiums and putting the squeeze

The Fortex Seafield plant, built with the assistance of $5 million from Freesia.

on outside operators. PML had to pay premiums to get stock but did not have the processing facilities to engage in the marginal costing that allowed processors to justify the procurement premiums. The company folded in 1987.

One of the more controversial moves during 1986-87 was Freesia's 25% (later 31%) shareholding in processing industry newcomer Fortex at an initial cost of $4 million (later rising to $5 million), to enable it to build a single chain multi-shift plant at Seafield in Canterbury.

Hamilton Logan, Richmond chairman to 1991, who attempted to encourage farmers to take up greater ownership of the company, with David Wright (left) and Mike Moore.

Fortex, which made much of its marketing skills, had, like Advanced Foods and PML, been squeezed out by other processors. It was shut out of slaughtering arrangements with CFM by new owners PPCS, and lobbied to gain acceptance and finance for its plans. Both the chairman John Austin and managing director Graeme Thompson were particularly persuasive. Freesia considered Fortex an innovative company that should be supported. The proposal included cutting and packaging 100% of product.

Freesia also took up an invitation to invest in Richmond following its 1987 restructuring, a further development of the John Anderson/ Southpac plan for the company. The invitation was ostensibly to get Freesia to act as a 'white knight' with a block of shares to prevent possible takeover activity by an investor tempting farmers to sell. The directors preferred Richmond to remain a farmer-owned Hawke's Bay company after being the subject of an unsuccessful takeover bid when Brierleys made its first foray into the meat industry in 1977. In fighting off that bid they had adopted a constitution that effectively limited the voting powers of major shareholders and Freesia found that despite a 19% shareholding it was limited to less than 3% of the vote.

This irritated Freesia so when Richmond made a move that could have given a voting majority to the trustees of the staff share scheme, Freesia took out an injunction to prevent it. It brought both sides together to negotiate a more equitable constitution, giving farmers the first option on buying out the shares held by Freesia. However, despite extensive promotion by the former chairman Hamilton Logan and some directors, farmers were not anxious to invest in a meat company in the post-crash environment. Only 350,000 shares or 10% of Freesia's holding were sold over a five-year period.

The transfer of Advanced Foods to Freesia brought with it the continuing problem of securing a supply of raw material to honour the Board's contractual commitment to Bernard Matthews. Various options to resolve this vexed issue were considered over the years.

It also brought the directors of Freesia into closer contact with GFW, firstly through the relationship Peter Egan had with the senior executives of the company and with Pat Goodman. In addition GFW held the other 50% of the Advanced Foods shares. As Jim Thomson recalled: "We got involved, through the machinations of GFW, with the Waitaki situation, I think because of our association with them in Advanced Foods."

Mick Calder resigned as secretary of the Board in July 1987 to take up the post of chief executive of Freesia. On returning from a three month management course overseas, he discovered the Freesia board had decided that Waitaki held the key to the future of the industry. In typical fashion Peter Egan had begun negotiations with GFW for Freesia to buy into it. As Waitaki was the biggest meat company, if Freesia could get a reasonable share of it, Egan reasoned, it could exert considerable influence on the industry.

At the same time, and just after the share market crash, it was considered a good time to take up a shareholding in Bernard Matthews. This was to be Freesia's first and only investment in off-shore processing and marketing operations, but not for the want of trying. Other projects included potential investments in a lamb processing company in France, an importer in Germany, two different meat processors in the UK and a beef importing operation in the US, but none of these came to anything. Later the company promoted the idea of a lamb cutting plant in Bahrain in association with the Bahrain New Zealand Cold Store (BANZ) but could not raise any interest among the New Zealand meat companies.

The Waitaki deal resulted in a complicated arrangement with GFW involving both shares and convertible notes. To manage the shares, Freesia negotiated the establishment of a separate joint venture shareholding company, Garway Meats, to be a nominee shareholder for the benefit of each partner.

The 23% shareholding in Waitaki acquired by Freesia was transferred into Garway and matched by the transfer of a similar number of shares held by GFW. In addition GFW undertook to vote the remainder of its Waitaki shares with Garway except in specific circumstances. Freesia had 50% of the votes in Garway and, therefore, nominally exercised a degree of control in excess of the 23% of Waitaki that it had acquired.

The Waitaki move was signed in March 1988. David Frith congratulated Freesia on its investment and noted that the deal had delivered one element of the Board's vision in that producers now owned approximately 70% of the industry through the producer co-operatives as well as Freesia's investments. He commented later: "Whether we liked it or not we were still very much involved, even with the Waitaki purchase. It was part of the restructuring of the industry. You could either just leave it to the world or have the farmers involved; and it (farmer involvement) was part of the deal with government."

Waitaki had more market representation than the other companies and was considered the leader in product development. There were a number of positives to the purchase.

But it did not please everyone. Farmers were facing their own problems of high interest rates on significant debt loadings and showed little interest in their majority control. If farmers now owned 70% of the industry the reaction appeared to be "So what?" – it would still be controlled by management.

Reinvention
1987

"The reason why we need to have statutory control is because we have a classic market failure, to use your own terminology, just as we have with local bodies, and with government and in a thousand other ways in the economy. If you're going to talk about economic purity where's it going to start and where's it going to stop? There's no such thing anywhere, at any time, as a level playing field." Owen Jennings, president of Federated Farmers, at the Producer Boards' Seminar, July 1988.

The Board moved out of ownership and intervention into an environment where intervention was increasingly becoming unthinkable. Pressures for change, impacting directly or indirectly on the Board (and on the concept of the producer board) were coming from an increasing number of directions making it essential for all meat industry participants to rethink their roles.

Once the Lange/Douglas Labour Government began implementing the deregulatory crusade central to its philosophy – and Geoffrey Palmer had set off on his great quango hunt – it was inevitable that all structures and systems which imposed rules and regulations would come under scrutiny. The hallmark of this reform was its comprehensive and usually zero-based nature. What had been valued and accepted in the past had to justify its existence for the future. Roger Douglas' 'Better Way' followed free market, non-interventionist policies.

The Government intended to have new legislation governing producer boards in place by 1988.

Former MIA executive director Peter Blomfield recalls the period from 1985 to 1987 as a time of intense discussion about the future roles and functions of the Meat Board and the Meat Industry Association.

New Board chairman David Frith was quick to realise the Board's future industry leadership style would be different with the emphasis on facilitating and co-ordinating rather than directing and controlling. Frith, deceptively mild in manner, operated from a comparatively strong base of personal power and with a clear vision for the industry's direction.

He knew he was taking the chair when opinions had become polarised by the period of ownership and levy-paying farmers were divided on the need for the Board. "About a third thought 'Well let's get rid of the Meat Board, it wasn't any use anyway'. One third was terribly disappointed that we didn't turn into a single seller, and the other third said 'OK, let's get on with it'." With hindsight, a no-win – or at least no-credit – situation.

Relationships with the processors and exporters had to be re-negotiated in every area, from promotion through to shipping, and inevitably it was a rock-strewn route. The Board's relationship with farmers was also irrevocably changed, and what it could deliver on their behalf was no longer so clear cut. Many of its initiatives, such as the push to revamp port works

Agriculture Minister Colin Moyle pictured with the Reconstitution Chart for the meat industry. "I've cut out the chump chops... carved up the scrag ends... and stuffed the bonehead. This, of course, means the end of the flap." Cartoon by Wrathall, from Truth, date unknown.

costs, were destined to be unpopular with at least one very vocal sector. DEVCO, which despite the odds had been a modest success, was about to become a major embarassment.

Opinions hardened in both political and farming circles against the possibility of the Board ever intervening in the market again. The only certain way to achieve that was to abolish the Board; if that could not be done then the next best thing, according to David Frith, was to "avoid contact, and criticise and blame the Board for any problem of the meat industry, which included poorer sheepmeat prices after 1985 than had been predicted by the meat companies".

By 1987 both the Board and the Meat Industry Association were significantly different organisations. Even their location changed. The Board moved from Massey House to the renovated Dominion Farmers Building, then known as Seabridge House, at 110 Featherston Street. The MIA later moved from Europa House, across the road, two blocks up to Wool House.

At MIRINZ in Hamilton, there was also a changeover, as Lester Davey retired and Doug Wright became director.

Within the space of a year, the Board had a new chief executive and its membership had changed significantly. Former Waitaki chief executive John Neilson now sat on the Board as a new government appointee replacing Fred Dobbs, and unionist Blue Kennedy would shortly join him in place of Reg Rusk.   Michael Kight had died, and Roger Marshall did not seek re-election. The two new producer members, elected in an eight-man contest, were Jim Bull and John Acland. Gavan Herlihy joined the Board after Adam Begg's retirement.

Herlihy had worked for the Board's Economic Service. None of the candidates had gone through the usual route of Electoral Committee or Federated Farmers, although John Acland regularly attended the meetings as a PPCS director and chairman of CFM. Jim Bull was a millionaire who had sold his potato business and was now a large-scale sheep and beef farmer in the central North Island.   Acland had resigned first from Apex then from PPCS, feeling the company was straying far from its core business in its investments.

A facilitator and co-ordinator by nature, with a firm belief in working together in one industry-wide forum, he had become increasingly disturbed

David Frith's 'new look Board' pictured in their new boardroom at Seabridge House. The proceeds from the sale of Massey House were used to purchase Totara Park House in London, to maintain the focus on marketing.

Seated, left to right: former chairman Adam Begg; deputy chairman Mervyn Barnett; chairman David Frith; chief executive Jim Thomson; secretary Mick Calder. Standing, from left: Blue Kennedy, John Acland, Norman McRae, Jim Bull, John Neilson, Brian Mooney.

The Riverlands plant in Marlborough, processing 600 cattle a day, developed by John Buxton for Brierleys in the early 1980s.

at the future implications of the 'us and them' attitudes being deliberately fostered by some parties on both sides during Board ownership.

"I was always keen to try to pull people together for the good of the bigger picture. For the good of the industry, I believed we needed to move closer together, the farmer and the industry should be more involved, and that's why I was always keen on the idea of an industry board."

John Acland's independence and integrity were put to the test at his first Board meeting. Both David Frith and Mervyn Barnett stood for chairman, and Acland voted against Barnett, a longtime friend and colleague. It is a measure of both men that they remained friends and Barnett became David Frith's staunchest supporter – 'the steel in his spine'. With Norman McRae, they formed a formidable triumvirate.

Meanwhile the MIA had reshaped itself into an executive council of 12, a structure which better acknowledged the financial contribution and influence of the major processing players and restricted the representation of exporters to four positions.

By the time Joe Ryan left the chairmanship of the MIA in 1987, there had been an almost complete generation change at the head of the major meat companies. During Board ownership Athol Hutton had taken over at Waitaki, and Sandy Murdoch at Alliance. Max Toy was appointed general manager of AFFCO in August 1985, and took over as chief executive when Trevor Gibson retired the following year. Also in 1985, Stella Clark became MIA secretary. The Canterbury Venison Company and Fort Export became the Fortex Group, with Sir Charles Hilgendorf one of its founder directors.

In 1986 Southpac had installed John Foster as CEO at Richmond and Graeme Lowe began to build a company in his own name. When Ian Jenkinson decided to retire from PPCS (but not Apex) in 1986 and the company prepared to advertise for a successor, he told his board they had the ideal person already there, marketing manager Stewart Barnett. The changeover at the major companies would be completed when John Prendergast took over from Spencer Hagen as managing director of Weddel in March 1988. In 1987 Brierleys put its meat activities, including the Huttons plant at Eltham and the Riverlands Meat operation in Blenheim, under the control of John Buxton who had managed Riverlands before the Brierley takeover.

John Buxton, chief executive of the Riverlands Group, in 1989 a small specialist export beef operation with plants at Eltham and Blenheim.

Joe Ryan notes that the MIA found it increasingly difficult to reconcile the representation needs of a membership which encompassed huge multi-plant operators and tiny exporting companies.

"My view was that the smaller companies had to have a voice in the organisation, because if they didn't, they could do all sorts of damage. Nobody said anything to me directly, but I sensed people thought I was too accommodating of the smaller ones, and should have defended the big boys more. They didn't have a successor lined up for me, and they appointed Spencer Hagen as acting chairman."

Following the recommendations of a commissioned report by McKinseys, the MIA brought in Sir David Beattie as an independent chairman. The former governor-general and judge was to prove a very effective chairman, and continues in the position to the present day. This meant the deputy chairman became industry spokesman, a role taken by John Foster from 1988 to 1992.

David Frith was convinced the Board was essential to producers' long term interests. It would need to play a central role and retain its statutory powers. But it would have to tread carefully, in particular in separating advocacy from any hint of intervention. He deliberately moved towards facilitating collective decision-making through mechanisms such as the Meat Industry Freight Council and the Special Access Markets Committee (established in 1988 and 1989 with equal representation from the Board and MIA). From the start, he recalls, he wanted people to "stand up and be counted" and more formal structures which made it less easy for people to walk away from decisions they had reached.

In much of this he was supported by the Ministers of Agriculture and Trade, Colin Moyle and Mike Moore. In the April-June 1987 issue of the *Meat Producer*, Moyle said he could see a continuing "surveillance and licensing" role for the Board, but not involvement in generic promotion as brand marketing took over.

Mike Moore declared himself a supporter of producer boards: "Instinctively I like them… I think the Meat Board is the instrument which can bring a lot of the companies together to solve some of the bitchy narrowmindedness which has existed in the industry.

"I think unfair tasks were given to the Board and an unfair comparison made between it and the Dairy Board which was perceived to be so successful… I have a lot of time for Meat Board politicians who have done a tremendous job in a difficult time."

In short order, after 1985, meat producing farmers had lost the certainty of subsidy for their production and payment for their produce. They lost a guaranteed purchaser in the Board and, soon after, the comfort of a nationally-comparable pricing system when the weekly 'national' schedule became the first meat industry icon to crumble under the steely gaze of the Commerce Commission. The requirement for companies to set their own competitive schedules in an environment of declining livestock numbers and processing over-capacity was a touchpaper for the procurement fireworks that followed.

As an adjunct to this, the Board's role in monitoring schedules diminished as some companies declined to supply information, and the lack of analysis of schedule price comparisons made it more difficult for farmers to make informed decisions on the sale of their stock. Even after two farmers from North Canterbury, Rod McKenzie and David Meares, stepped in with the AgriFax service in April 1987, there was no guarantee of information from all companies.

Even if it had wanted to, the Board could not restore the certainties of the previous trading environment. Furthermore, some of the key elements of the new situation were particularly difficult to put across because they were not what farmers wanted to hear. Now, no one sector could expect to profit out of proportion to any other and a measure of trust and support – and supplier loyalty – between farmers and companies was necessary.

At the same time a strengthening philosophical position was being taken against the concept of producer boards, particularly by officials at Treasury and MAF.

In 1987 the MIA's Peter Blomfield – remembered, overall, as a friend of the Board – was invited to join a Treasury Task Force considering the functions of the Meat Board.

MIA chief executive Peter Blomfield and its new independent chairman, former governor-general Sir David Beattie visiting PML in what would be the producer-owned marketing company's last year of existence.

His personal view, later reported in a memo to the MIA executive, and energetically lobbied with opposition agriculture spokesman John Falloon, was that most of the functions and activities of the Board could be divested elsewhere. The entire shipping function including freight negotiations should go to the MIA; grading and quality control should be the responsibility of the companies; the MIA might act as a registration board for exporters; Federated Farmers could safeguard producer interests. He saw the Board having value in semi-government roles such as the Iran contract and the administering of VRA, possibly generic promotion in development markets, and acting as a research and development stimulus.

Thinking aloud, he said such an emasculation would raise the question of whether there was any need for a Meat Producers Board at all.

On the other hand: "Consideration could be given to the establishment of a Meat Board as opposed to a Meat Producers Board with strong industry and producer representation. This Meat Board could have some functions from the MPB and the MIA."

In other words, an Industry Board. This concept of a structure with joint representation from producers and processors had been put into practice with the Game Industry Board, established in 1985 for the fledgling venison industry. (For a variety of reasons including market access and separate slaughter facilities, but also to set it apart from what it saw as a sector lacking in innovation, deer farmers firmly declined to become allied with the red meat industry.)

The Industry Board concept was also suggested in a background paper prepared for Minister Colin Moyle in 1987. In line with government policy in other areas, like the 1988 State Sector Act which restructured most government departments, the paper focussed on separating policy, regulatory, commercial and representation activities in the producer boards of the future.

A specific concern was the Board's referee/player involvement with com-

North Canterbury cousins Rod McKenzie and David Meares, who set up Agri-Fax to fill the information gap after the Board ceased to publish a national schedule. Initially they collected schedules by fax from exporters and compared them on an equal net price basis and published the results. However, when the procurement wars heated up even they were starved of current information.

mercial interests through Freesia. To improve accountability the paper suggested changes to the more corporate model, introducing performance and efficiency reviews along with direct elections, and the appointment of people with commercial expertise to replace the current government appointees.

The paper recommended that "the problems which arise from the overlap of regulatory and commercial roles be addressed (in part) by removing the Meat Board's control, acquisition, licensing, shipping, transport and packaging powers… the Meat Board's power over grading… would be removed also." Removal of the latter power should follow an appropriate period of transition, but others could be removed immediately. There was also the suggestion that, in line with the proposed amendment to the Commodity Levies Act, the Board's right to levy producers should be tested by ballot every five years.

The paper acknowledged the importance of quota management, and suggested responsibility for the identification of restricted markets and the allocation of rights should "rest with a sector-neutral body". With the separation of roles, the paper argued, the Board would be left with no statutory function and therefore would not need a statutory basis.

As the debate developed over subsequent years, the Ministry of Agriculture was to hold to most positions argued in this 1987 paper. It followed the Treasury line of minimal regulation, with the little necessary performed by a "government agency".

Likewise, there was a consistent thread to the positions of other participants, though some possibly evolved more than others. While there were definite ideological differences, it has to be said there was also an element of self justification and even 'role creation' in each side's arguments.

From the start, the Board argued that what might be philosophically sound in the New Zealand context could have disastrous consequences in overseas markets, where a strong statutory body was important to a number of significant customers.

Consistent in the MIA argument was a determination to avoid any Board involvement in what were seen as commercial areas, which included, increasingly, aspects of classification and quality. Particularly reprehensible to the companies was the use of the powers of control during the period of ownership, and transport in the challenge to Waitaki going outside the shipping conference. It didn't matter that the former was spurred by government and the latter backed by the High Court.

When Federated Farmers joined the debate, it was usually to put a far-right position that would strip back Board powers as much as possible. But high-profile chairman Brian Chamberlin spoke out against 'armchair theoreticians' in 1988, telling the Meat & Wool Section membership, "I am confident that if it had not been for our producer boards, we would be even worse off now than we actually are".

But despite this confidence, the erosion of the Board's powers continued.

Free Marketing and Controlled Markets 1985-87

"This industry has a foot in three centuries, born in the 19th, developed in the 20th and now looking at the 21st. Will it become another dinosaur, will it be to New Zealand what coal has been to the United Kingdom or steel has been to the United States, or will it face the future and become a sunrise industry?" Mike Moore, address to 'Towards 2000' Meat Marketing Symposium 1987.

With the end of Board ownership it was time for the companies to demonstrate their much vaunted marketing or selling abilities and prove their claims that they could produce superior returns.

While they had the advantage of not dealing with the massive volumes the Board had to contend with, the livestock throughput – their life-blood – had also diminished.

As they had been working towards taking back ownership in October 1986, not suddenly at short notice in December 1985, the surprise announcement of the Board's withdrawal had the companies scrambling to reorganise their finances as well as their marketing.

Joe Ryan put the MIA perspective in its annual report of 1985-86, revealing some of the opposing viewpoints and showing something of the intensity of the infighting and political lobbying that went on. Ryan refuted Board claims that the industry had agreed to the three-year phased transfer, asserting the companies were always aiming to resume marketing in 1986. He also commented that the industry had stood firm against the Board's proposed consortia to service the Middle East and Greek markets.

According to the MIA report, the industry understood that the MIC could not resolve the Middle East issue and had not given the Board a mandate. Consequently the action taken by the Board to withhold supplies from the companies operating in the Middle East was provocative and premature, and the MIA was making no apology for taking its case to the Government. The report reiterated that the industry had been seeking an orderly return of marketing to the companies by October 1986 with the aim of "eliminating the confusion that had developed over the future direction of export marketing".

The Board and its staff considered this revealed a certain aptitude for selective memory of the events of the previous three years. The Board's intervention had started in part to relieve the industry's marketing problems which developed with the build-up in production and stocks. The quickly forgotten references to the need for a structure to dispose of 'homeless product' and pass the financial responsibility to the Board also raised some hackles. So the free-market era began with a degree of bitterness on both sides.

The MIA claimed also that under Board control "there was a clear disin-

Fletcher Challenge announces its arrival in the food industry, which began when it purchased the DMBA plant in 1982.

centive to companies to invest further in new plant and the establishment of offshore bases." Again the Board believed this situation was more imagined than real, particularly the comment relating to new plant. Waitaki closed its aging Picton plant in 1981 and opened a $43 million sheepmeat processing facility at Blenheim in 1983. A group including Barry and Michael Giles built a lamb, goat and deer slaughter plant at Mamaku, and C S Stevens upgraded its Sockburn plant for export in 1982. The Farmers Meat Export plant at Whangarei was upgraded in 1983.

The companies had possibly been too busy dealing with the risk-free throughput bounty that had landed on their plates. As John Drayton baldly put it, "The decision on SMPs, the decision of the Board to own product, from the angle of a processor, that was manna from heaven. I had money coming out my bloody ears."

This was confirmed by the 1986 report from Sir Lewis Ross, 'The Financial Performance of the Meat Processing and Freezing Industry', which showed that from 1982 to 1985 processing profits of the 13 companies and 32 plants surveyed increased by some 72% from $53.2 million to $91.8 million. It was noted the 1985 figures reflected the considerably higher kill as well as a strong surge in by-product revenue.

In the MIA report Joe Ryan said that though the industry foresaw difficulties with the "premature return" of marketing, it accepted the challenge.

The companies had announced an initial 1985-86 season schedule equivalent to the Board's previously announced National Pool 90% schedule (with 10% to come), but the MIA conceded that subsequent schedules had drifted down because market prices had declined and the value of the floating New Zealand dollar had strengthened.

They claimed, however, that the schedule now gave farmers accurate signals about the need for a mix of grades properly suited to market requirements. It was a backhanded way of saying that the previous SMP-dictated schedule had not matched market requirements.

The Group system of export market monitoring and control which had been introduced in 1984-85 was to be continued, as it was "the most appropriate and established means of undertaking marketing in an orderly and disciplined way".

To reinforce the message that the companies had given an undertaking to the Government to operate a disciplined marketing arrangement, the MIA was to repeat its support for orderly marketing over the next few years. In the words of its 1987 annual report: "A rather complex system of control has been necessary because of the way production rather than marketing factors have dominated the supply situation."

The arrangements, including proposals for managing the transition from the Board's selling structure, were detailed in a paper presented to the Board's January 1986 meeting, a month after its decision to withdraw. This indicated the plans had been in the melting pot prior to the Board's decision. Key elements related to the UK and included the establishment of an agreed market-related shipment programme, the operation of a cost, insurance and freight inclusive (cif) purchase price common to all importers, and commitments by importers to "sound selling prices" while not colluding or at least

Challenge Meats' Jon Lamb, who thought he could revolutionise the New Zealand meat industry with a flurry of innovative ideas and fresh thinking.

not being seen to be colluding.

The five exporter Groups would be responsible for the entire export to the UK of carcasses and primal cuts which would be purchased and imported by the five importers, each representing one of the Groups.

The five companies in the UK had virtually decided amongst themselves that the number of importers should be reduced and they were always labelled the 'SAFF' – the Self-Appointed Famous Five. They were Towers & Co Ltd (Group A), Associated NZ Farmers (UK) Ltd (Group B), the PPCS-owned NZ Lamb Co (UK)(Group C), W Weddel & Co Ltd (Group D) and Thomas Borthwick & Sons Ltd (Group E).

Doug Brydges, who managed the UK-owned Towers, pictured with a scene of Smithfield when it was a stock market. At that time, in 1990, Brydges was also the chairman of IMTA, the Imported Meat Trades Association of the UK.

The decision to use only five importers was greeted in New Zealand with somewhat more muted tones than the outcry that had erupted when the Board had made its announcement to reduce the number of importers from 32 to eight, and had supposedly destroyed the business of some of the smaller New Zealand operators. There was comment among the wholesale and distribution companies in the UK and Europe, however, that the marketing system seemed to change each year and they never knew who they were going to be dealing with next. In their view there had been three different marketing systems in four years.

In reality, the Group system had special provisions for the export of further processed product. So although there were nominally five designated carcass and primal cuts importers, in fact 27 different companies imported New Zealand lamb into the UK during 1987.

The exporter Groups did establish agreed selling prices for the five importers, which were generally adhered to in the beginning, but later divergences occurred as UK domestic supplies increased and the pressure came on.

The proposal also sought to limit the Board's activities in the UK to "statutory duties to farmers (which were not defined), obligations to the EC and above-the-line media expenditure on generic advertising" – all other promotion would be the responsibility of the five importers. So in the space of three months the industry had thrown off controlled marketing under a single-seller and adopted a group approach operating under a very prescriptive system – another form of controlled private enterprise. And it still required the backing of the Board's statutes to hold it together.

Not surprisingly, the Board itself still promoted the idea of planned, orderly marketing and hankered after a producer-controlled marketing role either directly or through Freesia. Other operators were also looking at joint marketing operations. In November 1986, even before the Allison report, which subsequently recommended it, was finalised, the directors had reached agreement in principle with AFFCO and Alliance to merge their marketing interests in a venture with Freesia.

Attempts were also made to bring Richmond into the group, but eventually the company decided to go its own way. The arrangement with the shareholders of ANZF progressed to the stage of drawing up a shareholders' agreement to establish a profitable operating structure for processing and marketing. It was given the project name of Farmco. After extensive discussion and negotiation it was finally accepted, though, that the idea of a

John Foster. Quoted in the 'Self-destruction' issue of Meat Producer, *April-June 1989, he said: "Farmers owning the industry is like wetting yourself in a dark suit – nice warm feeling, but no-one notices."*

Barry Brooks (at right) pictured with the man who sold him his first order of meat at the historic Smithfield market, once the predominant point of sale and price-setter for most New Zealand lamb. Barry Brooks established his Brooks of Norwich lamb cutting operation, which by 1988 was the biggest in Britain, in 1970. Brooks initially used New Zealand lamb because it was cheaper but saw many opportunities for innovative ways of marketing, labelling and packaging "the best lamb in the world". PPCS took 50% of Brooks of Norwich in 1987, enabling the company to do most of its further processing in the UK market place, and became 100% owners in 199. Barry Brooks is a regular visitor to New Zealand, where he owns a deer farm.

totally integrated marketing and processing company was unlikely to eventuate, due mainly to differences in directorial and managerial aspirations.

The continuing push for orderly marketing was also exemplified by the 1987 'Towards 2000 – Meat Marketing Symposium' organised and sponsored by the Board, the MIA and the Market Development Board (forerunner of Trade New Zealand).

The general consensus from discussions among all parts of the industry was there were advantages in working together to gain critical mass to penetrate some markets, but there was still a role for the entrepreneur.

Also, despite New Zealand's moves towards a freer market economy, the symposium attendees agreed that very few meat markets were free and open so there was a need for a system to deal with trade restrictions or state buying organisations.

Therefore some issues could be addressed as an industry, but others should be left to the individual companies. Joe Ryan asked: "How do we maintain that enormous energy that's available from the private enterprise system and still not cut one another's throats?"

Some, like John Foster, wanted to speed up the cutting of throats. "How do we get more blood on the carpet and get the thing sorted out?" he asked. But he also modified his stance and conceded that the most practical solution, put forward by Sandy Murdoch of Alliance, was to divide issues into those that should be done collectively and those which were sacred to individual companies. So modified free enterprise marketing was still in vogue.

These moves towards a separate marketing structure contrasted with the view expressed by Minister of Overseas Trade Mike Moore in his address to open the symposium. "In my opinion, the single most devastating action a government has taken in your industry was to assist in the separating of marketing and production, and at the same time pump up production with the assistance of taxpayers funds. Companies responded to these signals in logical fashion. They were able to neglect marketing because that was somebody else's job and emphasised production. Success was therefore measured by the number of carcasses delivered to the works door. The net result was a structure that now, thank God, is on the way to becoming part of

history."

PPCS went its own way, in keeping with its established culture of independence. In 1987 it acquired 50% of Brooks of Norwich – a company which the *Meat Producer* said was then operating the single biggest lamb cutting and processing plant in the world.

Newly recruited marketing whizz, Jon Lamb of Challenge Meats was aiming to reach 100% further processing, despite the fact that, as he told the *Meat Producer* (Jan-March 1987), others in the industry saw this ambition as "hysterically funny". On product development, the company chose to work with the Danish Meat Research Institute rather than MIRINZ. It also struck out on an independent marketing route by establishing its own marketing office in London when its ideas (or at least those of Jon Lamb) conflicted with those of its Waitaki partner in Towers, and Athol Hutton.

After the Towers operation was later sold to Hillsdown Holdings, Waitaki set up its own offices, managed by Tim Ritchie who had been general manager of Towers since 1983. Towers continued to trade in New Zealand lamb and other products under the guiding hand of Doug Brydges. With hindsight, the decision to sell a long-established New Zealand-owned marketing and distribution resource was seen as parting with the family silver, but personalities can override practicalities and common sense in the meat industry.

Despite these independent sorties the major companies generally considered there was a need to develop a marketing structure with 'critical mass' to sustain offshore representation and to match some of the strengths of the supermarkets. 'Convergence', a term favoured by Alliance's Sandy Murdoch to describe aggregation or co-operation among companies by way of strategic alliances mainly for marketing strength, was regarded as being almost inevitable.

Murdoch and his team developed the idea of separate processing and marketing consortia in the North and South Islands using Freesia's investments in the various meat companies. The proposal involved the integration of AFFCO, Richmond and Waitaki's North Island operations trading as Wellington Meats. In the South Island Fortex and Waitaki, with the addition of Alliance, would trade as Southern Meats. A series of jointly owned companies would handle the marketing in world market regions – UK/Europe, North America, Middle East and North Asia. But this idea never got much further than a position paper with a diagram of the structure. So the Farmco concept turned towards sharing the costs and risks of the establishment and participation in offshore distribution and marketing.

As procurement competition warmed up in 1987 the proposed shareholding companies backed away from Farmco on the grounds that it would hobble their operations. If Farmco took ownership of product in New Zealand or operated for all shareholder supplier companies in all markets this would "affect the ability of companies to maximise procurement strategies". Centralised marketing would put companies operating in different parts of the country with different peak procurement months into direct competition.

Support for the Farmco concept continued on the basis of its New Zea-

The 'Tombstone' advertisement recording the sale of some New Zealand family silver. In September 1986 Towers, then owned by Dalgety Crown, Farmers Meat Export, Southland Frozen Meat, Towers International, Waitaki International and Wesfarmers, was sold to Hillsdown Holdings plc. Hillsdown continued to import New Zealand lamb.

land office being responsible for establishing or investing in targeted marketing companies offshore, central planning and monitoring and co-ordinating flows of product to markets. However, the supplier shareholders would deal directly with companies based in the market.

An extension of the ANZF/Freesia plan was a proposal put up by Bernard Matthews to establish a joint venture between processing companies and Bernard Matthews plc (BMplc) covering at least 65% of the New Zealand lamb sold in the UK. The joint venture would co-ordinate the supply of product to be marketed exclusively by BMplc in the UK and later in Europe.

The proposition was originally presented to the Board and to Freesia in January 1986 and was subsequently put to the individual shareholders of ANZF and then Waitaki. There was lukewarm response from the companies who were intent on launching their own marketing programmes. ANZF was, for example, basing theirs on the 'Butchers Best' brand.

Although Freesia and Matthews persisted, negotiations dragged on for too long. Then there was a serious difference of opinion between Bernard Matthews and Athol Hutton, when aspects of the deal were discussed in London, that put paid to BMplc thoughts of co-operation in marketing for a considerable period.

Leading Local Quality
1987-97

"The short-stay tourist may have only one or two opportunities of trying lamb and the odds of him or her having a poor experience have been pretty high... Some of the advertising for pork, chicken and cheese is aggressive, with direct protein comparisons between cheese and meat. Seeing this, many sheep and beef farmers and their wives feel a sense of irritation." Jock Mills.

For the first time in 1987, New Zealand meat was extensively promoted to local meat eaters, the ordinary shoppers. Television and radio advertising gave New Zealanders a taste of the type of generic promotion long carried out overseas, telling them "there is nothing in the world like your own beef and lamb".

Like Siamese twins, the New Zealand domestic and export meat markets are joined at birth. Though destined to walk together, they have not usually marched in step. This is despite the fact that export-processed meat has always had a presence on the local market, and a proportion of the meat, both beef and lamb, produced on most farms is sold locally.

To some degree, high prices and high demand on the export market drains supply and pushes up prices on the local market. Traditionally, there are tensions between the call for retail prices to plunge when they fall at wholesale overseas, and the retailer claim that stable pricing is better for long-term business.

While some of the major export processors (AFFCO, for example) have long been major players on the domestic market, with substantial wholesaling businesses, others, like PPCS, process only a small proportion of their throughput for local trade. Similarly, there is an overlap between the membership of the Abattoirs Association, and the MIA.

Separate representation for the abattoirs, licensed to process for the local market only and often owned by local bodies, was established in 1973.

A different infrastructure operates for purely local trade supply, with a proportion sourced by butchers buying stock direct from saleyards. They have it slaughtered on a toll processing basis at the nearest plant, then complete the further processing at the back of the shop.

Although a high proportion of meat production is exported, New Zealanders remain big meat eaters by world standards and the local market still consumes a half-billion-dollar basketful of red meat ($485 million for 360,000 tonnes in the year to June 1998 at wholesale prices). Local sales now account for a diminishing 10-20% of lamb and mutton, and around 20% of sales of beef, an increasing quantity.

Over the years it has suited the agendas of the Board, the meat processing industry and the farmers to have separate rules, standards and structures for the meat sold on the New Zealand market. For the farmers, the much less rigid local classification and grading systems provided an outlet, not subject to strict schedule pricing, for product of less consistent size or with heavier fat cover than acceptable for export, or in the case of beef, at lower weights.

It is not entirely surprising that this had led to a perception that meat available locally was inferior and that 'export graded' implied excellence. What little promotion there had been within New Zealand – for instance a chefs' symposium held in 1972 – was at first aimed at the tourist not the local consumer.

Until 1976 'meat processed for local consumption' was completely outside the Meat Board's area of interest, operating as it did under the Meat Export Control Act. Then, faced with inflation's inroads on income from export-graded product, the first moves were made to extend levy collection to cover locally-processed meat. As reported by the Board's annual report, farmers accepted this extension on the basis that all farmers (except cull cow producers) sent some of their stock to the local market, and that the Board's activities benefited all farmers.

Prime Minister Muldoon, however, rejected the proposed amendment to legislation just as it was about to go to Parliament. The Board persisted by raising the matter at every Electoral Committee meeting, and was finally successful late in 1979. The Meat Export Control Act was amended to allow the Board to collect levies from meat processed for local consumption, and the basis of collection for all slaughter levies was amended. Instead of a 1.5c per kg basis, levies were collected per head. It was an administratively simpler system but it meant levy income dropped rather more quickly as stock numbers fell.

Most farmers accepted the Board's argument that overseas-focussed spending was to the benefit of all farmers. But others – notably the Electoral Committee and some breed societies – were quick to argue that some money should also be spent on local promotion. And some, perhaps, were slow to realise how effective promotion of lamb overseas had built visitor expectations that the meat would be served superbly in New Zealand.

A Board management paper prepared for the Electoral Committee in 1981 highlighted the paradox that greater demand within New Zealand would have little or no effect on overseas prices. But having more lamb, 'the national dish'

Little local butcher shops like this one at Rawene are a vanishing breed, but meat consumption in New Zealand is on the increase and some specialist butchers are making a comeback. Photo: Rod Slater.

in hotels and restaurants frequented by tourists, might act as an extension of overseas promotion. The problem was that New Zealanders eating out tended to shun lamb, even if tourists sought it. It was a catch-22 situation. Lamb wasn't often found on the menu, and the roast, most often served, might not be of top quality. As well, the paper said: "Some 50% of all visitors to New Zealand are Australians on whom lamb promotion would be lost".

Willi Thomas, founder of Fortex's Courier Cuts, with shipping manager Fran Boswell.

The Board had already funded some local lamb demonstrations by food gurus such as Alison Holst, Des Britten and Graham Kerr. This could continue, the paper recommended, or the Board might run an educational campaign to "lift the image of cheaper cuts through a more imaginative approach, thus releasing more prime cuts to earn overseas funds".

Crucially, at that point, meat consumption, especially of beef, was continuing to increase. In 1978 New Zealanders consumed 30kg of lamb and mutton per head, and 57kg of beef compared to 10kg of poultry and 3kg of fish. "The Board does not believe… there is any need or justification for the promotion of red meat in New Zealand simply to increase the volume of sale. Not at this time anyway. The final point is the Board has no legislative authority at present to promote meat within New Zealand", the paper concluded.

The ground was to shift under this decisive position almost immediately, at first in the cause of the tourist palate. Taking another look at its legislative powers for promotion, the Board decided it could interpret them as including the local market. In 1983, through DEVCO, the Board arranged the sale of export lamb to some leading restaurants. Shortly afterwards, the Promotion Committee, chaired first by Michael Kight and then by Fred Dobbs, began work on what was to become the Lamb Cuisine Award, a strategy "to put top quality export lamb regularly on to the menus of New Zealand restaurants".

Consumption was, in fact, levelling off, and would begin to decline, mirroring trends elsewhere in the world, and reflecting both reducing production and increasing competition. Between 1986 and 1993, New Zealand's total meat consumption would decline by nearly 22% per head. Red meat consumption fell from 232,000 tonnes to 161,400 tonnes, with white meat consumption rising from nearly 93,000 tonnes to over 121,000 tonnes during the same period.

Mike Moore, Minister of Trade in the 1984 Labour Government was a fervent promoter of New Zealand primary products. (Such was his commitment that for a time he tried a lean meat-based weight loss diet prescribed by the Board.) The Minister was the logical guest of honour when Fred Dobbs launched the Lamb Cuisine Award in November of that year. Moore praised the Board for having done "more in the past 12 months than in the past 10 years" and said: "One good lamb meal presented to an overseas visitor (is) worth more to the economy than one export lamb carcass".

With the Lamb Cuisine Award, New Zealand consumers were being taken seriously. Seven participating suppliers, including CFM in the South Island, Waitaki's Tenderkist Meats, and AFFCO made available regular supplies of tender A C & A lamb normally used only for export. Fortex later targeted this market when Willi Thomas set up Courier Cuts, a daily nationwide air freight delivery service for restaurants.

A Lamb Cuisine Advisory Panel anonymously evaluated participating restaurants and annually awarded a plaque to those qualifying. To encourage the

Peter Thornley, winner of the Lamb Cuisine Gold Plaque.

creative use of the six cuts offered, including the lamb racks and fillets almost unknown to the domestic market, the prestigious Lamb Cuisine Gold Plaque was introduced the following year. The roll call of its winners would include some of New Zealand's most notable chefs including Peter Thornley, Varick Neilson and multiple winner Hennie Sillemans.

By 1985 the Board was much more active on the local front. Robyn Cameron came to manage the Lamb Cuisine Award and stayed on to launch much bigger things. She recalls that, during the difficult period when the ownership position was being resolved, she was thinking about the opportunity to increase local retailer awareness of consumer needs. The Board said it would back her, if she could show others thought it was a good idea to set up a structure to do this. Particular encouragement came from Allan Frazer, then group manager planning development, and Board member Roger Marshall.

They got support from abattoirs, meat retailers, wholesalers and members of the old Beef Promotion Council. The Red Meat Promotion Council, soon to be renamed the New Zealand Beef and Lamb Marketing Bureau, with Robyn Cameron as general manager, and Denis Denton from Woolworths as its foundation chairman was established in 1986 with seed money of $20,000 from the Board. Its annual funding consisted of $600,000 of levy money from the Board, including the $400,000 previously designated for the Lamb Cuisine Award. Such was the mood of support and enthusiasm to get on with the job, that retailers as well as wholesalers agreed to be levied a 'campaign charge' of $3 for every head of cattle and 30c per head of sheep slaughtered.

One of the Bureau's first activities was a comprehensive survey which showed that meat was most popular among the aging sector of the community and losing popularity with families with children. A followup survey in 1988 showed a fall-off among traditional consumers, both in the older age group and working class families.

To counter this, in 1987, the Board invested $2 million in a campaign to halt falling consumption.

The Bureau began a programme including television advertisements, and

Bruce Monk, Michael Groves and Robyn Cameron with the Beef and Lamb Marketing Bureau logo and the first edition of recipe cards devised by Elisabeth Pedersen.

catchy recipes for easy meals. It also began the much less visible, but arguably more effective, campaign to educate health professionals on the value of meat in the diet. This aspect of the work, along with liaison with food service professionals, was managed by public relations specialist Debbie Armatage, also in charge of the Lamb Cuisine Award. Other members of the Bureau's team included former butcher Bruce Monk and *New Zealand Herald* food writer Elisabeth Pedersen who became well known throughout the country for their demonstrations of meat cutting and cooking at Board-sponsored field days and other occasions.

Suddenly red meat was much more visible – which it needed to be, as competitor products were still increasing their promotional spend. In another successful Board-supported initiative, Jeanette McIntyre of Women's Division Federated Farmers co-ordinated a nationwide competition for recipes which were collected as the *Lambtastic Cookbook.* However, when Board staff promoted the book at subsequent field days, many farmers responded with: "But we don't eat lamb. We eat hogget and mutton, the lamb goes for export".

"Give 'em our best" was the theme of the local campaign in 1988, with the launch of new lean (Heart Foundation approved) cuts devised by Bruce Monk, using the technique of 'seaming out' legs of lamb and rumps of beef. In 1991 these cuts won the UEB award for the most outstanding new or improved food product of the year. However, although Alison Holst described them as "the best thing to happen to meat in this country for years", butchers and other retailers proved harder to convince and the new cuts remained a relative rarity on shop counters.

Other difficulties included access to 'export quality' tender meat for ordinary buyers. (This was also shown by the enthusiastic response when Fortex extended its mail order service, as Gourmet Direct, for domestic consumers in 1992.) For most people it came down to where you happened to live. For example, from 1986 Hawke's Bay consumers were spoilt for choice of export quality convenience products offered at Richmond's three supermarkets. In turn, as a 1992 *Meat Producer* article pointed out, the company shrewdly used their preferences as "market-testers for the export trade".

Alliance's ambitious Ashley Lean and Tender programme, an extension of the Waitaki Tenderkist programme, using modifed atmosphere packaging, was launched in Christchurch. It struggled against consumers unwilling to pay the additional prices or unfamiliar with how to cook the new look, ultra-lean cuts, and with supermarket butchers concerned at losing their jobs. Ultimately the programme was a victim of the cost-cutting necessitated by the company's dire financial straits in 1992.

From 1986, meat destined for the local market was not graded but given a simple description, administered by MAF, on the basis of leanness, sex and age. For butchers wanting to order to exact specifications, and as keen as their counterparts in export markets to have newer product types like large lean lambs for their customers, it was a frustrating experience. As in Britain, butchers were losing ground to supermarkets in the selling of meat, and large chains had the critical mass to call their own tune on standards and specification.

As well, chicken and pork continued to outspend red meat promotionally and without asking for retailer contribution. To set up an industry-wide alli-

Elisabeth Pedersen (centre) on
her mission to educate the
consumers of tomorrow about
beef and lamb.

ance for local promotion had been a considerable achievement; holding it to-gether through the first years was an even bigger one. While the Bureau made progress in promoting meat, other initiatives such as reinstating some form of national grading for local processing were not so successful. Also, not every-one appreciated Robyn Cameron's forthright manner and determination to move things along.

There was an almost audible sigh of relief from some quarters when she left to become a nutrition consultant, and Ian Lamb took over the Bureau in 1991. His credentials included, as a former marketing manager of the Pork Industry Board, the introduction of the successful 'Trim Pork' concept. Under Lamb, working with nutritionist Belinda McLean, the Bureau switched tack to an intensive campaign highlighting the importance of meat in providing iron in the diet.

Armed with sobering research showing the impact of a lack of iron on the intellectual development of children and energy levels in women, the Bureau began a fairly low-key pamphlet and speaking campaign to the theme 'Iron, the Body's Gold'. It was a timely move. For the first time, in 1993 New Zealand-ers ate more chicken than lamb, principally because, as Ian Lamb pointed out, of health and convenience perceptions fuelled by a promotional spend four times larger than for red meat.

By 1991 the Bureau was a large body, exclusively male and combining producer and New Zealand Retail and Allied Trades Federation (NZRATF) representation. The long-time chairman was Denis Denton, meat manager of Woolworths. Membership at one point, when each major supermarket chain had its own delegate, reached 28. It included Bill Bly of the United Breeds Society, David Lonsdale (NZRATF), Alastair Chapman (National Association of Retail Grocers and Supermarkets), Norris Everton, representing the whole-salers (also Abattoirs Association president); Allan Frazer of the Board; Bill Garland (Meat and Wool section chair, Federated Farmers); Todd Heller (NZRATF); Board director Gavan Herlihy; Brian Lynch of the MIA; former

Board member Roger Marshall of the Sheepbreeders; Rod Slater from NZRATF; Graham Snell of the NZ Stock and Station Agents; and Alan Wilson (Abattoirs Association).

The 'Iron' campaign was to become a major success for the Bureau, reversing many of the negative perceptions if not immediately increasing local consumption. A tribute to its effectiveness was the fact that the original public relations campaign, run with minimal funding and targeted mainly at health professionals, was copied and extended by the very well-funded Australians. Their TV advertising about the need for iron, later proved a real winner for the New Zealand Bureau.

But for Ian Lamb the campaign would become associated with personal tragedy when his pregnant wife, deliberately eating iron-rich foods, lost unborn twins after contracting listeria from mussels. His inevitable loss of focus only added to the problems of holding together an organisation which was asking its retailer members to do what no other product group was doing – contribute to promotion costs.

Denis Denton, longtime chairman of the Beef and Lamb Marketing Bureau.

Other influences were working against a common commitment. Lowe Walker, never a contributor to Bureau funding, was an active and growing participant in local beef trading. The 1993 decision to include beef processed for the local market as qualifying product for the US quota caused friction between the MIA and the Abattoirs Association whose president, Norris Everton, predicted most of the 23 existing local processors would be wiped off the map. (In fact the only closures have been at the Chatham Islands, Takaka and Motueka; others like Thames and Opotiki later upgraded for export.)

There was no lack of other issues. New joint food standards with Australia were being proposed, along with a national nutrition policy for New Zealand. A 1993 MIRINZ survey showed an overall improvement in tenderness of meat available for sale across the country, but some was still unpleasantly tough. The Board's quality manager Kevin O'Grady was offering assistance to local processors to set up systems which would make tenderness more predictable, but very few were interested.

By 1994, despite some measurable changes in consumer attitudes and even a halt in the meat consumption decline, the structure and funding basis for the Bureau finally collapsed. Retailers, not required to commit funds to promoting any other product, no longer saw any reason to do so for meat. Voluntary contributions from processors had also fallen from a peak when they represented 95% of all meat sold locally.

Electoral Committee members were scathing about the situation at their August meeting with the Board and called for more accountability for local promotion activities. They criticised red meat's loss of local market share, the focus on selling by price, and the lack of convenience products compared to competitor proteins. Like other farmer groups they were acutely aware of the lack of any branding in the meat business. A speech by the Dairy Board's Robin Fenwick, originally made to a sheep and beef farmer gathering and reproduced in the *Meat Producer*, made wounding comparisons between pet food and meat in terms of product information, presentation and packaging.

A fresh start was needed, free from factions and with a sustainable funding base. The Board offered bridging finance, plus the ultimatum that the parties had to devise a workable proposal which conformed with the general Board requirement that any initiative with the industry should be jointly funded.

Denis Denton chaired the transitional group which looked at options. Newly elected Board member Bruce Jans, along with the Board's general manager industry services Allan Frazer, and the MIA's Brian Lynch were then charged with setting up a new structure which would function effectively. Together with domestic processor representative and previous Bureau member Andy Tomlinson, from Masterpiece Holdings, they eventually became the nucleus of a new more tightly focussed bureau.

They sent out contracts in November with high hopes of a sign-up before Christmas. One local trade group held out, however, and it was not until March 1995 that it was clear the new structure could proceed. News of the final go-ahead coincided with lamb featuring as the most popular meat in the prestigious Corban's Food and Wine Challenge.

By then former local trade butcher and Olympic yachting manager Rod Slater, also a member of the earlier Bureau, had become acting, then permanent general manager. It was an inspired appointment popular both with the trade, and with the farmers, who appreciated his upfront humour and straight talking style. (His signoff at the Board's interim AGM was a flash of America's Cup red socks.)

Rod Slater's rebuilt team included marketing expert Debbie Armatage, returning after a spell working with television, as well as Elisabeth Pedersen who extended her recipe development and food consultancy work. Centred in Auckland, there was no longer a place for the regional representatives – at the time Stewart Milne, Jim Cameron and Peter Truman.

The funding came solely from producers and processors, with a commitment for three years. The only freeloaders were two export and five local processors. (They accounted for only 10% of product.) Processors contributed 20c a sheep carcass and $2 a cattle beast, with 1c a kg levied on bone-in and 1.5c a kg on boneless cuts. The Board agreed to match this up to $1 million. In line with the focus on women's health, the first high profile promotional activity announced was sponsorship for netball coaching.

With no retailers involved in funding, this ended the lengthy involvement and support of Denis Denton, now national meat manager for Woolworths. In a career which began with Borthwicks local trade he was behind a number of innovations including the introduction of boxed beef supply. More recently, he had become one of the first to use new information about the animal stress and tenderness relationship. He set up the strict quality and hygiene specifications that pushed Woolworths to the forefront of domestic meat providers and gave prominence to beef and lamb in its trend-setting new stores like 277 in Auckland.

The new Bureau picked up the momentum created by the iron campaign, the new funding enabling it to use the Australian-devised television advertising which immediately struck a chord with its target audience of younger women. Shortly after the campaign began, Debbie Armatage reported the Bureau was "absolutely inundated" with requests for more information about red meat and iron in the diet. Such has been the success of the campaign, including another series of advertisements comparing beef and spinach as a source of iron, that

Rod Slater, general manager of the Beef and Lamb Marketing Bureau from 1995. Photo: BLMB.

by the 1996 Board AGM Rod Slater was able to tell farmers iron had become the number one health issue identified by women.

In mid-1995 it was announced that the Board had asked the Bureau to manage the introduction of the Quality Mark, testing the idea for possible extension at a later date to offshore markets.

Debbie Armatage at one of the many Beef and Lamb displays at field days.

The Quality Mark – originally Quality Origin Mark – was a concept which Board directors Barry Dineen, Bruce Jans and Brent Rawstron, along with Allan Frazer, had long been promoting as a means of extending the existing lamb rosette into an internationally recognised symbol of quality and origin. Working with brand consultant Brian Richards their efforts, supported by promotions assistant Philippa Lorimer, and, for a year, by former Dairy Board brand manager John Baird, met with a mixed reaction from the wider industry and less than wholehearted endorsement at the Board table.

Consequently it was an achievement to gain approval to proceed with the Mark for the local market. The aim was ambitious: to create a whole new 'story' for New Zealand beef and lamb, incorporating aspects like safety and tenderness. While tenderness protocols for lamb were well established, it would be a world first to set them up for beef. In addition to the nutritional story already being told by the Bureau, it would, as Bruce Jans pointed out, also be a world first "in underpinning generic promotion of red meat with a range of food safety, eating quality and animal welfare standards".

To involve local processors, the approach was to encourage them to find their own way to deliver predictable and repeatable export quality tenderness, emphasising that even the installation of conditioning tunnels need not be expensive. It had long been known that much locally processed product, especially lamb, was acceptably tender. In some cases this was because the abattoirs had the facilities to do AC & A. In others it was a function of older chillers or the ability to store product longer – and the fact that the meat was never frozen, so did not suffer cold shortening.

What the new Bureau offered was assistance with documenting and achieving processes which would guarantee repeatable tenderness. In a substantial below-the-line cost contribution, the Board supported this by helping individual plants develop their own tenderness protocols and provided assistance from quality staff including Kevin O'Grady and Graeme Clent and the production supervisory team. MIRINZ meat scientist Kevin Gilbert also made an important contribution to the protocols for tenderness management. This time, there was a substantial level of acceptance, and a spinoff was a significant increase in understanding of beef tenderness on both sides.

It had been hoped the new Quality Mark would be launched in 1996, but the exhaustive process of negotiating agreed standards was still not completed. Late in 1996 the Board underscored its commitment to the Mark with $10 million, to be allocated over three years. Enormous effort went into gaining support from all sectors of the industry, with letters sent to every farmer and an explanatory video specially prepared for them.

The approach of the Quality Mark prompted a rare display of consumer pressure against meat treated with growth promotants, mainly through the major retailers but also by farmer Edna McAtamney of Southland. As originally announced, such meat would be permitted to carry the Quality Mark. However,

The Beef and Lamb Quality Mark.

in July 1997, Board chairman John Acland reversed this. "When retailers representing over 80% of the red meat sold on the local market made it clear consumers wanted their meat to be free from growth promotants, this is a market signal we were bound to follow in the interests of our producers."

In the event, it was not until September 1997 that the exhaustive process of developing auditable quality systems for processing and retail, along with repeatable tenderness, was finally completed. The time taken to develop the infrastructure, and the sunshine yellow and Pacific blue design, paid off in very positive public acceptance for the Quality Mark. By launch day, 50 processors and 450 retailers were involved with the scheme.

The Bureau manages all aspects of the Quality Mark on contract to the Board. At the same time it continues with a wide range of other local promotional work funded jointly by the Board and meat processors. In 1996 the new Beef and Lamb Hallmark Award replaced the Lamb Cuisine Award to encourage excellence in preparation and presentation of both types of meat. Prominent chefs were named Beef and Lamb Ambassadors. Other initiatives include the Food Service Panel and the regular food service newsletter *The Point*. Work with health professionals and the netball sponsorship, which has firmly established the image of beef and lamb with teenage girls, continues.

Once the cinderella product, meat for local consumption is now up there with the best of local products – appropriately at a time when New Zealand and Pacific cuisine is in fashion. ANZCO's Angel Bay burgers, developed for the local market, won the premium product award at the 1998 Salon International d'Alimentation (SIAL) food fair in Paris. Tenderness is increasingly consistent, to the point where it looks possible to reset the standards of acceptability. Allowable fat trim has been reduced, so Quality Mark meat cuts are now Heart Foundation-approved. Quality Mark follow-up shows its impact has been positive on a number of fronts.

Most important, total consumer spending on red meat is rising. New Zealand is the only country in the Western World to record an increase in demand for beef and lamb in recent years. In the two years since the launch of the Quality Mark, consumer expenditure on beef and lamb has increased by 12% and 15% respectively. To June 1998 per capita consumption of lamb was 10.22 kg and 38.73 kg for beef. As a long-time supporter of local promotion, it must have given Allan Frazer much satisfaction to report the increase in demand for red meat, measured by people's willingness either to pay more for the same amount of meat, or to take more at the same price. "There are a number of reasons for this increase, but I believe we can attribute at least some of it to the Quality Mark and other programmes which have increased awareness of the importance of red meat in a healthy diet."

Offshore Activities
1988-89

"The replacement of Meat Producers Board control by the private sector importers (together with a few fringe operators) turned into a disastrous combination of delayed deliveries, wishful thinking, price cutting, price increases, top class meat, dross class meat, deeply held convictions that the future involved highly processed meat, deeply held convictions that the future involved unprocessed lamb carcasses and manufacturing mutton... And so it went on."
Ingham's 'Meat Business Monitor', 25 September 1988.

By early 1988 virtually all of the proposals to set up farmer-oriented co-ordinated marketing on a commercial basis had foundered as companies concentrated on production and procurement. But the idea of co-ordinated marketing persisted and attention switched from New Zealand to the integration of the UK operations of Associated New Zealand Farmers, under Geoff Lorigan, and Waitaki, managed by Tim Ritchie. The proposal would combine the commodity trading activities of ANZF with the further processed and chilled product lines of Waitaki and merge the wool and by-products operations as well.

Geoff Lorigan developed the idea further, bringing Challenge Meats as well as Giles of Smithfield Ltd (an ANZF subsidiary company involved in commodity trading) into the group, with Freesia providing the funds to facilitate the integration process.

Ironically, given the earlier sale of Towers, the merger of Challenge Meats and Waitaki in June 1988 in New Zealand also joined their marketing operations in the UK, putting together the Towers partners, but without the facilities. The move reduced the number of marketing groups to five again.

An extension to Geoff Lorigan's proposal was for the new group to acquire other marketing operations and possibly extend its activities into Europe – a move that was not favoured by the shareholders of ANZF back in New Zealand. They had their own special relationships which they wanted to maintain. In Germany, for example, Alliance had built up a strong connection with Prime Meats and had picked up marketing arrangements with Peter Malt when they had acquired C S Stevens; AFFCO used Intermondo as its agent. These companies had particular strengths and distribution networks in the German market.

Prime, under the guidance of Heidi-Marie Zimmer and Gunter Bagowski, had developed a retail marketing strategy that involved cutting to exacting specifications and packaging under the Weida brand, and there was a natural reluctance to share this relationship with some of the other New Zealand exporters.

Prime's marketing approach was a significant development in the European market and at one stage Freesia considered investing in the company to secure a closer relationship with New Zealand. However, Prime was looking for supply assurances as well as equity, and Freesia was in no position to deliver.

Ironically, the preference to operate separately in Europe meant companies occasionally used more than one agent in the same country and there were instances of different New Zealand companies in fierce competition using the

Bernard Maurel of European importers Reyns and Maurel, pictured with Murray Roberts of AFFCO.

same agent. The difficulty then was to determine for whom the agent was actually working and a cynic's conclusion was that it was most likely the agent himself. The Board's office in Brussels put together a 15-page document detailing the various relationships between European agents and New Zealand exporters.

The consideration of alternative structures for the marketing of New Zealand lamb in the UK intensified during 1988 as political and access issues became more urgent, both in Europe and at home. Spain and Portugal had joined the EC in 1986 and some difficulties had been experienced in gaining access there for New Zealand lamb.

Both countries took unilateral action contrary to the EC Sheepmeats Regulation because of their concerns about the increase in lamb imports. The Board's 1987 annual report politely noted that potential opportunities for imports were blocked by Spanish government authorities "because of a series of unfortunate events, such as a misunderstanding over quarantine regulations". These were eventually sorted out but they raised tensions in the Community.

The European Commission had also reviewed the operation of the Sheepmeats Regulation and its report signalled the intention to look at internal support measures. It also proposed negotiations with third country suppliers to improve the operation of voluntary restraint agreements. Concern was expressed that lower prices for New Zealand lamb were increasing the cost of price support for domestic lamb. In practical terms this meant that the EC was looking for reduced volumes and increased prices through a minimum import price regime.

The Board, spurred by the growing disquiet about the decline in sales and wholesale (not retail) prices for New Zealand lamb in the UK market, contemplated various strategies and structures to halt the slide and to stabilise prices. An AGB Attwood analysis of wholesale and retail prices for New Zealand lamb from 1980 to 1988 revealed that the latter had moved up 40 pence to 117 pence per pound over the period while cif prices had declined by 8 pence to 42 pence per pound. These were clear grounds for accusations of weak selling if only the culprit could be nailed.

Back in New Zealand prices to producers for both meat and pelts had declined all season. By the autumn farmers were receiving around $15 for a PM grade lamb compared to an average of $23 for the previous season.

Neil Taylor, director of the Economic Service, reported in 1987-88 that net farm incomes were down to $20,700 per farm – the second lowest figure after 1985-86 since its series was started in 1961. This was disastrous. Confidence in sheep and lamb production was sinking rapidly and high levels of inflation in the domestic economy were not helping either.

Farm equity levels sank and the spectre of mortgagee sales hovered in the gloom. The *Meat Producer* ran its 'NZ Farmer – R.I.P.' issue which catalogued the impact on rural New Zealand of the combined effects of the economic restructuring and the downturn in overseas prices.

It was felt the Board had to be seen to be taking action to halt the slide, but the political climate was obviously against direct intervention. The Minister of Finance Roger Douglas had recently set up a caucus agricultural sub-committee to review producer boards and MPs known to be supportive of intervention were excluded.

Don Harwood, the Board's European director, pointed out his concerns: "The importers of New Zealand lamb have not shown any ability to work and act in a cohesive manner in the interests of developing the market and in the long term interests and benefit of the total New Zealand industry." He also drew attention to the prospect of the European Commission introducing minimum import prices if New Zealand could not control its pricing.

Concerns were raised by the companies as well, and resulted in a plethora of papers on alternative structures to deal with the situation. These ranged from the ANZF/Waitaki/Challenge merger proposals to the Waitaki 'Boilerplate' concept developed by marketing manager Craig Boyce. It proposed the establishment of a single company to buy all commodity sheepmeats product for shipment to the UK and a mirror company in the UK to act as a single primary importer. Further processed product was still to be kept separate.

Don Harwood, Meat Board European director 1985-88.

An alternative proposal from the international consultants McKinsey's, who were working for Waitaki, was for the establishment of a joint venture between ANZF and PPCS for the carcass trade while Waitaki would retain an independent organisation to market consumer-ready cuts to the retail trade. Also included for consideration was the option to reduce the number of importers to three or even two, a solution favoured by Weddel and PPCS.

There was even a proposal for a single-desk seller (the New Zealand Meat Export Authority), which found little support among the Board's staff especially without any commitment from producers. An option that found some favour was a joint Board and industry approach similar to ANZCO/Janmark. There was an abundance of ideas but very little support for a co-ordinated approach.

The idea of a single channel for sales to the UK and Europe was promoted by the Garway Task Force established by GFW, FCL and Freesia – a combination that may have put the kiss of death on any proposal for industry co-operation. Peter Egan of Freesia had tried the soft approach by talking to various key people but Barry Brill of GFW decided on the direct approach and sent out a 'confidential' paper, which received the usual industry treatment. Within days, copies were circulating in the UK, and the idea was scathingly criticised by the trade.

A typical response came from John Prendergast of Weddel New Zealand in a letter dated 6 September 1988, and copied to the Government (David Lange, Roger Douglas, Mike Moore and Colin Moyle), Market Development Board (Peter Shirtcliffe), Federated Farmers (Brian Chamberlin), MAF (Malcolm Cameron), the Board (Jim Thomson), AFFCO (Max Toy), Richmond (John Foster), Alliance (Sandy Murdoch), Waitaki (Barney Sundstrum) and PPCS (Stewart Barnett).

Prendergast advised: "We do not believe that a single-desk system for the UK holds significant advantages for New Zealand… We believe that the concept of a single channel comprised of heterogeneous elements for the UK is no more likely to be successful than NZL (DEVCO) was for North America." He advocated, instead, a reduction in the number of exporter and importer groups and the closing of the loophole which allowed a large number of companies to export further processed product. The groups, he said, needed to commit to a

SIAL, the Salon International
d'Alimentation, is one of the
main showcases and contact
points for the food industry.
One of the halls at the 1990
fair.

SIAL, the Salon International d'Alimentation, is one of the main showcases and contact points for the food industry. One of the halls at the 1990 fair.

marketing plan covering all sheepmeat products, within a system that prevented companies operating outside the groups. Shades of things to come.

His final comment set the proposal in the context of the times: "Barry, it does seem that some of the proposals put forward in the name of improving the industry's position, are more designed to restore the fortunes of certain members of the industry."

Given the precarious financial state of some companies, the prevailing attitude was that it would only be a matter of time before one of them fell over – which would relieve the pressure. The likely candidates were Waitaki or AFFCO. Consequently there was no advantage in assisting anyone to stay upright.

Even so, it was generally conceded that something needed to be done on the marketing front. On 14 July 1988 the Board wrote to the MIA noting it "shares the concern of many exporters and importers about the decline in the position of New Zealand lamb on the British market". In the Board's view an important component in a solution would be stronger and more co-ordinated arrangements to ensure better matching of supply to demand and more stable pricing.

The Board indicated its support for the 'Boilerplate' approach (perhaps with some modification to recognise particular exporter or importer skills) and offered to assist the industry to put it in place, provided MIA members were committed to the proposal.

The industry prevaricated and, surprisingly in view of its past experience with marketing intervention and the existing political ideologies, the Board began developing the idea of a commercially owned single exit point for all lamb and mutton exports initially to Europe, but eventually to other regions.

It was encouraged by the fact that the companies had apparently committed themselves to the Meat Marketing Corporation as the direct seller and/or co-ordinating body for special access markets in the Middle East, North Africa, South and Central America. In addition, a government-commissioned review of the Kiwifruit Authority had supported a single-selling entity and there were indications of support for the concept from both Fletcher Challenge and GFW.

The driving force was the perceived need to increase the return to the farmer. Yet by that stage some companies were claiming prices were improving. Also, the Economic Service reported that export lamb returns in 1988-89 had improved by 18.4% over the previous year, adding that the average return of $19.35

per lamb included premiums. The procurement wars had heated up again.

A Board marketing task force was established in mid-1988, comprising Allan Frazer, Mervyn Barnett, Jim Thomson and Trevor Playford, to examine the options for achieving enhanced returns through a more co-ordinated marketing approach for the European market. After consultation with industry executives, the Economic Service, Freesia, Watties and the Government the preferred approach was "to encourage the adoption of a single exit point structure for sheepmeat and offals for all of Europe through a company designated as Euromark. Shareholding and directorate would be provided by New Zealand processing companies in the main, with provision for minority Freesia/NZMPB interest." A timetable was proposed for approaches to the Government, Federated Farmers and to likely supportive export companies with a view to implementing or scrapping the project by February 1989.

Bill Joyce, Meat Board Middle East director from 1984-87 and again from 1992-96, with Mr Al Munajem, a major buyer of New Zealand lamb, at the Saudi Food Fair.

The proposals brought a welter of criticism, much of it published in the *Meat Producer.* John Foster of Richmond led the charge. "Euromark is an absolute disaster. We have had too many changes to the marketing system over recent years. The system we have of co-ordinated selling through four Groups is working and, even more important, maturing. It needs a chance to grow up."

He acknowledged that returns to farmers were inadequate and pressure from them through Federated Farmers was understandable, but claimed the industry had markedly improved its performance in both processing cost reduction and market returns. "One of the principles underpinning many of the current discussions is that farmers are natural owners of the meat industry…This is emotive stuff. If farmers at the end of the restructuring owned the whole of the industry, it would be like wetting yourself in a dark suit – it gives you a nice warm feeling but no-one notices the difference."

Robbie Burnside, chairman of PPCS, was also critical of the Euromark proposal: "It places sheepmeat marketing in someone else's hands. Unless we control the total destiny of our products we won't achieve maximum returns." Euromark would separate the product from the marketplace and interrupt the valuable flow of market signals back to the farm, which he presumably considered effective despite the distortions of the procurement premiums.

Others were similarly critical. The MIA report for 1988-89 stated: "There was little enthusiasm amongst the industry for the Euromark scheme." The industry believed that some refinement of the Group scheme along with any commercially driven rationalisation of operations would be in the best interests of the industry and New Zealand as a whole.

Jim Thomson recalled later that there was continuing antagonism with industry, farmer and national politics dominating the whole situation. "There were a lot of different agendas, and the Board had the opportunity at one stage through its financial influence, investments or holdings in the majority of the industry… to create something which could have operated as efficiently as the dairy industry operates." But because of the rivalry between companies owned by the producers there was no interest in a common objective.

The producer board system itself continued to come under fire as the Government sought to deregulate the industry further and limit the powers of the boards. Speakers at 'The Producer Boards' seminar organised by the Institute of Policy Studies, in Wellington in July 1988, again suggested a need to rethink

Robbie Burnside, chairman of PPCS, one of the trenchant critics of the Board's Euromark proposal.

the role of the boards.

Rowland Woods, who had worked for the Board in Brussels during the seventies, examined the case for change in the terms of statutory intervention. He concluded the existing structure did not provide the necessary environment for success, as producers needed access to strong, versatile, highly competitive marketing organisations, able to respond quickly and flexibly to an increasingly diverse and rapidly changing set of market conditions. While some statutory intervention was justified changes were needed in both the substance of statutory intervention and the way in which it was delivered.

Other papers discussed such matters as equity issues, 'weak selling', and accountability. The resulting debate underlined the gathering momentum for questioning the need for producer boards at all.

In the face of concerted opposition the Board flinched and the Euromark proposal was dropped. However, the Board was still concerned about the need for co-ordination in response to the developments in overseas markets and the low returns to producers. In the view of Mervyn Barnett, the Board's deputy chairman, farmers needed to receive $35 per lamb to make their farming operations viable. He pushed this line so vigorously that in time he was being referred to as '$35 Merv'.

The Board's withdrawal from marketing arrangements in Britain had also meant a change in generic promotion, which had been included as part of the general marketing programme during the period of ownership.

In 1986 generic promotion was jointly funded by the Board and the major importers on a trial basis, leading to a reduction in the overall level of promotional support available to the trade. This arrangement was replaced in July 1987 by the New Zealand Lamb Promotion Council (LPC), consisting of the Board and the five primary importers, to fund and organise generic promotion. As the single largest contributor, the Board paid one third of the promotional budget, with the balance being allocated pro rata amongst the importers.

The funding arrangement continued with exporters paying 0.66 pence per pound on product destined for the UK and the Board contributing 0.33 pence. The LPC became a hotbed of disagreement over the direction, mix and timing of the promotional spend, so the structure and funding were often subject to review.

Tony Collett, manager of the LPC. The map behind him shows the different consumer demographic areas in the UK.

The Board's Market Tentacles 1980-91

"I can remember a number of occasions being in Japan when the market was pretty unsteady, and the industry generally was trying to maintain reasonable pricing. And you would find a 10-tonne parcel being offered by some small operator from New Zealand at half a cent lower, and that suddenly became the market price. Someone like Ces Stevens would be sitting on a 40,000-tonne order, trying to negotiate the price, and suddenly he's shot. That happened often." Ron Cushen.

While most attention during the late 80s was focussed on the lamb market in the UK and Europe, other parts of the world were also subject to analysis, debate and change.

Although the Board was still the prime contractor for the single-buyer markets, particularly Iran, the industry was using the Meat Marketing Corporation to organise the sales and co-ordinate shipping. Nominated companies were appointed as agents. Brian Freeman had retired and Wayne Geary (ex-Borthwicks and the Board) took up the position of manager of the MMC, with assistance from David Shaida, Tony Fawcett and Kevin Whyte (also ex-Board).

The annual contracts were negotiated by a team led by Norman McRae and Hassan Shaida for the Board and various company representatives such as Bruce Bishop (Weddel), Stewart Barnett (PPCS), Craig Boyce (Waitaki) and Alan Henry (Alliance). The tonnages in each succeeding contract reduced as production declined in New Zealand but payments reverted to cash, with the accompanying and inevitable letter of credit problem each year. The reduction in New Zealand's lamb production was regarded as a useful lever in negotiating higher prices, although this did not happen as regularly as expected. Still, the annual contract was regarded as an important sales outlet, as it shortened supplies to other major markets.

In North America, the newly renamed Lamb Company was almost another victim of the rising tide of overseas protectionism and changing marketing circumstances in New Zealand. As DEVCO, the company had had fluctuating levels of profitability over 25 years of trading. The US and Canada had proved difficult markets to crack, with low per capita lamb consumption and diverse markets spread across the continent.

Even though all the major processing companies owned DEVCO, they had set about modifying its operations to suit their own purposes, secure in the implicit understanding of financial backing from the Board in the form of 'promotional funds'. The common view was the companies used DEVCO as a convenient outlet for the output from their cutting rooms and pushed the company to pay more than the market would bear on the grounds that the Board would continue to support it financially. In 1979, the Board had increased its involvement by becoming a 50% shareholder.

The policy that required DEVCO to take all cuts in natural proportions

Bruce Bishop with Roy Andrews, Weddel's Smithfield manager.

Brian Comfort, president of
the New Zealand Lamb
Company (North America) Ltd
from 1987.

was also a convenient ploy; there was no need to find markets for the more difficult cuts like shoulders as DEVCO would take them. The companies also made sure that DEVCO's exclusive licence applied only to the mainland US. Hawaii and Puerto Rico were excluded. One attempt by DEVCO to sell legs into the higher priced UK market in the mid-70s was quickly scotched.

Despite its exclusive licence DEVCO succumbed to pressures to allow some exporters to develop niche markets under its licence as long as certain conditions were adhered to. One example was NZ Food Enterprises, a joint venture established by entrepreneur Dave Donaldson and Hellabys in 1980 to develop the sales of lamb cuts and other New Zealand food items in California under the Spring Valley brand. Donaldson, successful in manufacturing and exporting forklift trucks, had during visits to North America explored the idea of an integrated food marketing and distribution company. The lamb product was to be exported frozen but thawed prior to sale so it could compete with the domestic product and achieve a premium over the frozen equivalent. However, the company found that developing the market took considerable resources in terms of finance and manpower and the prices they achieved did not make the scheme viable.

DEVCO encountered several major problems before and after the Board's withdrawal from ownership of sheepmeats. During 1985, in response to New Zealand's anti-nuclear stance, the US withdrew the previously negotiated 'most favoured nation' status between the two countries, which required material injury to be proven in countervailing duties petitions. Almost immediately there was a petition for countervailing duty against imports of New Zealand lamb from the American Lamb Company.

The resulting investigation by the US Commerce Department found that a number of New Zealand government programmes such as SMPs, export market development schemes, land development grants and fertiliser subsidies conferred bounties or grants that disadvantaged US producers, notwithstanding their own system of subsidies and grants. On 3 September 1985 the US Government imposed a duty of NZ36 cents per pound on all lamb exports to the US. At the time it was equivalent to about $NZ11.00 per lamb and had a heavy and direct impact on DEVCO, the only licensed exporter.

DEVCO found that procurement could be more efficiently managed under Board ownership. There was no requirement to take cuts in natural proportions. Sales volumes increased, inventory levels were reduced and more emphasis was given to the production and marketing of vacuum-packed consumer ready cuts leading to profit improvements. This may have led to a degree of complacency and an imprudent decision by company management late in 1985 to purchase, in excess of their requirements, a large volume of boneless lamb and long loins from the Board. It has been suggested the company management wanted to stay 'on side' with the Board in the hope of holding on to its exclusive licence.

Later reports indicate that some of the boneless lamb could have come from 1982-83 production and was freezer burnt. It was well outside the specifications of any available customers, and the company suffered a considerable financial setback. It was also suggested the product had been forced on the company, but Board staff maintained it was a management decision. As well there were severe liquidity problems as the US market began to decline. To cap all this off, senior management in the United States were being investigated by the Packers and Stockyards Administration for unfair trading practices. The flamboyant Wayne Rice had been so plausible he had managed to maintain the trust of the New Zealand directors – including CEOs of the biggest companies – when his honesty was directly challenged by a US attorney, but he was ultimately disgraced.

As its financial position continued to deteriorate, in March 1986 DEVCO was renamed the New Zealand Lamb Company (North America) Ltd. With the company coming under pressure from its bankers both in New Zealand and the US, an investigation of options was commissioned from Southpac under the guidance of John Anderson. An extraordinary general meeting in June 1986 decided to endeavour to trade the company out of trouble with some assistance from the shareholders. A payment schedule for supplier creditors was drawn up with the smaller ones being paid off as early as possible and plans were made to liquidate surplus product in the US. The banks pressed for a restructuring of the company including an increase in capital. Support was available from some of the shareholders but insufficient to achieve another objective, removal of the Board as a shareholder. In fact, the Board was a major contributor to the restructuring, using $5 million from the Reserve Account to take up half the $10 million preference shares issued to shore up the balance sheet.

The Board was also under pressure from the Government for the market in North America to be opened up for other exporters. A letter from Ministers Moore and Moyle to the Board in September 1985 stated that restrictions on access to markets should be withdrawn; in the case of North America by 1 October 1986. A task force of Mervyn Barnett, Barrie Saunders and David Wright from the Board, and Peter Shirtcliffe from the Market Development Board reviewed access to the North American market during the early part of 1986. Despite advice from Ron Cushen, then chairman of the Lamb Company, that the central marketing operation was working and it was "horse sense not to tamper with a successful operation" the task force concluded the US market should be opened for test marketing from 1 October, 1987.

The Board accepted this recommendation but not another that, while the development market status for Canada should be reviewed, the Lamb Company should continue to have the sole licence for frozen and chilled cuts only to that market. The exclusive licence for all lamb meat was to remain but would be subject to review in five years. The recommendation that the Board should review its continued involvement as a shareholder in the company was also considered, but not acted on.

The Board invited companies to submit marketing proposals that demonstrated ability and commitment to service the US lamb market on a long-term basis. If the test proposals were acceptable, after 12 months companies could apply for permanent licences. Thirteen companies submitted marketing plans during the first two years, but only a handful made any

Barrie Saunders, the Board's public relations manager from 1983-87 and one of the task force reviewing the North American market. He went on to be the North American director until 1989.

Minister of Agriculture Colin Moyle.

Graeme Harrison. As head of ANZCO and the Board's North Asian director from 1984 he had a tough and often lonely task. He kept fit for it by training for marathons, often making a circuit round the Imperial Palace in Tokyo.

significant progress. The North American market required more marketing activity, planning and promotional input than many had appreciated. In addition the existence of the countervailing duty reduced the expected profitability and was an effective disincentive to investing in a marketing infrastructure.

Unfortunately, many tried to buy their way into the US market by cutting prices to capture market share from the Lamb Company rather than develop their own relationships with new distributors and customers. Again this predatory competition put pressure on the Lamb Company.

At the same time there were changes in management both in New Zealand and North America. Terry O'Regan had replaced Norman Donkin when he retired at the end of 1986, but the financial crisis caused him to reconsider and he resigned in June 1987.

When news of the financial problems broke the Lamb Company – which at one point had enjoyed nine successive years of profit – was painted as a failure. It was another instance where the ordinary New Zealander gained a lasting negative impression of the meat industry and its apparent lack of business skills. As the Board was involved, it could not avoid some of the flak, which served to obscure some real achievements.

Norman McRae says: "I think DEVCO did a great job in putting discipline into the quality of the product going into North America. It certainly did a first-class job in Canada in terms of stripping out of the market a price that was substantially above everything that was commodity. It's a classic case of a single-seller working. The other lesson that comes out of that whole North American operation is that as soon as you make an exemption you demolish the advantage of a single-seller. You either have a single-seller operation or you don't have it."

Chris Newton, who had moved from the Board to ANZCO, was seconded to the Lamb Company as acting general manager while the problems were sorted out. He left in 1987 and Llew Pointon took over as New Zealand manager. The directors also decided to shift the management of the company to North America and Brian Comfort was appointed president of the group. He set about developing a survival and recovery plan for the company, including centralised financial control under the management of Ed Michaud, and a leaner staffing structure. The company gradually began to come right under Comfort's guidance and that of Graham Valentine, ex Coopers and Lybrand, appointed as the independent chairman of the New Zealand parent company.

Meanwhile, ANZCO, the Board's other marketing operation, was having a fight to establish itself as the exclusive marketer to North Asia. It was decided to open an office in Japan and both the company and new Asian director Graeme Harrison had to survive antagonistic local importers, who threatened boycotts, organised bullying and used blackmail tactics. However, with support from some major companies in Japan, principally Itoham Foods whose founder Denzo Ito had been a regular purchaser of New Zealand mutton for 20 years, the company gained a foothold and some grudging acceptance. ANZCO also moved to establish its presence in Taiwan and Hong Kong.

When the Board withdrew from ownership the development market status for North Asia and exclusive licence arrangements were maintained. It was necessary, however, for ANZCO to establish its own procurement operation in New Zealand with some assistance from the partners in the Janmark consortium. Writing in the *National Business Review* Warren Berryman noted: "Many a meat company executive would like to see Harrison come unstuck… they want to prove the Meat Board wrong in serving notice on 38 exporters and assuming total control."

After the shaky start, ANZCO and Janmark expanded operations in the market with the addition of further processing facilities in Korea for re-export to Japan – despite a Korean ban on imports of sheepmeat for domestic consumption. Southern Foods Ltd was set up near Tokyo, to process chilled lamb for the retail market. Graeme Harrison commented later that credit was due the Board for the way it backed up the company. "In the market, being associated with the Meat Board gave us extra status and authority."

As sheep numbers declined in New Zealand the company had to develop other sources of supply to maintain customer relationships and supply continuity. In 1989 it began to source an increasing volume of product from Australia, to the vociferous displeasure of New Zealand producers who considered that their funds were being used to support their trans-Tasman rivals. The last quarter 1993 *Meat Producer* reported: "At almost every Electoral Committee meeting someone argues that prices to New Zealand suppliers will be driven down if Australian product is also used (by the company)." But Graeme Harrison took the marketing perspective. "The most important thing is the commitment to the customer, year round. We cannot be in business unless we serve our clients. We have made a commitment to supply mutton as a manufacturing component, and we have to honour that commitment." Even so, mutton sales to Japan declined as competition from alternative manufacturing meats expanded.

Changing market conditions and indications of liberalisation of the Japanese beef import regime prompted a change of direction. In 1988, as the beef market began to inch open Graeme Harrison toured New Zealand with a report on the future of the Japanese market and inviting companies to supply beef using ANZCO's connections. There were no takers as companies had their own selling arrangements. To supply the developing market opportunities ANZCO followed a route well trodden by other marketing companies with a need to obtain supplies. It began integrating backwards and investing in processing assets, firstly in New Zealand and subsequently in Australia. This raised the ire of New Zealand meat companies who considered it inappropriate for ANZCO and Janmark to have the exclusive licence for sheepmeats to North Asia and to be licensed to export beef. The MIA considered this would be inequitable, as it would give ANZCO an unfair advantage over other companies not able to offer a full range of products to their customers.

In a bold move in 1989, ANZCO entered two joint venture arrangements with Japanese companies: Southern Nissui Ltd with Nippon Suisan Kaisha, to operate the Southern Pastoral farm in the Manawatu; and Five

Star Beef Ltd with Itoham Foods Inc, initially to set up a trial beef feedlot at Hinds in mid-Canterbury.

Five Star Beef later went on to construct the large-scale feedlot at Wakanui on the Ashburton River, and negotiated custom processing arrangements with Alliance at Sockburn. The company also moved into the Australian beef market in 1990 with the establishment of ANZCO International (Australia) Pty to acquire Bush's Pet Foods from Goodman Fielder Wattie and to build a beef supply network under the management of Tak Asai, previously vice president of ANZCO Japan. By that stage ANZCO was operating a truly multinational group of companies spread around the Pacific Rim.

Although much of the attention had been focussed on sheepmeats during the middle and late 80s, beef had also been under some pressure particularly in the major North American markets. The countercyclical provisions of the US Meat Import Law had come into play during 1982 and 1983 as projected imports threatened to exceed the quota levels. The quarterly determination on the projected import levels meant that the calendar year quota provisions were only invoked in the latter part of the year when most of the volume from New Zealand had been shipped. As a result New Zealand was virtually shut out of the market for the final quarter in both 1982 and 1983.

In addition, increasing concern about diet and health issues was adversely affecting beef consumption in favour of poultry meat in North America. Production of both poultry and pork were increasing and government incentives to reduce dairy output by encouraging the slaughter of dairy cows, compounded the beef supply problems. Prices, including those for imported manufacturing beef, were declining, and dropped steadily to reach an average of US86 cents per pound in 1985 compared with prices of over $US1.40 per pound in the late seventies.

There was sufficient concern for the 1985 US Farm Bill to include provisions for the establishment of a 'check-off' or levy on both domestic and

Surrounded by prominent guests from Japan at the opening of the Five Star Beef Feedlot are the Mayor of Ashburton, Geoff Geering (second from left), Kenichi Ito, chairman of Five Star Beef Ltd and president of Itoham Foods ltd, and Mervyn Barnett, chairman of ANZCO and a director of Five Star Beef Ltd. They are about to perform the Kagami-Biraki ceremony, striking open the barrels of saki to be served to guests.

imported beef for promotion purposes. This eventually led to the Cattle-men's Beef Research and Promotion Board's attempts to improve the image of beef in the US. Their budget of $US75 million annually included $US6 million levied from imported beef.

The fluctuating but declining trend in beef prices in the overseas mar-kets had an impact on beef schedule prices back in New Zealand and some price support was provided. This had left an accumulated deficit of $4 mil-lion in the Beef Stabilisation Account by the end of 1985. Even though the Meat Export Prices Committee slashed the minimum prices for beef for the 1986 year, a strong New Zealand dollar and increased manufacturing beef production, as a result of the US Dairy Herd Buyout Scheme, led to de-pressed prices and a requirement for minimum price supplementation for three weeks in May of 1986. This increased the deficit to $5.5 million by the end of the 1985-86 season.

Beef marketing was considered to be so mundane a matter that the MIA annual report for 1987-88 carried the comment: "As usual, beef marketing has continued with little need for Association involvement". Nevertheless mention was made of VRA restrictions at the end of 1987 in the vain hope that they would not be invoked again in 1988.

Peter Gianotti, the Board's North American director - market services, from 1987 to 1990.

Back in the sheep camp, New Zealand had been debating sheepmeat access with the EC following the 1988 report on the regime and against the background of the plan to move to a single market in 1992. These moves, as well as the gradual liberalisation of access for beef, were running parallel to the GATT Uruguay Round negotiations. With market access issues con-tinuing to be of major importance, the Board decided in 1989 to reorganise and enhance its overseas representation. Don Harwood was transferred from London to reopen the Board's offices in Bahrain as Middle East director. Allan Frazer filled his position as European director. At the same time Eu-ropean representation was beefed up with the appointment of Neil Taylor to the Brussels office as director, trade policy and David Wright as director, Continental Europe. At the Economic Service, Rob Davison took over as director. In North America, Laurie Bryant took over from Barrie Saunders with Peter Gianotti continuing there until 1991. In a further strengthening of trade policy expertise, Cheryl Craig became the Wellington-based trade policy manager.

Later, the Board reviewed these overseas representation arrangements to support the market development activities of the companies, moving the centre of its European operations, to be headed by Neil Taylor, from Lon-don to Brussels. Allan Frazer and David Wright returned to New Zealand, Wright to move to a position with Richmond.

In recognition of the UK market's importance and as most meat compa-nies had offices or strong partnership arrangements there, the London of-fice was retained under the management of John Mabb with assistance from Martyn Saines. However, the European market was growing with the em-phasis on higher value cuts, so the balance of value if not volume was swing-ing in that direction.

Between the Trade Titans
1983-97

"(Producer boards), and other New Zealand representatives, formed part of a highly effective team effort by 'New Zealand, Inc' in the run-up to the GATT agreement. When I see or hear intemperate and sweeping criticism of our producer boards, I wish the authors of such comments could have been exposed to my experience of seeing the boards at work. Without their influence and their presence… our promotional, marketing and negotiating would have been seriously weakened." Former New Zealand High Commissioner George Gair, at the 1994 MIA Conference.

As the General Agreement on Tariffs and Trade, the Geneva-based global giant of world trade, stirred into life for the new Uruguay Round in the early 1980s, protectionism still loomed large in the world agricultural trade picture. The playing field was strewn with bumps, many placed there through unilateral actions outside of GATT. It was an area where the US had been particularly inventive, aided by Provision 301 of its Trade Act which allowed it to make its own 'fair trade' rulings.

The delicate balance of the world beef trade was upset by the implementation of the US countercyclical provisions in 1982 and 1983. To add to the misery, bargain basement beef from the EC was everywhere, "devastating the beef industries in traditional supplying countries" in the words of the September 1984 joint statement by the Southern Hemisphere Beef Producers, meeting in New Zealand. The subsidised stockpile, boosted by the slaughter of dairy cattle after milk quotas were introduced in March 1984, was heading for 600,000 tonnes.

Ireland, once a niche producer, had jumped with particular enthusiasm onto the subsidised production bandwagon. It captured 30% of a Canadian market traditionally supplied by Australia, New Zealand and the US. Irish and then Danish beef, offloaded through Canada to the US to avoid duties seemed likely to trigger VRA restrictions early, and prompted both countries to apply specific countervailing duties against subsidised exports.

Australian Agriculture Minister John Kerin managed to stave off perceived threats to developing Pacific Rim beef markets when he brokered a gentlemen's agreement with EC trade commissioner Frans Andriessen that subsidised beef would not be sold in North Asian Pacific Rim markets.

In other responses, Korea had closed its markets to beef imports. Canada proposed its own countercyclical Meat Import Law. From January 1984, the US banned imports from 14 countries, including Ireland. But at the same time, its exporters were increasingly frustrated by the complex tendering requirements and tight quota limits Japan placed on beef imports through the all-powerful Livestock Industry Promotion Corporation.

GATT, looked to as the referee to bring order to this chaos, had a style and culture of its own. Free from the requirements of larger organisations to have a proportionally representative staff, it was able to recruit for ability and excel-

Janet Skilton, of the Board's market access team, pictured with some of the country-by-country analyses she did of the impact of the GATT round on the New Zealand meat industry.

lence; its numbers often included New Zealanders. Under the urbane Swiss diplomat Arthur Dunkel, its director general during most of the Uruguay Round, the style was European and there was a conviction of the need for fundamental reforms.

As a tiny country between trade titans, New Zealand at the GATT risked the fate of the mouse watching elephants mate. But, in fact, its influence was to outweigh its size. A number of factors, including a well-rehearsed strategy on the part of the Government negotiating team, backed up by the sustained efforts by the Meat Board as its meat industry advocate, combined to make New Zealand a clear winner from the seven years of negotiations.

For a start, New Zealand was a founder member of what became known as the Cairns Group. These agriculture-based countries met in Queensland just before the first formal meeting of the Uruguay Round in 1986. The unlikely alliance included members from Latin America, Asia and the Pacific along with Australia, New Zealand and Canada, and crossed most existing boundaries and linkages. For that reason alone the grouping was a force to be reckoned with. Its success in ensuring that agriculture had its place on the agenda in the negotiating round gave rise to expectations of improved access as well as reduced production-linked subsidies and export restitutions which seriously affected New Zealand's agricultural trade prospects.

Even more significant was that, as the world of trade met at Punta del Este in Uruguay, New Zealand, led by its new Labour Government, was shaking off agricultural supports and subsidies at breakneck speed. From being protectionist, albeit on a modest scale, New Zealand catapulted to the top of the league of support-free farming. The rush of market forces into agriculture, while bringing pain and suffering down on the farm, elevated New Zealand to the highest moral ground. It could argue for free trade without a shred of hypocrisy. It was a handy position to be in.

The run-up to the GATT coincided with the arrival of David Frith as chairman of the Meat Board.

Patient, persistent and persuasive, a skilful strategic thinker never at a loss for options, he was to raise the Board's already highly regarded tradition of annual relationship-building and lobbying visits into a diplomatic art, and hone to perfection the role of meat ambassador.

Right from the start, there was a clash of philosophy and style between the two trade titans, the US and the EC. The US, ambitious, competitive, confidently justifying its own use of export subsidies and farm support as a 'counterattack' to what was happening elsewhere, pushed the 'fair trade' agenda hard.

'Pierre' Shiratake, who worked for New Zealand meat in Japan for over 30 years, most recently as the Board's Japan representative, pictured in the Tokyo office. His involvement with promotional activities started when mutton was being promoted as a table meat fit for sumo wrestlers, to the much more sophisticated recent seminars for chefs and organised tours of Japanese media to see the New Zealand meat industry.

The US Meat Export Federation shows the flag in Japan. By 1989, as the liberalisation of the Japanese beef market approached, the USMEF, with the assistance of the USDA, was spending more than $NZ15 million a year on beef promotion in Japan.

In the more conservative corner, joined by Japan and Korea and many smaller developing countries, was the EC. Passionate in defence of the socio-economic welfare of its farmers (and the complex price support mechanisms by which it ensured their incomes), the EC was, however, anxious to see progress in aspects of the negotiations, which implied the need to make concessions on agriculture. In addition the Eurocrats, conscious of the growing cost of the CAP megalith, saw advantage in being able to explain to their own farmers that reform was being forced on to them.

But the conflict of interest with the US was further heightened when in 1988 the EC banned the use of any hormone-based growth promotants in beef. One of the consequences of this decision was the development of a flourishing black market in substances such as clenbuterol (Angel Dust) complete with Mafia-like infrastructure. Another, because it effectively shut out imports of beef from the US where the controlled use of scientifically approved substances was allowed, was to sharpen up the discussion on non-tariff trade barriers in the GATT. The US-led position was that 'sound science' should be the only basis for trade bans relating to plant and animal health or sanitary/phytosanitary (SPS) aspects.

'Mid-term review' for the GATT was in 1988. But other events took centre stage. For the New Zealand sheepmeat business, top priority was the second review of the EC sheepmeat regime, brought forward because of concern about the rising cost of subsidies. New Zealand got wind of a proposal within the EC to cut the VRA quota by 40,500 tonnes or 18% – because imports of New Zealand lamb were seen as the main cause of the high cost of the sheepmeat regime to the EC.

By this stage linking sheepmeat and butter access had become the negotiating tactic of the European Commission. What became clear during the negotiation, however, was that the main target for constraint by the Community was not butter but sheepmeat. Some years before the advent of the European 'single market' New Zealand's butter sendings were still confined to Britain and affected only two or three member states. But sheepmeat, and particularly the prospect of increasing arrivals of chilled product, aroused fears in a number of member states.

Board chairman David Frith was quick to point out that the true cause of the rising cost of the common Sheepmeats Regulation was the weakness of the policy itself. "I don't see why unsubsidised New Zealand sheep farmers should be the whipping boy for the failings of those programmes."

By 1989 the two sides, represented by the New Zealand Minister of Overseas Trade Mike Moore and EC Agricultural Minister Frans Andriessen, had reached an agreement providing for the reduction in overall tonnage from New Zealand to the EC from 245,000 to 205,000 tonnes over a four-year period. In exchange the existing 10% Common Customs Tariff would be eliminated and New Zealand exports of chilled lamb could increase by 1500 tonnes in each of the four years, from the base level of 6000 tonnes.

Delays in resolving the arrangements for the internal regime meant the deal could not be ratified until December 1989 but in typical EC fashion it was backdated to be effective from 1 January 1989. The 10% levy paid on all New Zealand sheepmeats sent to the EC during 1989 was refunded to the importers, putting New Zealand exporters into the invidious position of having to seek reimbursement from them. Many importers denied there was an obligation for them to repay, which caused some tension between the companies and their supposedly loyal agents.

For the New Zealand beef industry, as signalled by Graeme Harrison in his far-sighted report, developments were increasingly driven by the flexing of export muscle by the US. This was highlighted by the unilateral action, supported by Australia and New Zealand, which forced Japan to put in place a series of market opening measures leading to 'full liberalisation' by 1991. The threat was that Japanese imports would be banned from the US (using Provision 301) unless US beef and oranges were allowed increased access to Japan. The agreed liberalisation measures included steadily increasing import quotas teamed with decreasing tariffs, and a move towards direct end-user relationships instead of channelling all purchases through the LIPC.

(Perhaps symbolic of the negotiating approach used by successive US trade representatives was the crowbar said to have been given by President Bush to Carla Hills on her 1989 appointment. Many of the US teams were, disconcertingly for their Asian opposite numbers, led by women.)

The US, Australia and New Zealand also successfully challenged Korea's 1984 ban on beef imports. Korea was required to open up its market "or otherwise bring into conformity with GATT the beef import measures" by 1997; the Korean liberalisation was to follow a pattern similar to Japan's.

US beef exports began expanding by leaps and bounds and by 1988 were just over 300,000 tonnes – about the same as New Zealand's total global shipments – with most going to Japan.

Meanwhile, GATT director-general Arthur Dunkel set December 1990 as the target date for completion of the Uruguay Round negotiations, and had scheduled the final talks for Brussels.

In Brussels, the Board took part in formal annual consultations, but was also in contact with the Commission at least once a week. Day-to-day monitoring of changing bureaucratic requirements was an art form in itself. Over 12,000 documents were processed each year in the administration of the VRA alone. On behalf of exporters, there was plenty of fast talking to do. It might be to explain a shipment of chilled lamb, mistakenly accompanied by certificates describing it as frozen, had not in fact thawed out on the wharf, or to persuade officials that a day's difference in arrival date at a crucial time should not incur huge amounts of duty. Back in Wellington, Christmas and New Year were always very busy times for Gary Donaghy and Mary Malone of the Board, who were responsible for ensuring New Zealand lamb shipments came as close as possible to but never over the VRA limit.

Distance made no difference to the vigilance needed in maintaining New Zealand's interests, particularly relating to sheepmeat access. Anything published, as well as anything publicly spoken, on behalf of the industry, was and still is today noted in Brussels. EU representatives, both from member states and the Commission, paid regular visits to New Zealand. While local farmers were scathing at the industry's apparent lack of enthusiasm to promote chilled lamb, it was essential, even in local publications, to downplay the relatively limited development actually happening, because European farmers saw it as a

The Board's European trade policy manager Neil Taylor and Continental Europe director David Wright, pictured outside the European Commission building in Brussels. Neil Taylor counts it as one of the ironies of market access that the two key officials for New Zealand in the EU sheepmeat regime were a Frenchman, Michel Broders and the Irishman, Michael Hammell. With both, New Zealand established good working relationships. And in reality, he says, New Zealand poses no threat to the French sheep industry because its values are totally different and its sights are set in other directions. "The typical French flock is about 80 sheep, many of them herded on open meadows, where they earn a subsidy for keeping the fire risk down. They are valued as part of the rural lifestyle, a world apart from production systems in New Zealand."

direct threat to their fresh domestic lamb.

The Board in Europe had some unique strengths, played to the hilt both by European director Neil Taylor and by David Frith during his regular visits. The Board made good use of its status as a source of authoritative information on the New Zealand meat industry, official but non-government.

For frontline New Zealand GATT negotiators, there was high quality technical input; for key Commission representatives certain strategic information was offered exclusively. The Board could open doors closed to others like government officials or meat exporters, sound out opinion and glean information without signalling New Zealand's negotiating bottom line. A close and synergetic relationship was forged between the Brussels office and the New Zealand representatives to the European Community.

Street theatre from local farmers, with produce and protests spread around Brussels, marked the countdown to the proposed GATT deadline. Mike Moore, who had been heavily involved in negotiations, came to Brussels, as did his National successor, Philip Burdon.

No agreement was reached. Agriculture was a major rock on which the talks foundered, with a number of aggressively charged clashes between the US and the EU. In hindsight, Neil Taylor says, no side was prepared enough to make a crunch decision. "It was a complete waste of time. It was as if they were trying to get to the end point without doing the hard yards between."

While the GATT process was regrouping, with the US and EU working towards areas of compromise, other moves were being made in the freer trade arena.

On 31 March 1991 the Japanese beef market was 'fully liberalised'. The previous quota was replaced with a tariff to move down from 70% to 50% in 1994. The role of the LIPC, which had managed all aspects of the market including the ratios of grainfed and grassfed, chilled and frozen product, came to an end, allowing direct relationships with buyers. The same year Taiwan lifted restrictions on its beef imports, but with a bias to the US. Korea allowed mutton imports for domestic consumption.

Five years after the offending New Zealand export subsidies had been removed, the US reassessed the countervailing duty (CVD) on imported lamb. From 1992 it remained on the ITC's books at zero. CVD monitoring ceased in 1995 after the Board requested an ITC review which included a final visit to New Zealand to assess the subsidy situation.

But the EC was still struggling with its beef stockpile and the US was still imposing what David Frith called the "absurd and indefensible" beef Voluntary Restraint Agreement (VRA), which was triggered each year from 1991.

The atmosphere was tense as the end of the four-year derogation from the EC sheepmeat VRA approached in 1992. French farmers were hijacking truckloads of lamb and burning them in protest against imports – principally British and Irish – which they saw as responsible for their depressed prices. Gestures against New Zealand were relatively few, but did include a break-in to the Paris Embassy, peacefully resolved over tea and Steinlager.

Hopes had been high that a GATT agreement would have removed the need for annual VRA negotiations. New Zealand sheepmeat exports to Europe were increasing and the industry saw the 205,000 tonne quota as a real restraint and

The Board's market access team of the early 1990s. Trade policy manager Cheryl Craig at right, with Edward Richards.

220,000 tonnes as a realistic target. When David Frith, with UK director Allan Frazer and Neil Taylor visited eight European capitals in 1992, and met with agriculture commissioner Ray MacSharry and GATT deputy director-general Charles Carlisle, along with a number of agriculture ministers and sector representatives, they constantly repeated one message: New Zealand would develop markets for its chilled lamb responsibly without the need for special restrictions.

Beef market access activity switched to Korea in 1992, with the first of what would be a series of combined Board and meat industry visits to discuss beef liberalisation.These bilateral negotiations ran very much in parallel with those conducted by Australia and followed the lead set by the US. After 18 months, negotiations concluded with an agreement to introduce direct purchase relationships through a simultaneous buy and sell (SBS) system which would apply to an increasing proportion of product previously purchased by tender through the government purchasing agency LPMO. In form much of the Korean liberalisation followed the pattern set for Japan; the differing Korean style came through in implementation.

Japanese farmers protesting against the liberalisation of trade in beef and oranges, initiated by the US and supported by Australia and New Zealand.

The Board recognised the increasing importance of the Asian market, and decided to increase Asian representation by opening an office in Hong Kong early in 1993. Laurie Stevens was appointed to the post with the responsibility of co-ordinating regional development of beef and sheepmeat in the rapidly developing 'Asian Tiger' economies. In addition, John Hundleby transferred from the Trade Commission to manage the Tokyo office. To facilitate new relationships in Korea, Chris Bryan opened an office for the Board in Seoul in 1994, with Gun Hee Yi taking over later.

Further changes to global beef dynamics were signalled as Uruguay sought a clearance from Foot and Mouth Disease to export fresh beef to the US. The US, Canada and Mexico were moving rapidly towards the creation of NAFTA, the North American Free Trade Area, which came into force in 1994. A major impact of this, besides freeing up across-border flows of beef and beef animals, was the imposition by Mexico of a 25% tariff on all other suppliers. Aimed at the EC, it virtually killed off a promising new New Zealand beef market overnight. The drastic devaluation of the peso had a similar effect on the lamb trade.

In June 1993, GATT gained a new director-general, former Irish government minister and EC commissioner Peter Sutherland. Sutherland had a formidable reputation intellectually and for his energy and determination to get things done. He set a December deadline for concluding the negotiations.

Much effort went into the New Zealand positioning in the run-up. The Board had used the past three years to develop some comprehensive information showing effectively the impact of any change in access totals or tariff level. The two-year old Brussels office, officially 'opened' with fanfare by the Prime Minister earlier in the year, hosted a policy conference. The *Meat Board News* of 14 October 1993 reported that all New Zealand ambassadors in Europe, and other top-level representatives were invited to be briefed by Board CEO Warwick Bishop, Neil Taylor, UK director John Mabb and the three regional managers for Europe, Andrew Burtt, Mark Neiderer and Francois Richard, on "issues and developments relating to meat". Minister of Overseas Trade, Philip Burdon en route to the Cairns Group meeting and GATT discussions in Geneva, was also in Brussels.

As the *Dominion* later reported (July 1998), Peter Sutherland managed to "cajole, flatter and bully" GATT's participants into agreement, banging down the gavel he used to keep discussions moving, for the last time on 15 December 1993.

The New Zealand meat industry emerged a clear and immediate winner, with a 10% boost to its access to both the EU and the US, from implementation date. One of the best things, as Warwick Bishop pointed out, was an end to the annual uncertainties of the US VRA and the EU sheepmeat regime.

Sheepmeat access to the EU increased by 20,000 tonnes to a total of 225,000 tonnes, while still retaining the zero tariff. And – though nobody would highlight it until it was signed, sealed and delivered some 18 months later – there was no specific limit on chilled lamb.

It is likely that some of the Community's trade law experts had been uncomfortable with the way New Zealand had been forced to accept the constraint on chilled lamb in the first place, and the conclusion of a monumental negotiation bringing benefits for the Europeans as well as agricultural exporters was an appropriate opportunity to abandon it. Nevertheless, credit must also be given to the quality of the New Zealand negotiators and the excellent personal relationships that were built up between New Zealand government negotiators and Meat Board advisors and their European counterparts, notwithstanding competing trade interests.

"A senior Commission official laughed when I later asked if we had played our cards right, or if we could have done better," Neil Taylor recalls. "She said: 'As usual, New Zealand doesn't ask for the sky. You are realistic in your demands, and we know you'll be true to your words. You don't try to cut corners or be too smart'."

A 'Eurocrat' enjoys a day at Kawau Island. Rolf Mueller, deputy director-general of the agriculture division of the EU, DGVI, is pictured with David Frith at right. David Frith assiduously maintained relationships with politicians and officials in Europe, visiting at least once a year. He recalls one meeting with the French Agriculture Minister which started with a fiery presentation of his objections to New Zealand's lamb exports. Then talk, over a cup of tea, turned to rugby and other topics, and the meeting stretched out amiably. Suddenly the Minister excused himself to rush off to Parliament, where he was just in time to save a confidence vote. "It's probably the only time I've come close to bringing down a government," Frith says.

Following the GATT agreement, the US Meat Import Law disappeared, and New Zealand had a tariff-free quota of 212,745 tonnes access for beef, an increase of nearly 30,000 tonnes over the 1994 VRA. Limits on mutton and goatmeat were removed. Canada allocated a country-specific quota, but also offered the possibility of low-tariff imports above that level. Tariffs in Japan continued to reduce progressively from 50% to 38.5% by the year 2000. South Korea was committed to increase minimum quotas, and other market liberalisation, by the same year. The EU agreed to reduce both the value and volume of subsidised exports such as beef and poultry, competing with New Zealand sheepmeat and beef, particularly in the Middle East. And the SPS provision was signed off. In future, plant and animal health-related non-tariff barriers to trade would only be imposed if justified by 'sound science'. The Ministry of Foreign Affairs and Trade publication *Trading Ahead* predicted the value of the GATT victories would lift New Zealand's GDP by 2-3% over the following decade.

GATT was signed off in Marrekesh, Morocco on 15 April 1994. The US implemented the agreement from January 1995 and the EU from July that year.

The World Trade Organisation (WTO), still based in Geneva and initially headed by Peter Sutherland, was born as the new body to hear trade disputes. One of the first on its agenda was the US challenge to the EU ban on growth promotants. Despite the finding in favour of the US in 1997, the EU has so far resisted such imports, and is now suffering retribution.

But the ink was barely dry on the SPS agreement before the outbreak of Bovine Spongiform Encepalopathy (BSE or 'mad cow disease') in Europe showed where the ultimate trade barriers lie. As British beef farmers found to their endless frustration, if the customers don't trust it, the country – even a borderless EU neighbour – won't buy it.

Much had changed with the Uruguay Round agreement. But much also stayed the same.

Export subsidies and producer support systems were not wiped out overnight, in the US or in the EU. Access restrictions like Japan's 'safeguard' clause lurk in the fine print. Many of the market opening initiatives will not be complete until after the year 2000, and the WTO will have begun a new round of talks by then.

Not for the first or last time Canada showed it marched to its own access drumbeat with continued attempts to impose beef import quotas that, in the words of Warwick Bishop speaking to *Meat Board News* in June 1993, "flew in the face of logic, reasoned argument and its commitment to the Cairns Group". In 1997 Canada tried to impose a compulsory 'check-off' or levy on imported beef, to fund promotion and research for the local product.

US sheepmeat producers continued to look to protectionist weapons – appeals to government to introduce quotas, or country of origin labelling – to assist a nationwide flock of eight million which was the size of the one in Southland. Faced with successive Farm Bills reducing subsidies, and growing imports from both New Zealand and Australia, they also attempted in 1995 to introduce a compulsory 'check-off' which would levy imported sheepmeat to pay for promotion of the local product.

A referendum showed even domestic producers were divided on this, but it was not until July 1997, after an extensive lobbying effort first by Trevor Playford then by Bill Joyce as the Board's North American representatives, that it was finally laid to rest. Barely a year later there was a petition to the International Trade Commission claiming injury from imports and calling for safeguard tariffs. Before that, there had been yet another call for country of origin labelling to be applied to imported lamb.

The market access 'minders' for the New Zealand meat industry have been conditioned not to relax. More than ever before, every 'i' must be dotted and 't' crossed in the EU quota documentation and management. Some in Europe still find it hard to believe there isn't somewhere a binding 'agreement' limiting chilled lamb sales which, on average, have climbed about 1500 tonnes a year.

It would be foolish to assume no envious eyes are sizing up New Zealand's share of the sheepmeat access. The rules could easily be reset less favourably. There is still a tightrope to walk.

US sheep are raised in totally different conditions from those in New Zealand. This flock in Wyoming has a permanent shepherd.

High Productivity 1987-97

"I had some sympathy for the meat industry in that people used to say 'we're getting robbed blind by the grading system, they're stealing our product'. I used to say 'But they're not. There might be inefficiencies there, there might be inconsistencies, but they're not robbing you. They might be robbing certain categories, but they're not making any money, therefore there's not a problem'." Richard Johnstone.

Meat classification provided, in the post-ownership period, one more example of a much firmer industry stand being taken against Board initiatives. The companies had continued to ignore attempts to introduce standards for conditioning and aging and in 1987 successfully countered the Board's proposal to introduce a 'Q grade' to indicate lamb tenderness. Their alternative proposal was a minimum standard.

But there was clear evidence that the market was not satisfied with what was currently being offered. That same year David Frith and Jim Thomson took Sir David Beattie and Peter Blomfield of the MIA with them for their annual lobbying and market visit to Europe. David Frith recalls: "We got a roasting from the European business because the quality had gone down the drain.

"They (the MIA) were confronted with the problem. And of course they thought we had jacked it up. Because the importers said, we have got to do something about this quality. It's really starting to hurt us. And Allan Frazer had done quite a lot of work on Q grade with them.

"Peter Blomfield went away and talked to these fellows privately, and they said, come and look at the stuff. This has just come back from Supermarket X."

The evidence was one of the levers by which the Board eventually got agreement from about 80% of the industry that all lamb sent to Europe should be A C & A.

"Weddel were terribly opposed to the cost of manning it… PPCS were grumpy about it. But it was actually very significant and very important," David Frith recalls. "It was a serious quality issue, and you wonder how long it would have gone on if the Board hadn't been there to address it. And of course, now people wouldn't be without it… It was probably their idea!"

The industry-wide Quality of Product Acknowledgement Agreement was signed by the managing directors of all processing companies in 1988 and fully implemented from October 1989.

The agreement undertook to progress in two stages towards the use of AC & A to deliver repeatable standards of tenderness in lamb. The Board appointed Mark Cassidy, formerly with CFM, to the new job of quality assurance supervisor, and the team of production supervisors took on the task of monitoring compliance with tenderness protocols, which soon reached 98%.

Brenda Duff checking a carcass. She became the first woman on the supervisor team in 1991. From 1988 the Quality of Product Acknowledgement agreement brought new responsibilities for the supervisors in checking tenderness, using the Product Quality Index (PQI).

On the breeding side, improvements to the sheep flock were gathering momentum. Farmers were beginning to make use of technologies like the ultrasound scanner to select leaner animals for breeding. At MAF's Invermay Research Station, the then director Jock Allison began the search for top performing rams, a project picked up by Waitaki International and later Animal Enterprises. Options like the highly prolific Booroola breed were also being investigated.

In an initiative by MAF, new sheep genetics had been introduced in 1985. By 1991, after five years of quarantine the new breeds, imported from scrapie-free regions of Scandinavia, would be added to the national flock. The Texel, with its blocky back end, promised exceptionally fast lean growth; the Finn offered huge increases in lambing percentage; and the Oxford Down fast growth.

As these potentially highly productive animals waited out their quarantine, the removal of SMPs and other economic pressures sent out some strong market signals about the profitability of farming. Land formerly used for sheep and beef farming switched to forestry, horticulture – and dairying.

The switch to dairying in the second half of the 1980s came at a time when US market indications were that money could be made in manufacturing beef. And 'lean' was becoming one of the US beef industry's big weapons against competitor products.

These prospects prompted a surge of growth in the unique New Zealand business of bull farming. In other respects, though, farmers seemed reluctant to adopt suggested improvements to beef productivity and management. Despite years of attempts by various groups, Beefplan never captured the imagination or the support of the influential Angus and Hereford breeders. After struggling through several incarnations it was sold to a group of breed societies.

In the 1983-84 season, bull slaughterings were 16% of the total export kill. Ruakura scientist Chris Morris picked up a theme earlier argued by Massey's Bob Barton. He urged increased retention of dairy bull calves, which would otherwise be slaughtered at a few days old as bobby calves, as a quick means of increasing beef output, and highlighted the good growth potential of cross-breeds.

Over the following five seasons bull slaughterings increased 108% while total export slaughterings increased 43%. Analysis by chief Economic Service economist Brian Speirs, in the April-June 1990 *Meat Producer,* showed that for 1988-89 bulls made up 24% of the export beef kill.

Bulls provide the largest quantities of the leanest beef. New Zealand had long established a reputation for reliable assessment of the exact leanness of its boxed beef exports, most of which was 90% lean or more. Initially this was assessed visually (VL or visual lean), later by chemical sampling (CL or chemical lean). In an arrangement seen by some sellers and importers to offer a lucrative leeway for reinterpretation, the CL rating was always shown in code. Through the combined efforts of the Meat Importers Council of America (MICA), led by Graeme Goodsir, the Board and some companies, led by Waitaki, the rating was shown in clear from 1988 onwards.

Mark Cassidy, who joined the Board to manage the new tenderness protocols.

Peter Packard, Beef Council chairman, presents second prize in the 3 entire male beef competition class to Dr Lockwood Smith, Minister of Agriculture. Beef competitions are used to encourage production of beef to the specifications required by the market, such as fast lean growth.

The innovative Beef Contracts established by John Buxton of Brierley-owned Riverlands Foods helped farmers bridge the steep capital cost of setting up in bull farming. The programme, started in the South Island under the management of Malcolm Monteith, provided some payment guarantees as well as incentives for out of season production. It was a structure that, with some amendments, has since been widely copied. The rise in bull farming also altered the dynamics of the beef-dairy industry relationship, reducing as it did the need to run a traditional beef cow herd.

Beef grading had remained relatively unchanged while the makeup of the national herd became larger and leaner through widespread use of exotic cattle including Friesian-cross dairy calves. Farmers became increasingly vocal about the lack of recognition for increased yield, or an improved amount and proportion of saleable meat cut from the carcass, a figure which varied between breeds and often even more dramatically between different animals of the same breed.

In the Beef Grading Review of 1986-87 extensive trials led by Dr Barry Hogg of MAF Ruakura attempted to establish if there were any 'typical cuts' from which a reliable yield calculation could be made. The trials, on 568 steers, heifers and cows at a number of works, showed a clear relationship between leanness and high yield – that the yield of saleable meat decreased as carcasses became fatter. Good muscling conformation was also linked to higher yield.

The yield trials, co-ordinated by Mick Wilkin from the Board, showed a "disconcerting" variation in cutting techniques and hence yield. The trial report noted this varied from an average of 66.39% of the carcass as saleable meat down to 62.25% between processing plants. It got to the point where it would be "difficult for meat processors… to very accurately specify their product". It was a strong argument for national standards for preparation and trimming.

The trials also highlighted the up to 2% weight lost through evaporation in the chiller. This might be insubstantial to an individual producer but from an overall company standpoint it was a powerful reason to investigate the technique of hot boning, where the carcass goes directly to the boning table after slaughter and from there into cartons. The process can be completed within 40 minutes. Lowe Walker started trials of the technique at its Hawera plant in 1991, and was followed by Wallford Meats at Waitoa. Hot boning, which eliminates the need for hanging or chilling, dramatically increases processing efficiency and is ideal for beef which will ultimately be ground or manufactured, but a number of tenderness and packaging issues had to be resolved before the process could be used for table cuts.

Many of the findings of the grading trials were absorbed into the revised beef classification from October 1988. Beef cattle other than bulls and manufacturing cows were now classified according to three muscling classes as well as six fat categories. It was expected that up to 12% of prime carcasses would go into muscling class 1.

Beef development initiatives were regrouping. In 1988, the Beef Council was established, on the initiative of the Board, and with support from other groups, to promote the development of the beef industry. Chris Le

Cren of Canterbury was the first chairman. Almost immediately long-time Beefplan stalwart and new Beef Council member Peter Packard set up a very active Northland-based offshoot, along with consultant Bob Thomson and, until his untimely death, Peter Taylor, the energy behind regular breakfast meetings.

Beef grading soon faced further pressure as the transition to a liberalised Japanese beef market got under way. Japan's preferences in beef were the absolute antithesis of the lean grassfed product being sent to the US. Japanese consumers would pay astronomical prices by New Zealand standards ($225 a kg) for beef from its homegrown and heavily marbled Wagyu cattle. In descending rank of market preference, with prices set accordingly, came imported grainfed beef and then imported grassfed beef.

Japan's own grading system focussed on marbling or intramuscular fat, meat colour and fat colour. Marbling was classified in 12 categories from the best or highest ranking, a snowstorm of fat through the meat, to the least desirable with barely detectable fat. Most New Zealand beef ranked one to three on the scale. It scored equally poorly on the colour spectrum, with the predominantly yellowish fat of pasture-fed animals and typically red-brown meat colour.

Across the Tasman, the transformation of the Australian beef industry was already well underway, with significant overseas, principally Japanese, investment in new feedlot industries. Every type of cattle, from Jersey cows to 'allsorts' were being fattened but the clear preference, and the biggest money was for black cattle.

While New Zealand meat processing industry leaders had reacted cautiously to Graeme Harrison's 1988 report that Japanese beef market liberalisation would be a watershed event, farmers had their eyes on the possible prize. Satisfying the Japanese market had the potential to turn the New Zealand grading system and beef production upside down. Traditional breeds, especially Angus and Hereford, might again have their day for their better marbling potential, and older, fatter animals might once more fetch a premium.

Classification was part of Australia's full-on assault on the Japanese market. In the late 1980s it had moved away from a simple grading system similar to the US one – Prime, Choice and Select – which was enjoying huge success and customer recognition.

Australia introduced a detailed carcass description 'language' covering every combination and making it possible for complex specifications to be prepared at either the 'on hoof' or 'on hooks' stage. Though there were similarities to New Zealand's beef grading system, there were many more subdivisions, too many more in the opinion of a lot of Australian producers.

Within plants, classification authority AUSMEAT had devised chiller assessment, a similarly detailed analysis of the beef carcass in terms of marbling, meat and fat colour, (in line with Japanese standards), pH, eye muscle, and estimated lean meat yield.

In New Zealand, killing sheet information for beef and sheepmeat producers was mostly a summary of numbers by grade and price, varying according to company format. Australian producers now received a standard-

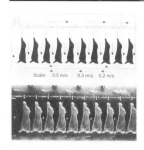

Computerised images allow MIRINZ to calculate the efficiency of a freezer. Developments like this and machine vision are paving the way for Video Image Analysis, which it is hoped will truly measure the saleable meat yield of each individual beast.

ised 'feedback' sheet detailing their performance on the above criteria, and signposting production changes which might be needed.

At this early stage, there was an implied invitation for New Zealand to take up the system. AUSMEAT's architect John Hall felt it ridiculous to have a proliferation of different description systems through the beef export world and time for everyone to speak the same 'language' in the interest of informed buyers.

The Australians also saw the advantages of mechanically measuring yield, and generous research money went in to investigating techniques such as Video Image Analysis (VIA) to give exact readings of yield for each carcass. New Zealand producers, long concerned about the fairness of payment for what they knew was widely varying yield, could now look across the Tasman at a system offering almost unlimited potential for payment according to different quality attributes.

The Five Star Beef feedlot at Wakanui, which aimed to produce marbled beef with white fat took its first black cattle in 1991, the year the Japanese beef market was deregulated. Cattle numbers in the South Island began to climb, fuelled both by the feedlot and by the swing to dairying in the region.

In the US, where fat was being trimmed from feedlot beef, leanness ruled and health consciousness was rising, McDonald's was trialling the McLean Burger, 91% lean and only half the fat and three-quarters the calories of a regular burger. McDonald's experiment was to prove a costly demonstration of the disparity between customers' calls for healthy food and their actual eating patterns, and was quietly laid to rest about 1995.

A study carried out by Brian Chrystall of MIRINZ at the time when 'cholesterol' was becoming a dirty word showed the natural health advantages of raising cattle on pasture. New Zealand beef had less fat than its British counterpart, nearly 50% less fat than Australian beef and about 60% less than the American product. As well, a higher proportion of the fat in New Zealand beef was unsaturated.

With the encouragement of the Board's North American representative Mike Muirhead, researcher Dr Dale Huffman of Auburn University prepared and trialled burger formulations using New Zealand bull and/or cow beef. Taste panels rated them highly.

Other market development for bull beef involving the Board and companies included inviting organisations such as Burger King and Arby's of Roast Beef sandwich fame to New Zealand. Burger King was to become a staunch supporter of using lean beef from New Zealand and Australia in its North American formulations, in contrast to McDonald's which uses only 'American' beef in the US.

As well, further processing uses for beef were being considered, and not just at the MIRINZ Processed Meats unit which had been investigating reformed products for some time. In 1991 the Board, through the Meat Research and Development Council (MRDC), and the Trade Development Board funded a study led by MIRINZ meat scientist Rob Archibald into 'intermediate meat products' such as chopped or seasoned beef, designed to meet the needs of food manufacturers.

For these sorts of reasons many of the dynamics of the global and New Zealand beef industry were different by the time the Beef Grading Review Committee began a new review late in 1993. Graeme Clent took over as chief production supervisor from Mick Wilkin, who retired in 1993 after 27 years with the Board.

Mick Wilkin, chief production supervisor from 1985-93, who co-ordinated the major beef yield trials in 1987.

Producer concern to move away from 'the great averaging machine' was increasing as was pressure to use newer technologies, like the pH meter in operation in Australia, to give more specific rewards to quality attributes. Such information was also available at innovative plants like AFFCO's Manawatu Beef Packers, but was not payment-linked.

Producer awareness of the role of animal management and stress in meat quality was growing, assisted by the very successful Board-funded research programme in 1993. Kevin O'Grady, whose expertise was in quality systems, had joined the Board to take over the quality manager role. This was the opportunity, some said, for the Board to again take the lead in giving quality pointers and gathering information necessary for product traceback and therefore product improvement. It was an opportunity missed, lost or blocked.

Several of the participants, including review chairman and Board member Richard Johnstone and beef consultant Bob Thomson, argued for the Board to set national standards for beef quality attributes. The counter-argument, from company superiors within the MIA, if not from industry members on the Committee, was that any such recognition should be on a company basis only, as quality was never an absolute, but represented 'fitness for purpose'. As always, Graeme Lowe was a firm voice for keeping Board involvement to a minimum.

There was a strong push from some quarters to adopt all, or the chiller assessment part, of the AUSMEAT system; critics said you would need to be a lawyer to administer it.

The final brief to the Review Committee, recorded in *Meat Board News*, reflected the effectiveness of pressure from the processing side of the industry at a time when classification was one of the Board statutory powers very much up for discussion. The review could go 'as far as the scales'; in other words, weight, conformation and fat cover as before.

The review bent over backwards to be consultative, starting with a broad invitation to farmers to say what they wanted from the beef grading system. Once the extensive range of replies was analysed, the response boiled down to: improved reward for yield, with objective measurement, preferably through new technology. Despite predictions, only 1% of carcasses had graded conformation class one according to the standards set at the last review, making it relatively meaningless for payment purposes.

From 1991 to 1993 the MRDC funded another extensive study into assessing the total saleable meat yield of cattle from cuts. The study by Alan Kirton, Roger Purchas and others found the cuts that gave the most accurate prediction were a combination of the topside, knuckle and outside cuts. However, it also found that the limiting factor was the variation in preparation of cuts because of different operators and different market specifications. Again, it pointed to the accurate and cost-effective new technology such as Video Image Analysis (VIA).

The other limiting factor was the lack of an accurate individual animal identification system which would trace the cuts back to the original carcass and farmer so appropriate rewards could be paid. Such a system was to be a long time coming.

By the time the Committee agreed on its findings Board member Richard Johnstone had lost his seat (perhaps because of a lack of success in effecting change) and fellow Waikato beef farmer and 'Farmer for Positive Change' Tim Brittain took his place.

The final report recommended a simplification of the existing system – and even clearer signals of the value of leaner carcasses. The cut-off point for 'excessive' fat levels (F) is at 17 mm rather than 24 mm and for the first time a separate category of TM identifies bull carcasses with over 3mm fat.

The main aim of the changes, as outlined in the *Meat Producer* for the third quarter 1995, was to make it easier to identify lean, well-muscled carcasses and those with excess fat, now including bulls. "The best" is now more achievable, the article said. In line with long term lobbying by producers, the boundaries between P1 and P2 muscling class had been changed so that "more prime animals producing lean high yielding hindquarter cuts will be on the top step of the payment scale". The cut-off point between P2 and P3 was also changed and lifted.

Any of the rewards for market quality characteristics like tenderness and meat colour, which producers had also asked for, would be delivered through companies. AFFCO at their Asia-focussed Manawatu Beef Packers Plant and Richmond through their Pasture Prime Asian Beef programme overseen by David Wright, both provided extensive quality information, but any hope this might be gathered to add to a national information database on the beef herd was dashed.

Producer participants in the Beef Grading Review Committee remember it as a frustrating experience because elements within the MIA successfully blocked any meaningful moves away from the existing system.

The agreed results offered lean pickings for producers, even the hoped-for objective classification through VIA was still in development. Despite formal discussions between the Board and Australian Meat and Live-Stock Corporation (AMLC) in 1993, the mood of the Australian meat industry had swung right away from sharing intellectual property for the greater good. It was also decided not to try to align new grading descriptions with AUSMEAT, now led by former AFFCO man Ian King.

Though the Hennessey probe, introduced with such high hopes some years back, was now being used in some situations, the *Meat Producer* article pointed out that in practice it still could not outperform "a well-trained grader's eye". Its frustrated inventor was also unsuccessful in an attempt to win a seat on the Board.

There was a breakthrough agreement on a new voluntary classification, designed to meet the needs of the catering industry in Asia, and also buyers for whom the description 'bull beef' conjured up an image of strong, dark meat from an older animal. Young Lean Beef (YLB) a voluntary classification, could be used for beef from animals not more than 26 months of age.

Taste tests by Arie Graafhuis and others of MIRINZ, conducted in Singapore and later in other Asian countries, showed consumers found meat from the young bulls tasty and succulent, typical of the New Zealand beef animal.

The Board adopted a 'coach' rather than captain approach to newer quality initiatives, giving no direct support to issues of national relevance such as farm quality assurance and national information and identification. The job of promoting these went to private groups like Jamie Ritchie's Hawke's Bay Farm Assurance Scheme and Bob Thomson and Chris Canning's Beef Improvement Group (BIG).

Meanwhile companies were collecting increasingly valuable information about the beef they were processing. Undoubtedly, certain suppliers known to produce top quality meat, both beef and lamb, were being rewarded by special payments. But in line with many other payments in the free market this was not being done on any transparent, nationally comparable basis. The argument from major companies like PPCS was that their own databases were big enough to provide viable information. Collective initiatives like BIG took a further knock when independent exporter Benmore, a strong supporter, went into receivership in 1997. BIG was later to be revived under Richmond's ownership.

The basic information from companies to farmers was still the killing sheet, though other more detailed information was increasingly available to chosen suppliers.

As with beef, so with lamb. Developments in grading and classification after the end of the 1980s tended to be on a company basis. PPCS, for instance, supported a Lincoln University initiative to scan live sheep for leanness.

A 1990 analysis by the Economic Service showed that the national flock was moving quite rapidly towards leanness, but not so quickly towards heavy. 22% of throughput graded PM, 23% YL and 23% YM. Two years later, in the *Meat Board News* of 15 July 1992, Economic Service director Rob Davison pointed out that taking a lamb up from PL to PM increased its price by 41%, up to PX +30%. Bull beef returns would increase by 10% with every step up the weight range. He recommended more farmers invest in scales.

New breeds selected for high productivity, pictured at Andy and Hamish Ramsden's Woodville farm in 1996. The lambs, already 24kg at two months old, and growing 300g a day, are half East Friesian, a quarter Finn and a quarter Romney. The cows are Friesian-Salers cross with Charolais calves, also a high-performance combination.

The meaty Texel, introduced in 1991.

The most recent major initiative for an amendment to national lamb grading started in the UK market when Allan Frazer was director. Concerns were relayed about variation in conformation, but these were hard to pin down and equally hard to measure. However, they were supported by Mick Wilkin who said New Zealand lamb was lacking "eye appeal". The concerns built to a level where it was considered a new 'E' grade should be introduced to recognise carcasses with an extremely full conformation.

The customer case was not clear-cut enough to persuade industry members of the review group that a new national classification should be added. At the 1992 review of lamb grading, an additional E classification was provided for in the YM, PM, PX and PH classes. Originally intended to be mandatory from October 1992, the deadline was delayed a year and eventually use of this grade became voluntary. From the producer end, *Meat Board News* of 24 September said, the E grade was seen as a means to recognise "the top 5% on the basis of superior muscling". For example, the widely perceived greater yield of Texels had been dismissed as insignificant by most processors.

Among those who believed there was a bigger picture to be reviewed, and were initiating substantial variations to the classification system, was Craig Hickson of the aptly-named Progressive Meats Ltd, who had transferred his customer-focussed innovations from the Board to his own processing plant in Hastings in 1980. With Progressive, in association with the Heavy Lambs Trust, Craig Hickson used incentives to cajole producers into meeting all sorts of quality specifications and now operates his own quality audit system.

He introduced the 'scattergram' as a more graphic means to show farmers how close the total line of sheep supplied was coming to the target weights, along with a number of other incentives to produce more specifically to time and to quality both of meat and pelt. More recently Progressive (now also with businesses in Feilding and Gisborne) has abandoned the use of Board classifications as a payment system and pays on the basis of simple target market specifications such as Mediterranean, France, North America.

The scattergram was later copied by many others, including Fortex. In line with its self-proclaimed role as industry innovators, Fortex commissioned extensive in-plant yield trials aimed at supporting a classification/ payment grid providing more steps than the official Board version and more possibilities for scaled payment according to precise quality and yield.

More than ever before, as the 1990s began, lamb producers had a wide range of market niches to aim for and a growing list of different specifications. The days when there was one perfect lamb type to aim for were long gone. Price signals from Britain and, especially Germany, made it clear consumers would pay high prices for lamb. And opportunities for lamb in the giant US market were growing as domestic production declined.

At the same time, as Board CEO Warwick Bishop highlighted in the 1993 strategic plan, changes in land use had greatly reduced the available area for meat production. It added up to producing more from less and farming more intensively: more lambs per breeding ewe and per hectare of available land.   Of the breeds released in 1990, the prolific Finn was to prove most popular. And the productivity of the national flock was beginning to accelerate rapidly.

From 1995, ultrasound scanning was increasingly used to identify ewes bearing twins and triplets. There was a mindset change. Once twins, and certainly triplets, were something to be avoided, now the push was to lift the average lambing percentage, getting more lambs, better mothered and faster growing. This time the change was largely driven through the schedule and by individual companies. The direction though, was strongly supported by the Board through the Meat Research and Development Council and Sheep Research Council, with projects like the major survey on reproductive wastage and '200 by 2000' initiative to lift lambing percentages towards 200% by the new millennium.

The Oxford Down, another large lean breed introduced in 1991, but proving much less popular.

The proof of the changes driven through classification and the schedule can be seen in changes to the composition of the national flock. In 1972 25.6 million lambs were processed, in 1997 the figure was 25.3 million. But, as Economic Service director Rob Davison points out, significant productivity improvements have been achieved over the years. In 1972 64.4% of lambs processed graded P (almost all PM) and 32.4% graded Y (mostly YL). The 1996-97 production was a mirror of this with 56.9% grading Y and 32.1% in the P grades. YM, accounting for 34% of the kill, was the predominant grade; in 1971-72 it was PM with 41.5%. Some processors are being presented with lambs that are too lean, or even devoid of fat.

Over 25 years, the average carcass weight is 17.3% heavier at 15.94 kg. This means shipping weights have stayed fairly constant, although there has been a huge increase in cut and boneless product with less than 30% (compared to nearly 87%) exported as carcasses.

Since 1971-72, the average beef carcass weight has increased by nearly 28%. This has been due in part to the use of growth promotants but mostly to more intensive production systems. Beef cattle numbers have risen and fallen back to levels similar to 25 years ago, but the dairy herd has grown by 30% and export beef tonnages are 51% higher.

Officially, the sheepmeat classification system was last revised in 1992 and the beef classification system in 1996. A great deal more description and quality information is being generated and in many cases passed back to producers, but it is being done on a company basis.

Both Waitaki and industry newcomer Challenge attempted to boost the available number of large lean lambs by appealing directly to farmers' back pockets. When Waitaki offered $25 a head – twice the schedule price for an equivalent 18-25 kg lamb – for the WX lamb they were deluged with suppliers, many of whom preferred to ignore the fine print that required them to sign a contract and supply on the shoulder of the season. Challenge, newcomers to the business, were even less well equipped to manage the marketing of all the additional shoulders and flaps acquired along with the cuts they needed for their branded products. There was no surprise when these schemes later folded, victims of their own popularity with farmers, as much as anything.

Waitaki   NZR Times

Registered at P.O.H.Q. as a magazine   No. 24 August 1985

50,000 WX lambs needed in '85-86 with supply over 12 months

Prolific Finn lambs. The Finn was the new breed that really took off, its prolificacy helping to give a substantial lift to the average national lambing percentage.

In the 1997 legislation the Meat Board's responsibility for quality was carefully circumscribed and it was to be in consultation with the wider meat industry. From the start of the 1999-2000 season, classification for both beef and sheepmeat will be voluntary, so companies will have freedom to develop their own specifications for supplying farmers to meet.

The Meat Board-administered classification system has been an important benchmark reference just as the schedule itself is an important benchmark for the increasing number of alternative payment systems, such as contracts, which have developed between individual producers and the companies they supply.

There's a sad irony in the fact that it was the classification system which created friction between the Board and the new Minister of Agriculture (and enthusiastic part-time beef farmer) Lockwood Smith, after a dispute over the classification of meat from his prized Belgian Blue heifer as L – the leanest grade, usually destined for manufacturing. And there was further irony in the fact that the Board-audited description system took the blame when the major point of contention – the low price for ultra-lean meat – was a company issue.

Even those who criticise other aspects of the Meat Board's activities almost universally praise the soundness and integrity of the classification system and the judgement and skills of the people who administer and audit it. It is internationally understood and valued to the extent that some competitors have shamelessly tried to reproduce it. It delivers what it promises, consistently and repeatedly. Customers – even the super-critical French – value it highly.

THE FORTEX FORMULA
YIELD GRADING GRID
A BETTER SYSTEM FOR REWARDING FARMERS

This overlay is for use with your Fortex Scattergram on your stock management report and with the Fortex Yield-Based Payment Schedule published weekly in newspapers throughout the South Island.

Place it over your **Scattergram** to see how to aim for best returns next time you draft.

Place it over the current **Yield-Based Payment Schedule** to see the latest prices being offered in the various cutting families.

GR Equiv						
	ALPHA	LO2	MO1	FXO2	FXO1	FXO
	BETA	LP2	LP1	MP1	FXP2	FXP1	FXP
		IL	IM	IX2	IX1	IX

9 10 11 12 13 14 15 16 17 18 19 20 21 22 23 24 25 26 27 28
WT Kilos

Lay this sheet over your Fortex Scattergram or the Yield-Based Schedule in the Fortex newspaper ads. Match up this corner of the diagram to obtain accurate figures.

This information will help you with your farm management decisions and quality improvement.

FORTEX GROUP

GOING TO MARKET, FOR FARMERS

The Fortex Formula was an attempt to pay farmers on the basis of meat yield.

No Midas Touch
1987-90

"Simply because of the opportunity to have a restructuring, the potential was there to create a farmer-owned structure which would have effectively controlled the ownership of the industry, without legislation. Because of inter-company rivalries and a lack of political will to do those things, it didn't happen." Jim Thomson.

Some farmers were scathing in their condemnation of the Freesia shareholding in Waitaki. In their view the company was moribund and should have been left to collapse under the burden of its debts. In 1990, with the benefit of hindsight, Electoral Committee member Lindsay Malcolm described the investment as "ill timed and strategically bad". It was overpriced and it allowed the corporate shareholders to extricate themselves with honour, preventing the natural rationalisation that would have followed a Waitaki receivership.

The Freesia directors were aware that Waitaki's financial position had deteriorated as the negotiations progressed because of some ill-considered foreign exchange transactions, but the outcome was far worse than they anticipated. The early forecasts of a profit of more than $20 million for the 1987 year had declined to a shaky $5 million by the time the deal was signed. This eventually became a loss of some $50 million by the end of the financial year.

There was also some disagreement within Freesia about the decision to invest. Farquhar McKenzie and John Holdsworth had resigned and been replaced by Norman Geary, ex-Air New Zealand and managing director of Mount Cook, and David Spence, ex-CFM and investment banker. Geary in particular was to exert considerable strategic influence over the future development of Freesia.

Norman Geary, who took over as Freesia chairman in 1987, pictured in Japan during a North Asia review.

The partners in Garway were well aware that there was more to be done and a restructuring task force was established. Consultants, McKinsey & Co were commissioned to analyse the state of the industry and review the options. As earlier consultants had, they concluded the industry suffered from an imbalance between available processing capacity and declining stock numbers.

The answer was further rationalisation through the closure of nine North Island and six South Island plants, or 45 out of the total of 155 sheep and cattle chains. The focus was on the South Island where it was estimated only 77% of the sheep killing capacity was being used.

The Garway Report was sent to the Prime Minister David Lange, Agriculture Minister Colin Moyle and other ministers, in part to get politicians to recognise that the industry was in a parlous financial state and also in a forlorn attempt to generate some support for the anticipated high costs of restructuring. In the new age of 'Rogernomics' it was not surprising the Government's response was that the corporates should find commercial

David Spence.

Bernie Knowles completed the Freesia Board lineup.

Pat Goodman, chairman of Goodman Fielder Wattie (GFW) which by 1986 had increased its holdings in Waitaki to 70%. Fletcher Challenge (FCL) and GFW as 'the corporates' attracted much farmer scorn when their meat industry investments turned to loss-making dust. Brierley Investments, the other major corporate in the meat business, did not get involved with producers and largely escaped the opprobrium – and managed to exit with profitability intact when it eventually sold to ANZCO.

solutions to commercial problems.

The immediate answer was for the company to negotiate closures with the costs being shared among the parties. Waitaki and Freesia discussed the issues with both Alliance and PPCS as part of a wider plan to develop the marketing proposals, but Alliance was having its own problems in sorting out its 1987 C S Stevens acquisition. In mid-1988 PPCS negotiated to buy the Marlborough and Finegand plants from Waitaki as well as contributing to the closure of Islington and Burnside and their retention on the understanding that they would not be used for sheep or beef slaughter operations. In a separate but related move, Challenge Meats (the old SFM) merged with Waitaki, with Fletcher Challenge providing $100 million of subordinated debt to assist the deal.

Michael Turner reported in the *National Business Review* on 20 December 1991 that Challenge Meats had recorded a loss of $31 million in 1987 and "FCL, admitting failure, had to write off another $65 million when selling the business to Waitaki in mid-1988. FCL got no cash out, instead giving Waitaki a $100 million subordinated loan..."

The chairmen of the two major corporates – Pat Goodman of GFW and Hugh Fletcher of FCL – announced the deal and advised both companies would be making an orderly exit from the industry. Hugh Fletcher had become somewhat disillusioned with the meat industry, particularly the procurement side. As he said, he would never consider building a pulp and paper plant without controlling the source of the raw material.

So Freesia was associated with two major corporates, both relative newcomers to the industry with little knowledge or experience of its politics and hidden agendas. The three were lumped together by the media and the companies as the 'corporates' and were always first to take the heat from the companies or their bankers in any financial readjustment.

The transaction did, however, put two big corporates with substantial financial resources in control at Waitaki and those resources were going to be needed as the procurement war continued unabated. Waitaki's result in 1988 was an unparalleled loss of $97 million and the company and its major shareholders came under considerable pressure from its syndicate of 18 national and international banks. Further action was necessary.

The first requirement was to ensure Waitaki was financed for the 1988-89 season. In order to satisfy the banks the shareholders were required to provide some evidence of their support for the company. This involved the negotiation of a Shareholders' Agreement for Facility Stabilisation with the banks, which included agreement for a short-term trade factoring arrangement to finance Waitaki's receivables. Factoring involved buying the company's receivables at a discount and holding them until payment was received in accordance with the sale terms. This provided a faster cash flow to the company.

FCL, GFW and Freesia provided the equity for the establishment of a trade finance company, initially called Spike Finance but later formalised as Waitaki Trade Finance, which operated for most of the 1988-89 season. The corporates also undertook to develop acceptable commercial rationalisation plans for Waitaki in relation to the other operators.

Some sweeping plans to rationalise the processing capacity in the North Island were developed by former National MP, Barry Brill of GFW, which involved the possibility of Waitaki making uninvited, surreptitious moves on Richmond with some assistance from AFFCO. However none of these came to pass.

Freesia staff: Trevor Miles, manager of finance and investments, and Mick Calder, chief executive.

Meanwhile, Fletcher Challenge was convinced the meat industry structure was inappropriate and the future lay in restructuring along the lines of the dairy industry. Driven by Michael Andrews who headed the primary industry sector of FCL, and later became managing director of the company, the case was made for the formation of a national pooling arrangement, which harked back to earlier Board proposals. Also suggested was the separation of the slaughter and processing operations from the marketing and distribution.

The general view was that this was a 'king hit' solution that would require co-operation from most of the companies in an industry in the throes of a procurement battle and not renowned for long-term mutual consideration. The industry view, via the MIA, was that rationalisation was needed but none of them wanted to make the first move.

Trevor Miles had joined Mick Calder at Freesia and they set about developing the Freesia restructuring plan in this new environment. The plan centred on Freesia gaining majority ownership of Waitaki. The corporates had also indicated that farmers were the 'natural owners' of meat processing facilities. The Freesia Plan involved the transfer of ownership of the shares in Waitaki from GFW and FCL to Freesia (at a nominal value based on the wish of GFW and FCL to exit the industry with dignity), but with some subordinated funding being maintained.

Subsequently Waitaki's assets would be transferred to farmer-owned companies in the North Island (AFFCO and Richmond) and South Island (Alliance), with possible side arrangements for particular plants. Rationalisation of the capacity in each island would then be the responsibility of the farmer-owned companies negotiating with other operators to best advantage. There were also proposals for the co-ordination of marketing through a central structure controlled by the farmer-owned companies.

To implement the plan an agreement was signed by FCL, GFW and Freesia providing for a "substantial reorganisation of the meat industry" and noting that "they will all support an attempt to expedite actions to implement such reorganisation". In addition, Waitaki had initially agreed to establish a restructuring committee to work with Freesia to implement the proposals.

The funding arrangements provided for some assets to be sold to finance the plan. As an alternative there was a proposal for a government guarantee, but little conviction that it would be considered favourably.

Another facet of the plan was to ensure the rationalisation arrangements contemplated were not jeopardised by falling foul of the Commerce Commission. The Board and Freesia sought relief by way of a Statement of Economic Policy from the Government to the Commission under the terms of Section 26 of the Commerce Act.

AFFCO's Max Toy, who doubled the number of plants under his control from six to 12 in 1990, when his company took over Waitaki's North Island assets. Two of the plants taken over, Waingawa and Longburn, were closed and would never operate again.

The statement issued on 22 September 1989, and signed by the Minister of Commerce David Butcher, indicated the Government supported the rationalisation process to reduce processing capacity, and that it was in the public interest for this to be achieved as rapidly as possible. It requested the Commission take into account the public benefit of achieving rationalisation of the industry as soon as practical. This was the only time that a Section 26 Statement has been issued by the Government. It certainly assisted in ensuring the smooth progress of the Waitaki restructuring process.

The directors of Waitaki decided they could not allow one of its shareholders, Freesia, to manage any restructuring of the company. They believed the company should devise and manage any reorganisation, but in conjunction with the major shareholders and the banks. In their view the company's South Island operations were improving and therefore they did not fully accept the need for their reorganisation or rationalisation.

The North Island operations were certainly at risk and they initiated discussions with the other operators for the disposal of assets and an associated closure programme. Jardens acted for Waitaki and Southpac advised AFFCO and Richmond. Richmond later decided that it would not participate in the ownership restructuring, but would be prepared to contribute to any closure programme.

As the North Island negotiations progressed, the major corporates continued to push, with the encouragement of the banks, for an exit strategy involving the divestment of the South Island operations as well.

The resulting strategy was for AFFCO, led by Max Toy as CEO, to acquire Waitaki's North Island processing assets and for Alliance, under Sandy Murdoch, to take over Waitaki and the balance of its operations in the South Island. The plan was formulated so it would not trigger a clause in a previous agreement that gave PPCS first option to buy any of Waitaki's South Island plants offered for sale.

Barney Sundstrum led the Waitaki team in negotiating the sale of its North Island plants for a 25% shareholding in AFFCO and two directors on the AFFCO Board. However, to assist in the funding the banks required that

The Waitaki management team: from left Mark Russell, secretary, Philip Galvin, treasurer, Richard Grant, finance manager, Tim Ritchie, operations manager, and Barney Sundstrum, managing director.

50% of FCL's subordinated debt be transferred to AFFCO in return for one director – Phil Pritchard. The AFFCO preference shares held by Freesia were to be converted to a loan but Freesia was to retain two directors – Owen Pierce and Norman Geary.

AFFCO's board was now increased to 17 directors and the banks insisted that a financial adviser (David Dorrington of Price Waterhouse) should also be present. It was an unwieldy structure at the best of times.

The AFFCO arrangement was finally settled late in 1989. But with AFFCO still in poor financial shape the Freesia directors and its appointees on the AFFCO board were nervous of the outcome. They considered early action was necessary to restructure the management and direction of the organisation and rationalisation of capacity should begin as soon as possible.

The real complexities arose with the Alliance negotiations as its CEO Sandy Murdoch, who had a reputation for going to the brink then backing away, insisted the company deal with only one shareholder and not the three corporates individually.

For its part GFW did not want to be directly involved with any continuing investment in the industry. This forced the corporates into an unlikely coalition called Freesia Meat Holdings (FMH), with tortuous negotiations to sort out priorities. In addition, Freesia negotiated to take up the 19% of Richmond shares held by Equus for the benefit of Waitaki and to acquire the 50% of Advanced Foods held by GFW.

Both FCL and GFW negotiated at management level but brought in directors when they wanted to exert some pressure. This caused some friction between the two of them and left Freesia, usually in the form of the consummate mediator Mervyn Barnett and his 'reasonable farmer' line to act as the go-between. Barnett was not averse to pushing hard on behalf of the producers and on one occasion, after leaving a meeting in Fletcher Challenge House, he decided Peter Egan had let the corporates off too lightly. Egan was told to go back and ask for more – which he did.

Alliance chief executive Sandy Murdoch (right) had just gone from managing four plants to nine after his company took over Waitaki's South Island assets. He is pictured at a Meat Board field day at Mount Linton with, at left, Alistair McGregor of Mount Linton and Board chairman David Frith.

Packaged lamb products under Waitaki's Taranaki brand. From product development to industrial relations, Waitaki had been an enterprising innovator whose brand is still recognised overseas today. In many ways, it was a good buy for the producer.

Unfortunately the subsequent deal signed by Michael Andrews was vetoed the next day by Hugh Fletcher. This resulted in Mervyn Barnett insisting that all future documentation with FCL be signed first by Fletcher.

To add to the complications facing Freesia, Fortex decided to step up the pace of its five-year strategic plan. Showing a sublime indifference to concerns about over-capacity, it wanted to expand its processing operations into the Otago area by building a new plant at Silverstream – new capacity but, as its directors argued, it was "the right sort of capacity".

Freesia believed it could not continue to hold shares in Fortex when it had been negotiating with Alliance. Also, while the Fortex proposal was logical from its viewpoint it compromised Freesia's advocacy for reductions in capacity. As Jim Thomson later commented, Fortex was "willing to accept the funding, but reluctant to allow any input into policy. I think we were very fortunate that the funding arrangement was terminated when it was."

Freesia negotiated to sell its shares at around $1.35 per share at the end of 1989 and was subsequently criticised by some farmers for accepting a relatively low price compared with the values recorded when Fortex was later floated on the Stock Exchange. Eventually Freesia could at least say that it got its money back.

Alliance also insisted on a number of concessions from the corporates, including some additional capital ($24 million from FCL and $6 million from GFW) to enable Alliance to buy out the Waitaki minority shareholders. There was also an indemnity arrangement, to provide against the possibility of 'black holes' in the Waitaki operation that were not identified during the due diligence process. All of this had to be organised in a way that preserved the Alliance co-operative status. And it was achieved in only two or three legal documents.

On the other side, the FMH transaction involved the three corporates, and a chart of the process drawn up by lawyer Rob McInnes from Rudd Watts & Stone looked like a computer wiring diagram as it covered 17 different financial transactions and 52 legal documents. It got so complex that, at one stage, Peter Egan was one of the authorised signatories on both sides of the transaction.

The Alliance agreements were finalised in March 1990. Alliance took over Waitaki and its South Island plants plus the 25% shareholding in AFFCO. FMH as the corporate shareholder gained 37% of Alliance shares, with the right to appoint three directors. These directors were Norman Geary and Mick Calder for Freesia and Jeff Jackson representing the FCL interests. Phil Pritchard took over early in 1991 when Jackson was appointed chief executive of AFFCO.

Alliance was in a reasonably sound financial position and expected to consolidate its position after undertaking some capacity rationalisation and, because of the spread of works it now owned, it could negotiate from a position of strength. Sandy Murdoch, chief executive of Alliance, reportedly intended to make the most of the advantages resulting from the takeover. He saw the proper future form of the industry as 'convergence' into an oligopoly – a few operators, all large enough to have the critical mass to negotiate freight rates and to commit market resources.

The industry was reaching the nirvana sought by many previous leaders and was finally ready to settle down to a prosperous future. Or was it?

A Shift in Work
1987-97

"We started out to have a flexible and multi-skilled workforce. Each worker signed an individual contract, based on the current award… (we) started with a mix of experienced meat workers, semi-skilled workers from other industries, and people chosen for qualities such as ability to work with a team. Our aim is to give everyone at least three major skills. When necessary – such as when there are absentees – they can be assigned to other work around the plant… I'm all for worker participation. People have so many good ideas." Robin Reid, general manager, Weddel Feilding, in Meat Producer *third quarter 1992.*

Fortex's compact new plant at Seafield near Ashburton was built with a single sheep and lamb chain, using the latest inverted dressing technology. Graeme Thompson intended to make it at least twice as productive with shift work. He had already established shifts in the associated cutting plant ahead of the nationwide agreement, gaining an exemption from the main Award. The workers at Seafield, where a deer slaughtering plant had been operating since 1982, were members of the 'related trade' branch rather than the Meat Workers' Union.

Initial discussions with the union's Jack Scott went nowhere and little further progress was made when Roger Middlemass took over. As Graeme Thompson tells it in his unpublished memoir: "I decided to bring the whole issue to a head, run the gauntlet and start the shift work without any agreement, using the existing shift agreement in the cutting room as a document suitable for extension across the slaughter floor."

In some ways it was Oringi replayed. Fortex recruited 45 new workers from the Ashburton area, which gave enthusiastic support. The workers had to fight their way through a 200-strong picket, many of whom, Thompson later discovered, had been released on pay by rival companies. Most of the workers crossed the lines under the eye of the media. Shortly afterwards, Labour Court Judge Goddard ruled the work practices illegal, giving the parties four weeks to return to him with an agreement.

According to Anne Knowles, in effect this meant: "If you want to slaughter on shifts, you've got to reach agreement with the unions. That single action got Fortex at the top of a slippery slope. They had to put in an arrangement that guaranteed income regardless of what the weather was going to do and the season was going to do, and they also paid an enormous premium to get the agreement." The rest of the industry, determined to avoid any guarantee of a full season's work, agreed that Fortex and the union should have their own separate agreement.

The deal ultimately worked out included acceptance of the union's offer to compress four days' work into three 11-hour days – for five days' pay. Included among the benefits was a guarantee of $2^{1}/_{2}$ days work year round, five weeks' holiday, medical insurance and superannuation.

It was, as many on the union side privately acknowledged, a steal – a jump in wages and conditions so large it attracted criticism from other MIA members

Jack Scott, national secretary of the Meat Workers' Union during the period when Fortex negotiated its slaughter shift agreement.

Les Tubman shows farmers computerised skid identification during one of the regular information tours at Fortex Silverstream. The Maitland Discussion Group members were amazed to find their guide was a union delegate, working as part of the management team.

and politicians like Ruth Richardson and local MP Jenny Shipley. It also proved spectacularly effective. In his next negotiations, Thompson and the unions hammered out a four-shift deal which saw the plant used round the clock, cementing at the same time a new, more collaborative union-management relationship.

The Fortex agreement was the beginning of the end of the 'chain' as a meaningful unit for plant productivity comparisons. Over a million lambs were processed at Seafield on one chain in a season. To achieve that throughput by conventional means would have needed at least three chains.

Graeme Thompson had paid highly for a competitive advantage that would not last long, but it gave him a national profile as a successful innovator. However, he had achieved his shift agreement under a different award, which made him separate from the rest of the industry.

Following the Labour Relations Act of 1987 the MIA worked hard, according to Anne Knowles, "to get everybody to see there could be only one contract covering people. Was it going to be this useless national arrangement that only catered for a very small part of the terms and conditions of employment? Or was it going to be something much more meaningful that could incorporate not only hours of work, but what people actually got paid, and what they actually did."

Jack Scott of the union, meanwhile, warned in *Meat News* of 19 October 1987: "Workers need the national award for protection because it is enforceable in the courts. Without it, employers would be able to dictate lower wages, no holidays and no sick leave to their workers, and workers would be powerless to retaliate."

During the 1987-88 season, the employers' aim was to remove Clause 13, which allowed second-tier bargaining, from the Award. With the strong prospect of strike action, it took some selling to the meat industry executive. But again solidarity delivered results, and the very diverse employer group developed a new mindset and collective strength.

It was not until August 1988 that the Award increase was agreed without Clause 13 and, in keeping with industry policy, without backdating. The unions had missed a season of wage increases and the employers had positioned themselves strongly. Over the next two years, Anne Knowles was one of a small group who worked with the then opposition National Party to formulate what became the Employment Contracts Act.

The new plants which proliferated from 1987 onwards began to negotiate the shift agreements that made small into efficient. The change was not without strife. For example, South Pacific Meats at Morrinsville had a particularly torrid time introducing its second shift.

The most trouble-plagued of the big older plants were closing down, among them Shortland (Auckland) where mutton and lamb processing had ceased in 1982, Islington (Christchurch), Burnside (Dunedin), both in 1988, and Waingawa (Masterton) in 1989.

The whole employment environment was loosening up. Mike Brooks, who worked with the Retailers Federation before he took over industrial responsibilities at the MIA, after Anne Knowles left to join the Employers' Federation, says: "Once Sunday trading came in about 1990, it was obvious seven-day work would go across the board". Chinks were appearing in other rigid demarcations and new relationships were being developed.

Not long after John Prendergast became Weddel's managing director he faced problems with Westfield, another Auckland plant. Prendergast says the "big rambling early 1900s site" was plagued by absenteeism. As prospects for beef looked good, the company decided to close only the sheep operation. A 10-week strike ensued. Negotiations over redundancy were conducted with Ken Douglas of the Council of Trade Unions, and eventually settled in accordance with the company's first offer.

"I got to know Ken Douglas very well at that time and developed a healthy respect for his strategic work for the unions," John Prendergast recalls. "We always had very open discussions and I think he helped shape my attitude to unions quite considerably, that we could work with them and involve them."

Also notable was the fact that the Gisborne Refrigerating Company at Kaiti did not come out in support of their colleagues at Westfield. Unfortunately the stand-alone beef operation didn't prove viable and was closed a year later in 1989.

As part of its 'de-merger' from Weddel Crown, Weddel New Zealand had taken over the disused plant at Feilding, which had not operated since failure to reach agreement with workers in 1984. A new, state-of-the-art plant was built on the site, and a new employment approach was taken. "We pre-empted the Employment Contracts Act," John Prendergast recalls. "All the workers went through a very sophisticated interview system. How and why they wanted to work, because they were not necessarily from a meat industry background. We wanted the right people for the introduction of Total Quality Management." However, good relations were established with the Meat Workers' Union, which was employed as bargaining agent. As a sign of good faith, and in expectation of no theft, workers were allowed to park their cars within the perimeter fence.

The action now shifted to the South Island. Almost as soon as the legal documents had been signed and sealed with Alliance's 1990 takeover of Waitaki the enlarged company was hit by a debilitating strike over redundancy compensa-

Leading from the top – Weddel NZ chief executive John Prendergast, seated at left and general manager livestock and public relations, Munro McLennan at right. Standing is the general manager, marketing, Duncan Evans. John Prendergast told the Meat Producer: *"We've moved away from the old autocratic confrontational style to a consultative one. It's not a consensus style, however. I still make decisions."*

"Whipping the guts out of 3200 sheep or 400 cattle a day is filthy, soul-destroying, boring and dangerous. Freezing workers suffer from repetitive strain injuries, nasty cuts and infections diseases such as brucellosis and ringworm. The work is production-motivated and profit-driven. And yet the companionship between the men and women who work on the chain is 'mighty'."
Auckland Freezing Workers Union president Frank Barnard (left) and secretary Graham Cooke summed up the meat workers' lot for Meat Producer *editor Anita Busby in 1988.*

tion, despite assurances no jobs would be lost.

Following the company rationalisations of previous years, and with rumours of more to come, the unions were seeking a national redundancy agreement. To further their claims, they had imposed loadout bans on all plants where such agreement did not exist. Under the Labour Relations Act, strike action was lawful for unions seeking redundancy compensation.

AFFCO, the other partner to the Waitaki deal, had anticipated the problem and reached agreement with the unions as part of the North Island settlement. Loadout bans there were lifted after Ken Douglas intervened, even though no other company entered an agreement.

The strike, affecting all nine of the Alliance plants, started in mid-March and dragged on for seven weeks. Management decided on a tough approach rather than conceding, but this was seen in some quarters as no longer appropriate, and Tony Forde left the company not long after the strike was resolved.

The Employment Contracts Act of 1991 (ECA) represented a watershed in industrial relations. It swept away the structure of awards and arbitration and put the employment relationship on the same basis as any other commercial contract. It also encouraged direct negotiations between employer and worker, removing the special status of the union as a bargaining agent. The Freedom of Association clause allowed people to choose which, if any, union they wanted to belong to. One of the most significant changes was the removal of ownership of work, defusing all demarcation disputes at one stroke.

In some respects, however, the ECA only clarified and codified what was already underway. Both unions and employers had seen the writing on the wall, even if the message was different. The employers' hand was on the pen, their view was in the ascendancy, perfectly fitting the aspirations of the National Government elected in 1990.

The unions recognised the need to regroup and find new strategies in the face of new realities. The most powerful force, in Roger Middlemass' view, was rising unemployment. Anne Knowles believes credit should also go to the effort during the previous past decade to make it clear to all parties that change had to happen.

There was no thunderclap when the ECA came into force on 15 May, the day before the National Meat Workers' Award expired. "It was uncannily quiet… like, what happens next?" reflects Mike Brooks. His industrial relations role at the MIA is a much lower profile one focussing on human resource issues like health and safety. Frontline advocacy is now an individual company responsibility.

The ECA provided for all current terms and conditions to roll over until new negotiations began. The Meat Workers' Union approached the MIA asking for a rollover. The employers, however, had been working towards this moment and had company agreements and plant contracts drafted and ready to go. They wanted separate plant agreements to recognise individual circumstances and conditions and reduce the union's ability to have company-wide strikes.

Trevor Arnold, representing Richmond, recalls being a lone voice for letting the dust settle before making any new moves, at a pre-legislation meeting of the MIA industrial committee. "I said the industry's been set up to pave the way. The Meat Workers' Union have come to us and want to roll it over, let's just roll it over. All the companies around the table, except Lowe Walker, said no, this is a grand opportunity to sort the unions out. We were outvoted. But we all agreed about separate plant contracts."

The irony is that the only two companies which ended up then, or shortly thereafter, with separate plant contracts were Richmond, after a battle, and Lowe Walker, for tax purposes already organised into separate companies which could each negotiate a contract.

Richmond literally went public as part of its push for separate plant agreements, publishing an open letter to its employees in the Napier *Daily Telegraph,* 11 September, 1991.

Four of its nine plants, including the newly acquired export-upgraded former Otaki abattoir which had previously suffered continuous disruption, had already signed separate plant agreements. Richmond pointed out that many of its competitors already had plant agreements while *none* had signed company agreements.

The real opportunities for new contracts came with new and smaller plants. As Anne Knowles points out, there are different dynamics with a smaller and self-contained workforce, as there are when the work is not so seasonal.

Smaller plants like Waitotara, and newly established King Country Lamb were most active in pushing for shift work. Passively or sometimes aggressively anti-union, many of these smaller plants also preferred to recruit staff without industry experience or industrial relations histories, and train them to the company culture.

It was a much greater challenge to change the culture of an existing business with 3500 workers at five locations, but Weddel tackled it. After Prime Minister Jim Bolger officially opened the rebuilt Weddel Feilding plant in 1991, workers joined invited guests and head office managers at a sit-down lunch where personal place-cards ensured a mix of people at each table. It was a symbolic occasion.

Weddel's move towards arguably the most radical change in workplace relationships had begun before the ECA. Its 'TCS' or Total Customer Service was a house name for Total Quality Management. This involved the concepts of worker participation, team-building and problem-solving across hierarchies and boundaries. Based on the Deming philosophy of individual responsibility for quality, and continual improvement, TCS involved all 14 unions at the various workplaces. The company's core collective contract was regarded as a trend-setter.

The most concentrated activities took place at the giant Tomoana plant, where Lynne Elmes, general manager workplace development, and one of the scheme's architects, was based. But with John Prendergast leading by example, Weddel attempted to apply the concepts across all of its plants. Less than two years after it started, the million-dollar investment in TCS had led to a definite culture change and was paying off with big reductions in accidents, absenteeism, contamination and the cost of rework.

New work patterns were cutting costs in other companies as well. When, in 1993, Booz Allen & Hamilton compared local beef plants with those in Australia, the US and Argentina, New Zealand 'hot boning' plants (small, new, and mainly operated by Lowe Walker) topped the efficiency table on many counts, with traditional 'cool boning' plants not far behind. This was a major achievement as they were being measured against the mammoth US plants with massive economies of scale and year-round supply of standard-sized ex-feedlot cattle. It was also a complete turnaround from the 1970s when John Foster said high process-

Waitotara, one of the new breed of small processing companies which set different employment rules. At left chairman Rod Pearce with general manager Scott Weir.

Taking responsibility for quality, Weddel Kaiti lamb slaughterman, Rene Farmer, measures a sample of his own work. One of the outcomes of the TCS culture change was greatly improved communication and understanding of the overall business. Weddel Tomoana byproducts manager Andrew Watt said; "Before we started, surveys in all our plants showed people had very little idea of how their job fitted in. At least one person had been working for 35 years without seeing what other sections did."

ing costs almost justified shipping stock to Australia for slaughter.

The world meat industry looked at New Zealand with new eyes. Giant US company IBP, invited here by Richmond, came, looked and decided not to buy in New Zealand but, as Trevor Arnold recalls, described their ideal as a beef plant in Australia "with New Zealand management".

Labour flexibility was one of the major innovations in many contracts. The new contracts at King Country Lamb, a non-union plant, provided for the same workers to take turns sweeping the floor and working the slaughterboard.

Weddel pledged its workers there would be no job losses resulting from the TCS initiative. Fortex was seen as the leader in worker conditions and a number of staff were shareholders. But all the goodwill in the world could not fund redundancy payments for the workers when first Fortex (in March, to a chorus of "I told you so" from informed quarters) then Weddel (in August) went into receivership in 1994.

Some ex-Weddel workers have carried on their TCS practices to the delight of new employers, like the lamb processing team which moved on to Richmond Awatoto before that too was closed down. But no employee now enjoys the kind of conditions that ended when Fortex did.

Changed employment and economic circumstances are fully reflected in the meat industry, which still employs up to 18,000 workers, some of them for only a handful of weeks a year.

Individual contracts vary widely in their clauses and conditions. The average wage of the meat processing worker has slipped down the national averages, and the occupation's appeal as a career has diminished. The workforce is older; the job has less appeal to students and, with increasing use of plants around the year and around the clock, there are fewer opportunities. Productivity has increased. In at least one workplace, workers pay for their knives and other equipment, and are responsible for their maintenance. In a recent, 1998 finding, the Employment Court backed a meat company which fired a man who was absent for two weeks and did not respond to a request to make contact.

New work methods such as the walking beam are almost a move back to the days of the solo butcher. But the pace has lifted and the days have lengthened, with the typical shift 10 hours long. The meat processing industry is high on the list of repetitive strain injuries, a problem for employers seeking to reduce their ACC levies.

Industrial action continues but not on a national basis. In some places, innovations have been slow in coming. Only in the past year has shift work been introduced at Richmond Takapau, and the company has begun to employ on a seasonal basis to break the seniority stranglehold in some plants. There have been battles at the non-union Riverlands plants at Bulls and Eltham, and a hostile relationship with the unions exists at Taylor Preston, a mid-sized multi-species plant which, defying the drawbacks of location, operates at Ngauranga in Wellington.

Union coverage is only a small percentage of the workforce. In some plants only one or two are covered and in at least one plant union representatives are banned from the premises. Conditions can be "brutal" in plants like these, says Roger Middlemass; the Auckland-Tomoana union succeeded in having the contract at a Waikato plant declared harsh and unreasonable.

But there are still queues when jobs are advertised. Unemployment has turned the tables completely.

Meeting at the Freight Council 1989-95

"We achieved <u>huge</u> reductions, like 35% over a two or three year period, and we actually worked together, with farmers and the industry. Another victory was persuading Cool Carriers to reverse a decision not to include Napier in its calls. We really got stuck in on that. It was perhaps the first time real rigour had been applied from the New Zealand end. The partnership of Meat Board diplomacy and meat industry raw aggression was very effective." John Foster.

For the meat companies, control of shipping was a logical part of their individual marketing activities. The Board's direct involvement of industry representatives in the European shipping negotiations for the first time for the 1985-86 season was too little and too slow.

As later described by Allan Frazer to the Electoral Committee: "The Board recognises that exporters now have staff with experience in shipping matters and therefore can assist in negotiations and it is for this reason it invited company representatives to participate… The industry has always been consulted prior to any negotiations but the Board considers continuing participation by the industry in actual discussions as desirable if a united negotiating stance is to be achieved, with any subsequent benefits being passed to the exporting sector and the producer."

From the MIA perspective: "It is appropriate for those who pay for the freight to be consulted" and their contribution to negotiations put extra pressure on the shipping lines for space, and helped to bring in changes to rates including a box rate, giving incentive for more further processing. The Board had a representative on the MIA shipping committee, which continued to "provide information facilitation" to help with forward planning.

At that stage, as outlined in the *Meat Producer*'s Oct-Dec 1986 issue, the majority of New Zealand shipping was covered by contracts negotiated by the Board. The three-year contract to the UK was operated by member lines of the New Zealand Tonnage Committee (NZTC) which included Associated Container Transportation Group (ACT), Overseas Containers Ltd (OCL) and the New Zealand Line. These three lines were also part of the NZESA conference shipping to Europe and the Mediterranean. Other carriers were Compagnie Generale Maritime, Hamburg Suedamerikanische, Hapag-Lloyd, Lloyd-Triestino, Nedlloyd Lijnen, Scancarriers A/S and the Baltic Shipping Company.

Four container lines were licensed to operate the US East Coast service: Pace, Columbus, New Zealand Line and Antwerp Bulk Carriers (ABC). Three containers serviced the West Coast: Blue Star, Columbus and New Zealand Line. For the Japan/South Korea trade the members of the New Zealand Eastern Shipping Committee were Japan Lines, Mitsui OSK, Crusader Swire Container Service and the New Zealand Line.

Rates for all these routes were negotiated by the Board, which signalled in the *Meat Producer* article that a number of aspects would be actively reviewed

Gary Donaghy, Board shipping manager and secretary of the Meat Industry Freight Council.

Graham Archie of Hawke's Bay Export Cold Stores with the first trial unit load of lamb carcasses, which went from Napier on the Reefer Dolphin. *Photo: MIRINZ*

when each contract came up for renegotiation. In the case of the North American trade, this would include investigation of an alternative unitised service based on wrapped pallet-loads.

With shipping to smaller markets there were no formal arrangements, but the Board monitored the level of service and the rates being offered. The Board no longer had direct involvement in the charter trade it started during the years of ownership. The industry consortium, Meat Marketing Corporation was responsible for establishing freight rates and conditions for services to Africa, the Middle East and the USSR.

Changes in the available types of shipping paved the way for the cost saving trend to continue. The new generation of relatively small reefer ships was more than a match for the massive container ships in flexibility of service. New packaging developments meant it was possible to ship smaller 'unitised' pallets of cargo. This was an advantage when smaller shipments were involved and a distinct plus for the North American trade where port health requirements meant containers were opened at entry. One problem remaining until labour market reform was manning which continued obstinately at levels required for the older, larger ships. Also, many innovations were resisted by workers as much as they could.

The same US lines which had led the way in containerisation, were now in the forefront of diversification away from container ships. Because the conferences were completely containerised, this meant including other service providers. From 1980 onwards, the brakes went on fast-rising offshore freight costs. The shipping section, prominent in the Board's annual reports, began to record "no increase", and later even some decreases, in freight charges.

The meat industry was benefiting from the world-wide over-supply of all types of shipping.

Meat News reported in 1990 on $30 million savings in freight to North America and $21 million to Europe, with four new carriers designated.

Trials were also proceeding with the European lines and these too were opened up to palletised services from 1991 with the addition of new designated carriers. At a time when rationalisations were taking place, especially in the container trade, this meant few if any seriously interested companies were excluded.

Within New Zealand, structural change was proceeding apace, bringing in many of the reforms recommended by the PCEK report in the early eighties. Rail zone charges were restructured, increasing some costs for lamb shipments but cutting them for beef. In 1988 the Port Companies Act became law, opening up the ports to private ownership.

The Meat Industry Freight Council (MIFC) was established in 1988, with equal representation by the Board and the meat companies. It was the first of the joint decision-making committees which became the hallmark of the Frith Board's reconfiguration of the role and activities of the Board. The logic behind each structure was the same. Instead of being on the outside making a fuss, the industry was invited to come in and be accountable for decisions, which would then form a recommendation to the Board.

The MIFC met for the first time in April 1989. Representing the meat industry were Richmond CEO and MIA deputy chairman John Foster, Bruce

Martyn Saines and John Mabb of the Meat Board's London office watch the unloading of trial shipments at Sheerness.

The Meat Industry Freight Council. From left: John Miller, MIA; Graeme Arnold, Copax; Jim Thomson and David Frith, Board; John Foster, Richmond and Bruce Sloane, Weddel.

Sloane, shipping manager for Weddel, and Graeme Arnold of PPCS subsidiary company Copax. The Board was represented by chairman David Frith, CEO Jim Thomson, and Board member Norman McRae. The secretary was Gary Donaghy from the Board.

Both David Frith and John Foster look back on the MIFC years as a time of positive achievement, when new ways of negotiating were used successfully. The industry members had no qualms about upping the ante in negotiations, something that longtime European conference negotiator Alan Bott must have found quite disquieting. He would certainly have realised things had changed when David Frith, concluding a lengthy phone discussion round midnight New Zealand time, asked for Bott's home number to follow up that evening UK time.

It was no longer a discussion about increases. It was a question of savings, and not just single figure percentages. As David Frith recalls: "In the past they had always used their accounts to justify the increases. We said, we're not interested in that, we're interested in what we are going to pay."

Another change to long established practice was that all negotiations were held in New Zealand. Invitations to go to Britain were politely declined. Just to push home the point that this was a different environment, the negotiators went home without an agreement after one of the first rounds of discussion. David Frith says: "It was tactical, to some degree. But we weren't going to agree unless we had a really good deal. And they hadn't met our bottom line."

From 1987 the balances of power began to change, a trend which gathered speed during the MIFC years. The Board stranglehold on negotiation and the container companies' and conferences' tight grip on services both began to crumble as part of a wider environment of deregulation. Cost cutting was further enhanced by the deregulation taking place throughout the New Zealand economy. In the transport area, for example, there was the possibility of using more road transport. The meat industry actively added to the pressure from many quarters for port and labour market reform. The lack of reform, a Treas-

Monitoring the temperature of carcasses being loaded at Timaru. Under the Iran protocol established in 1990, the Board employed additional staff to check that carcasses were always handled at the required temperature. The protocol was negotiated after the trade to Iran lapsed over questions of guaranteeing temperature controls. The Board's area supervisors had the ultimate authority to decide whether exports could proceed. A long time part of the production supervisors' role was to keep what Joe Ryan calls a "wharf-wise" eye on anything which could affect the condition of product at ship's side prior to loading.

The Lauritzen Lines' Erikson Frost *loading the second trial of self-contained units of frozen lamb carcasses, at Bluff. MIRINZ worked with Lauritzens and their New Zealand agent McKay Shipping to develop the 'Meatpak' concept which could load units of up to 60 carcasses at one time. Strapped together with high tensile stretch cling film, they could be easily handled so reefer ships could be loaded in days rather than weeks. Photo: MIRINZ*

ury paper suggested, was costing the country $800 million.

For the first time in 1989 Air New Zealand involved meat and other export industry representatives in discussions on proposed freight increases. The MIA used the opportunity to lobby for a change in the legislation under which freight rates were approved by the Minister of Transport.

The same year, the Board and other producer boards formed the Agriculture and Horticulture Shippers' Organisation, registered under the Labour Relations Act, as a "platform to exert more control over all aspects of shipping, and in particular waterfront industrial matters". But in 1991, the Employment Contracts Act rewrote most of the rules for all industrial situations.

In 1990, the Board's production supervisors gained a new shipping role as auditors for the Iran temperature protocol. The new procedures, as the MIA pointed out, put additional requirements on all involved in on-wharf handling, including working at times in temperatures lower than -12° C. They were conditions it might have been impossible to negotiate in pre-waterfront reform days.

Costs, which had reached $450 million for 740,000 tonnes in 1986, were down to $350 million for 770,000 tonnes by the time the *Meat Producer* surveyed shipping again in 1990. "Conventional refrigerated vessels as well as container ships will carry New Zealand's meat cargo to North America from January next year. Cargo will be collected from regional ports such as New Plymouth and Napier, as well as the four main container terminals, through which product has been channelled in the past.

"The new arrangement, bringing in four new carriers for a total of nine carriers to North America, offers potential savings of up to $30 a tonne, or nearly $7 million on the 230,000 tonnes annually sent to North America.

"Companies sending meat to the US and Canada will have greater freedom to select from the designated carriers the one which provides them with the best possible deal on service and rates, to suit their operation. The agreement (for one year only) follows last year's settlement for the European trade, which cut back previous costs by $28 million over its two-year term."

The writer, shipping expert Dave McIntyre, commented that "from within the shipping industry, the perception is that the meat industry won a particularly good deal in the contract it signed with NZESA". In what was to become a pattern, the two year contract, replacing three year ones, saw a significant drop in rates the first year and a relatively small clawback the second. The contract provided differing peak and off-season rates, gave a 25% subsidy on inland transport costs from areas like Hawke's Bay and Southland, distant from container ports, and also allowed two trials of alternative shipment methods.

The pattern of opening up access to more participants, and negotiating down costs, continued through the 1990s. In effect, the trades, beginning with the North American, were opened up to all who wished to be involved. By 1992, 15,000 tonnes was being shipped outside the conferences on conference routes. The smaller ports were having their days in the sun. Lauritzens and Cool Carriers were calling at Timaru, Napier, Bluff and Dunedin.

The Board estimated that, as a result of its negotiations with the NZESA, producers had earned 65 to 70 cents more per lamb and shipping costs now made up only 20% of the wholesale price per animal in Britain. Savings of $12 million on agreements to Europe, US and Hawaii were reported in 1994, the year the MIFC began managing the arrival marketing programme to the EU, as required under the VRA agreement.

Now individual industry companies became much more involved. While the MIFC negotiated and recommended to the Board the overall freight rates, individual companies were increasingly able to negotiate within this framework for prices and services to suit them. There had been a growing clamour from larger companies like AFFCO and Alliance (which together shipped over half of NZ's meat exports) to use their size as a negotiating strength. Other companies were pooling resources to maximise best freight rates.

A Railfreight Iceliner, designed to bring carcasses at perfect temperature to the Port of Napier.

The transition was complete – and successful because of the way it had been managed. David Frith says: "I would defend very strongly the time we took to phasing (from) the Board doing all the negotiations to having an industry council, to letting the industry do it itself. We had a very nice clean transition, driven I believe by conventional shipping changes.

"We were getting smarter on the changes in international trade, and using that to our advantage, and it was the first time we had any leverage. We used it collectively, and we got significant savings."

By 1995, when removal of the shipping powers was being discussed as part of the review of the Board's role, only a framework of control really remained. 'Transport', once one of the prominent sections in the Board's annual report, was now relegated to not much more than a footnote to information about the exercise of the Board's statutory powers. Shipping similarly took a much less prominent role in the annual reports of the MIA. Now it was over to individual companies, or groupings of companies, to negotiate their freight rates directly. Some, notably Lowe Walker, publicised their successes, others kept this, like other commercial information, to themselves.

The Meat Board's remaining transport responsibility was its participation in scheduling the marketing programme as part of the quota administration, and some focus, as part of its support for quality initiatives, on trucking as a link in the meat quality chain.

Despite all the mergers and rationalisations which have taken place, many of the names listed in the 1971 annual report still ship meat from New Zealand, and choice of service is still possible. AFFCO's Ross Townshend recently noted the company had 41 different carriers for its export product.

Air freight tonnages remain modest, even if the value per tonne can be spectacular. Most of the tonnage is still destined for the hotel trade in the Pacific.

Former Board member Fred Dobbs believes a bulk air freight revolution is just around the corner. But in the meantime, a positive advantage of sea freight has emerged. A sea voyage is just enough, for chilled meat in controlled atmosphere packaging, to continue the aging process to a level of tenderness freshly processed local meat simply can't match.

Creative Tension
1990-92

"Farmers, while able people, are not necessarily in touch with all aspects of the export mix… I personally favour some representation of all the sectors on the producer boards. I want to see much stronger diversity, to give an industry perspective. At this stage it's right that farmer producers should control the boards. They are paying the levies and they have the most at stake. But I'd like to see this evolve… The next stage of our development must involve not just farmers, but all sectors, working together in putting together strategic proposals and marketing plans.

"By the end of this three year term, I'm determined to see a meat industry that knows where it's going."   Minister of Agriculture, John Falloon, in the Meat Producer, *last quarter, 1991.*

An amendment to the Meat Export Control Act, heralded in 1985, finally came in December 1989 and led to the appointment of commercially experienced Board members. Barry Dineen (Shell Oil), Jim Macaulay (National Bank), Graham Ansell (Ministry of External Relations and Trade), all current or former chief executives, and Ross Finlayson (Amalgamated Marketing) joined the Board in March 1990. They replaced John Neilson and Blue Kennedy, the outgoing government appointees, and lifted the number around the Board table to 11.

In other ways the legislative amendment shored up the existing position and direction being taken by the Board. It defined 16 functions which included promoting the development of existing and new markets, promoting the consumption of meat in general and New Zealand meat in particular, promoting access to markets and providing information on market requirements, encouraging efficiencies, and undertaking research.

The 1990 annual report stated: "The Board's purpose, as defined by statute is to maximise the return to New Zealand's meat producers. The Board seeks to do this through a strong producer ownership position in the New Zealand meat processing industry; orderly and well co-ordinated marketing of New Zealand meat, plus improved trade access; co-ordination of international promotion to develop a consistent image and greater awareness of the qualities and benefits of New Zealand meat; cost efficiencies from continuing research and development, quality control and streamlined distribution." Orderliness and co-ordination were still high on the list and the Board was entering another phase of consultation and discussion.

Jim Macaulay had just retired as chief executive of the National Bank when he joined the Board as a commercial appointee in 1990. His successor at the National Bank was John, later Sir John, Anderson, an influential figure in the meat industry throughout his banking career.

Following the theme promoted for some time by Treasury and MAF, the new Act also called for more consultation with the industry on licensing. A separate clause spelled out the Board's responsibilities in quality control and establishing grading standards. It also gave the Board responsibility for by-products. This, as the *Meat Producer* of April-June 1990 reported, was "not something that had been sought or lobbied for, so the practical implications are still being sounded out".

The revised legislation also gave the Board the powers of a natural person. As CEO Jim Thomson explained, this allowed the Board to buy or sell shares in a company without gaining the approval of two ministers, or provide capital to a subsidiary such as Freesia without written approval.

In other words, the Board could invest in the industry more directly. For example, it could set up joint ventures with companies for promotion, or establish the Meat Research and Development Council (MRDC), which was ready for launching in early 1990.

The MRDC was a major new initiative on behalf of meat producing farmers, and the beginning of a significant new level of industry co-operation in research. The MRDC, a response to the changes affecting the meat producing sector through government restructuring of science, was driven at Board level by producer representative Jim Bull.

Following the recommendations of the Science and Technology (STAC) Committee in 1988, most future science funding would be contestable. Any allocation through the Foundation for Research Science and Technology (FORST) from the diminished Public Good funding pool would have to be well argued for and its contribution towards the overall policy aims, set by the Ministry of Research Science and Technology (MORST), of increasing the economic wealth of the country, would need to be clear. It was an area where the benefits from being seen to be working together to a common industry purpose were overwhelming.

MIRINZ director Doug Wright reacted with equanimity to the idea of contestable funding, but for his organisation, as for other scientific establishments, a considerable culture shock was in store. MIRINZ's total available funding was reduced, because of lower Public Good funding, as was the certainty of access to funding from the Board and industry. MIRINZ's eventual success in gaining overseas contracts to supplement its income by as much as 40% was to cause some disquiet. When Doug Wright went on to become a science advisor with FORST, Graeme Longdell, formerly the head of the MIRINZ development engineering section, became its managing director.

Alan Royal, formerly head of MAF's Meat Division and then its Wallaceville research centre, was the first executive director of the MRDC. The MRDC, funded by producer levies paid to the Board, became the central clearing-house

Jim Bull of Hunterville moved out of the potato business and into meat, becoming one of the biggest sheep and beef farmers, and being a producer representative on the Board from 1987 to 1993. He gave a lot of impetus to the Board's new research and development strategies.

The MIRINZ Board, 1990-91, the first year of new funding arrangements through the MRDC. Standing, from left: Hamilton businessman Bill Gallagher, scientist Gordon Leary, and Doug Longdill from AFFCO. Gallagher and Longdill were new appointees to the Board. Seated: Meat Board member Gavan Herlihy, chairman and MIA chief executive Peter Blomfield, MIRINZ director Doug Wright, and secretary Lyn Frazerhurst. Photo: MIRINZ

Graham Ansell, chief executive of the Ministry of External Relations and Trade, whose previous postings included time as ambassador to Japan and as head of the New Zealand mission to the EC.

for all meat industry research funding, including MIRINZ, which had formerly been funded equally by the MIA and the Board separately. Processing industry interests had equal representation on the MIRINZ and MRDC boards through the MIA, even though, in what was to become unpalatable to levy-payers, processor money was no longer put into any research benefitting the industry generically.

In its foundation year MRDC pledged up to $12 million – almost a third of the Board's annual income from levies – to projects designed to enhance on-farm and processing productivity. It commissioned work from a range of providers including the universities and crown research institutes such as AgResearch (formerly part of MAF). Research spending priorities were set through wide industry consultation, with the Sheep Council (1989) and Beef Council (1988) set up to help identify on-farm research needs.

A significant number of Board-initiated consultative structures were in place and working effectively by the time the National Government came to power in 1990. This was acknowledged in a February 1991 letter to newly appointed Agriculture Minister John Falloon from MIA chairman Sir David Beattie, saying that since the legislation changes and new Board composition there had been improved consultation between the Board and the MIA, especially in shipping, licensing, market access and research.

But he went on to say the MIA believed it now appropriate to request the formal separation of the Board's regulatory and commercial functions, and a review of the functions and structures necessary to service the New Zealand meat industry in the most cost-effective manner. "This may be the present situation, a reoriented Meat Producers Board, a Meat Industry Board or a Meat Board." The review would include the role and functions of the MPB and MIA, and maybe also the Ministry of External Relations and Trade and MAF in relation to trade access.

Sir David cited October 1990 briefing papers from MAF to the new Government, saying all commercial activities such as Freesia, Janmark, ANZCO and DEVCO (the Lamb Company) should be separated. As he put it: "Those acting as referees and setting rules for entry into production, processing, and marketing should be separated from those actually undertaking those roles."

The strength of this sort of feeling, not always coming from the MIA side, contributed to Jim Thomson's decision to resign as chief executive of the Board in February of 1991. He recalls: "There appeared to be a continuing resentment of the Board's ability to still be a player… At best the presence of the Board was tolerated. But the impression was also created that there was a continuing effort to reduce the Board's ability to intervene or compete. The point was expressed by a number of the companies, particularly those with farmer shareholders, that the Board should be wound up. And the money that had been put into the industry should be written off and just left there because it was really the farmers' money anyhow.

"I resigned because of an awareness that my philosophies were never going to be able to be implemented through the structures that were there. There was not a political will which seemed to coincide with what I believed could have provided a better direction. And to that point at least my philosophies weren't totally shared by the Board. And unless there's that support, it just ain't going to happen."

The Producer Boards Amendment Bill aimed at reducing the statutory powers of all producer boards, was still on the table. The legislative timetable at that stage was for policy decisions to be completed in 1991 and a Bill ready for introduction in 1992.

The MIA's position was made aggressively clear in its 1991 draft strategic plan. Top of the list of key success factors: "Constrain the power of the Meat Board". In line with the revised legislative timetable, it aimed to "separate statutory powers from commercial activities of the Board by 1 October 1992; eliminate the statutory powers of the Meat Board, specifically acquisition, shipping, and market access/licensing if the former (is) not achieved."

These objectives were backed up by calls from industry leaders for the Board to separate its statutory and commercial activities. Graeme Lowe, in particular, was critical of the role of Freesia and commented to the *Hawke's Bay Herald-Tribune* on 4 October 1991 that "he was concerned at the way Freesia was a player and a referee in the industry".

Like his National predecessor Duncan McIntyre, John Falloon was an agriculture minister whose connections with the meat industry, especially in Hawke's Bay, ran deep. John Foster recalls giving the fledgling politician, then a Federated Farmers provincial president, a run-down on the evils and inefficiencies of the industry which could be detected in his thinking throughout later years.

A definite 'dry', he was among the Government members keenest to continue the deregulation drive. At the same time he wanted to inject fresh ideas to override the stalemates which had developed in the past and, with the assistance of Catherine Petrey, co-opted from MAF's policy division, he actively promoted new thinking and new perspectives.

This was a minister more likely to seize new ideas than be swayed by arguments of tradition or past practice. The MIA's message of more commercial freedom and less intervention was in tune with the Minister's thinking.

He saw the lack of co-operation between sectors as an irrational hindrance to progress, and became increasingly convinced that a new industry board structure bringing producers and processors together would strengthen the meat industry's performance offshore.

"If we simply go on being fragmented, arguing with each other, we will continue to go down in our share of the world market for meat and wool," he told Radio New Zealand on his return from visiting Europe and the Middle East in November 1991. The meat industry needs to "bury the divisions, develop trust between sectors and users of the product... following the model I suppose of the Dairy Board's joint venture companies."

Speaking to the *Meat Producer* he urged farmers to become "informed and active challengers of existing structures", which he saw as too conservative in their approach to problems. He wanted direct elections and further change in the composition of boards. For the Board, this meant a series of reviews that occupied it periodically for the next six years.

It was increasingly important for the Board to explain its evolving role at a time when this was becoming more and more complex to communicate. Unlike the further processed products and quality initiatives during the ownership period, the Board's new activities and strengths were less tangible and more

Barry Dineen, chairman and managing director of Shell Oil NZ Ltd., when he was appointed to the Board.

Brett Sangster, Board communications manager from 1987-94, pictured with one of the display boards used at field days around the country to inform farmers how the Board was investing its levy money.

difficult to explain. The commitment to consultation meant decisive action could more easily be blocked and credit for proposals diverted.

Some of its new structures, such as the Lamb Promotion Council in London, were struggling. Back home, relationships were less than comfortable with organisations like the Beef Council which wanted to expand its funding and functions and was reluctant to acknowledge the Board's backing. Through the Electoral Committee, the Meat Board was inextricably linked with the Wool Board – for better or worse – and as wool prices headed downwards it was almost always worse.

Additionally, some on the Board and in management, burned by negative criticism from the industry since the intervention years, became reluctant to highlight some of its best initiatives or even point out when the Board was involved and levy-payers' money was being used.

At the same time the policy for Board publications was to "maintain an independent editorial stance". While this allowed for wide-ranging coverage of industry issues in both the *Meat Producer* and *Meat News*, it let many legitimate opportunities to explain Board roles and activities go begging. For example, comment on valuable overseas activities such as the market access visits by David Frith was restricted for fear they would be seen as junkets. Activities like the first-ever meeting of all meat company chairmen, convened by the Board, also had little coverage.

On top of that, some of the necessary messages were not too palatable. There was the fact, for example, that farmers needed to focus their support on one company and, for the industry to remain viable, producers could not receive a disproportionate share of profits. David Frith and the Board had to walk a tightrope between acknowledging the farmer's wish for competition and encouraging new entrants in a way that would not upset the industry.

The Board was offering leadership, but the new 'facilitative' model was harder for farmers to identify with. While Federated Farmers leadership had been amongst the most enthusiastic followers of the free market line, some of its rank and file, and some outside its membership, would have welcomed a degree of intervention to ensure reasonable prices.

Farmers also took very hard the end of free access to farm advice from MAF after its restructuring. The MRDC, under Alan Royal, moved to fill this gap by setting up a nationwide network of monitor farms. These aimed to show by practical example how 'average' farmers could plan their businesses and lift their productivity, with positive spin-off for the surrounding community.

Early on, it was clear the monitor farms were a success. But the MRDC had been set up with its own logo and identity and deliberately launched at arm's length from the Board. Not surprisingly, it was a prime example of what communications manager Brett Sangster described as the 'Doughnut Effect' – sugar and glory to the external participants and invisibility for the funder at the central core. It got to the point where many farmers assumed the BNZ, in reality a minor sponsor, was the funder of the very popular farming videos paid for by the MRDC.

The extent of levy-payer ignorance of Board activities was shown in 1992 when a survey commissioned by Brett Sangster showed 40% of farmers believed the Meat Board still sold meat.

These findings prompted a decision to become much more proactive in different communication strategies and to make greater use of publications, particularly the renamed *Meat Board News*, to highlight Board structure and activities. It also gave impetus to a new strategy – holding a number of small farmer meetings around the country, logistically difficult and often attracting only a handful of people, but providing the face-to-face communication seen to be the most effective way of communicating with farmers.

Summing up the first hundred meetings, the *Meat Producer* reported that the questions most often asked were about the Board itself. "What does it do? How does it spend levy money and how is it accountable for the spending? Where does it sit with other players in the meat industry – and who are all the organisations often described only by their initials like the MIA and the MPC?"

Meanwhile possible legislative change was a constant backdrop and from 1992 onwards farmers were increasingly being asked to have informed opinions on aspects of the Board's operation and its accountability mechanisms.

In a number of less formal ways, the Board and the MIA were working together. Both recognised the need for decision-makers such as bankers to understand how the industry worked. In early 1992 they organised an 'information programme' for the media, bankers and economists, involving a two-day visit to Hawke's Bay for a briefing on issues affecting the meat industry, with tours of Lowe Walker, Weddel and Richmond.

The dynamics of the Board/industry relationship changed in 1992 with the arrival of two new chief executives. Warwick Bishop, formerly with Works Corporation, joined the Board in March, after a period of nearly a year during which David Frith had acted as both chairman and CEO. Brian Lynch took over in June, when Peter Blomfield retired after 18 years at the MIA.

With the passing of the Employment Contracts Act in 1991, the MIA had at one stroke seen its previous main focus and purpose removed. What had been a central and active role in industrial relations was reduced to a lesser advisory one. The Association was ripe for reinvention. From the start Brian Lynch made it clear he saw the MIA and the Board as separate but essentially equal contributors to a strategic forum addressing key issues for the industry.

Interviewed in the third quarter 1992 *Meat Producer,* he said he would like to see the MIA taking a more assertive role in putting industry views on things like trade access, an area in which, as a former diplomat, he had personal contacts and expertise. He saw the new directions of the MIA being closer to the Board in shipping, trade policy and market-based information. Soon the Association established its own economics section, three floors down Wool House from the Meat and Wool Boards' Economic Service.

Brian Lynch's redefinition of the role of the MIA would put further pressure on the Board to lobby, communicate and use the media effectively, often, from the Board's perspective, seizing headlines more properly its and adding to existing confusion about the roles of the two bodies.

Asked by the *Meat Producer* to comment on the claim that "it seems to suit some MIA members to paint the Meat Board as public enemy number one, or deny its share of credit for successes achieved", Brian Lynch said he accepted there had been strains in the past, but believed a better relationship now existed. "A bit of creative tension now and then isn't necessarily bad so long as it con-

Bringing the Board to the farmers. In 1992, there was a move away from large-scale Board presence at field days. Instead numerous small question-and-answer meetings were held in homes, woolsheds, cookhouses and, if fine, outdoors, in an attempt to find a more effective way to communicate with farmers. Pictured is Board member Gavan Herlihy, standing, with the general manager, production, Peter Gianotti seated at left.

Warwick Bishop, who left the practical world of Works Corporation in 1992 to immerse himself in politics as chief executive of the Board.

Ross Finlayson of Amalgamated Marketing, a pioneer of numerous markets for New Zealand meat and more recently the chairman of Animal Enterprises (Lamb XL) which brought new exotic sheep breeds to New Zealand. At the time of his appointment to the Board he was also a director of Fortex. Appointed to the Board for one year in 1990, his tenure was repeatedly extended and he finally stepped down in March 1999.

tributes to the main goal... farmer loyalty is fundamental to the success of the industry as a whole."

A year later the concept of consultation was sorely tested when both the Board and the MIA produced strategic plans. Though complementary in many areas, the targets proposed by the two sector partners diverged wildly in places.

Greater 'creative tension' was also developing between the Board and its third industry partner, Federated Farmers' Meat & Wool Section. Federated Farmers as a whole was also facing the need to redefine and reassert its role. Previously funding of the organisation had been assured through a proportion of slaughter levies collected at the same time as those for the Meat Board. However, with the passing of the Commodity Levies Act, Federated Farmers would depend on voluntary funding. It was already facing a loss of membership and criticism for lack of relevance and unwieldy structures that blocked enthusiastic newcomers, especially women.

The attitude of Federated Farmers had been made evident when its president Owen Jennings nailed his colours to the mast in *Straight Furrow* on 16 October 1991: "The meat industry needs to decide whether it is going to be an open competitively based industry or whether it's going to be a controlled and regulated industry. It's trying to be both and failing. If you and I, the farmers, are going to live by competition then let's get on with it and do it. There is no halfway house. Turn the Meat Board into an industry board with minimum powers, drop the Board-owned commercial interests...and other interventions and let the market dictate who does what and how. The best will survive and the poor will go belly up."

While some of its members would welcome aspects of co-ordination and intervention, Federated Farmers wanted to reduce the powers of the boards especially the non-trading ones. It was almost a case of those at the back shouting "forward" and those in the front crying "back".

Under long time chief executive Rob McLagan it had already developed an industry in issuing press releases critical of everything that contravened far right wing philosophy. The Meat Board had long been among the targets. In 1993 former Concrete Association chief executive Theo Simeonidis – as much of a stranger to the meat industry as professional engineer Warwick Bishop was at the Board – became the new chief executive for Federated Farmers. Where Warwick Bishop found difficulty in taking some of the more extreme traditional enmities seriously – and found the politics and emotions the hardest part of the business to manage – Simeonidis, often using the Official Information Act, slipped easily into attack mode and made the Board a major target for shrill criticism and sustained enquiries through the Federation publication *Straight Furrow*. This added to the "away with the producer boards" chorus coming from a number of quarters.

In a particular irony much of the criticism was orchestrated by Barrie Saunders, the former Board North American director now a PR consultant, who counted both the MIA and the Business Roundtable among his clients.

A Better Marketing Mousetrap 1988-91

"The historical view held within New Zealand agriculture over the last 30 years that competitive advantage is derived from a more efficient production base, is unfortunately, in isolation, found wanting. The vast majority of capital investment in the agriculture sector has been committed to production and processing facilities. The skillset in the industry is largely production based. At a time where the requirements are for added value research and development, distribution horsepower and visibility to the consumer through focussed marketing expenditure the meat industry is, in my opinion way behind the eight ball." Andrew Meehan, chief executive, Southpac, April 1991.

The apparently fruitless search for a better marketing mousetrap faltered during the brief manifestation of Euromark in 1989, but was not abandoned. The concerns with the poor marketing performance of the industry combined with the much publicised, frequently debated 'problem' of weak selling still encouraged the optimists in their quest for the Holy Grail.

But while the search was conducted into the nineties ostensibly in the name of orderly marketing and better returns, it became embroiled in industry politics. The newer entrants were suspicious of the motives behind some initiatives, which were considered to be taken by the industry establishment to preserve its creaking structures and fragile financial support. Producer board reform proposals exacerbated the turmoil and intensified the squabbling over the various marketing issues.

The recurrence of the procurement wars in 1988-89 and their continuation through to 1990-91, especially in the South Island, seriously affected meat company profitability. This served to confirm the view of many analysts that industry attention was focussed too much on production to the detriment of reaping the potential benefits that existed in the marketplace.

The Board and bankers continued to express concerns that the industry suffered from a lack of combined selling strength in most world markets. As one report noted: "New Zealand does not send a provincial rugby team abroad to do the job of the All Blacks – neither should the meat industry."

The declining financial performance of the companies and the possible collapse of a major company through lack of banking support, with AFFCO and Alliance picked by their competitors as the likely contenders, led to a series of reviews during 1990-91. It was also a period of intense lobbying of the companies by stakeholders and bankers to get some action to avert the downward spiral. The Government was operating in a 'more market' mode with little inclination to intervene, so the solution had to be generated from within.

Freesia Meat Holdings and its constituent corporate shareholders (FCL, GFW and Freesia Investments Ltd) had looked at marketing issues as part of overall restructuring moves that were being considered in the late eighties. They had convinced themselves of the structural weakness of the industry, justifying a managed solution to the problem either at the production or the marketing

For the new markets, new marketing structures were called for, such as the Joint Action Group or JAG, which brought together exporting companies for a common market development purpose. The Board's marketing manager for beef, Liz Francis, pictured here at celebrations for the opening of the Board's Hong Kong Office in 1993, has put considerable energy into JAG and industry groups to develop beef markets in Asia. In 1997 Liz Francis became the Asian regional manager, operating from Wellington.

ends or both. In doing so they had flirted several times with the idea of a 'single buyer approach' to marketing.

The Freesia team favoured a structure based on a commercial adaptation of the Dairy Board model, which bore a remarkable resemblance to the National Pool arrangement developed by the Board in the latter stages of its market intervention. The proposed organisation, the New Zealand Meat Marketing Council shortened to 'Meatmark' (a new organisation, not to be confused with the Board's company in the UK), would buy up all product and use the exporting companies and distributors to export and market the product. Meatmark would co-ordinate the plans of individual marketing companies to ensure returns to the industry were maximised.

After being regularly dusted off and given a new coat of paint the Meatmark proposal was just as regularly returned to its shelf because it was regarded as commercially and politically too difficult to implement.

These interventionist views were in marked contrast to those in the 1990 report of the Porter Project, which promoted voluntary industry groupings as the path to export success. The meat industry was notably absent from the published examples. According to Jim Thomson, its rapid-fire take on how the industry operated was so wide of the mark it was dumped. But the report did comment that slow progress had been made by New Zealand meat exporters towards the Porter-style solution of active pursuit of opportunities to differentiate their products. Such a differentiation strategy would require heavy investment in the marketplace and in forward integration along the marketing chain. However, such developments were constrained by low profitability in the industry and a general focus on production efficiencies rather than marketing.

The general Porter message was to advocate competition in the market as a means of achieving efficiencies and better returns. The idea of actively encouraging New Zealand meat exporters to compete against one another in the marketplace did not sit well with the Freesia analysts and raised the real or imagined spectre of 'weak selling'. There was also the view that controlling marketing structures through processing companies would not work because of their

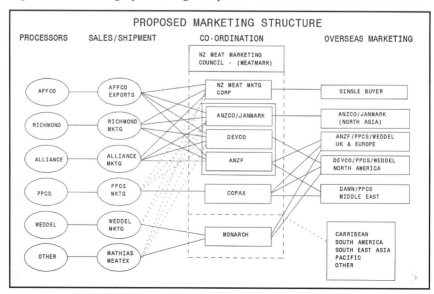

Wiring diagrams abounded during the attempt to find a better marketing mousetrap. This one, devised by Mick Calder of Freesia, shows the relationships in a proposed new 'Meatmark'.

production focus. The concept of separating marketing from production was again seriously considered although it was not acceptable to some of the companies.

This view had been summarised by Max Toy of AFFCO when he advised his board in 1989 that "procurement, processing and marketing must be linked together". This required the processor to have equity in the marketing company to provide efficiency in the flow of product through the system. AFFCO management recognised the advantages in integrated marketing (marketing companies owned and operated in common with like-minded operators) as long as the shareholding was in the hands of the processor.

As Toy said: "The marketing company leads the processing company by the demands of the marketplace. Conversely, because of the direct ownership aspect, they are also partly driven by the attainable desires of the New Zealand processor." Both ends fighting against the middle, but in the meat industry context the production end generally prevailed.

Max Toy recognised the merits of establishing New Zealand-owned companies in the marketplace and he ventured that integrated marketing companies such as Associated New Zealand Farmers (ANZF), the Lamb Company and Janmark could and should evolve by market and by product. The natural evolution would be the development of regional sheepmeats companies in Western Europe and the Middle East and regional beef companies in the US and Japan.

Steve Gray joined Freesia in 1991 as financial analyst in place of Trevor Miles, who went to manage Advanced Foods. Gray did not have a background in meat but quickly focussed on the marketing issue. In a strategic review of Freesia's operations, he commented that marketing was the area where the biggest opportunities for enhancing returns existed.

"In many areas it would appear that New Zealand companies tend to see each other as competitors to sell against rather than as a group whose common 'enemy' is the overseas producer of competitive protein products. The New Zealand lamb producer's greatest competitor is probably home raised pork and chicken and not even UK lamb, let alone another company's New Zealand lamb! We need a market structure that recognises this and at the same time removes the financial or stock pressures that create 'weak' selling."

In his view New Zealand had a dominant product position in the export of lamb and a dominant market position in the UK (and to a lesser extent the Continental markets) by reason of the VRA quota. There was an opportunity to exploit those dominant positions by creating an appropriate structure with processing separated from the marketing function.

As the financial state of the industry deteriorated in 1990-91 Freesia Meat Holdings formed a task force to review the state of the industry and commissioned a new study by Pappas Carter Evans & Koop (PCEK). The report entitled 'Securing a Profitable Future for the New Zealand Meat Export Industry', published in July 1991, indicated the industry was in crisis and virtually unbankable again due to declining stock numbers, operating inefficiencies, extreme farm gate procurement competition and declining marketplace returns.

Richmond's market development efforts in Denmark went as far as designing and organising special freezers to display its lamb in supermarkets.

The study looked at possible solutions at both the production and marketing ends that were commercially feasible and within the existing legislative framework. On the marketing side the report proposed the establishment of a Meat

Marketing Council. The aim was to "provide a horizontal forum to ensure the actions of individual players are co-ordinated and do not jeopardise the returns of all exporters."

The council would be based on the revamped MIA marketing committee and include representatives of the Board, and would establish a code of conduct aimed at setting minimum levels of market discipline. Membership would be compulsory for all exporters who would be required to submit marketing plans to the Council. So the idea of more formalised co-ordination was reborn.

The problems besetting the meat industry were widely understood in the early nineties and many analysts had suggested solutions. Ernst & Young developed a concept involving the merger of the interests of AFFCO, Richmond, PPCS and Alliance with the formation of a series of regional toll or custom processing co-operatives and a central procurement, marketing and finance organisation as a possible solution.

The central organisation would involve Freesia taking over the Board's shares in the various commercial marketing activities and putting them into the central marketing organisation along with the shares held by the companies in marketing ventures.

It was labelled 'Super Farmco' because essentially it was an adaptation of the 'Farmco' model first mooted by Freesia in 1986. Again, the suggested separation of procurement and marketing was not an option the processors could live with.

Geoff Lorigan of ANZF in London was also mulling over the structure for marketing New Zealand lamb in the UK. His principal shareholders, AFFCO and Alliance, were under pressure from their banking syndicates and some improvement in returns from the major lamb market was of obvious interest. He had developed the idea of a Single Entry Point (SEP) structure with a SEP for commodity product Europe-wide and separate SEPs in each EC country for value-added products.

However, he found the agents he had selected to deliver the structure (Freesia and/or the banking syndicates) were not able to force such a marketing structure on the industry – the erroneous idea that Freesia could use its investments to push the companies around was in vogue for only a short period in 1990-91.

Lorigan's alternative was a modified strategy called Limited Entry Points (LEP). This would amalgamate the European commodity import activities of ANZF, NZ Lamb Co/Brooks (PPCS) and Towers (Fortex), which handled some 70% of the trade. Weddel Swift and the newly established Richmond Lonsdale, created when Richmond acquired its long term importing partner Dalgety Lonsdale, would remain as independent importers, and all other non-aligned New Zealand exporters would be required to choose one of the three. There would be similar but separate structures for the import of value-added products. It was really a proposal to reduce the groups from five to three and to close the 'further processed products' loophole. Along with everyone else in the industry, he lobbied unsuccessfully for the companies to make some changes.

Amongst all of this two overseas-based marketing gurus visited New Zealand in June and July 1991. Dr John Morris, a New Zealander based in the US and Professor David Hughes from the UK were relentlessly critical of the marketing efforts of the meat sector during their 'Marketing New Zealand Meats Profitably' seminars around the country.

They identified a number of key problems including: "A commodity orientation rather than the required market orientation, endemic mistrust between producers and meat companies and to a lesser extent between producers and the Board, the practice of averaging prices to livestock producers (which) obfuscates market signals, concentration on throughput at the expense of longer term development of higher value-added markets, etc" – all the usual suspects.

Their advice: "Meat companies, notwithstanding their present financial exigencies, must increase their focused research and marketing representation in key target markets." They also advocated switching from a commodity to a market orientation, requiring meat companies to make long-term commitments at the most senior management level.

Many of the Asian meat promotions, like this one at Food and Hotel Asia, focussed on the total New Zealand food experience.

The heretical idea of the industry being market-led rather than production-driven was one of the main forces behind another review of the industry initiated by Rick Christie of the Trade Development Board (TDB) in July-August 1991. The review involved a combined team from the TDB (Ifor Ffowcs Williams and Janette Malcolm), the Board (Tim Ritchie and Bill Joyce), and Freesia (Mick Calder). The team also included consultants Tony Caughey and Terry O'Boyle who had taken an interest in the industry during a separate investigation into the by-products side of the business.

There was also the family connection with Simon Caughey, the marketing manager of AFFCO, and one of a new team brought into the company by new chairman Peter Jackson. Other new appointments at AFFCO that year included Jeff Jackson (no relation to Peter) as chief executive and former Elders chief executive Allan Barber as chief operating officer. Former chief executive Max Toy moved to London to head ANZF, after Geoff Lorigan left to pursue his own business interests.

In addition to their promotion of a market-led industry the TDB had advanced the need for innovation in market and product development and "an environment that encourages participants to compete on aspects other than price".

The result of the team's efforts, 'Sheepmeat Marketing – Building a Sustainable Future', in August 1991 was presented to an executive committee of the Board set up to examine the future structure for the marketing of New Zealand's sheepmeats. The committee's report focussed on industry profitability and bankability and noted that industry losses were anticipated to top $100 million in 1990-91 and that equity ratios of major companies were at dangerously low levels and deteriorating.

A draft of the report had commented on the declining performances in both the farming and processing sectors of the industry. "There is an additional ingredient in this cocktail for disaster. The banking sector, whose direct meat company exposure is greater than $1.5 billion, says that the New Zealand meat industry will be technically unbankable for the 1991-92 season." Farming leaders were quick to remind the bankers that their exposure to farm debt was many times greater. Farmers and meat companies relied on each other, so financial failure in the meat processing industry would have much wider repercussions.

The draft report went on: "The banking sector accepts that an enforced exit of one or two major processors will not solve the long term structural problems facing the industry. This would merely be a case of postponing the inevitable, as today's winners became, in time, tomorrow's victims. Even new participants in the industry, whose entrance fee was in the form of cheap assets from failed companies, would themselves, in turn, become victims. Simply, the downwards spiral of failure is self perpetuating and indiscriminate."

The final and abridged report advised: "Regardless of what is done in the domestic market (to address over-capacity and procurement practices), the industry must obtain better returns from the marketplace to build a sustainable future."

A more co-ordinated marketing approach was required and the team believed this could improve annual industry returns by $80 to $100 million. Eight options were considered including deregulation, co-ordinating committees operating with or without coercion, 'Super Farmco', regional marketing companies, and even a dairy industry model.

After reviewing each of the options in terms of selected criteria – market-led, bankable, sustainable, commercial rather than imposed – the team echoed Max Toy's earlier remarks and recommended that the optimum market structure would be achieved with the establishment of regional marketing companies for key markets and for key products.

In addition it suggested there was a requirement for a Meat Council to provide a regulated planning mechanism.

The report was presented to the Board, which approved negotiations with the industry to develop a marketing structure built around the proposed regional marketing companies. The report was to be used as briefing for a meeting with the MIA on 6 August 1991, but it was decided an approach to each of the major companies to outline the proposals would be more productive. The most positive response – a conditional willingness to consider the proposals – came from companies such as AFFCO and Alliance that were under financial pressure. Others expressed the attitude of "let the dinosaurs fail".

Subsequently the Board looked at a suggestion from Bill Joyce, its general manager industry services, to 'franchise' the key market areas as a way of achieving regional co-ordination and limiting the number of companies operating. The Board would set a franchise value on sheepmeat marketing in each

Ngauranga Meat Processors, advertised for sale in 1991, having been restored to viability after the collapse of the Welpro joint venture between Wellington City Council and Gracelands Export Ltd.
The promotional brochure says the plant is sited "in the natural funnel for the Wellington, Horowhenua and Wairarapa catchment area, comprising 2014 farms, stocking some 3.7 million sheep and lambs and 1937 farms carrying some 128,000 beef cattle", according to 1989 agricultural statistics. The plant is now owned by Taylor Preston.

region, and would allow any company which paid a fee and met other obligations, such as opening a representative office, to market there. The franchise fee would be held in trust and the interest used to fund promotion in the area.

The MIA itself had been reviewing marketing options for sheepmeats. The Iraqi invasion of Kuwait (followed by Operation Desert Storm) had unsettled the market in the Middle East and, in the wake of the collapse of the Berlin Wall and the beginnings of the reunification of Germany, returns from EC markets were declining.

The EC's Private Storage Aid scheme for lamb introduced in 1990 was used regularly during 1991 as prices fell and the UK announcement that the Variable Premium Subsidy would be removed from 31 December 1991 further disrupted the market. As with the removal of SMPs in New Zealand in 1985, the decision encouraged producers to sell lamb to gain the higher support prices before they disappeared.

Processing and packing high value tenderloins at Ngauranga Meat Processors.

In recognition of the problems, the MIA advised that a Lamb Marketing Working Party had been formed with the Board "to consider strategies in the immediate and longer term". The MIA had initially considered further co-ordination through the Group system operating on a global basis but with the number of Groups being reduced to three. The leaders from each Group plus representatives from the Board would develop market plans and monitor performance under the umbrella of a Market Development Council. The council would rely on the Board's licensing powers, particularly those under section 9D of the Meat Export Control Act which provided for the Board in consultation with the MIA to impose conditions on licences relating to quantities and classes of meat exported to specific countries. The idea of a marketing council was back in vogue.

At that stage there were over 50 fully licensed exporters plus another 33 using the Board's licence MEL 235 under the probationary system. In addition, there were 16 countries around the world designated 'Special Access Markets' for sheepmeats: Iran, Iraq, Jordan, Egypt, Syria, Morocco, Tunisia, Algeria, Libya, Canada, Mexico, Chile, Peru, North Asia, South Korea and the USSR. The licensing of specified exporters for each of those countries, such as the informal Metco Consortium (PPCS, Alliance and the Board) to Middle Eastern countries other than Iran, and Weddel for frozen sheepmeat to South Korea, was reviewed by a joint committee of the Board and the MIA which provided a recommendation to the Board. So the notion of issuing specific or conditional licences was not new.

The various marketing proposals generated were used by the corporate stakeholders and the bankers to exert pressure on the companies and members of both the Board's and the MIA's working parties.

All the deliberations culminated in a two-day meeting of the MIA executive starting on 5 August 1991, which included a meeting with the Board on the second day. The Board representatives (David Frith, Tim Ritchie and Bill Joyce) used the marketing committee's report as the basis for their position, and outlined the need for commercial solutions with co-ordination and discipline.

Chairman Sir David Beattie advised the Board the MIA had agreed to develop a strategic marketing plan and assess the structures necessary to maximise returns to New Zealand, by 1 October 1991. The aim would be to incorpo-

Alliance marketing manager Alan Henry took over the role of negotiating the Iran contract from the MMC, along with Dale Kwok of PPCS.

rate strong disciplines in the major markets with price guidelines and monitoring, bonds and penalties.

The MIA's market planning exercise took the commodity marketing approach. It centred on filling the Iran contract for the Meat Marketing Corporation first; this would shorten up the volume available to other markets and theoretically provide a firmer pricing base.

The plans then covered the proportion of the EC quota to be shipped to the UK, to be calculated in accordance with each company's assessment of what it expected to sell in the market, rather than the previous approach of allocating pro rata to the kill. Companies' overall allocations would be subject to a market release programme ordered by the shipping panel or monthly to control the marketing flow of available product. The plans would then deal with the rest of the EC followed by the other market areas.

The plans were still production-driven as each company was first committed to supply a share of the Iran contract in accordance with its level of kill and these percentages would apply to the total EC quota as well. Companies that could not fill their share of the Iran contract would face a penalty of 25c/kg for lamb and 10c/kg for mutton to be passed to the MMC to purchase the shortfall.

This arrangement forced companies to contribute to the Iran contract. Its principal target was Fortex which was not set up to supply frozen carcasses and had bragged about it at the expense of the other companies. Fortex was attempting to get out of the commodity trade though events would show that it could 'sell and be damned – but sell' with the best of them if driven to it.

Graeme Thompson of Fortex, a member of the MIA executive at the time, recalls: "On the one hand, I appreciated that the industry had to supply the Iran contract because there was nowhere else for those carcass lambs to go. On the other hand, as a company we had invested millions of dollars to do what we needed to do to reflect market conditions, add value and find markets. We argued that we had done all those things so why should we have to (supply carcasses). We lost the battle in the end. I had to pay $2 million into the coffers, which basically went to our arch-rivals PPCS and Alliance. Because they were major suppliers of the contract they got our $2 million."

Sir David Beattie followed up the joint meeting with a letter to the Board dated 7 August to confirm the decisions, particularly those relating to Iran and the UK/EC. It went on to advise that the MIA intended introducing a system of bonds as a guarantee of "good behaviour" with attendant monitoring requirements and penalties for breaches of agreed price guidelines. All the arrangements would be covered by a co-operation agreement to be put in place before the start of the new season. The MIA had noted the Board's proposal for a Meat Council, which would be considered in due course.

In addition Beattie advised the MIA did not consider it appropriate for beef to be included in the discussions. "The international beef market is quite different from the international sheepmeat market in that New Zealand is not a prominent player in the market and therefore does not run the same risk of competing against itself. They (the MIA executive committee members) feel that care should be taken not to allow a problem in one area to cause unnecessary reactions in other areas. The same applies to offals, pelts and hides."

By inference, the obverse of this statement is that the MIA was acknowledging that by competing with each other in lamb trading the companies risked reducing the available returns. The Board had always contended that competitive trading in lamb inevitably left some value lying on the table in overseas markets, but the companies claimed that was the cost of 'efficient' marketing.

In the MIA's view beef exports were not a problem because good returns were being received from all markets. In other words, prices were up on the previous season. This optimism existed despite the fact that the European intervention beef stockpile had increased to more than 900,000 tonnes and the US had imposed voluntary restraints for the first time since 1988. A principal cause for the optimism was that the end of Japanese beef import quotas had come on 1 April 1991 and Korea was starting on a similar liberalisation.

Of course, the market planning proposals put forward by the MIA executive did not suit everyone. Tim Ritchie, who had returned from managing Waitaki's operations in London to the new position of executive assistant to the chief executive at the Board, reported on the deluge of discussions and meetings that took place jointly and separately during August. The Board continued to pursue its regional marketing company proposal and advised the MIA their plans did not go far enough as "they did little to address commercial solutions necessary to fully capture the ongoing market potential". The MIA retorted that the Board's proposal was not practical as "no artificial barrier should be placed between the processor and the end-user". But the proposals for establishing a council continued to be developed.

While the Board had support from the TDB for its proposals it became clear there would be difficulties in putting together a regional marketing company structure. There was no enthusiasm from the companies and the Board had no mandate from producers or government to impose a solution. The Board noted that the last relevant communication from the Government, which had called for deregulation and a transfer of marketing back to the companies, had been five years previously in 1986.

Even though further debate was proposed the regional company concept was quietly dropped. But the idea of franchising market regions was still a possibility.

In 1991 Graeme Thompson of Fortex chartered a giant Russian Antonov transport plane to take 120 tonnes of time and temperature-sensitive chilled lamb from Christchurch to Brussels. The plane arrived two days late – its agents having been tempted by a "lucrative proposal to pick up a load of weaponry for the Iraqi army." Worse, there was no sign of the requested refrigeration. "The agents' representative explained that when they got high in the air, they opened special vents in the fuselage to allow cold air to flow through the holds," Thompson recalls.

Faced with the expensive prospect of cancelling the deal, he decided to go ahead, and rely on the refrigeration engineer accompanying the cargo. With 120 tonnes of meat on board, the plane had to restrict its fuel load and land frequently – at Brisbane, Perth and Singapore. There its crew went shopping and the meat had 9 hours in the Singapore sun. The plane flew to Karachi, then "disappeared".

The captain decided to turn north over Afghanistan to Tashkent, saving fuel by flying low. The easily identifiable Russian transporter came under fire from the Afghan Mujaheddin. Avoiding the Stinger missiles depleted the fuel and they only just managed to land at Tashkent. There the captain offered US dollars for fuel but the airport officials wanted meat, eventually marching the crew at gunpoint into the terminal and helping themselves to 5 tonnes of meat. After the angry engineer threatened terrible repercussions, they returned 3 tonnes and accepted a balance of US dollars as payment for the fuel.

Though the cargo arrived at Brussels two days late, the chilled lamb survived unscathed, and everyone got their chilled meat for Easter, with deliveries being made that same day.

The Ownership Paradox
1990-92

"Market forces at work bear a remarkable resemblance to war being waged – exhilarating action for observers and some participants, pain for the loyal and less nimble, fortunes to be made by the few, and the likelihood of a lingering sad aftermath… Somewhere, vultures of the battlefield are calculating how long the South Island companies can survive a haemorrhage of payments out of proportion to markets overseas.

"It doesn't take a psychic to predict that if the trend to per head buying continues to accelerate, while overseas lamb prices drop or stagnate, the South Island bubble will burst. The odds, because of their proportion of the ownership, are that the producers will be picking up many of the pieces." Janet Tyson, Meat Producer *Second Quarter 1991.*

The split of Waitaki between AFFCO in the North Island and Alliance in the South was greeted ambivalently. It was either hailed as the final step in securing majority producer ownership and control of the industry, or regarded as a desperate throw of the dice by the corporates endeavouring to preserve some of the value of their investment as they sought an orderly exit. In the rationalisation rat-race, it was the farmer-controlled companies that had survived – so far.

In fact, while the debate and discussion over Waitaki had been going on farmers had been quietly getting together and setting up more of their own smaller single-chain processing operations. Blue Sky Meats, under the guidance of Ross Wensley had started a single-chain sheep plant in Southland in 1987, with a substantial farmer shareholding, plus input from Mathias Meats and New Zealand Equities.

A group of farmers in the Wanganui region, headed by Rod Pearce, had looked at the merits of working together to combat the power of the big meat companies by using alternative methods of processing their stock. In 1988 they decided that a new processing facility was feasible and formed a partnership with Mathias Meats, Graeme Lowe and New Zealand Equities to combine marketing, finance and industry knowledge with committed suppliers. The Waitotara Meat Company was floated with investments from 160 farmers plus supporters and its processing plant established in 1988.

The Board's 1990 annual report noted: "After a dramatic period of upheaval and restructuring, the New Zealand export meat industry is now largely in the hands of producer-owned and controlled companies and companies in which producers have a shareholding." But to make the achievement worthwhile, sheep and beef farmers had to work to ensure the industry was efficient and profitable. "New Zealand's farmers have been delivered a once-in-a-lifetime opportunity to take greater control of their own destiny. It is up to them to make it work."

The contrary view had it that market forces should have prevailed. Many farmers were convinced that a weakened Waitaki should have been left to collapse. The surviving companies like AFFCO and Alliance, and possibly some

Blue Sky Meats chairman Ross Wensley.

newcomers, could then have operated more efficiently than the collapsed 'dinosaur'. This view ignored the fact that the corporates (FCL and GFW) were mindful of the effect a major collapse would have on their own relations with financiers and the stock market.

The banks had also been unenthusiastic about a collapse of a company of Waitaki's size and worked assiduously on restructuring arrangements. A collapse would allow new operators in at a cheaper capital cost with lower financing charges to compete against the surviving companies, so setting off more intensive procurement competition. Further procurement competition would impact severely on the survivors and their bankers, so there was considerable interest in an orderly rationalisation.

Finally, the Board had been concerned about the impact on importer and buyer confidence in overseas markets. Waitaki handled about 30% of New Zealand's meat exports so a collapse would have seriously dislocated marketing arrangements.

Barry Dempsey, whose Waitane Meats venture at Gore was short-lived. PPCS took over the near-new multi-species processing plant in 1994 after Waitane went into receivership.

Some commentators questioned Freesia's credibility in investing in bricks and mortar – and predominantly in co-operatives – when its original objective had been to invest in the market. Some farmers considered the co-operatives had become debt-ridden and inefficient, and Freesia was responsible not only for the debts but also for supporting inefficient companies.

Freesia justified the investments because it had been set up to encourage producer ownership and control of the industry. However, the farming press reported many farmers considered producer ownership was a lost cause as they were not convinced that they owned, and much less controlled, the companies in which they had shares, so there was no requirement to support them. Michael Turner, who had a lot to say about the Alliance situation, having cut his teeth at the *Southland Times*, noted in the *Dominion Sunday Times* of 6 October 1991: "Freesia then realised what our man in the black suit already knew – that farmers would not support plants they owned if there were better commercial options".

Dick Davison, chairman of the Meat & Wool Section of Federated Farmers, was reported at the time saying that farmers wanted more influence in the industry in the hope that it would lead to more discipline in the market. "But in terms of farmer ownership, influence and control, we've gone backwards." He said in the same issue of the *Dominion Sunday Times* that each time the industry came close to "commercial maturity" someone rescued it, but he believed that farmers now wanted that to stop.

The opposition to the new ownership arrangements was stronger in Southland where farmer shareholders considered the corporates had forced Alliance into the transaction, aided and abetted by the bankers, Freesia and, to a lesser extent, the Board. In fact, a majority of shareholders had voted for the transaction at an extraordinary general meeting in 1989. But memories can be short in the meat industry.

Recent meat company financial results were not good news. MIA chairman Sir David Beattie reported in the 1990 annual report: "The 1989-90 processing season was extremely poor for companies because farmers held back stock to rebuild flocks and herds following the run down in recent years, and the dramatic effects of the drought on the east coast of both Islands." As well, about 12

The Meat Producer *recorded, in its April-June 1990 issue, that 70% of processing capacity is in control of the producers.*

FORTEX GROUP

Structure and funding of key companies in 1990, showing ownership and Freesia involvement, if any. Fortex had some start-up funding from Freesia, a substantial producer shareholding and was about to be publicly listed.

new small plants had started operations in the previous three seasons, putting considerable pressure on the procurement market and continuing the premium battle through 1989-90.

Individually, companies could justify paying above-market premiums because they were increasing throughput to spread their high fixed cost overheads. This could continue in the short term so long as they covered their variable costs, but in the end it made processing unprofitable and eroded what little equity there was left.

However, the companies were competing for a finite number of stock each year, so that one company's gain in market share was another's loss. It was a zero sum game, which required deep pockets or very understanding funders. The pressure proved too much for two of the newer operators and both Gracelands (a joint venture with the Wellington City Council's WelPro at Ngauranga) and Ventec (at Tirau) went into receivership in 1990. Despite this ominous message other proposals for small plants were on the drawing boards.

Bankers started to take an even greater interest in the industry. They were in a unique position as the four major banks (BNZ, ANZ, Westpac and National) were, together with several overseas banks, involved in the syndicates financing the bigger companies. In addition, these banks separately provided finance for the smaller companies and had funded the newer operations.

The banks preferred to provide only seasonal funding but had been inveigled into funding long-term core debt as well, which left them very exposed to the vicissitudes of the industry. They were sufficiently concerned about reducing their risk and exposure to suggest there should be constraints on the funding for new processing plants.

However, the BNZ had made an exception with the new Fortex plant at Silverstream. It was, after all, the darling of industry onlookers. Funds were provided even though the final cost, when it opened in 1991, was considerably in excess of the original estimate.

In contrast, the banks were concerned about the viability of AFFCO after the Waitaki deal and had insisted on appointing their own financial adviser, David Dorrington of Price Waterhouse, to monitor the activities of the company on their behalf. They also started to tighten up the funding arrangements with meat companies generally to limit the erosion of capital that was one of the outcomes of procurement competition.

The battles of the previous two seasons and the poor financial results caused a slight lull in procurement activity in the North Island in 1990-91. In its *Annual Review,* the Economic Service reported average lamb returns for 1990-91 were 8.4% lower than the previous year. However the situation differed between islands: "Strong procurement competition between South Island companies resulted in little change in previous season's prices which was a contrast to the North Island where export lamb prices were provisionally down 25%."

The competitive activity coupled with the threat of another strike at the Alliance plants led to a further weakening of farmer confidence. Farmers either switched their allegiance to other companies or spread their risk by splitting their drafts between Alliance and other operators. The company had also recognised the need to rationalise capacity and had developed a strategy which involved some plant closures. It was a move that did not endear them to the

AFFCO NEW ZEALAND

AFFCO was a producer co-operative with substantial Freesia funding.

unions or to the farmers in those areas serviced by the affected plants.

The transport sector benefited from carrying stock out of traditional supply areas. This was especially the case when South Island companies were competing so fiercely they were also buying stock in the North Island with freight free offers to take the lambs south. Transport companies from as far north as Otorohanga were carting stock for transfer to the South Island. As John Hermans, a Rail Ferries master commented: "You always knew when the procurement wars were heating up. We started carrying stock from North to South or vice versa, and when things got really crazy we carried it both ways."

The reduced confidence, rationalisation and procurement competition had an immediate financial impact on Alliance. Owen Poole had joined Alliance on a short-term basis to assist in reorganising the company following the Waitaki merger. He recalls: "Following the strike it was apparent we were getting into a bit of strife. So I looked at where we were likely to be at year-end and what could be done. We started a plan – 'Agenda for Change' – discussing it with directors and the banks."

This led to the decision to close Ocean Beach and Kaiapoi in 1991, and the scaling down of operations at Makarewa and Mataura with the loss of 1450 jobs.

"One thing led to another and the company lost a lot of money, $152 million, split roughly between operations and asset write-down," says Poole. "Bankers lost confidence, we ultimately convinced them that the plan was robust and worth their continuing support. However they wouldn't provide any additional finance. We had to raise the money through selling our non-core assets, and try and coincide that sell-down with the requirement for cash through the rationalisation."

The bankers insisted on appointing their own financial adviser, Rob Thompson, senior partner of Coopers & Lybrand, to monitor the affairs of the company and to introduce some discipline into the finance section.

New Alliance chief executive Rick Bettle had a background in the dairy industry and more latterly in Wrightson Ltd, a subsidiary of Fletcher Challenge. The new AFFCO chief executive Jeff Jackson, was also ex the dairy industry and then Fletcher Fishing. This led Michael Turner to report in the 20 December 1991 issue of *National Business Review*, that the appointments were seen as moves by FCL to protect its investments. He went on to note that despite the divestment of Waitaki being promoted in the name of increasing producer control of the industry, FCL appeared to be gaining stronger influence. "A joke doing the rounds is that if FCL put someone in as chief executive of the Meat Board – a position left vacant this year (following the resignation of Jim Thomson) – it would have the industry sown up. The irony is that FCL is trying to get out of the meat industry."

He also noted that after the problems that led to the Alliance loss had become obvious some of its shareholders had said the best investment FCL could have made in the industry would have been to let their co-operative fall over. The Alliance farmer shareholders heaped much of the blame for the decline in confidence and the financial loss on to the corporates. Some of that antagonism spilled over onto the directors as well since they had recommended acceptance of the deal to the shareholders.

Alliance was also a producer co-operative with substantial Freesia funding.

The upshot was vociferous anti-corporate and anti-director groups baying for blood, specifically the replacement of all directors. Most important was the 'Cairns Group', under the leadership of local farmer Dennis Cairns with assistance from Tony Forde, ex Alliance general manager.

They generated enough heat for Alliance to arrange a series of farmer meetings to address the situation and to attract the attention of TVNZ which dispatched Linda Clark and Ross Stevens to investigate. The resulting programme aired many of the grievances and noted the increase in transfers of stock for slaughter out of Southland to competing processing companies, "across the Gore Bridge".

The programme interviewed local farmer, and anti-corporate, John Morrison from Mossburn. He was the spokesman of the Mossburn group, formed in 1989 to "oppose Meat Board interference in private enterprise", including the Waitaki-Alliance merger. Morrison was described as having a penchant for ringing the *Southland Times* and providing a story during a lengthy tirade against those currently in his firing line.

He depicted the corporate directors as "those shiny-arses from Wellington" who should consider their positions and resign. "Those three directors (Mick Calder, Norman Geary and Phil Pritchard) representing the Meat Board and Freesia are responsible for the precarious financial position of Alliance, and they should go." He was immediately labelled a "swede hopper from Southland".

Hugh de Lacy described the situation in the *Mercantile Gazette:* " The phenomenon of farmers railing against the company (Freesia) which was created by their own producer board supposedly to protect their own interests, highlights the underlying anomaly of the producer board trying to be both the half-back and the referee.

"The farmers of Southland see Freesia as the half-back who flicked on to the Alliance backline the rapidly deflating ball that was once Waitaki Meats, after being the referee that blew up the resolved ruck of the Waitaki retrenchment, and then awarded itself the put in to the subsequent defensive scrum. Alliance's farmer shareholders are rightly outraged at being fed the hospital pass that is the likely $160 million loss the company is likely to bear this year. They don't accept Freesia's protestations that they called for the pass and that Freesia only delivered it on request."

The agitation by farmer shareholders had the partly desired effect of farmer directors agreeing they should each resign and be subject to the will of the shareholders. But for the sake of continuity it was decided this should be over a two year period. In addition to the two directors retiring by rotation (George Pinckney and Hugh Simmers) another four directors (John Falconer, Owen McStay, Jim McIntyre and Peter Wilding) resigned with only four of them standing again. Jim McIntyre and Peter Wilding did not stand.

Only John Falconer was re-elected and Bruce Anderson from South Canterbury, Murray Donald and Kathie Henderson, both from Southland, were voted in. The corporate directors were not subject to the same electoral process and they remained. Kathie Henderson was the second woman voted to the Alliance Board, following in the footsteps of Christine McKenzie, elected two years earlier and the first woman director of a New Zealand meat company.

Alliance then started down the long road to restructure the company ac-

cording to its 'Agenda for Change', while coping with the procurement war and the demands of the bankers. It was a matter of balancing the operations, and introducing the productivity improvements and cost savings.

The proposals for divestment of 'non-core' assets such as the shareholding in Southland Farmers Co-operative were not regarded kindly by the shareholders. But as the buyer was Southport the trauma was less than it might have been. It was the consideration of closures or the scaling down of operations of other Southland plants that caused more anguish.

Some commentators, including Michael Turner, writing in the 6 October 1991 issue of the *Dominion Sunday Times,* considered AFFCO, with more emphasis on beef, was in a better financial position. AFFCO had formed a joint venture – New Zealand Beef Holdings – with ANZCO to market beef in North Asia, in the face of criticism by other industry members such as Graeme Lowe, who opposed the granting of a licence on the grounds of the Board's referee-player involvement. Nevertheless, optimism about the company was somewhat at odds with financial results as AFFCO had recorded a loss of $11 million in 1990 followed by another loss of $86 million after extraordinaries in 1991.

AFFCO pointed out that, apart from rationalisation costs stemming from the Waitaki transaction, excessive procurement premiums had contributed to the loss. In December 1991 the company announced it was appointing financial advisers to put together a restructuring plan which involved finding $100 million through a private equity placement. It was aiming for a structure that would retain farmer control after the equity injection – a fairly tall order. With the complexities of the arrangements, and the ebb and flow of the financial tides in the industry, the project took longer than originally contemplated, and stretched the goodwill of the various banks and financiers such as Freesia and Fletcher Challenge almost to breaking point.

The troubled AFFCO also felt the need to slate the performance of some other meat companies. Fran O'Sullivan reported in the *National Business Review* in December 1991 that AFFCO, in making its announcement, was also critical that while it had disclosed its losses other meat companies were not so forthcoming.

It argued that Fortex's announced 1991 profit of $2.89 million could be stripped back to a loss of nearly $3 million if the company's depreciation policy of not charging against major assets in their first year's operation was reworked and if presold goods were not excluded from the inventory valuation. It also pointed out that PPCS's $17.4 million bottom-line profit would be substantially reduced if above schedule pool payments were shown as an ordinary operating cost instead of a post profit net adjustment. Each of these companies had been established according to the co-operative ethic – but that ethic did not extend outside the company.

King Country Lamb was sufficiently confident in the future of the industry to start building its single-chain lamb processing plant at Benneydale in 1991. Also AFFCO, after lengthy joint venture negotiations with ANZCO had come to nothing, decided to go it alone and redevelop its Feilding plant as a specialist beef operation – Manawatu Beef Packers. Others lured by the sirens' song included Cromwell Meats Ltd and Waitane Meats Ltd, both establishing single

Weddel was the only major overseas-owned company remaining in New Zealand. It was a private subsidiary of Union International of the UK, part of the Vestey organisation.

Lowe Walker was a staunchly independent, privately-owned company.

The Riverlands Group was part of Brierley Investments Ltd, later to be publicly listed as Huttons Kiwi.

Craig Hickson of Progressive
Meats, who has made a
success of sticking to his core
business of processing.

Freesia Investments.
From 1987-90 Freesia
invested over $100 million to
give farmers ownership and
control of the meat processing
industry.

chain plants in 1990, and Thames Abattoir upgraded to export the same year, becoming Coromandel Meat Processors.

Keith Taylor had joined forces with the Preston local butchery family to form Taylor Preston and buy Ngauranga Meat Processors – the reincarnation of WelPro – from Graeme Lowe who had acquired it from the Wellington City Council in 1991 (but only after Peter Norman, John Drayton and Weddel had all tried to put it on a commercial footing). In addition, Pro Pacific established its short-lived sheep and goat meat operation at Opotiki in 1991. There was no shortage of new companies, even though stock numbers were not increasing.

However, moderation was to be short-lived as procurement heat was turned up again the following season. Companies had lowered their debt levels and placated the bankers, but they had also salted away some fighting funds. They were ready to 'reward' their stock suppliers with higher returns or to take another swipe at their competitors in the struggle to determine the 'last man standing'.

This time there was extra pressure as lamb numbers declined by some 3.5 million due to the continued run down of the national flock and harsh winter and spring weather. The export lamb kill fell by 4.5 million and procurement prices increased by around 40% to an average of $39.50 per head. Mervyn Barnett's $35 lamb had been achieved, but at some cost.

The continuing procurement battles and their effect on processor profitability during 1990-91 had been of considerable concern to the shareholders of Freesia Meat Holdings (FCL and Freesia) among others.

Mick Calder had completed a study of the merits of co-operative ownership particularly as it related to the raising of capital and the lack of producer/shareholder loyalty to their company. He noted that voting restrictions tended to restrain company developments. There had been moves by co-operatives in Europe, such as Kerry Foods, to introduce equity capital to assist in the expansion of their operations and division into separate processing and marketing entities.

He suggested similar consideration might be necessary for the meat industry co-operatives in New Zealand. These comments and proposals were roundly castigated by Brian Cameron, a director of the PPCS co-operative who declared that changes to the co-operative structures were unnecessary and Calder's lack of understanding of meat industry co-operatives was appalling. Subsequently, some co-operatives did resort to alternative structures and techniques to gain access to capital; others went to the wall for the lack of it.

A new PCEK report, *Securing a Profitable Future for the New Zealand Meat Export Industry*, was commissioned by Freesia and published in July 1991. On the procurement side, it said the industry was facing extreme farm gate procurement competition due to declining stock numbers. It was virtually unbankable without some structural adjustment, but the study concluded 'free market' solutions would not help the meat industry as it was suffering from serious market failure. It was felt that the underlying supply and demand conditions of the industry were such that free competition would lead to higher than optimum production costs and lower than necessary product prices.

An 'ownership paradox' was also compounding the situation. While farmers owned the industry, particularly through the co-operative structure, they

John Upton (left) of Mathias Meats, Raj Gundavda, of US Agrex, and Graham Cooney of Blue Sky Meats at the 1991 SIAL Food Fair. Blue Sky Meats was founded in 1987 and it was Graham Cooney's first visit to the major food fair. He told the Meat Producer *he found it valuable to get first-hand views from customers, which had implications for both processing and procurement back home.*

were also suppliers and had accepted the benefits of extreme procurement competition while placing the viability of processors – their companies – at risk. They did not sufficiently value their shareholding in any meat company to consider that they were obliged to support it. In fact some held shares in competing companies.

The industry exhibited all the elements of 'Empty Core Markets' as identified by Abigail Williams of Texas A&M University, which are "chaotic with frequent episodes of cut-throat competition". In contrast to vigorous competition, which is healthy: "Cut-throat competition results in chaotic markets in which all forms earn below normal returns, in the long run as well as the short run." In such circumstances non-market solutions including co-operation amongst the companies, were justified and necessary to reach a stable equilibrium.

The report recommended three key initiatives: (1) the introduction of a livestock quota system with Tradable Killing Rights (TKRs) related to the export quotas, to limit cut-throat competition; (2) provision of liquidity for co-operative shares to allow shareholders to benefit in the market value of their company; and (3) establishment of a Meat Marketing Council to co-ordinate the actions of all of the players.

The first two recommendations were treated with the usual industry scorn, and given little support. Farmers were against TKRs or any other moves that would lessen the procurement competition, and mean lower prices. They also argued restraints on the procurement market were covert actions by the companies and their bankers to shift their risks back onto producers. The co-operative issue was strongly resisted as a move by the corporates to try to wrestle control away from the farmers. The marketing council would come to fruition as the Meat Planning Council.

The Meat Planning Council 1991

"I wouldn't have got it off the ground without the banks. They were saying, this industry's beginning to look unbankable, and there has to be some collective effort to make it profitable, both for the farming side and the other side. And they were turning to the Board and the Government, and the Government was saying 'We're not touching it'. So the banks became very proactive. They saw the Meat Planning Council as the industry at least getting together and addressing some of these issues... there were many meetings and many phone calls. And some very interesting people came into line. I remember several who, one day were against and the next day were for it." David Frith.

The banks continued to gnaw at the bone of the industry's bankability. It was reported the overseas banks involved in various meat company funding syndicates wanted a clear statement of where the industry was heading to persuade them to continue their support for the 1991-92 season. The banks also commented on the declining market conditions overseas and queried whether the marketing solutions being discussed were trying to "breathe life into a corpse".

The proposed solutions were only addressing the delivery of a product to market without actually marketing it, which raised a comparison with the marketing operations of the dairy industry. The banks were looking for a longer-term structural solution endorsed by all interested parties. They suggested another Task Force.

The Government had also been under pressure from the TDB, which had even drafted the terms of reference and proposed the names of possible

About 400 farmers came from around the central North Island to hear debate on the issues surrounding the Meat Planning Council. The panel of speakers at the Te Kuiti meeting included John Foster (Richmond), Colin Henderson (Wairakei Group), Jeff Jackson (AFFCO), David Carey (King Country Lamb), David Frith and Jim Bull (Board) and Bill Garland (FF Meat & Wool Section).

members for a Task Force. It noted that "all interested parties have been developing potential solutions for the past several months. The underlying causes of the crisis facing the industry are not new and have been referred to in many previous reports and debated at length for years."

The Task Force would consider many of these proposals. Its nominated members were the Meat Board, MIA, "current industry bankers in whatever groupings chosen by them", Federated Farmers, TDB and Freesia. The terms of reference envisaged the Task Force would deliver its advice within two weeks of its establishment, which was proposed as 14 August 1991. The Task Force never eventuated as it was the Government's preferred option not to become actively involved or set up new structures and to let existing parties work together to reach a solution.

The Meat Planning Council (MPC) was that solution. By mid-August agreement had been reached between the Board and the MIA on the format of the MPC, to be in operation by 1 October 1991 for an initial period of five years. The MPC would comprise seven meat company chief executives ("as no major player was prepared to delegate authority to another on matters affecting his business") and four from the Board, but with voting to be on a 50:50 basis. The council would discuss both sheep and beef matters and there was provision for two of the MIA representative positions to alternate according to whether sheepmeats or beef were being considered. The volte-face on beef came from the need to sort out the allocation of quota for the US market. The 'rules' governing MPC activities were to be encapsulated in a commercial agreement between all licensed exporters.

Jeff Jackson, former Fletcher Fishing chief executive, who took over from Max Toy at AFFCO in 1991.

The establishment of the MPC represented a "bold first step of a process intended to return New Zealand's meat industry – at all levels – to profitability". The joint announcement from David Frith and Sir David Beattie on 23 August highlighted the international marketplace as the "crucial arena" for solving industry problems, rather than the areas of livestock procurement or restructuring. "Getting it right there (in the market) will create an environment whereby desirable improvements will flow on throughout the structure of the industry – right back to the farm gate." It was a rather forlorn hope since events were to prove that some MPC decisions actually fuelled the procurement competition.

The immediate requirement was the 'Commercial Co-operation Agreement' to be established with all licensed exporters with a key element being 'marketplace franchising'. The right to export to any area would be dependent on agreement to conform with specified conditions, including the provision of market plans, and the lodgement of an 'export franchise fee' to be held in trust.

If an exporter did not adhere to the agreed terms the franchise fee would be forfeited and the funds used for export market development activity in the area where the transgression occurred. In the event, the franchise fee became a performance bond put forward in the form of a bank 'stand-by letter of credit' in favour of the Board.

The whole exercise ran into an immediate storm of protest from the smaller processors and independent exporters who considered they had not been consulted adequately and their interests and concerns were being ig-

Rural News

Editorial

Death of a dinosaur

WEDDEL's ignominy was complete last week with the announcement there would be no money for $70-odd million worth of unsecured creditors followed by the Commerce Commission's decision to allow North Island meat companies to buy the failed company's five plants and keep them closed forever.

So the Vesty dinosaur is finally dead, although it was not given a pauper's funeral. The consortium's paying $50 million for the plants, having outlayed $2 million on a plethora of consultants and assorted travelling shiny arses.

The events of 1993 and 1994 helped make the reputation of Ron Clarke and Rural News *for hard-hitting headlines and no-bullshit opinions. Ron Clarke continues to review the meat industry's imperial fashion parade, now for the* New Zealand Farmer.

Colin Henderson of Benmore Products, founder of the Wairakei Group which aimed to counter the power of the bigger companies in the MPC.

nored by the meat industry establishment.

Not all exporters were members of the MIA, and some who were considered the structure of the executive committee and voting systems gave them no real influence. The executive committee was dominated by the big companies – the dinosaurs. The committee was chaired by Sir David Beattie and comprised Stewart Barnett (PPCS), Rick Bettle (Alliance), John Buxton (Riverlands), Alan Clark (Meatex), John Foster (Richmond), Jeff Jackson (AFFCO), Graeme Lowe (Lowe Walker), Gray Mathias (Mathias Meats), John Prendergast (Weddel) and Graeme Thompson (Fortex).

Colin Henderson of Benmore Products considered the big companies would dominate on the MPC as well. The MIA representation (with allowance for the sheepmeat and beef alternates) was to comprise all of the executive committee except Sir David Beattie and Alan Clark. While he had no problem with some of the MPC requirements, such as providing a market plan, he was concerned "*who* was sitting in judgement – a number of people who had already tried to knock out the smaller guys, particularly me. I'd had my fair share of treatment.

"Both the North Island and South Island meat industries were in disarray. There were a lot of new plants in the North Island and Fortex was on a roll. The big guys were shaking in their shoes and couldn't come up with anything that would address the massive overcapacity problem and the inefficiencies prevailing in the older plants. The only opportunity of putting any constraints on the new wave of entrants was in export marketplaces especially in the US and EC quota markets. You didn't have to be a rocket scientist to work that out."

The total lack of consultation added to the distrust. It fired up Colin Henderson to convene a meeting of the disaffected parties at the Wairakei Hotel, after which they became known as the Wairakei Group. "There were about 30 different companies involved, many of them also MIA members. The only ones not in were AFFCO, Weddel, PPCS, Alliance and Richmond. The big five – or really the big six because the Meat Board was on that side."

As Henderson recalls, David Frith and Tim Ritchie were invited to address the meeting but they fanned the flames when they equated telling the delegates what was going to happen with industry consultation. "I said we've got news for you. We've all got a significant investment in the industry and we won't be treated like that," said Henderson.

The group then cranked up the PR machine using Ron Clarke of *Rural News* who leapt at the chance to support the underdog and malign the dinosaurs. The campaign was to let the farming community know that the 'big guys' were trying to use the MPC to press gang the 'new boys' into line.

Farmers had backed the new smaller operators because they had energised the procurement wars. "The big companies were terrorised by the farmers," said Colin Henderson. "The support that Benmore got from farmers sending stock to us was unbelievable; so many people told us that they had been sending their stock to AFFCO for years but would switch procurement away from them. We ran shed meetings and hall meetings. Clarkie helped put the issues in black and white. There was a massive groundswell of support."

The MPC issue dominated the MIA conference in Queenstown in late September 1991. Guest speaker Dennis Hussey of ACIL Australia was loudly applauded by members of the Wairakei Group for his forthright criticism of the scheme. He commented that the industry had a history of under-performance and appeared to have "lurched from crisis to crisis, searching unsuccessfully for a solution to unacceptable commercial outcomes... I believe that the proposed Meat Planning Council is setting the industry up for another spin in this revolving door of intervention and barriers to entry, consolidation of vested interests, eventual collapse of arrangements, and the commercial pain of further adjustments to asset values."

Peter Egan, chairman of Freesia was more fulsome: "I am a great believer in a planned approach, both for the companies and the industry and I support the establishment of the Meat Planning Council. A global approach to planning with a time horizon that extends beyond 12 months is what will be required in the future." The applause was a little more muted.

The MIA had initially indicated it would be looking to the Board to impose licence conditions to either make all licence holders become members of the MIA or ensure they posted a bond and were committed to the MIA proposals. Later this changed to hoping to persuade the Board to license only those companies that signed the co-operation agreement. In the event the Board used its powers to incorporate conditions into meat export licences enabling it to give directions to licencees under Sections 12 and 14 of the Meat Export Control Act, including a direction that the licencee "would adhere to the terms of the agreement establishing the Meat Planning Council".

A final Heads of Agreement to establish the MPC had been drafted by the Board and the MIA and sent to all exporters under cover of a letter dated 7 October 1991. This noted that as part of the arrangements each licensed exporter was being asked to be party to a 'commercial' agreement between the two principals, which they were asked to sign and return by 25 October.

A series of meetings in Auckland, Wellington and Christchurch over a

Minister of Agriculture John Falloon (centre) meets key New Zealand lamb importer representatives in London, November 1991. From left: Doug Brydges, managing director of Towers; Peter Firth, director of Weddel Swift, Ken Rouse, NZ Lamb Company, and Max Toy, chief executive of New Zealand Holdings (the UK name for Associated New Zealand Farmers).

Though there was a change of government when National, under Prime Minister Jim Bolger, was elected in November 1990, there was no return to the earlier days where farmers took priority. David Frith says he enjoyed working with Labour ministers like Mike Moore, even if he did often ring from overseas in the small hours of the morning. "When National came in I thought this will be easier, I know most of these guys from way back. But I got the distinct impression of 'We know what to do, David, thank you, we'll call when we need you'."

Rick Bettle, Alliance CEO from 1991-95 and current chairman of the Lamb Company. A newcomer to the meat industry when appointed to Alliance, he took a very active and vocal part both within the company and in the MIA.

two-day period was proposed as the final consultation prior to implementation. The aim was to tell the industry what was going to happen and to avoid political discussion. It was during those meetings that concerns about the contents of the document were raised, but inevitably politics came into it as well.

The stonewalling approach adopted by Colin Henderson and Warwick Wilson of Crown Meat Export in claiming inequities and lack of consideration of the smaller organisations had the desired effect. To get the process moving again the Minister of Agriculture, John Falloon, called a meeting at his home in Wellington on the evening of 15 October to get people to express their views on the issues and, more importantly, to talk to each other.

Those invited were John Foster, John Buxton, Rick Bettle, Peter Jackson, Graeme Thompson, Stella Clark (MIA), David Frith, Tim Ritchie (Meat Board), Ken Douglas, Peter Harris (CTU), Royce Elliott (MAF), Dick Davison (Federated Farmers), Colin Henderson, Warwick Wilson (Wairakei Group), Graham Scott (Treasury), John Anderson (National Bank), Gordon Hogg, Catherine Petrey (Minister's Office). Some of these were members of the informal agricultural strategy committee the Minister had set up as a sounding board on agricultural matters. Paul Spackman from the Prime Minister's Department kept Jim Bolger well informed on developments.

It was during these discussions that John Anderson, representing the banks, is reported to have made it very clear that funding for the industry as a whole was closely related to the setting up of the MPC.

All participants were asked to comment on the issue and raise their concerns. During the discussions Colin Henderson said they wanted representation. "The Meat Board and the MIA threw up their hands in horror. I said we don't want a vote, we want representation." There was no way, he said, that they could rely on getting their views to the MPC through the MIA.

The meeting and subsequent discussions between Colin Henderson, Warwick Wilson, Tim Ritchie, Board secretary Trevor Playford and MIA secretary Stella Clark resulted in some significant amendments. These included the need for the MPC to treat all parties on a "fair and equitable" basis and the appointment of an observer, Eric Cammell, now retired from AFFCO, to represent the interests of the smaller companies. As well, they clarified issues relating to licensing and the approval of market plans.

The schedule of alterations ran to six pages for a document covering 28 pages. An industry intent on deregulation internally was moving back to a detailed prescriptive mode of control of marketing operations. And that was just the start of things; paper output would consume large tracts of trees.

The Board described the MPC as "a top level policy forum". The rules required companies be represented by their chief executives and not their subordinates so decisions could be implemented; the only alternate to a CEO unable to attend meetings was that company's chairman.

The MPC was set up with six goals: (1) to create a climate to encourage meat companies to be market-led, not production-driven; (2) to foster innovation in market and product development; (3) to encourage export market competition beyond price battles; (4) to create greater marketing effort in the Pacific Rim and the Middle East; (5) to improve targeting of promotion and marketing; and (6) to develop strategies to ensure maximum earnings for exporters.

It was even considered that the MPC could lead to an industry board, based on statutory support for the developing commercial relationships. The one area the MPC could not discuss was procurement.

In the end the MPC began operations slightly later than the planned start date of 1 October. The Board reported the MPC was concentrating on bringing a more rigorous and focussed approach to sheepmeat export planning and pricing. Four franchise markets were designated for sheepmeats: the UK, Continental Europe, the Middle East and North America. Franchise values were established according to broad bands of the volume of product supplied to each of the markets.

CTU economist Peter Harris was among many who weighed in with their opinions on the meat industry's problems and possible solutions.

Warren Berryman, writing in the *National Business Review* on 11 October 1991, immediately labelled the MPC a "buzzard's cartel" which was "operated by the Board and big private sector meat companies and backed up by the Board's statutory power to banish non-conforming companies from the meat exporting business". In the *National Business Review* of 20 December 1991, Berryman reported the Commerce Commission was keeping a close eye on the MPC which he depicted as "the Meat Board cartel set up to rig prices for export sheepmeat".

In the end it came down to a question of the powers and legal situation under the Board's Act in relation to the export activity, which was the MPC's aim, rather than any collusive livestock trading practice in New Zealand, which was covered by the Commerce Act. Michael Turner pointed out, also in the *National Business Review* on 20 December 1991, that "without the MPC the banks probably would not have renewed seasonal funding lines for AFFCO and Alliance". He asked whose interests were best served by the new MPC, on which Jackson and Bettle sat, particularly when the Meat Board, which was supposed to represent producer interests was also an investor in AFFCO and Alliance which were heavily indebted and "propped up by" Freesia.

Even though the MPC was set up to deal mainly with marketing issues, it did not please a number of farmers who had benefited from the procurement battles of the previous two seasons and saw the council as a device to stifle competition.

John Morrison of the Mossburn Group asked the Commerce Commission to investigate the MPC because he considered it would restrict competition amongst meat exporters and protect the larger established exporters. "We believe that it's simply a barrier to new entrants into the meat industry, thereby reducing the competition for the firms that the Board's got all its money in."

In his view some of the present industry participants were not efficient because of the debt loading they were carrying. On the 14 October 1991 edition of 'Rural Report' he said: "Newcomers may not have the debt loading that the incumbents have and so therefore may bid higher for the lambs. This means that the present companies, namely Alliance and AFFCO and PPCS may well be outbidded (sic) for the farmers' lambs. That's what they are afraid of."

Pressure from the banks, and from some of the corporate shareholders, as well as the Meat Planning Council's work in moderating some of the price fluctuations overseas, resulted in a more measured approach to procurement pricing in 1991-92. Companies produced reasonable financial results for the first time in three years.

The chairman of the MIA reported on the favourable environment resulting from improved market returns, and, more particularly, the rationalisation in the New Zealand industry. "The process of rationalisation has been helped by improvements to the domestic economic environment through the virtual elimination of inflation, lower interest rates, reduction in protection for manufacturers, transport reforms, meat plant delicensing and other moves to cut costs and improve efficiency, plus the flexibility offered by the Employment Contracts Act. This progress has significantly enhanced the ability of participants in the meat industry to improve their returns to companies and producers." Rogernomics was having an effect.

Moderation of some of the more extreme competitive activities also brought the industry to the attention of the Commerce Commission. In January 1992 it announced it was seeking assistance from those who produced, sold, and transported livestock "to be its eyes and ears in monitoring prices to make sure there was no collusion to fix prices".

The disciplines and co-ordination introduced by the MPC had some effect, but the general view was that favourable market conditions led to steady and sustained improvements in returns from key markets during 1992, and particularly from the UK.

The industry's response to the MPC challenge to establish closer relations with markets outside the UK was conditioned partly by the growing interest in chilled product which required more monitoring, precise handling and distribution than its frozen counterpart. The MIA reported in 1992: "To extract maximum benefit from their marketing systems and retain better control of the distribution chain, New Zealand companies have in recent years expanded their offshore operations." It noted that New Zealand controlled operations had been established in Bahrain, Belgium, Germany, Canada, Japan, Singapore, UAE and the US.

"This process will continue with the growth of chilled and differentiated products and as companies extend their hands-on reach into the marketplace." However, representation was generally for individual companies so the fragmented approach continued, and dreams of achieving critical mass to take on the big retailers were still just that.

The Meat Planning Council also broadened its focus to include monitoring of the negotiations on sheepmeat access to the EC, or EU as it became on 1 January 1993, a review of the Special Access Market system, and "structures for more effectively allocating exporter entitlements to volume constrained markets" – the quota allocation systems. The debates and squabbles over quota allocations and marketing arrangements were to become even more protracted and bitter than the 'turf wars' that had erupted with the MPC proposals.

Divestment
1991-97

"Freesia tried to be a catalyst to give the farmer a better return. We thought getting the costs out and getting processing capacity closer to stock availability would achieve that, and less competition in the procurement market would mean some co-ordination in the marketplace." Peter Egan.

Somewhat overshadowed by MPC developments in 1991, the Board initiated a review of lamb marketing in North America (US, Canada and Mexico) including the impact of the proposed North American Free Trade Agreement (NAFTA) and the promotion activities of the Australian and US meat industry organisations.

The review committee comprised Graham Ansell and Tim Ritchie from the Board, John Foster and Graeme Thompson (MIA) and Pat Goodman of GFW plus the Board's Andrew Burtt as secretary. Their work covered not only the current market conditions and New Zealand's performance in the market since the 1986 review but also the operations and activities of the Lamb Company in Canada and the US and the Weddel-led consortium in Mexico.

The committee's recommendations were reviewed and largely endorsed by the Board in March 1992 and passed to the MPC for their consideration. It was a rather long chain of command especially since any licensing decision of the MPC had to go back to the Board for implementation. The price of co-operation, perhaps?

The Board echoed the review committee's opinion that the marketing of New Zealand lamb should be conducted in a more co-ordinated manner "under an overall New Zealand promotional umbrella to maintain and develop the high quality image of the product in North American markets". In the specific markets the single licensee arrangements for Canada (the Lamb Company) and Mexico (Weddel consortium) should be retained.

However the Lamb Company should put in place co-operative arrangements that allowed other New Zealand suppliers to exploit specific market niches in Canada without undermining its existing activities. Also in Mexico, other suppliers should be given the opportunity to supply the Weddel-led consortium.

For the US it was recommended that the existing multiple licence system should be retained so long as the co-ordination conditions of the licences were rigorously adhered to under the guidance of the MPC.

It was also recommended that the Lamb Company "should consider the advantages of restructuring its operations, through commercial negotiations, to achieve autonomous entities in each of the US and Canada." In doing so the company could consider broadening its share base and promoting the sale of the Board's interests in the company – including the shares held by the Meat Industry Research Trust.

However, there were several barriers to be overcome, including some

Pat Goodman of GFW and Graeme Thompson of Fortex are serenaded during their visit to Mexico as part of the North American Review.

pre-emptive rights clauses in the company's articles, before that could be achieved. The first step came with the 1992 decision by the Board to reconstitute Freesia as Primary Resources Ltd (PRL), an investment holding company, and as part of that arrangement to transfer to PRL its Lamb Company preference shares and an outstanding loan.

In December 1991 the Board had announced a review of Freesia's structure and role. As the annual report said: "It was prompted by the Board's desire to ensure that there were no aspects of its operation which could inhibit the development and success of the newly formed Meat Planning Council." It was also an acknowledgement that the Board's 'referee-player' status was a major sticking point in developing new directions and relationships with the companies.

Subsequently the Board advised the Electoral Committee in March 1992 it was establishing two commercial holding companies to more cleanly separate its statutory responsibilities from its investment arm (Freesia) and its commercial trading arm (ANZCO/Janmark).

The announcement indicated the Board had adopted an approach similar to the Government's State Owned Enterprise model. The two holding companies were to be directed by independent, commercially-oriented boards of directors, none of whom were Board members or staff, and would be managed under a directors' charter or statement of corporate intent against which the Board would monitor their performances.

Primary Resources Ltd was finally set up in August 1992. PRL ostensibly took over the Board's shareholding in Freesia Investments as well as acquiring from the Board the preference shares in and a loan to the Lamb Company, and a loan to Advanced Foods Ltd. Peter Egan, David Spence and Jim Macaulay resigned as directors of Freesia as part of the process of downsizing and re-launching as PRL.

Technically, it was just a change in name and direction but it was styled as a new company which, as David Frith recalls, was essential. "It was cosmetic. If we'd just said, now Freesia doesn't have any Board members on it, we'd never have got away with it," he says. "But by saying this is a new company, and we've got new directors, people could get their minds

The official opening of the Five Star Beef feedlot, a joint venture between the Board subsidiary ANZCO and Itoham Foods Ltd of Japan. From left: Prime Minister Jim Bolger, Board and ANZCO director Mervyn Barnett, Joan Bolger, ANZCO managing director Graeme Harrison and Jenny Shipley, MP for Ashburton. Grainfed beef from the feedlot was on the menu for the official lunch.

Three generations at the formal opening of Five Star Beef. Standing, from left: Pam Frith, the current Board chairman, David Frith, Board member and future chairman John Acland.
Seated: Lady Judith Ormond, former Board chairman Sir John Ormond, and Rosemary Acland.

around that.   And nobody challenged it, did they?"

The directors were Norman Geary (chairman), Bernie Knowles and Mervyn Barnett, who announced he would resign from the Board in March 1993. Mick Calder continued as the CEO. The statement of corporate intent changed the focus of the company. While Freesia had previously been positively engaged in investing funds in the industry, the emphasis was now on the active and ongoing management of those investments and possible divestment of them.

David Frith commented that the Board had been criticised repeatedly for its investment activities which farmers and meat companies contended had allowed it to play the role of both player and referee. The aim of PRL was to separate the roles.

He also noted in the *NZ Herald* of 11 August 1992: "The divestment of the investments is not a fire sale. It means a commercially driven exit, in whole or in part from each respective company over time." PRL had been looking at investing in marketing operations in France and Germany, but the new approach meant that the company was moving into reverse.

Later in 1992 the Board announced the formation of Meat Enterprises Ltd (MEL), a holding company to take up the shareholding in the ANZCO/ Janmark group of companies including Five Star Beef Ltd, Southern Nissui Ltd and New Zealand Beef Holdings Ltd. The directors of MEL were Mervyn Barnett, Murray Gough, ex-CEO of the Dairy Board, and Rob Thompson from Coopers and Lybrand. This time the statement of corporate intent was directed more at the structuring of the group for eventual divestment to a commercial operator.

While farmers were by now almost unanimous in their call for the Board to dispense with Freesia, ANZCO was a different matter. Many wanted ANZCO sold off and its earnings given back to levy-payers. ANZCO had started as a specialist sheepmeat organisation but moved into other products as the markets opened. As a group it had aimed to form strategic alliances with market leaders "to fast track market development and reduce financial exposure". It had therefore formed beef joint ventures, including the Five Star Feedlot, with two of Japan's leading food companies, Itoham Foods Inc and Nippon Suisan Kaisha Ltd.

It had also formed a joint venture with AFFCO in 1991 to market beef in North Asia – New Zealand Beef Holdings. At the time of its formation ANZCO's New Zealand manager Paul Phillips said: "Other New Zealand beef companies had been canvassed to see if they were interested in such a deal but they had walked away from it". AFFCO already had a well developed business in Japan and ANZCO aimed to take advantage of those strengths and build on them.

It was seen that ANZCO had spun its $350,000 seed funding into marketplace gold through its joint venture feedlot, and the time it had invested in marketplace relationships. Now it was positioned to take great advantage of the liberalisation of the North Asian beef market. If it was to be divested, there was a strong argument that farmers should see some of the proceeds.

PRL's first divestment move was the restructuring of the finances of the Lamb Company, repaying the outstanding loan and the accrued interest. It was also designed to set the scene for the eventual sale of the preference shares held by PRL and the 50% of the ordinary shares held for the benefit of the Meat Industry Research Trust.

Late in 1993 PRL prepared an information memorandum for the sale of Advanced Foods and endeavoured to attract New Zealand operators, without any measurable success. The only real interest came from the originators of the whole Advanced Foods arrangement, Bernard Matthews plc.

In addition to selling the company, PRL had to consider that the Board was seeking a release from the contractual arrangements relating to supply and access to the UK market it had signed with Matthews when it had control of the export of sheepmeats in the mid-eighties. In the circumstances, a sale to Bernard Matthews plc provided the opportunity to achieve this though it did give the buyer a negotiating edge. The cancellation of the contract was part of the sale agreement negotiated, and Advanced Foods was sold in August 1993. At the same time the shareholding Freesia had taken in Bernard Matthews in 1987 was sold.

There was also the need for Matthews to secure a more consistent and long term contract for the supply of carcasses to the Advanced Foods plant. Peter Egan had always regarded the lack of a secure supply as an Achilles heel. He had had numerous battles with Waitaki and then with AFFCO to get a supply commitment, but only short-term deals were available. He had threatened on more than one occasion to build a slaughter chain at Waipukurau so that Advanced Foods could do its own procurement and processing.

Advanced Foods had managed to stitch together a working arrangement with Progressive Meats and a more informal deal with AFFCO. It was this latter understanding that Bernard Matthews' managing director David Joll concentrated on and turned into a more formal longer-term arrangement to

One of the Meat Board's biggest field days was held in March 1992 to showcase the new Five Star Beef feedlot. Among the hosts were chief economist Brian Speirs of the Economic Service and Paul Phillips of ANZCO (right).

the benefit of both parties.

The more difficult task for PRL was to find an opportunity and a means of exiting from its investments in AFFCO and Alliance. The legal agreements and understandings with the two companies, their bankers and the other corporate shareholders, particularly Fletcher Challenge, complicated the situation. Of course, the farmer directors of both of these meat companies always had the ready suggestion that the corporates should just hand the investments over to the farmers and leave. This was not regarded as a responsible option, either by the directors of PRL or by their shareholder, the Board.

A winter view of the Sapporo Beer Garden, one of ANZCO's longstanding customers for New Zealand lamb. Sliced thinly, it is used in the Beer Garden's famous Genghis Khan dish.

In 1994 AFFCO revived the financial restructuring programme started three years previously. Company rationalisation had involved the closures of sheep chains at Horotiu and Waitara and the beef chain at Taumarunui as well as rebuilding the works at Moerewa and Feilding. However the financial restructuring was to be delayed until 1995 by debate over the tradeable quota system.

The company then successfully attracted two cornerstone investors in the form of Dairy Meats and Peter Spencer's Toocooya Holdings, with each taking up a 10% shareholding in the restructured company. This move was not entirely accepted by some of the shareholders of Dairy Meats who considered they should have been more fully consulted before funds were committed.

The investments gave AFFCO the shot in the arm that was required despite adverse remarks from some business commentators. 'The Analyst' in the *Independent* commented on the proposed float under the headline 'AFFCO's prospectus: You can tell by the smell it ain't hay…' Even so, the company was successfully floated with some over-subscriptions, and listed on the Stock Exchange on 1 May 1995. Both Fletcher Challenge and PRL were required to continue to support the company until the bankers had converted their notes and sold the shares. This meant the corporates did not exit until early in 1996, both a little wiser for the experience.

By then, the Board had sold, through MEL, its 64% shareholding in ANZCO, which had added to its operations in Australia with the purchase of the McPhee Meat Packing plant at Blayney.

The purchasers were Huttons Kiwi, increasing their existing shareholding from 20.8% to 30%, Rangatira Investments 10%, and management which increased its shareholding from 10% to 20%. The existing partners in the company, Itoham and Nippon Suisan Kaisha, took up the balance. Due diligence began early in 1995 with the aim of completing the sale in February, but negotiations became a little more protracted and the deal was eventually completed in December that year for a price of some $35 million.

As well, negotiations for restructuring the shareholding within the Lamb Company had come to a head. Rick Bettle had taken over as chairman of the company. Mick Calder, who could see his role at PRL disappearing with every divestment, had switched from PRL to become company secretary of the Lamb Company.

In another complicated deal, seemingly typical of any PRL transaction, the shareholding in the Lamb Company was reorganised before a series of transfers, which saw PRL, the Meat Industry Research Trust and Jim Bull (who had taken over the Borthwicks shareholding) exit as shareholders of the company in June 1996. ANZCO became a shareholder and Richmond increased what had been a minimal holding, so the Lamb Company was owned by AFFCO, Alliance, ANZCO and Richmond – all held together by a shareholders' agreement.

In some respects, PRL had succeeded in bringing together the co-ordinated marketing operation, involving most of the major operators, that had been one of the primary aims of Freesia.

However, as the Lamb Company's earlier incarnation DEVCO had been a larger consortium, cynics would say that they had succeeded only in putting a fair proportion of Humpty Dumpty back together again.

Alliance was also moving towards its eventual aim of restructuring out its corporate shareholders. It had settled the indemnity arrangement with Freesia Meat Holdings in 1993 and addressed many of its cost and effi-ciency issues as part of its 'Agenda for Change', but it was still under a tight rein from its bankers. John Waller of Price Waterhouse, who had consider-able experience in company restructuring as well as managing receiverships, had taken over as the banks' financial adviser.

Still under some pressure to reduce its debt loading, Alliance had started developing its plan to raise $40 million from farmers and other investors over a two-year period. Rick Bettle stumped the southern South Island at woolshed meetings, giving as good as he got at question time, and in the process ensuring farmer involvement and support. The money was to come from raising $25 million in equity over three years through the retention of pool surpluses, conversion of rebates to shares and cash subscriptions, plus a $15 million capital notes issue. It also involved an initial move to convert the original shares held by the corporates and which carried special rights relating to the percentage share of the company, to ordinary A shares sub-ject to special conditions regarding voting rights and redemption.

In addition, Fletcher Challenge would take over Alliance's shareholding in AFFCO in exchange for its loan which stood at $35 million and for the issue to it of a further 2.2 million Alliance shares. There was a parallel arrangement with the Alliance bankers to convert some of their loans to convertible securities, with the proviso that they would be interest-free and not convert if the capital raising was successful. It was just another simple Freesia-related deal, much loved by lawyers.

The deal involved the usual round of tense negotiations within Freesia Meat Holdings between Fletcher Challenge, GFW (now Goodman Fielder) and PRL and parallel haggling between Freesia and Alliance over the terms of the arrangement. Mick Calder recalls being involved with Grant Niccol of Fletcher Challenge in the negotiations with Alliance directors and chief executive Owen Poole the night before the extraordinary general meeting held in August. John Waller of Price Waterhouse acted as the go-between while Mick Calder consulted by phone with both Norman Geary and Bernie Knowles into the early morning.

The final agreement was reached about an hour before the meeting. The capital raising plan and the conversion of the corporates' shares was approved by 91% of shareholders. Some farmers were not happy; John Morrison, now chairman of Northern Southland Federated Farmers, considered farmers had no choice but to vote for the plan. "It was a fait accompli. Shareholders were told to vote for the plan or lose your company."

The issue of capital bonds went ahead in 1996 after Alliance posted a profit of $18.1 million in 1994-95 as a result of favourable climatic conditions leading to a high seasonal sheep and lamb kill. The issue for $15 million was over-subscribed and dealings with the company's bankers became a little more amicable.

The A shares issued to the corporates were redeemable at valuation but subject to the condition that the company's finance ratios did not move below agreed limits after the redemption. In June 1997 the corporates gave notice, under the provisions of its constitution, for the company to redeem the shares at the end of the financial year. It was a foregone conclusion that this would result in another round of tortuous negotiations over a fair value for the shares.

Christine McKenzie, pictured as she learned she had become the first woman elected by shareholders to be a meat company director, for the Alliance Group.
Photo: Southland Times.

The value hinged on the recent financial performance of the company and more particularly on future expectations. Naturally, Alliance prognostications were much less optimistic than those of the corporates. Also, there was the usual haggle between the corporates over the unwinding of the shareholding in Freesia Meat Holdings. Eventually, and with considerable input from the legal fraternity, the valuations and other arrangements were agreed and the redemption settled on 1 December 1997 at a price of $1.52 per share.

Once the Alliance deal was completed the Board decided there was no need for PRL to operate as a separate organisation as its task was virtually complete apart from the sale of the Richmond shares. The remaining directors of PRL resigned and the responsibility for the operation of the company passed to the Board, with John Acland as the sole director and chairman.

The Richmond shareholding had been held over by PRL because it had provided a consistently good dividend, there was no urgency to sell and there would be no difficulty in arranging a sale. There had been various unsolicited offers from investors to take up the shareholding, but PRL had declined to sell. In addition, arising from the fracas that had developed between the two parties in the late 80s, there was a 'gentlemen's' understanding that PRL would consult Richmond prior to any sale but the final decision would be for PRL as the shareholder.

The Board's announcement early in 1997 that it was offering the Richmond shares for sale by tender ruffled the company's corporate feathers. It considered the Board was not acting in accordance with the understanding and being denied a say in the choice of any new shareholder.

The concern heightened when it became clear that the leading contenders were likely to be AFFCO or PPCS, both considered by Richmond as less than friendly potential shareholders. This was especially so as Richmond still considered it was a farmer-owned Hawke's Bay company. A resulting court hearing saw Richmond win the right to decide who their shareholders would be, and both AFFCO and PPCS were ruled out. The sale of

Board deputy chairman Jim Macaulay with the ingredients for a Genghis Khan, pictured when the North Asia Review team visited Japan. The team recommended ending ANZCO's exclusive lamb and mutton export licences.

the shares to HKM Investments representing a number of Maori Incorporations and trusts was finalised in December 1997 and completed the Board's divestments at the end of its 75th anniversary year.

It also brought to an end the roller-coaster existence of Freesia/PRL. With its investments sold off, PRL was put back on the shelf. The company had been raised from the ashes of the Board's intervention in the mid 80s to operate as a separate investment arm of the Board. Its principal function had been to weld together a producer-owned and controlled commercial structure to promote orderly marketing, but it became enmeshed in the rationalisation of ownership and capacity. Freesia's lofty aims had been to give farmers a better return by taking costs out, cutting procurement competition and adding co-ordination in the marketplace. However, the change in political and farmer attitudes towards a more competitive economy with less statutory control and intervention eventually made the Freesia/PRL approach politically unsustainable and hastened its demise.

With the complete disinvestment of the Board's interests in meat companies, influence had truly passed to their shareholders.

As the Board had reviewed and withdrawn the Special Access Market arrangements for the Lamb Company in Canada and ANZCO in Japan, and subsequently removed the arrangements for the other markets in the Middle East, the prospects of it entering the market in future were reduced to ashes.

The Board and PRL were not alone in endeavouring to rationalise or reorganise the ownership of companies in the meat industry at a cost of around $90 million, with some of this offset by the $35 million return from the sale of ANZCO. Brierleys made a number of raids and had persisted with Huttons Kiwi before finally bailing out in 1995. ANZCO took full ownership of the Riverlands processing assets as Pacific Beef and has continued to established itself as one of the bigger operators. ANZCO, now known as ANZCO Foods Ltd, includes ANZCO Foods (Australia) Pty, ANZCO International (Australia) Pty, Canterbury Meat Packers Ltd, with plants at Seafield and Blenheim, the Five Star Beef Feedlot, Pacific Beef Ltd, with plants at Bulls and Eltham, the New Zealand Casing Company, Crown Marketing Ltd and ANZCO Green Island Ltd. Rugby identity Eddie Tonks chairs the board, managing director is Graeme Harrison, and other board members include Murray Gough, Kenichi Ito, Naoya Kakizoe, and Norman Geary. Alan Grant and Max Toy are alternate directors.

Fletcher Challenge and GFW had tried, through SFM and Waitaki respectively, but having decided that the industry was not to their liking had difficulty in arranging their orderly exit, leaving considerable dents in their back pockets.

The banks, largely through the invisible hand of Sir John Anderson of the National Bank, had been more involved than they wanted to be but had managed to pull back without too many scars. Meanwhile, some of the companies were rearranging ownership for themselves.

Drawing the Watchdog's Teeth 1972-97

"Mr Lindsay Malcolm spoke to his remit and made the assertion that equity accounting presents the Board with an opportunity to camouflage and confuse. He also said that Meat Industry Reserve Account investments were easily accountable and that the Board had in the past gained a lot of kudos from full disclosure of the Meatmark accounts. He said that ANZCO has a monopoly status and should be subject to some scrutiny. Freesia Investments is the principal recipient of Reserve Account funds but appears to be pouring funds into the meat industry out of a bottomless pit... He said the Board only ever seems to provide full disclosure when things go wrong." Electoral Committee minutes, August 1989.

The members of the Meat Board had status, authority and access to influential people within New Zealand and overseas. Their ultimate accountability was to the producers, whose interests they were charged with representing. But until 1995, they were directly answerable only to a group of 26 – the Meat and Wool Boards' Electoral Committee.

Each July, farmers could vote for an Electoral Committee representative to make the twice-yearly trip to Wellington on their behalf. Committee members served a one-year term, although most would be re-elected unopposed for a number of years, unless some controversy arose.

The Electoral Committee functions, as specified by regulations under the Meat Export Control Act, were twofold. These were to receive the annual report and balance sheet of the Meat Board, and to elect producer representatives onto the Board. The latter power could strike fear and trembling into the grown men of the Meat Board, and of the Wool Board, for whom they performed a similar function. As Anita Busby wrote in the Oct-Dec 1989 *Meat Producer:* "Candidates about to appear before the Electoral Committee for a place on the Meat Board are as nervous as pimply youths setting out on their first date. The ordeal of exposing one's inadequacies and lack of knowledge to 26 men is apparently worse than anyone can possibly imagine. It is dreaded." The Committee elected two members for a three-year term on the Meat Board in March, and the Wool Board in August.

Over the years the Electoral Committee had developed an informal and undefined role to communicate important producer issues to the Board, and information given them back to the producers. This included the ability to submit remits.

Though the Board had no obligation to act on those remits, which covered the full spectrum from weak selling to sheep measles, from every permutation of pricing to proposed federation with Australia, it was unwise to ignore them. The Board in turn used the Electoral Committee to test ideas such as grading changes and the move to a local trade levy, and on occasions to set the record straight if it felt it had been misreported in the media.

Don Macnab of Wanganui, Electoral Committee chairman from 1978-87. He brought in the idea of announcing Board electoral results by handing each candidate a note, instead of lining them up at the back of the room and making a public announcement.

Aside from the elections, the two-day March session and one-day August meeting with the Board was largely devoted to a detailed briefing on industry issues ranging from port reform to Board investments and local and overseas promotion. It was an intensive backgrounding which gave the Electoral Committee members the opportunity to become what Brian Peacocke, in a 1981 study, called a "highly-informed elite".

The Committee had the chance to meet the Board's overseas representatives and others such as the US agricultural attache. The programme included a dinner with the Meat Exporters' Council or Meat Industry Association, traditionally used by the hosts to prime Committee members with what former Electoral Committee member Alan Grant describes as "hot air and half truths". As other on the Committee saw it, the evening set them up with awkward questions to ask the Board in public session.

The Electoral Committee interpreted its "receive the Annual Report and Accounts" as an opportunity to grill the Board on the topics of the day, especially those concerned with marketing and finance. As a watchdog for the producer, it was keen to show it had sharp teeth.

Members were dogged in their pursuit of detail on commercial aspects like ANZCO. Perhaps Freesia was the all-time most contentious issue, with chairman Peter Egan guaranteed a grilling every time he appeared. Overseas office spending and particularly the perceived cost of air travel for members and their wives was another popular topic, along with allegations of weak selling in various markets. While the Board always resisted making public any commercially sensitive information, or separating out consolidated finances, it did on occasion invite Committee members to have personal discussions on financial issues.

The indirect process of selecting producer representatives through an Electoral Committee was established shortly after the Board itself. Since 1957 Committee membership was made up of representatives of 23 districts defined according to sheep numbers and county boundaries (with two representatives for Gisborne and Southland). In 1970 numbers were ad-

Counting Electoral Committee votes at Seabridge House. From left: Chris Hampton of the Economic Service, the Board's electoral administrator Sandra Irwin and Trevor Playford, secretary from 1987-95.

justed to 26 to include a non-voting representative of the Meat & Wool Section of Federated Farmers. A further review in 1974 essentially retained the status quo.

Although most Electoral Committees readily lent an ear to lobbying by interest groups and would-be Board members they resisted any caucusing, priding themselves on taking an independent approach to the key electoral decision. Only on a few occasions was there bloc voting, and apart from its bi-annual visits to Wellington, the Committee usually had no separate existence.

The Electoral Committee system meant that a Board candidate was not faced with the time and expense of mounting a nationwide campaign for farmer votes. But in the run-up to elections most candidates followed the tradition of personally visiting each Electoral Committee member in their home district. This allowed candidates to acquaint themselves with the critical issues and, as Doug Archbold recalls, gave Committee members an unparalleled chance to "suss out the qualities of the candidate".

Longtime North Otago representative Lindsay Malcolm, who ultimately lost his seat to David Douglas, in the Farmers For Positive Change landslide.

On election day, candidates each made a presentation, followed by "no holds barred" questioning from around the Electoral Committee table. Considerable effort often went into preparing these presentations. Doug Archbold remembers that one repeatedly unsuccessful challenger startled the committee with a dramatic performance which involved stripping to his singlet, changing into a rugby jersey and brandishing a "large and venomous knife" with which he sliced open a rotten apple symbolising the Meat Board, "rotten to the core".

Votes were originally cast for both vacant positions at once, but later this was modified to a papal-style election where the first candidate to gain a clear majority was elected, then lowest-polling candidates were dropped off until the second majority was achieved.

Fred Dobbs, who as a government appointee did not have to run this gauntlet, recalls: "Every Board member had a fearful anticipation of the Electoral Committee. I have never seen such a cruel system, or one in which so much is asked in the way of accountability, and yet so little loyalty is given in turn. You have to sit before 25 members, each with a personal agenda, and you are quizzed without mercy. In the end you are given a piece of paper, handed down as a judgement, and you are either in or out. (However) I think the Electoral Committee has a lot going for it… the fact that it became the forum for a few voices who were articulate enough to command the floor with a limited knowledge is regrettable."

The aim was to be strictly fair and avoid strategic voting. Despite the fear and respect with which candidates viewed the Electoral Committee process, there were relatively few occasions when sitting members were beaten, and when they were it was normally in a contest of personalities rather than issues.

The drama of a successful challenge to a sitting Board member spread well beyond the boardroom. The way results were conveyed called for strong stomachs on the part of the candidates and their wives who, in a tradition established by Rosemary Hilgendorf, attended a lunch function at the Board on election day. Candidates were called in and handed a sealed copy of the

Doug Archbold of North Canterbury. Electoral Committee member from 1987 until it was disestablished in 1995.

results in front of the Electoral Committee by the Board secretary. The wives got the information in a similarly public and potentially distressing way, delivered by the chairman's secretary, for most of the period Marilyn Murray. It was a point of honour, Mavis Barnett recalls, to "keep control of your face till you could dash to the toilets". It did not help matters that a strong family feeling had usually developed amongst the Board members, and some associated with the Board didn't hide their feelings of disgust when a sitting member was ousted.

Meat industry issues might have brought out tough questions in public sessions, but it was wool that aroused the real passions of the Electoral Committee. The biggest wholesale turnout of both Electoral Committee and Wool Board members was during the Great Wool Debate over compulsory acquisition. There was no parallel upheaval in the Meat Board at the time of industry ownership from 1982-85.

A significant vulnerability of the electoral system was that it did not have its own electoral roll. Until 1970, eligible voters were taken from lists compiled by MAF, and originally only sheep owners were automatically included, though beef cattle owners could self-declare as voters.

From 1970, the roll was sourced from the annual agricultural statistics census. From 1976, farmers became eligible to vote for the Electoral Committee if they made a statutory declaration that they owned 100 sheep or 100 beef cattle. The disparity of these qualifications in terms of capital investment or farm size was to become an ongoing issue. Another concern was that not all owners of stock were levy-payers to the Board and vice-versa. Other problems included votes for companies, multiple ownership, and the fact that around 10% of properties change ownership each year.

The Electoral Committee gave its members a unique level of status and influence and they were expected to set high standards. Doug Archbold, new in 1987, was reminded of this when met at the airport by Mervyn Barnett and advised on appropriate dress, a suit if at all possible, and tailor-made cigarettes in preference to roll-your-owns, when in Wellington.

For many, membership of the Electoral Committee was an end in itself, and they made their mark as tireless advocates for a particular district or special farming interest. Grading was a favourite right round the table, while North Otago representative Lindsay Malcolm, a member of the Oamaru-based ABCO Board, never missed a chance to support local trade processors.

Among the most lively confrontations were those between Board chairman Adam Begg, a man of prodigious memory, and unrelated Committee member Aubrey Begg, a Southland farmer and ex- Labour MP. He kept an extensive file of press statements and speeches by Board members and other farming leaders, plus other relevant ephemera, as a means of keeping the Board accountable. He would challenge Adam Begg and scrabble through his file for a clipping to support his point. Adam Begg would reply succinctly, to the point, and occasionally he would quietly correct the quote or put it in context without reference to any notes.

For the more ambitious and for those who, like Mervyn Barnett in his outspoken challenge to the grading system in the late 1970s, gave notice of their leadership qualities, the Electoral Committee was an unofficial training ground for Board membership.

This path was followed by Sir Charles Hilgendorf, Crichton Wright, Michael Kight, John Daniell, Roger Marshall, David Frith, Mervyn Barnett, Richard Johnstone, Alan Grant and Bruce Jans. Amongst those defeated for a Board position were Dick Davison and Eric Roy, the latter going on to Parliament and to chair the powerful Primary Production Select Committee.

The grooming process for farmers identified by the Board as particularly promising usually included the award of a Nuffield Scholarship, ostensibly to study an aspect of agriculture overseas but most valuable as a passport to a lifetime network of influential international contacts.

Alan Grant was one who in 1985 forced himself into national – and international – prominence via television as spokesman for a group of mid-Canterbury farmers who slaughtered 3000 old ewes in protest at the 50c pittance they were being paid for them.

The next year he defeated sitting member Brian Lill for the Electoral Committee and a year later, in 1987, became deputy to the new chairman Richard Johnstone after drawing the long straw following two tied ballots with Aubrey Begg.

Aubrey Begg, former Labour MP and Electoral Committee member for most of the 1980s. After his death in 1989, Eric Roy took his place as Southland representative and has gone on to be a National MP.

Alan Grant had been awarded a Nuffield Scholarship in 1985, appearing before the selection panel the day after the 'Mayfield massacre'. In response to a question about the appropriate number of sheep for New Zealand he suggested the comparatively low figure of 50 million – and drew the response from panel member Mervyn Barnett that he had certainly done his bit to reduce them!

There was a surprise addition to the selection panel that day. Sir Charles Hilgendorf, determined that his protégé would be successful at his third attempt, had come along uninvited and even though he was no longer formally a member. With or without the force of his argument, Alan Grant's nomination prevailed.

Among the defeated candidates was Banks Peninsula's Robyn Grigg, put up as the first female contender by an equally determined backer, Selwyn MP Ruth Richardson, who took the panel's decision to the Human Rights Commission. The Commission backed the selection but the challenge gave wide publicity to the perception of an exclusive 'old boys' network' applying not just to the Nuffield but to other all-male establishments like the Board and the Electoral Committee. At a time when increasing numbers of women were being forced by economic circumstances to take a more active part in farming partnerships, it was not the best sort of image to be projecting.

Although large numbers of women, including the future Prime Minister Jenny Shipley, had been involved in the more inclusive Kellogg Rural Leadership course based at Lincoln College, then University, from 1979, this never seemed to translate into a position on the Electoral Committee or Board. In 1987, Hawke's Bay's Prue Humphries was one of three candidates defeated by Jim Bull for a seat on the Board.

Exclusive, conservative… these criticisms were increasingly applied to

Bill Garland, chairman of the Federated Farmers' Meat & Wool Section, 1993-95, and as such a non-voting member of the Electoral Committee. His predecessors, who included Dick Davison, Snow Petersen and Tim Plummer, and successor Edward Orr, all played an active part in Committee and Board politics.

the Electoral Committee, along with calls for a move to direct elections. Most of the critics were on the outside looking in. Those operating within the system tended to be staunch defenders, regarding it as effective despite some faults. The problem, accentuated by the differing individual interpretations of how the Committee communicated with constituents, was how to convey this to potential voters.

Generally, if the electoral process aroused any emotion amongst producers, it was apathy. On average, four Electoral Committee positions were contested each year with a voter turnout of around 30%. This, of course, added weight to the argument that direct elections would encourage greater interest.

The criticisms were of continuing concern to the Board and the Electoral Committee, which prided itself on the hard questions it asked and the rigorous process it put candidates through. A constant refrain was 'poor communication'. While some Committee members were energetic and inventive as informal links between the Board and the average farmer, with people like Richard Drake writing newspaper columns, others were less adept at the admittedly difficult task of providing farmers with the information they wanted.

One of the most consistent outside critics of the process was Federated Farmers. It saw a separate group gaining more privileged access to meat industry information than its own Meat & Wool Section and then not adequately passing it on to ordinary farmers. The relationship was never an easy one, with elements of professional jealousy and a compulsion by Meat & Wool delegates to play devil's advocate. In fact, there was often considerable overlap in membership between the Meat & Wool Section and the Electoral Committee and other structures like meat company boards, with longtime Alliance chairman John Falconer one of many to spend time on the Electoral Committee.

This concern prompted continual rumblings and at least two surveys of the effectiveness of the Electoral Committee system, one of them in 1980. In 1981 Rob Storey, then president of Federated Farmers, backed Kellogg scholar (and Hawke's Bay Meat & Wool chairman) Brian Peacocke's research project on the Electoral Committee. However, he found the conclusion "not condemning enough". Peacocke had decided that on the whole the Committee was doing a good job, even though, like the Board itself, it was reactive rather than proactive. It could be made to do better, and it was important to have a separate group.

Peacocke's study recommended the informal role of the Electoral Committee should be formalised and standardised so farmers knew what sort of information they would receive and how it would be communicated.

Little was written about the role and functions of the Electoral Committee, which gave its more enterprising members the scope to define their own, particularly in challenges to the Board to change direction, or in the championing of favourite causes. In 1984, Agriculture Minister Colin Moyle rebuked the Committee for stretching its mandate and presuming to be the driver of decision-making.

He would not, he said, "abide by the kind of master-servant relationship that the Committee appeared to have established in trying to make the Boards answerable to it". He was not "prepared to idly stand by at a time when the meat industry was going through a crisis, and see the Government's plans for the industry stymied by the entrenched conservatism of Electoral Committee members."

The Committee should, he said, keep to its two statutory functions and if necessary devise a suitable alternative system of electing Board members. By implication, a more direct system of election.

The same year an outspoken advocate for direct elections joined the Committee. Among the new members elected in 1984 (along with Tony Brennan, John Duncan, Rick Vallance, Dick Davison, Allan Kane and John Falconer) was Bruce Jans.

While keen to use the Committee as a forum for change, Jans' particular interest was port reform, believing his home port of Napier was at a disadvantage. He was also strongly critical of the indirect electoral process, describing it as " a waste of time and thoroughly out of date". The remit process was also totally ineffective. He proposed an overall revamp of farming organisational structures, "a redefining of areas, to make them interlock, not overlap", and suggested fining down the Electoral Committee, giving it more teeth and time on the job.

"It had some pluses, but overall it seemed to be focussed on electing clones of clones. There were many good people, I don't want to detract from their honesty and integrity, but overall I felt there was a mindset of not addressing the real issues or being proactive. When so much is going on, just to stand still is going backwards," he later told the *Meat Producer* (fourth quarter, 1994).

In the face of the various criticisms the then chairman, long-time member Don Macnab of Wanganui, and his deputy Colin Dick from North Otago, defended the status quo and the ability of astute members both to seek out information and communicate with farmers. Macnab estimated up to 500 questions would be asked in the course of any one meeting and members travelled anything up to 6000 km to talk to their constituents. However, the move for reform gathered momentum under the 'new generation' of members elected from 1984 onwards.

Just to call the Committee together for a meeting outside of the two specified occasions was difficult under the current rules. However Bruce Jans, Richard Johnstone, Brian Jeffries and Barry Cameron succeeded in doing so in February 1987 to discuss wide-ranging concerns about industry structure and its influence on farmer returns, the role and function of the Board, and the operation of the Electoral Committee system. The meeting, attended by 10 members plus the recently retired Hawke's Bay representative Tom Atchison, discussed reducing the Committee to 15, increasing allowances and providing a secretariat, and meeting four times a year. Bruce Jans put a personal case for direct elections.

The circumstances and holding of the meeting created acrimony and undoubtedly contributed to Don Macnab deciding to resign from the Committee and the chair, and Richard Johnstone taking over as chairman later that year. When Alan Grant became his deputy, both were involved in ef-

Richard Johnstone, Electoral Committee chairman from 1987-1991. Johnstone was a Board member from 1992-95.

forts to promote reform within the Electoral Committee system. As Alan Grant later told the *Meat Producer*: "People say it's a cosy relationship, that the Electoral Committee is perpetuating its own role, but I cannot think of a better system than the one we have got now. It's easy to criticise, hard to come up with a constructive alternative."

Both Johnstone and Grant were acutely aware the spotlight was coming on to producer boards as a whole and their accountability in particular. In a series of informal meetings they acknowledged many faults and difficulties – that the Committee was seen as elitist and conservative, and that more rigid performance measures were needed. Their recommendation was to enhance its status and powers, for example increasing terms of office to two years. They wanted to generate more 'positive tension', using the Electoral Committee as a more powerful tool in the increasingly important two-way relationship with groups like the Government agriculture caucus. To "assist in their understanding of the rigorous examination candidates are given", they also suggested a representative of 'MAF or Treasury' should take part in the electoral process.

The informal think tank proceeded to a more formal review which recommended "better communication". In a welcome step towards demystifying the process, a new guide book was prepared, describing the role and activities of Electoral Committee members.

The review group also considered the vexed question of eligibility to vote, and whether to base it on stock units to reflect the changing national flock and herd, but in the end stayed with the status quo. In its own words, the Committee also "confirmed the one man, one vote" principle. As Alan Grant told the *Meat Producer,* any form of "proportional representation" according to stock numbers was rejected as "an expensive bureaucratic nightmare".

In practice, a voting anomaly had been steadily growing, with the increased number of people farming in partnerships. Unlike other structures such as trusts or companies, each partner in a partnership had his or her own vote, following an amendment of the Meat Board regulations in 1976 when most farms had a single owner. With nearly two-thirds of all sheep and beef businesses now being farmed as partnerships, often with husband and wife, this allowed a large number of women to get their name on the electoral roll.

Another recommendation, not proceeded with by the Board, was that it would be desirable for the Electoral Committee role to "be extended to enable them to get the Boards to do things that farmers wanted, rather than having the Boards deciding on policies on the basis of their discretion or what they considered best for farmers". In other words, they wanted to shape policy, not be briefed on it, however comprehensively, after the event. It was just the kind of extension of mandate which had aroused the wrath of Minister Moyle.

The role of the Committee formed a main part of the terms of reference for the major independent review of the electoral process in 1992. The review panel, chaired by Sir Roderick Weir, founder of the stock and station company Rod Weir and Co and later a director of Crown Meat Export, also included Adam Begg, the immediate past chairman of the Board, Malcolm

Cameron, the former director-general of MAF (also formerly a Wool Board director) and Laurie Stanton of Pokeno, the most recently elected member of the Electoral Committee. Tim Ritchie, the Board's general manager corporate affairs, was secretary to the Committee, and Ken Armstrong of MAF Policy was an observer.

The Electoral Committee, pushed hard by its new chairman Alan Grant to make some moves in the direction of reform through some more formal procedures, made submissions. So too did the Board, in Grant's view "tending to be protective of the status quo". After an exhaustive round-the-country consultation process, hearing 121 submissions in a wide variety of places, the review committee recommended Board members should in future be chosen by a selection panel of six 'qualified electors' which would begin the process by actively seeking out candidates.

James Aitken, founder of Farmers for Positive Change and last chairman of the Electoral Committee.

The Electoral Committee would continue its other functions as a Producer Council with a statutory requirement to communicate with producers. Young Farmers' Club and women's group representatives would be given speaking rights. The Weir committee also recommended electoral boundaries based on stock units with differentiated sheep and beef numbers. There should be one vote per "stock owning entity".

While the Meat and Wool Boards were still assessing their response to the Weir committee recommendations, the report was overtaken by other events.

Former Electoral Committee chairman Richard Johnstone was elected to the Board in 1992. John Acland was elected to the Board for a third term in 1993, but Jim Bull chose not to stand again. Alan Grant, after just a year in the chair, was elected to the Board from a record 11 candidates in 1993. Margot Buick and Kathryn Ward, both former Kellogg scholars, were among the candidates.

Interest in the electoral process was picking up; a torrent of change was about to be unleashed.

Ironically, it was a wool industry issue which prompted the upheaval that proved terminal for the Electoral Committee and shook the foundations of the Board.

The Wool Board's decision to pledge funding to the International Wool Secretariat without directly consulting its levy-payers launched Hawke's Bay farmer James Aitken onto the national scene.

A complete political novice, he didn't belong to any organisation like Meat & Wool Section, and he didn't know his local Electoral Committee representatives or what they were doing. By his own acknowledgement he didn't know what sort of Pandora's box he was opening when he took up his wife's challenge to "stop moaning and do something" about the electoral system.

What James Aitken wanted was the personal right to vote for a Board representative. In other respects he was a strong supporter of the concept of the Electoral Committee, the more so once he understood its role and the depth of its questioning of the Board.

With the strong support of Tom Atchison, now more than ever convinced the Electoral Committee was a body that had outlived its time, he stood

Kathryn Ward, the first – and last – woman on the Electoral Committee.

John McCarthy, a member of the Farmers for Positive Change and representative for Wanganui from 1993. In 1999 he was elected as a member of the Board.

successfully for the Committee in 1992. A lucky turn of events meant his personal campaign snowballed into a nationwide movement. Contact with *Rural News* correspondent Warren Berryman, following an article criticising producer board lack of accountability, led him to the paper's editor Ron Clarke, already a trenchant critic of the Board. For the newly established challenger to the *New Zealand Farmer's* dominance of rural readership, this was an issue made in heaven.

In no time the Farmers For Positive Change (FFPC) was in the headlines, making play with phrases like the 'old boys' network' and relentlessly contrasting the enterprising spirit of the newcomers with the dusty bureaucracy they wanted to sweep away.

In July 1993 FFPC, campaigning for a referendum on direct elections, took 13 of the 18 contested seats (James Aitken was returned unopposed), and in August 1993 came to Wellington for the Wool Board elections. Kathryn Ward of Hawke's Bay was among their number, becoming the Electoral Committee's first woman member. (In 1994 dairy farmer Jennie Vernon became the first woman to win a Nuffield Scholarship.)

The group was determined to make its point about Wool Board directors. Many of them, despite a shared Christ's College education, met face-to-face for the first time at airport check-ins en route to Wellington the day before. Despite this, they had no trouble agreeing on strategy. Niceties about bloc voting were one of the first casualties of the new regime.

On the first ballot, 25 votes were cast for the incumbent Wool Board chairman Pat Morrison. 14 votes – also a majority – were cast for the other incumbent, John Wills. In keeping with accepted practice, Morrison was declared elected and a new ballot was held to choose between Wills and Tony Brennan who had originally polled 11 votes. This time, neither candidate received a majority. In the stalemate, Wool Board returning officer Gerald Barker informed the group that Wills would hold his place until next year's election.

There was a rush for legal advice, in the case of the new Wanganui representative John McCarthy, from his father, retired Court of Appeal Judge Sir Thaddeus McCarthy. Ultimately it was decided that the election could stand as it had achieved the right result though by the wrong means. Both candidates who achieved a majority of votes should have been declared elected on the first ballot. This raised the interesting question of whether recent elections of the Meat and Wool Boards could be declared illegal and all their decisions invalid.

The situation catapulted the fledgling group from idealism into political reality. James Aitken and some of his members were summoned to a late night meeting with Agriculture Minister John Falloon. There they agreed they wouldn't precipitate such a potentially destabilising crisis and would accept legislation validating the election of all current and past Board members being passed with all speed. It was, with the concurrence of Labour, in power when the illegal variation had come about.

For the Farmers for Positive Change, it was a quick introduction to the avalanche they were prodding. Further education in pragmatism and political expediency was to come.

There followed a famously unruly meeting characterised by open aggression from both newcomers and old guard. However, as a result of the agreement, Wool Board member John Wills retained his place, while chairman Pat Morrison was re-elected, earning many members the wrath of their constituents.

The Meat Board briefing sessions were characterised by a similar uproar although the tough questions bore a remarkable similarity to those asked on previous occasions. Mervyn Barnett's retirement meant a by-election was needed and for the first time presentations to the Electoral Committee were made in public. Bruce Jans was the successful candidate.

Then there was the referendum promised by the new members, but which an Electoral Committee had no power to authorise or funds to organise. Wool Board chairman Pat Morrison and an extremely reluctant Meat Board chairman David Frith eventually agreed to fund the referendum and planning began almost immediately. Members of the referendum sub-committee were James Aitken (chair), Tim Brittain, David Douglas (new members) and John Metherell (existing member) of the Electoral Committee. Other members were Bill Garland from Federated Farmers' Meat & Wool Section, Meat Board director Alan Grant and communications manager Brett Sangster, and Allan Kane and Patrick Conway from the Wool Board. Catherine Petrey from the Minister's Office, and Ken Armstrong from MAF Policy represented the Ministry of Agriculture, responsible for drafting any final decision into legislation.

The referendum was professionally designed by MRL and held over the Christmas 1993 period.   As well as options for direct election, it asked farmer opinion on voter eligibility. Thirty-one percent of eligible farmers voted. The results were decisive in two areas: a clear majority for ward-based representation, and for a change in voter eligibility to ownership of 250 sheep or 50 beef cattle. One of the options rejected was the levy-based vote promoted by James Aitken.

Views on how direct elections would actually be implemented were less clear, with farmers reluctant to let go of some kind of intermediate watchdog structure. This sort of 'shadow electoral committee' was defined in the referendum as an audit committee. The concept of the audit committee in many ways resembled the revised role of the Electoral Committee as proposed by the earlier Weir Committee, with no role in voting for the Board but an enhanced one to represent the views of farmers from around the regions.

Forty three percent voted for "direct elections but with an audit committee elected in parallel to board directors". Nearly 40% voted for an electoral committee system to continue. Only 21% chose direct election without an 'audit committee' or intermediate group.

With a less than a clear mandate, sub-committee members had to agree to disagree on some of the issues raised. But it was obvious the Minister was determined to keep up the momentum as part of the wider changes he was promoting for the Board. On the basis that a majority of farmers had voted for "some form of direct voting", John Falloon gained agreement to set up a new steering committee to review the role of the Electoral Committee.

Andra Neeley, member of the Electoral Review Committee.

It was quite clear there was only one direction the review could take. The possibility of maintaining any sort of Electoral Committee was non-negotiable. "It didn't fit the current model of public policy," David Frith recalls. With hindsight, he agrees the Board should have been more assertive in upgrading the status of the Electoral Committee, possibly moving to a three year electoral cycle and improving the funding.

The Electoral System Review Committee became known as the Cullwick Committee for its chairman Dr David Cullwick, a partner in Ernst and Young. Draft proposals were submitted for public review in July 1994 and the final report was presented to the Minister in September.

Other members of the committee were: Meat Board chairman David Frith, Wool Board chairman Pat Morrison, Electoral Committee chairman James Aitken and deputy chairman David Douglas, long-time Electoral Committee member Doug Archbold, Meat & Wool Council chairman Bill Garland, immediate past senior vice chairman Andra Neeley and Ken Armstrong of MAF. The Committee was supported by Paul Spackman, senior manager, Ernst and Young and previously with the Meat Board and the Prime Minister's Department.

The aim of this review was to propose a system that provided for the accountability of Boards and directors, identified the election of directors as part of the accountability process, and encouraged the participation of a wider number of farmers in the process. The new system should also promote the emergence of new directors.

The draft proposals attracted 124 submissions, mostly supportive of direct elections and many 'composite' responses from Federated Farmers' branches. Concerns raised included the manner in which wards would work, the possible capture of director elections if proxy voting was permitted, and the roles and functions of ward committees.

The Cullwick Committee finally recommended direct elections on a six-ward basis. But in another lesson of political realities and the power of other agendas, the Farmers for Positive Change representatives were not able to push through the audit committee concept despite their close involvement. The idea of ward committees was also rejected, although the report did suggest farmers could have the option of electing local delegates to attend annual meetings on their behalf.

The Cullwick Committee endorsed the value of a watchdog group but said it was better for such groups to be formed informally as and when needed. It also indicated the Board would have to make a decision on the question of setting up its own electoral roll, something that had always been pushed into the too hard or too costly basket. While the Board could access lists of farmers through the Statistics Department, the details of its levy-payers were held by the meat companies, which steadfastly refused to release them, citing the privacy legislation.

As the deadline for advertising for the March 1995 director elections approached, the Minister made it clear he was determined to proceed with the Cullwick recommendations, most of which could be brought in through regulation in advance of the legislative changes still being debated.

The Minister's final decision, that the move to new processes would begin in 1995 as a transition year, with elections held in September rather than March, was made so close to the November 1994 deadline for advertising the elections that notices appeared in the *New Zealand Herald*. It, unlike other major papers, had not been able to pull them at the last minute.

The Electoral Committee was laid to rest and new regulations gazetted the same month Sir John Ormond died, March 1995.

Cheryl Craig, formerly the Board's trade policy manager, became the new Board secretary early in 1995 when her predecessor Trevor Playford took over from Laurie Bryant as North American director. With the assistance of electoral administrator Sandra Irwin, she set about the enormous task of establishing a new roll of eligible electors.

Margot Buick, Fellow of the Australasian Institute of Food Technology, who made an unsuccessful bid to become the first female Board member. Formerly a meat quality expert working in the development section at Alliance, she is currently commercial manager of MIRINZ.

Compiling an electoral roll from scratch involved a massive information and communication exercise of advising farmers of their rights and their voter eligibility. The new regulation of one vote per business tended to disenfranchise many of those women who had previously had a vote as a business partner. There was also the perennial issue of privacy legislation which was again interpreted to mean that the Board could not, as a starting point, have access to levy-payer lists held by the meat companies.

Voting was conducted by postal ballot, the counting conducted by Board staff under the scrutiny of the independent returning officer, former Secretary of Justice David Oughton.

The first election under the new ward system gave conclusive proof that a new order had arrived.

Ironically, the first two sitting members to come up for election under the new system were the two whose vision for a reshaped Electoral Committee had not been pursued far enough or fast enough. In the northern North Island, Richard Johnstone was defeated by newcomer Tim Brittain, who made use of the new rolls to send the electoral 'sweetener' of a toffee to all voters.

In the South Island Brent Rawstron, who had conducted an imaginative campaign highlighting his niche export of $1000-a-tonne beef to Germany, defeated sitting member and deputy chairman Alan Grant.

Despite the quite widespread calls for a structure to bridge the transition between the Electoral Committee and direct elections, the Meat Board, unlike the Wool Board, steadfastly resisted calls to fund a 'second layer' of delegates to attend meetings on farmers' behalf.

James Aitken, who feels the Farmers for Positive Change can feel proud that they "said what they would do, came and did it, and went home" is still disappointed that the audit committee baby went out with the electoral bathwater. Looking back, Aitken says the FFPC didn't know what they were letting themselves in for. "We didn't come to turn the meat industry on its head... we wanted stability, and control of where our levies were spent."

Collusion and Collapse
1993-94

"Meat processing was a cosy industry when New Zealand had captive markets, limits on the permitted number of companies (quantitative licensing) and other regulations. Those days have gone. So have many old-style meat companies." The O'Brien Column – National Business Review, *10 February, 1995*

One of the assumptions of the procurement battles was that they would lead eventually to the collapse of the weaker companies and the survivors would reap the benefit by gaining access to the fallen company's stock. In other words, forced rationalisation.

These collapse scenarios tended to focus on AFFCO and Alliance which were still recovering from huge losses and it was assumed the corporates would not want to prop them up. AFFCO was considered particularly vulnerable as it had made several announcements about financial restructuring, but nothing had eventuated. It had announced a $75 million decline in the value of its assets in 1993, giving an equity ratio of 13%, and was considered to be surviving only through the goodwill of its bankers and the corporates.

In this environment Freesia ex-chairman Peter Egan quickly threw off his industry rationalisation mantle and joined the fray. He teamed up with Alan Straker late in 1993 to establish Greenlea Premier Meats Ltd, a single-chain beef plant sited right in the heart of AFFCO territory, in Hamilton. He recalls that he had tried to persuade AFFCO to adopt the single-chain philosophy when he was a director.

"I remember getting up at an AFFCO board meeting and saying to them, 'Gentlemen I have tried, but please have no objection if I now go off and do what I'm trying to convince you people to do'."

There was also an outside chance that Weddel could fall as its parent company Union International had been hit by a crash in its real estate investments. It was working its way through an agreement with its bankers to sell down assets over a three-year period ending in December 1994. The Weddel operation in New Zealand was highly geared having borrowed $50 million, guaranteed by Union International, to repurchase the company from Crown. Plans were afoot to float the New Zealand company as part of the overall asset sales strategy.

However, when the inevitable collapse occurred, the arrow initially veered off target and missed these so-called dinosaurs.

The 1993-94 season was one of unremitting pressure even though the seemingly never-ending GATT negotiations had finally reached fruition and provided some confidence. The slash and burn approach to procurement continued although Graeme Thompson of Fortex recalls that there was a degree of consensus in the South Island about overseas market trends and the effect on the level of the opening schedules. It was generally considered that an opening level of $42 per head was indicated. As Thompson recalls: "We were silly enough to come up with the schedule first. We fronted with a $42 schedule, and this was totally accepted. A week later Barnett (PPCS) comes out with $49. Well, we had huge egg on our face." It was also a perfect example of the industry poker game where bluffing is just another competitive tool. The Commerce Commission was later to misinterpret this unique industry idiosyncrasy.

During the early nineties the Fortex star had been rising and it had become the darling of the politicians including Minister of Finance Ruth Richardson, who held it up as a shining example of the new approach to management in the age of competitive market forces. The company had listed on the Stock Exchange in June 1990 at $1.80 a share.

Tom Scott sums up, in the Evening Post, *24 March 1994, the popular perception of why Fortex met its end. The reality was more complex and included over-hyped expectations – which meant the impact of its collapse was out of proportion to its significance in the wider meat industry – and systematic fraud. NZ Cartoon Archive.*

Graeme Thompson was named the 1990 Deloitte/*Management* Executive of the Year, and received the Bledisloe Medal from Lincoln College for his contribution to the farming industry in 1992, the same year as the company received the Tradenz Air New Zealand Exporting Excellence Award.

Fortex's new, very high technology plant at Silverstream was single-chain, multi-shift and designed to further process the entire throughput of lambs. It was a concept viewed with a degree of cynicism by 'old hands' in the industry who considered some carcass freezing would be needed to provide a buffer for the seasonal variations in throughput.

The company had begun to look at the prospects for developing similar processing facilities in the UK as a means of extending its business in the European region. This led to some comment that Fortex needed to keep pulling a rabbit out of the hat each year to keep its balance sheet looking good.

Then Fortex hit the sand. It had announced a $4.8 million loss for the 1992-93 year as a result of lower throughput and sales, and this, Graeme Thompson suspected, was the trigger for PPCS "to put the knife in" during the procurement merry-go-round the following season.

The intense pressure was reflected in the company's share price, which went from $1.03 in January 1994 to 70 cents a month later. An announcement in March that the company anticipated an interim six months loss of $40-$50 million caused TA Pacific, a Bahamas-based funds manager, to sell down its three months-old investment of $9 million, and the share price dipped a further 15 cents. Despite efforts to cobble together a rescue package the company went into receivership on 23 March, leaving many unanswered questions from share analysts, farmers who were owed some $7.5 million for stock supplied to the company, and the 1800 workers who lost their jobs.

The irrepressible Rick Bettle commented, "Dinosaurs 1, New Guys 0".

The extensive media coverage and analysis of the crash of the former high flyer highlighted the issues, adding to generally negative perceptions about the effectiveness of management in the meat industry. It was not until somewhat later that facts emerged which led to the conviction of both Graeme Thompson and his finance manager Michael Mullen for concealing bank loans and other fraud-related activities – which included the incorrect coding of stock as cuts of higher value than was actually the case. Both would be jailed in 1996,

PPCS chief executive Stewart Barnett, accused by Graeme Thompson of hastening the demise of Fortex.

Mullen for a year and Thompson until September 1998.

The analyses placed considerable emphasis on the intensity of the procurement competition in the South Island, with the spotlight being directed at PPCS. However, PPCS is said to have wanted Fortex to survive but only sufficiently to prove to farmers that there was competition.

In addition, the negotiations with the receiver over ownership of the Fortex South Island plants kept the pot bubbling. Initially 48 different parties expressed an interest in the plants. When both Alliance and PPCS expressed an interest, outraged farmers opposed to restrictions on their livestock selling choices suggested the Commerce Commission turn these applicants down. A third company was needed to ensure farmers received the best prices for their stock.

PPCS had recently taken over the works of the failed Waitane Meats Ltd at Gore and Venison New Zealand at Mossburn and was considered to be financially strong. Alliance was still strapped for cash and faced opposition from shareholders concerned about increasing debt levels. Virtually unnoticed during the Fortex furore was the announcement by another Southland meat company, Blue Sky Meats, that it had sustained a loss of $180,000 after posting a $1 million profit the previous year.

PPCS initially got the nod from the Commerce Commission to buy Fortex assets, but after long-winded negotiations with the receiver, the Skeggs Group picked up the Silverstream plant. Canterbury Meat Packers, a 50:50 joint venture between Phoenix Meat Co Ltd and Five Star Beef, bought the Seafield operation.

The Board was immediately in hot water because of its supposed involvement in the Seafield site through ANZCO, as part-owners of Five Star Beef, despite the separation resulting from the establishment of the MEL holding company. As the *Independent* reported on 12 August 1994, both Bill Garland of Federated Farmers and Stewart Barnett of PPCS claimed that the move went back on the Board's assurances that they were looking to withdraw from the bricks and mortar side of the industry. Stewart Barnett noted that the Board was still operating as a player and "setting the schedule in competition with our levy-payers". This gave, the *Dominion* claimed on 10 August, the new Seafield owners an unfair advantage.

Some commentators wondered why the Skeggs Group would bother getting into the meat industry. The *New Zealand Farmer* suggested that PPCS and Alliance were not going to lie down and let the new entrant take stock without a battle. As it turned out Skeggs ran into too many difficulties finding working capital. Further negotiations resulted in PPCS acquiring the plant from Skeggs in October 1994. Graeme Thompson was reportedly "shattered" when it was announced that they planned to mothball the 'leading edge' of meat processing technology slaughterboard and only operate the freezing, storage and further processing facilities.

The Fortex crash had other implications. It brought to a halt Weddel plans to float the company and caused AFFCO to reorganise its restructuring plans – once again. Weddel had split its business into two parts. Aotearoa Primary Products Ltd with John Prendergast as chief executive and David Sadler as chairman, would operate the Aotearoa (Cambridge), Whangarei and Feilding plants and the Hastings tannery. Weddel New Zealand, managed by Munro McLennan, with Union International's Terry Robinson as chairman, would operate the Tomoana and Kaiti plants, the McCallum Industries canning business, and farmer suppliers' collective Weddel Tararua.

As Munro McLennan later told the *Dominion*, "after the collapse of Fortex, interest in making meat industry investments took a severe blow".

John Prendergast recalls: "The prospectus was ready to go in March 1994. And suddenly we had the Fortex crash and the underwriters pulled the plug." Weddel continued in its current structure while Union International announced it had set aside $35 million from its asset sales programme for the recapitalisation of the company and until that was finalised it would continue to guarantee Weddel's bank borrowings. This guarantee did not prove to be as strong as it first appeared.

Under the white coats is an assortment of bankers and media people, brought to Hawke's Bay by the Meat Board and MIA to give them a better understanding of the meat industry.

AFFCO, which had suffered losses amounting to $117 million in 1993, was promoting its restructuring plans under a scheme of arrangement with the banks and other lenders, which also involved the raising of $50 million from farmer shareholders. If the capital raising was successful the banks, Fletcher Challenge and PRL would convert $146 million of interest-bearing debt into shares. The aim was to reduce AFFCO's debt from $216 million to $65 million and increase capital to $168 million. At the same time it was designed to restore farmer confidence in the company to counter some of the nervousness about supplying stock to a debt-ridden AFFCO, especially following the Fortex crash. The move would end AFFCO's co-operative status.

The Fortex saga also caused another rash of industry introspection involving the participants, bankers and other stakeholders and, finally, the Government. Various farming and industry luminaries ranging from the ex-Federated Farmers leaders Brian Chamberlin and John Kneebone to Bernie Knowles of PRL and AFFCO, James Aitken and Lindsay Malcolm of the Electoral Committee, Rick Bettle of Alliance and Peter Harris of the Council of Trade Unions all sought a change of approach in the industry.

Bill Garland of Federated Farmers Meat & Wool Section summed up concerns: "Fortex Group's difficulties are a tragedy for the meat industry. (It) reinforces the image that the meat industry has got major problems with company debt, overcapacity and the lack of profitability."

The common call was for less procurement competition to allow companies to put funds into market and product research as well as promotion. The prospects of a dairy industry structure were again canvassed as well as a completely free market with no constraints from organisations such as the MPC. Farmers' desire for procurement competition persisted, despite their concerns about security of payment from financially troubled meat companies.

The *Dominion* of 1 July 1994 reported that David Frith received a "guarded reaction" when he made an offer to the Meat & Wool Section of Federated Farmers for the Board to bring together the competing parties to seek some resolution of the procurement brawls, and to liaise with the Commerce Commission, which had prevented the MPC dealing with procurement issues. Frith commented that "although sheep and beef farmers had

Banker Chris Moore, the Board's communications manager Brett Sangster and another of the bank visitors in Weddel's Tomoana plant.

benefited from intense competition among meat companies for stock, farmers risked losing their considerable influence over the meat industry if they allowed it to continue down its present path."

There were comments about the meat companies' preoccupation with procurement, which was stripping money from the industry, and banker nervousness. The response from the MIA was that comments about the industry being "unbankable" were alarmist. It noted that "the industry's difficulties are not beyond the reach of sensible solutions." But it did recognise that the industry was handicapped until those solutions were found and implemented. Farmers, particularly those who had supplied Fortex and been left high and dry, sought their own remedies including faster payment than the usual 14 days industry standard, or sought Board backing for an industry insurance scheme.

Peter Harris, CTU economist, echoed the unheeded conclusions of several earlier studies of the industry in his analysis in 'The Basis of Instability in the Meat Industry'. He concluded there was a basic structural weakness in the industry and suggested that it "staggers from crisis to crisis" because of a cycle that traps it in a short-term commodity situation, trading unprofitably with diminishing equity.

"Meat companies have low equity, high fixed costs and excess capacity forcing them to maximise throughput to spread overheads; individually each company under-invests in product and market development, training and other investments that could improve returns in the long run; companies pay above actual market prices for stock in order to ensure throughput which depletes equity further and the company begins the next season in an even worse position. The industry never gets into a position where it is responding to long-term market imperatives."

He explored the various options that had been closely examined several times in the past, ranging from complete free market to a single seller, but concluded that none of these would work. He finally favoured balanced regulation and an adaptation of the fishing industry's tradeable quota system, the previously rejected notion of Tradeable Killing Rights, to stabilise the procurement sector.

Peter Harris's views received a lot of attention in the media. Jonathon Underhill, writing in the 13 May 1994 issue of *National Business Review* noted: "Reaction from various industry participants to Harris' work is that his comments are valid even though they come from a worker's perspective." Faint praise.

Peter Harris recalls the Meat Board was promoting the view that the industry was fundamentally sound and bankable and any problems could be laid at the door of management incompetence or the inability to deal with the vicissitudes of an inherently risky business. "There were snowstorms in Canterbury that year and all that sort of stuff; there was a bit of bad luck and a bit of bad management, but fundamentally there is still an industry problem to confront." There were issues that could not be overcome by companies acting on their own.

The unions were frustrated by the continuing lack of action and the prospect of further closures and job losses despite pay rates that were virtually frozen. As Harris recalls: "We got hold of Falloon and said look, we've been stumbling on like this since the 80s. How many more meat industry crises do we have to have before we do something about it?"

John Falloon decided to do something about it. The first move was a meeting with the MPC to get more industry stakeholders to agree there was a problem. John Falloon accompanied by Catherine Petrey, Ken Douglas and Peter Harris attended a meeting of the MPC on 24 March 1994. The response from MPC members was mixed. Some denied there was any problem, others blamed the banks, and the Board representatives tossed in commercial incompetence rather than structural problems. There was no consensus so the visitors left, still frustrated.

Separately, Rick Bettle had been questioning the rationality of the system and structure of the industry. In a rather enigmatic speech to Western Southland Federated Farmers on 29 March 1994 he noted farmers required a free market for their stock procurement but wanted controls on the marketing activities of companies when selling their product. In his view this removed a barrier to entry for newer companies, and attempted to ensure better returns for the producer by advocating controls so the buyer did not benefit from lower prices eventuating with competition.

He came close to suggesting that a single seller was required to benefit from the New Zealand brand name. In his view you either had deregulation in both procurement and export marketing or regulation at both ends. The existing system was a bad compromise. "The point of all this is that human nature is such that people love competition when it suits them, and endeavour to remove it where it does not." He suggested, somewhat provocatively, but true to character, that farmers should accept the good and the bad in the real free market, "and thrive in it".

Catherine Petrey recalls that Rick Bettle, wearing his MIA deputy chairman's hat, talked to John Falloon about the issues. "The Minister wanted to have a crisis meeting, create a forum to discuss it through, and everybody counselled against that, because there might be an expectation that something would occur." It was government policy not to intervene, or at least not to be seen intervening.

But Rick Bettle was very keen to get everyone in the industry to agree there was a problem. A subsequent meeting with the Minister was followed by informal discussions at the Basin Reserve during the cricket – Graeme Lowe was one of the fellow spectators – and a decision to set up a group to meet regularly about meat industry problems.

Catherine Petrey cajoled MAF into providing a meeting place and a secretary, even though "they were very much following the Meat Board line that if the banks do their money that's their bad luck".

The first meeting of the group was held in the MAF offices on 13 April 1994. The members were Rick Bettle (MIA), Ken Douglas or Peter Harris (CTU), David Frith (Meat Board), Bill Garland (Federated Farmers), Owen Symmans (Prime Minister's Department), John Asquith (MAF) and Catherine Petrey. Others were co-opted from time to time.

The initial meeting was kept quiet but Ian Templeton's *Trans Tasman* newsletter, always well attuned to meat industry news, somehow got wind

Graeme Lowe and John Foster, who worked together at Dawn Meats to blow some gusts of fresh air through the meat industry, remain friends despite each building up separate businesses after 1986. They are pictured in 1991 at the annual Richmond-Lowe Walker cricket match. Both have now retired from meat processing, and Foster's former company Richmond took over Lowe Walker in 1997. Photo: Graeme Lowe.

*Rob Davison, Economic
Service director since 1987,
whose farm business trend
advice was called on by the
'Secret Seven'.*

of it and labelled the group the 'Secret Seven'.

Notes of that meeting indicate the group met to determine whether there really was a problem and went through the ritual catalogue of ills. These included: the bankers' loss of confidence in the industry even though they were still financing new plants; over-capacity and emphasis on throughput and turnover rather than adding value; farmers' support for new entrants because the competition led to improved returns while being concerned the bankers appeared to be running the show; and demoralised and restless workers. The participants also agreed to provide other members of the group with copies of background source material, which was to be co-ordinated through Denise McCann, Rick Bettle's personal assistant.

A document titled 'The problems facing the New Zealand Meat Industry' was put together within a week of that first meeting. It included the Peter Harris analysis, several papers from Abigail Williams and colleagues on the 'empty core market' theory and the need for co-operation to overcome the problems, the Boston Consulting Group/PCEK report prepared for Freesia Meat Holdings on 'Securing a Profitable Future' and extracts from 'An Analysis of the New Zealand Sheep and Lamb Industry' by Booz Allen & Hamilton.

The work done by Abigail Williams had been used in a study carried out by CS First Boston and commissioned by Fletcher Challenge. Peter Harris reckoned Fletchers were looking for some way of getting the industry stabilised to a state where they could sell their equity. "They knew it was a bad mistake. They learned from the experience and they just wanted to get their money out. So they commissioned CS First Boston to look at a strategy for industry stabilisation, and they went around the key stakeholders in 1993, pre-Fortex."

The Booz Allen report had analysed the problem of uncertainty of supply of livestock as part of a wider analysis for Alliance and its bankers.

The membership of the 'Secret Seven' varied considerably. According to Peter Harris, up to 20 people were involved. He says the group had no title, no formal status, no terms of reference, no money to pay for research, and the participants were not formally representing their organisations.

An early paper prepared for the group indicates the number had swelled with the addition of Alan Pickering (ANZ Bank), David Byrch (BNZ) and Alan Jackson (Boston Consulting Group, which had taken over PCEK). Brian Lynch of the MIA and Rob Davison of the Economic Service were also pulled in at a later stage to contribute.

The core paper looked at whether or not there was an underlying problem in the New Zealand meat industry, "If there is will it go away without interference?", and "Do we require more or less regulation?" The group concentrated on procurement competition, the ownership paradox and 'empty core markets'. It concluded there was a problem that was unlikely to resolve itself. A free market on the supply side faced a controlled market on the selling side.

Other options, including the use of Tradeable Killing Rights (TKRs) as proposed by PCEK, were considered as a means of promoting some discussion among industry leaders. The option was even extended to suggest a levy on stock killed by TKR holders to fund industry initiatives on training, market development and product development. As reported in the *New Zealand Farmer* on 8 June 1994, Peter Harris went on to promote TKRs as "one way to create a degree of stability and to remove the short-term preoccupation with stock procurement".

Southpac provided an analysis that demonstrated the parlous financial state of the industry and its author, Jim McElwaine, joined the ever-increasing 'Secret Seven'. The findings of this report were almost strangled at birth by the Board, anxious to promote the idea that there was no real financial crisis in the industry.

Board chief executive Warwick Bishop applied his engineering training to reduce the McElwaine argument to its basic elements. "The analysis has some fundamental flaws. Firstly it bundles beef and sheepmeat together, when the bulk of the two products have quite different needs as regards seasonal funding. A company producing manufacturing beef complementary to supply from the Northern Hemisphere doesn't have a seasonal financing problem.

"There is a generalised assumption about the debt/equity ratios in the industry, and the assumptions about what is workable don't take into account the different operating realities of different industry sectors. In other words the pure traders, the processors and the exporters have all been linked together."

Board deputy chairman Jim Macaulay, who had formed a strong alliance with David Frith and moved firmly into the farmer camp, relied on his

The dance of the New Zealand dollar, 1984-94. The exchange rate is one of the external forces the meat industry has little power to combat. ANZ graph.

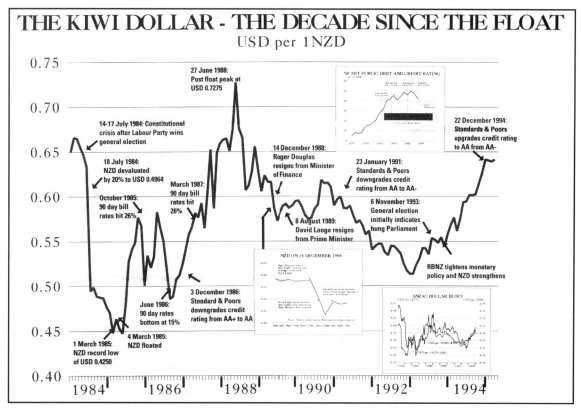

banking experience and contacts to reject the view that the industry was not bankable, even though the Southpac statistics and much of the comment from bankers at the 'Secret Seven' meetings suggested otherwise. In his view only the successful companies were representative of the industry.

"It does lump everyone together and doesn't include some marketing companies," he said. He wanted to use the amateur statistician's ploy of changing the sample to get a better result. But even when Jim McElwaine adjusted the figures to exclude the non-representative companies the results were less than adequate.

Outside of the 'Secret Seven's' deliberations Rick Bettle was stirring up discussion on structural and control issues in his own unique manner. In a speech to the tanning industry in Palmerston North in May 1994 he advised that cut-throat competition was destroying the industry. "Politicians have got to get involved in the meat industry or the whole of New Zealand will continue to be held to ransom by the farmer."

He also suggested that the Meat Board needed to assess its role and should either get in or get right out of the industry. He said many lessons could be learnt from the dairy industry where suppliers were committed to one company which changed prices once a year and spread payments throughout the period, and where marketing was done through a single-desk operation.

"The meat industry by contrast supplies a free market, yet once it passes through the farm gate the market changes." So, he was reported in the 1 June 1994 issue of *New Zealand Farmer,* the industry was not in a real free market. He went on to describe the 'empty core' characteristics of the procurement side of the industry: "This type of market is the most competitive market in the world – so competitive that there is absolutely nothing in it, which is a very dangerous situation."

Other farming and industry leaders joined the debate. Mervyn Barnett, now chairman of ANZCO and no longer a member of the Board, supported the call for an agreed industry strategy and suggested the MPC should take the lead. A pooling system with farmers receiving an initial price at the farm gate and a further payout once the product was sold could be the answer.

A similar approach was advocated by Bernie Knowles, who showed his dairy industry background when he added that farmers should be committed to a supply contract to a company to give certainty of throughput. He said a year's notice of withdrawal of supply should be mandatory. "One year is incredibly short notice, in terms of a farming lifetime."

James Aitken, chairman of the Electoral Committee considered that a summit meeting on the meat industry was overdue. A letter from John McCarthy, who considered the GATT agreement threw up some opportunities and challenges for the industry, supported him. "For the first time in some years farmers, workers, processors and bankers all have an interest in industry stabilisation and a quantum lift in sophistication of production and marketing."

In the 15 June 1994 issue of *New Zealand Farmer*, editor Tony Leggett turned this into a call for a leader of vision. "That's probably all it will need to bring some common sense and logical thinking to the marketing mess that has half the farming scene and a major export earner in organised chaos." The editorial suggested that James Aitken or Federated Farmers would be prime candidates for promoting a round table summit to resolve the issue.

The Board, on the other hand, took issue with Rick Bettle. Warwick Bishop, in a letter to the editor in the same issue of the *New Zealand Farmer*, claimed that competition and lack of political interference had been the saviour of the industry and the 'empty core market' theory was only one academic's view. Bettle should "focus his attention back on the game and not look to his coach on the sideline to intervene…Yes, it's tough out there, and with fewer sheep to process some meat companies will have to close or merge with others. That is what the free market and competition is all about… Welcome to the 1990s and the real world, Mr Bettle."

Bettle responded that there were several options that could be considered including the dairy industry and the free market. He also suggested the Board should assess its role. "Perhaps the Meat Board would be prepared to join me in this brave new world by removing the legislation attached to its own income."

John Prendergast, managing director of Weddel New Zealand Ltd and often a trenchant critic of co-ordinated marketing initiatives.

The issue was aired again at Federated Farmers' Meat & Wool Section conference in July 1994. The chairman, Bill Garland advised delegates that if they did not like the realities of the deregulated meat industry they could accept imposed disciplines or go dairying. The industry had problems but they needed to be solved commercially rather than by intervention. "Any industry-wide solution that forces farmers to commit stock for a full season or to go back to a national schedule will simply shift the problem of indebtedness and overcapacity back on to the farmer." So the likelihood of a commercial or any other solution involving managed procurement being accepted was remote.

At this stage Agriculture Minister John Falloon, perhaps prompted by the findings of the 'Secret Seven', started on a different tack. In a speech proposing changes to the producer boards, he suggested that meat industry participants should co-operate more in marketing. "Meat companies play games in New Zealand, ruin their balance sheets and then wonder why they cannot invest in marketing. Ultimately, I cannot see that the recent level of regulation in agricultural marketing will stay because it was put in place to sell to quota markets. But if we create coherence among exporters, we ultimately will not need the regulations."

The realities behind the theory and debate soon came sharply into focus. While the 'Secret Seven' were still deliberating their final report, Weddel New Zealand crashed. On 19 August 1994, over 3000 people were put out of work at the five plants and more farmers were caught with money owing for their stock.

In the months following the Fortex failure, the Weddel directors had discussed the option of a combined float of New Zealand and Australian assets, but this did not happen. Management then had to secure working capital for the new season. John Prendergast, who retired during this period, says: "They had to be very sure the guarantee was going to be renewed in December so they asked for a resolution from Union International. But the bankers in the UK wouldn't allow this so they had no alternative to putting themselves in the hands of the New Zealand banks. And I think the banks relished the opportunity… it was the easiest opportunity for them to achieve rationalisation in an industry in chaos in 1994."

There was also the prospect of an easy recovery of their debts assisted by the promised $35 million set aside by Union International. The ANZ Bank took the lead, appointing KPMG as receiver, led by Michael Morris and Alan Isaac, still working through the Fortex receivership.

The 'Secret Seven' report, co-ordinated by Alan Jackson, came to the same conclusion as Southpac and the Freesia/PCEK report of 1991. There was a problem, and it would not be resolved by standing back and looking at it. They noted that only one of the recommendations of the Freesia/PCEK report, the formation of the MPC, had been implemented, or "forced on the industry". However, the industry continued to generate unacceptable returns, increasing the desire of the banks to reduce their exposure to an unstable and unacceptably high-risk business. The issue of the 'empty core market' was raised once again.

The view was expressed again that a managed solution to the problem might not only be justified but necessary. Procurement stabilisation was singled out, even though it was recognised farmers would be unlikely to accept any voluntary change. The initial solution proposed was for the introduction of an 'Indicative National Schedule', almost a repeat of the Board's National Pool arrangement of 1985, with a few more freedoms. But it was generally considered it would be impractical to implement and would not pass the political acceptability test.

The group went on to consider 11 different options to resolve the problem. Some commercial solutions such as the dairy industry model or company amalgamations were rejected as being too difficult to implement. It was agreed that elements such as bankers imposing and monitoring capital and debt funding limits, changes to the disclosure requirements of the Co-operatives Act and redefinition of the structures and roles of industry bodies such as the Board were necessary to a total package. However, the group decided that an additional mechanism was needed to provide a foundation for rationalisation and investment.

Here the options were a fixed national schedule price system or tradeable killing rights, both previously rejected, or a revised export Voluntary Restraint Agreement (VRA) quota allocation system. The first two did not pass the tests for practicality, simplicity and/or political acceptability. The quota allocation system did, so it was the final element of the solution package. The group also concluded there should be encouragement of industry and company rationalisations such as AFFCO's proposed restructuring with its deferred redundancy arrangement.

The proposals may have been reasonably straightforward but putting them into practice was not easy. It was recognised that Rick Bettle could not advocate the recommended changes, so Peter Harris, David Byrch and Alan Jackson went on the road to sell the package. They did not make much progress against the opposition. Peter Harris recalls: "We did quite a few presentations, we went to the Board two or three times, and Federated Farmers, the GATT agricultural conference, and the Electoral Committee." There was opposition from Federated Farmers and the Board as well as some companies.

At the conference promoting the benefits of the GATT accord later in the year John Falloon was agitated at the attitudes of the companies. "He had some very angry words at one point with John Foster. He said, 'These people are trying to save your industry and you're standing up there and you're criticising them and the Board, and you're having a bob each way'," Harris recalls. "He got quite exasperated with a number of the players, the Board, Federated Farmers and the meat companies."

Keith Taylor, managing director of Taylor Preston.

Catherine Petrey remembers Bill Garland was "seeing things differently from the Meat Board and he was beginning to understand the crisis, and that it wasn't in farmers' long-term interest to have this auction at the farm gate." However support was not forthcoming from the president of Federated Farmers, Graham Robertson "who had more of a free market view".

While the banks could accept the concept of imposing financial limits on meat companies they were in the business of lending when the risks were acceptable. So they continued to support new initiatives while being very tough on the financially-strapped companies. Changes to the disclosure requirements of the co-operatives disappeared into the mists and the redefinition of the industry bodies got swept up in the producer board reform debate. But those considerations paled into insignificance when compared to the arguments that raged over the basis for the allocation of the proposed quota allocation system. It swamped consideration of all the other recommendations.

The Weddel crash prompted a further round of calls for a solution to stabilise the industry with some commentators predicting more closures. However, within two weeks a group of major North Island companies had moved to agree in principle to form a consortium (Trial Run Holdings Ltd) to buy the Weddel plants and keep them closed, subject to the Commerce Act, technical considerations and the attitude of the banks.

The *Independent* reported that the leaders were John Foster of Richmond, Graeme Lowe of Lowe Walker and Keith Taylor of Taylor Preston and that all North Island meat companies except three minor operators (Brierley's Huttons Kiwi, Peter Egan's Greenlea and the Myers family's Hawera Processors) were in support of the move. John Foster recalls that it only took a day or so for he and Graeme Lowe to come up with the idea. Brian Chamberlin agreed to act as consultant to the group and CS First Boston advised on the financial structure of the deal. The aim was to seek bank finance to be repaid over a three to five year period.

The move raised the ire of some farmers already smarting about the loss of payments for stock from the collapsed company. A group of Northland farmers led by Ken Whitehead believed farmers would bear the costs, as the consortium members would restrict the competition for stock to recoup the cost of the investment. This was the theme of a letter to the Commerce Commission opposing the consortium bid for the Weddel plants. In this view the consortium would be passing the cost of freezing company negligence on to the farmer. The consortium retorted that the deal would be paid for from increased efficiencies rather than any limitation on livestock pricing.

Up to 30 other parties were interested in some or all of the Weddel plants, so the consortium proposal was not a foregone conclusion. Consequently the consortium's offer had to be too good for the receiver to refuse. Even then there was considerable wheeling and dealing before arrangements were settled. Determining the contribution from each of the consortium members was complicated enough and exacerbated by proposals to introduce tradeable quotas. This raised the question of whether Weddel's allocation would go with the company or be put up for tender.

The Commerce Commission made an interim determination in November 1994 denying the application on the grounds that the anti-competitive effect of the proposal would outweigh any public benefit claimed by the consortium. The consortium had claimed there would be cost savings for the industry, better international marketing, increased security for stock suppliers, and more investment in further processing in New Zealand. The Commission believed the cost savings could disappear if or when new plants were opened and the other claimed benefits could be achieved without the Weddel plants being permanently closed.

Rick Bettle advised the Alliance shareholders at the AGM in December 1994 that he would complete his three-year term in June 1995 and would hand over to Owen Poole. He was reported as having become disillusioned with the meat industry. The industry had stabilised after the procurement wars, which led to the Fortex and Weddel collapses, but he predicted it would revert to the same pattern as people forgot about the recent upheavals and started investing in new plants.

The Commission called a conference in January 1995 to review the determination and the Trial Run Holdings proposals. Both sides marshalled their arguments. For the consortium, National Bank economist Arthur Grimes argued that one giant meat company in the North Island would be better than the existing system. He also used complex mathematical models to prove that as long as there was at least one other contender for the supply of stock, competition would not be diminished.

He was backed up by a team including Rick Christie from Tradenz, Neil Taylor from the Board's Brussels office and Gunter Bagowski of Prime Meats in Germany arguing the need for greater stability, reliability of supply and more emphasis on investment in the market for the long-term survival of the industry. Rob Davison of the Economic Service advised that as there was still ample capacity relative to the available stock numbers companies would not be putting the squeeze on producers. Other supporters included Alan Jackson, Paul Spackman, and John Yeabsley from the New Zealand Institute of Economic Research.

Two former meat industry leaders, Peter Norman (ex-Borthwicks) and Athol Hutton (ex-Waitaki) headed the anti-consortium brigade which included a number of individual farmers. They argued that the closures would limit competition for stock, reduce processing capacity and cause hold-ups, which would restrict the ability of farmers to produce at near full capacity. They also pointed out that the longer the Commission delayed in making a decision the less likely it was that any of the plants would open.

After a week of hearings the Commission reviewed its original determination and eventually announced it was authorising the consortium proposal. It had decided the proposal would result in some lessening of competition for the procurement and processing of stock, but any detriments would be less than the overall benefits.

The consortium had cleared one hurdle but other problems kept appearing. These included proposals from the local councils in Gisborne and Whangarei to keep facilities open to service the local market. There were also plans to appeal the Commission's determination, but they eventually faded, and Trial Run Holdings proceeded to buy the five Weddel plants from the receiver for $51.2 million and sell off the usable equipment to achieve their target of paying off the financiers within two years.

During the debate the president of Waikato Federated Farmers Graham Pinnell made a telling prediction: "The more plants the consortium closes, the greater will be the opportunities for a new player. If farmers become frustrated through delays in killing, having to pay cartage to remote works, or they perceive a lack of farmgate competition, history shows that they will support a new player." Within two years new capacity had replaced over 60% of that lost when the Weddel plants closed, and stock numbers had continued to decline.

The Commerce Commission had further dealings with the meat industry the following year when it acted on complaints from farmers alleging that meat companies in the North Island were engaging in price fixing. The allegations cited the members of Trial Run Holdings for colluding on procurement strategies which resulted in lower farm gate prices. The Commission subsequently executed search warrants on four major North Island meat companies – AFFCO, Richmond, Benmore and Lowe Walker.

The evidence showed the companies had been in regular contact and discussing prices. The companies did not dispute that they had been talking together but argued such conversations were generally full of misinformation and did not necessarily lead to price fixing. The final outcome of the long investigation and a lot of legal wrangling was that the four companies, plus a number of other smaller firms, were judged to have breached the anti-collusion provisions of the Act and were fined amounts totalling $5 million.

Despite all the financial disasters of the late 80s and early 90s new companies were formed and restructuring proceeded. Notwithstanding all of the closures, the industry that had consisted of 11 companies and 45 meatworks in 1986 had expanded to 29 companies and 64 plants in 1994, many of them now single-species and single-chain plants. It also showed that some investors were still prepared to take the risk despite the decline in stock numbers and financiers were prepared to back them, even though bankers had expressed concerns about industry viability and had made efforts to limit funding.

In keeping with the rough three-year cycle, the procurement situation calmed in 1994-95, aided by an excellent lambing percentage. In the case of beef, spirits were dampened by weakening overseas market prices and an appreciating New Zealand dollar.

Bruce Jans pictured with his company's new storage facility, bought after the Weddel collapse in 1994. The buildings, originally part of Whakatu, had been owned by Weddel since 1986. Known as Tomoana North, they were used for hides and pelts storage. For Bruce Jans, by then a Meat Board producer representative, acquiring the building was more than just a business transaction. His ambition had been to join the HBFMC Board but while he was still gaining experience and contacts as an Electoral Committee member the company had, in effect, ceased to exist after the Hawke's Bay restructuring which closed the Whakatu plant and allocated most of its associated facilities to Weddel. "Whakatu was the best. I was outraged that the rest of the industry had collectively decided to get rid of the best so the others should survive," he told the Meat Producer *in 1994.*

Extracting the Rent
1983-97

"Ladies and gentlemen, we've got a problem with salmonella. We can't find any." MAF chief meat veterinary officer Andrew McKenzie to the Meat Importers Council of America, October 1995.

"We've done all the spadework. It's now time to extract the rental, having spent the dollars upgrading our systems." Andrew McKenzie in the Meat Producer, *last quarter 1996.*

When a world-wide focus went onto food safety, with the outbreaks of BSE and then E coli, the New Zealand meat industry reaped the benefits of a far-sighted food safety strategy.

It had its beginnings with the restructure of MAF into four businesses in 1987. Meat Division, now headed by Andrew McKenzie, came under MAF Quality Management (MQM) which had responsibility for all export food products.

McKenzie accelerated the process, started by his predecessor Alan Royal, of shifting Meat Division from a prescriptive 'command and control' organisation towards a new attitude of partnership with the industry and acceptance that there might be many different ways of achieving a desired outcome. It changed the MAF/meat industry interface, and went hand in hand with a new focus on meat as a food, and meat hygiene as food safety.

He also gave greater determination to the drive to establish a New Zealand position on meat hygiene, at the Codex and in other forums. A foundation of this argument was the meat industry food safety strategy. In 1991, the establishment of the Meat Industry Hygiene Council (MIHC) provided the effective consultation forum lacking since the Meat Hygiene Advisory Committee had ceased to meet. Membership included the MIA (John Miller), meat company representatives (Dennis Butler from Alliance and others), the Meat Board (Peter Gianotti), the Abattoirs Association and MAF Quality Management. The MIHC was instrumental in getting industry acceptance of MAF's food safety strategy.

One of the key objectives of the strategy was the international acceptance of scientifically justified and cost-effective food safety and meat hygiene programmes, based on agreed risk analysis principles and methodologies. The New Zealand position was underpinned by ongoing research by people like MAF's Steve Hathaway, whose work included extensive microbiological analysis.

As it developed, the strategy also called for a greater involvement of industry in setting standards, the introduction of food safety and quality assurance systems, and a devolution of inspection services wherever possible. Compliance with standards would move from a 'defect checking' approach to one of auditing New Zealand systems.

Another positive step was the formal approval system for industry laboratories through the special company MILAB Approval Ltd, wholly owned by the industry, and self-supporting. This was both to ensure a suitable system of

Andrew McKenzie, chief meat veterinary officer for MAF Regulatory Authority during the negotiations which established equivalence for New Zealand with the EU and US. Photo: MAF.

international standard to meet the current testing needs of the US and EU but also to anticipate possible moves within the EU and elsewhere "to introduce compliance with the total quality management criteria of ISO9000 standards".

Once again, the New Zealand position was consistently presented at international forums such as Codex and on regular visits to customer countries. This included the concept of 'regionalisation'. If, for example, there was an outbreak of Foot and Mouth Disease, export restrictions would be placed only on the affected area instead of a whole country.

The new approach was symbolised in the new edition of the 'bible' of industry procedures – Manual 5 (Slaughter and Dressing), completed in 1993. Previous versions had set out prescribed procedures to be followed at the direction of MAF. 'Manual 5' became the first 'industry standard', agreed and accepted after nine rounds of consultation with all sectors. In a hint of future ways of working, compliance, although sometimes reluctant, was voluntary.

Further international endorsement of the New Zealand way of doing things also came in 1993 when New Zealand was host country for the Codex Committee on Meat Hygiene. As the MIA annual report noted, new codes for meat inspection and risk assessment took "exactly the same approach which New Zealand was seeking".

Even more significantly, the New Zealand influence could be detected when the concepts of equivalence, science-based risk management and greater harmonisation of standards were reflected in and supported by the Sanitary/ Phytosanitary (SPS) and Technical Barrier to Trade (TBT) agreements negotiated at the completion of the GATT Uruguay Round in March 1994.

In the last quarter 1996 issue of the *Meat Producer* Andrew McKenzie described the SPS and TBT as an important turning point in the international trade in food, animal and plant products: "(They) say what the outcome should be, rather than prescribing every detail of what you should do…They confirm that decisions about formulating sanitary and phytosanitary measures will be made by assessing the risks."

MAF's veterinary counsellors, first in London and then in Brussels had played a significant part in the shaping of the agreements through their dual role of promoting New Zealand's position and developing useful contacts. In 1994 Barry Marshall went to Washington to establish a similar position for North America.

World-wide, there was a greater focus on food safety after the first recognition of BSE (Bovine Spongiform Encephalopathy or Mad Cow Disease) in Britain in 1991. Following revelations that the disease probably originated with meal made from diseased animals being fed back to other animals, the spotlight went onto traceback. It became important to know the exact source of meat and details of animal feed and management.

Around the same time HACCP – Hazard Analysis Critical Control Point – made its way from specialised areas like the US space programme into more general food industry language. A risk analysis and prevention tool, HACCP looks for potential problem-causing areas within a process and devises ways to overcome them. In line with 'outcome-focussed' thinking it encourages those actually working in areas to take responsibility for devising strategies to overcome problems.

MIRINZ listeria expert Andrew Hudson (left) working with Roger Cook, editor of the new microbiological manual. MIRINZ experts like Peter Nottingham, Colin Gill and Graham Bell, as well as MAF scientists like Steve Hathaway, have contributed to New Zealand's leading position in meat microbiology. Photo: MIRINZ.

The Delphi logger, one of the temperature tracking devices which made it possible to monitor the condition of chilled meat throughout the transport process. The logger was marketed by Auckland-based Tru-Test distributors which developed it in association with MIRINZ, with computer software by the Board subsidiary MIR.

Jorge Ng and John Logie of MIR

Technician Andrea Rogers compares two agar plates, one positive for E coli O157:H7 (left) and one negative. E coli, a bacterium naturally present in animal gut, has been the source of some horrifying food poisoning outbreaks in the US. Photo: MIRINZ.

By 1993-94 MAF and the MIHC were conducting roadshows to introduce the concept of HACCP, and at the Weddel plants it formed part of the Total Customer Service (TCS) culture change. Also, increased focus came on avoiding microbiological contamination where it started – on the farm. Fortex, with a high proportion of its meat exported chilled, was one of the leaders in encouraging farmers to present their stock in clean condition. It photographed all stock on arrival and scored it from A to D, rapidly achieving big increases in the A and B categories on the basis of pride, not payment premiums.

In a further 1994 transformation MAF meat-related responsibilities were split between MQM, dealing with certification activities such as meat inspection and led by Derek Breton and MAF Regulatory Authority (MAFRA, later MAFReg), under Andrew McKenzie, which had the responsibility for policy.

By 1995 many aspects of the New Zealand food inspection system, including the increasing use of risk analysis in formulating food standards and guidelines, were reflected in the Codex system. As John Miller noted in the *Meat Producer* (last quarter 1996), New Zealand's approach to risk analysis was also being used by committees on pesticide residues and veterinary drugs. As the MIA noted in its 1996 annual report, even if Codex had no absolute force, the legislators of the EU and US were clearly taking notice.

"We decided there must be alternative ways of doing things and we started challenging the US and EU requirements and arguing for the concept of 'equivalence'; that our systems meet their safety outcomes," Andrew McKenzie said in a 1996 *Meat Producer* interview.

In preparation, MAFRA designed some surveys of New Zealand beef processing plants. This added to an increasingly valuable microbiological database which, for some companies, went back over 20 years and was unmatched by any international competitor. The first survey results showed, among other things, that salmonella could not be detected, and the overall microbiological counts were very low. The results were available when Andrew McKenzie spoke to the

Meat Importers Council of America (MICA) at their 1995 annual meeting.

Food safety and HACCP were the hot topics that year, just as one of the disease scourges of the past was finally beaten. Uruguay was about to gain quota access for fresh meat to the US, having achieved final clearance from Foot and Mouth Disease in 1993. The end was in sight for bans affecting Argentina as well.

The new threat was the tiny food poisoning bacterium Escherischia coli 0-157:H7, commonly known as E coli, which had caused the deaths or serious disabling of a number of small children in the US. The most highly publicised source was undercooked hamburger. It was first found at the 'Jack in the Box' chain but soon resulted in a number of other ground beef product recalls.

It was a dramatic, and emotive demonstration that the long-established 'scratch and sniff' meat inspection system, involving over 7000 US Department of Agriculture employees nationwide, was ineffective against contamination from an invisible bacterium likely to be present in the gut and on the hides of many feedlot-raised cattle. With lobby groups such as the parents of STOP (Safe Tables our Priority) demanding higher standards, the massive US Food Safety Inspection Service (FSIS) proposed a radical shift in its procedures. In the hugely detailed 'Mega-Reg' it proposed a move to a HACCP-based process putting responsibility for hazard identification and process control on to the individual plant operators.

Tom Nicolle of MIR, who went on to work with Hugh Barr at IRL developing the Prime Cut market optimisation model.

As the New Zealand industry had been confronted by the US and EC requirements in the 1970s, most of the US meat industry was aghast at the scope, scale, cost and practical difficulties of implementing what its own government required of it. A total mindset shift was called for, and powerful arguments were mounted against it.

But E coli remained a problem. In March 1996, food safety as an issue ballooned into the world headlines with publicity of much more widespread incidence of BSE than had been previously suspected. Then there were outbreaks of E coli in Japan later that year. The power of adverse publicity was shown in a slump in beef sales in most parts of Asia, a region where no European beef was sold.

Europe's response to the new cases of BSE, beside banning exports of British beef, was a much stronger call for traceback. Led by Germany, there was a new demand for country of origin labelling.

As with the 1986 Chernobyl disaster, the Board, supported by the industry, resisted the opportunity to spend generic promotion money to trumpet to the world the relative cleanness and safety of New Zealand meat. It was criticised, as it had been earlier, for not doing so.

But promotion was hardly necessary, as buyers from around the world made their own assessment of New Zealand as a source of safe meat. As lamb sales soared, demand from the EU for New Zealand beef, through GATT licences, also climbed steeply: sales climbed from 848 tonnes in 1994-95 to 5358 tonnes in 1995-96 and 9311 tonnes in 1996-97.

Recording physiological features using remote telemetry. Research, largely funded by the Board, has greatly increased the understanding of the factors involved in animal stress, and therefore, meat quality.

There were also calls for animal identification, allowing traceback to farm of origin, to become a national requirement. It was Meat Board (and MIA) policy that this be an individual company decision. It was already being implemented in various degrees: by AFFCO through its Marks and Spencer contract,

The Richmond (formerly Lowe Walker) plant at Dargaville has a curved ramp to the stunning box, which helps ensure cattle arrive in a calm condition at slaughter. Most recently built New Zealand meat works incorporate design features to enhance animal welfare, in line with the ideas of world authority Temple Grandin of Colorado State University.

by the Waitotara Meat Company and through the Beef Improvement Group.

When Andrew McKenzie and his team went to the EU in 1996 to argue for equivalence across a wide range of food industry systems, they were in the comfortable position of having ample evidence that New Zealand systems, whether they were to monitor growth promotant or residue use, or ensure micro-biological cleanness, were effective, and viewed as such by successive EU veterinary and other specialist visitors.

Even so, it was hugely satisfying when, late in 1996, negotiations were successfully concluded for a Veterinary Agreement with the EU. The agree-ment, which acknowledged the equivalence of New Zealand systems and cer-tification for food exports, was a first between the EU and any third country, and remains the most detailed. The agreement included the application of regionalisation for any outbreak of animal disease.

The low-key announcement from MAFRA late in 1996 that "several years of intensive work… is close to producing a world first agreement with the European Union which will ease the entry for New Zealand meat, dairy and other animal products into Europe" belied the significance of the event. It marked a complete turn-around from the vulnerable position New Zealand found itself in in 1971.

The logical next step was to seek equivalence from the US. In some ways, the task was more difficult than with the EU because it represented a bigger mindset shift. At the same time, the 'MegaReg' clearly pointed in this direc-tion, and for some years the US, Canada, Australia and New Zealand had been working as the 'Quadrilateral Group', a Codex committee set up to develop principles for establishing equivalence.

Andrew McKenzie reported after a US visit in October 1996 that FSIS staff would obviously "prefer replication of their standards and assessment of equivalence claims is problematic for them". But MAFRA took the ini-tiative in providing a case for equivalence according to the framework pro-visions of the World Trade Organisation's sanitary/phytosanitary agreement. There was powerful evidence in the completed microbiological surveys, which showed contamination levels were in most cases lower by a factor of 10 than those applying in the US "…which we attribute to more compre-hensive standards covering such areas as operating procedures and tem-perature controls", Andrew McKenzie said.

The 'Final Rule', familiarly known as the 'MegaReg', finally came into force in January 1997. Shortly afterwards, New Zealand was able to announce that equivalence in a number of aspects of meat hygiene and food safety had been negotiated with the US. Further agreement, on outstanding areas such as temperature control, would be achieved in 1998.

As the former Department of Agriculture, then the Ministry of Agriculture and Fisheries, briefly the Ministry of Agriculture, then Agriculture and For-estry, came under the portfolio of the Minister of Food, Fibre and Border Con-trol, the scene was set for a final stage in the devolution of responsibility for meat hygiene. Once the new Animal Products Act (replacing the increasingly inappropriate Meat Act) was passed, most verification and assurance services became contestable.

Meat Inspectors

Meat inspectors were literally the men (and the women, after Marama Apu and Marie Koperu began work at Ocean Beach in 1979) in the middle.

To preserve this independence, they were public servants, employed by the State Services Commission, until 1987 the central employing authority of the public service. Their union was the PSA.

They were not the employees of the meat company where they worked but plants could not operate without them. On their call, a whole plant could be stopped.

Their work automatically stopped as a consequence of many other types of industrial disruption and they were interested observers of a wide range of protest strategies and the annual increase in wage demands. They were fulltime employees with a strictly specified range of duties in an industry where the working season could be as short as 90 days. Yet because their services were essential their wage negotiations, like those of the meat workers whose industrial strategies taught them a lot, were just as subject to the annual pressure to settle… Add wage increases that one year reached 12.5% and there was a potent brew.

Privatising meat inspection was one of the cost-cutting exercises suggested by the Pappas Carter Evans Koop report in 1985, which recommended professional inspection firms licensed by MAF.

The meat inspectors were amongst the state sector employees most militantly opposed to the State Sector Act. Once it was passed, they became employees of MAF Quality Management and the focus of concern switched to who would pay redundancies averaging about $50,000 a person, or four times the industry average. (In fact, the legacy of SSC employment remained until the mid-1990s with the industry supporting the long-defunct Waitaki company in a case against MAF for the costs of meat inspection during the 1986 national strike.)

Over the next few years, negotiations between MQM, government and the MIA went back and forth, in tandem with the debate between meat companies and the Government about paying the cost of the inspection service. The Government finally decided that companies would pick up the total cost of redundancies from the 1991-92 season.

By then, companies were contracting with MAF for provision of meat inspection costs. From 1990 the companies were paying 100% for what could be called 'Clayton's' contracts: there was no choice of provider and many of the rules including the cost were set out in a non-negotiable fashion by that provider.

The meat companies argued that the service should be more flexible and ultimately contestable, by increasing the range of jobs the meat inspectors could do and also by transferring some of their functions to company employees. Over the years this did occur, with meat inspectors assuming responsibility for implementing health and quality reporting systems, such as AFFCO's ASQIS and Optihealth used by a number of South Island plants. In the new contestable environment it is likely to be extended further.

Meat inspectors stamp a carcass fit for export.

A Final Burst
1993-94

"If the current state of the industry is a measure of our ability to identify solutions, we would be better yakking about sex and rugby," Bill Garland, Straight Furrow, *7 November 1994.*

"The fatalistic approach favoured by some outside observers, that 'only a few more failures' will resolve the industry problems, is not a valid or acceptable solution." Sir David Beattie, MIA annual report 1993-94.

At the beginning of 1993 the only answer to industry problems was the MPC and its activities had had little impact on the procurement arena. The constraints of the Commerce Act and strong farmer opinion in favour of farm gate competition prevented any overt moves towards collective or possible legislative action to ameliorate the destabilising procurement problem. So the hope for a solution was pinned on better or more co-ordinated marketing.

The MPC's attentions swung firmly onto the quota allocation system in 1993. In the absence of a conclusion to the GATT Round at that stage, the USDA had determined late in 1992 that the trigger levels for 1993 imports would be exceeded and the VRA provisions of the Meat Import Law would be required for the third time in three years. This time, however, the VRA was applied early in the year, restricting meat access for the whole of the calendar year. New Zealand's VRA tonnage was set at 192,800 tonnes, less than the previous year and there were early indications the allowable tonnage would reduce even further in the following year.

The US decision raised the concerns of Canadian beef interests that imports would increase due to spill-over from the US and pose a threat to their producers. They lobbied for an inquiry and the resulting determination by the Canadian International Trade Tribunal supported the view that increased imports were likely and could threaten the domestic industry. A global tariff quota of 72,021 tonnes was imposed for 1993 and import quantities over that amount would attract a tariff surcharge of 25% ad valorem.

Christmas and New Year are some of the busiest times for Mary Malone, the Board's quota administration officer, who has the responsibility for monitoring exports against quota allocations and ensuring that they are filled to the last possible kilogram every calendar year.

This focussed the attention of the MPC on quota allocation systems and management. The Board rather blandly reported in its annual report that "debate raged over the best system of allocating entitlement to the higher priced US market and whether quota entitlement should be a tradeable good. No one system dealt effectively with individual meat company circumstances, making consensus decisions extremely difficult. Agreement was eventually reached for allocations to be based on export shipments in the current season with allowance for exporters' traditional local market sales. Sheepmeat access entitlement to the EU was also brought into the debate. For the 1993 season, access for beef to the US and for sheepmeat to the EU was based on the traditional system of share of national slaughter in the current year." That statement hid a multitude of sins – or more accurately – acrimonious conflicts.

Consideration of the quota allocation system had started relatively sedately back in July 1992 when the MPC decided to "set up a sub-committee to consider and make recommendations on a fair and equitable system for allocating exporter entitlements in quota markets". The sub-committee was Graham Ansell and Warwick Bishop from the Board, Rick Bettle (Alliance), John Buxton (Riverlands), Graeme Lowe (Lowe Walker), Graeme Thompson (Fortex), assisted by Brian Lynch and Stella Clark (MIA), and Bill Joyce (Board).

The sub-committee invited submissions from 71 licensed meat exporters and Federated Farmers and received 14 replies, indicating the lack of interest at that stage. Most of the submissions advocated the retention of the 'percentage of the kill' as the fundamental criterion for allocation under the existing system or its use as the basis for some modifications to overcome recognised faults. The principal suggestion was to use the previous season's kill to remove the element of uncertainty. Other options such as tendering (too complex and bureaucratic) and historical market share (difficult to measure as company ownership and forms had changed over the years) were considered and rejected.

The sub-committee then set all those views aside in favour of its own deliberations and recommended a system of tradeable rights. There would be an initial allocation based on the percentage of kill "owned at the time of slaughter in the previous production year" with 5% of the quota held back for allocation to new entrants.

This was presented to the MIA executive on 24 November 1992, and thrown out. Graeme Thompson of Fortex recalls: "I was on the sub-committee with Rick Bettle to come up with a changed formula for the allocation, and we basically carried it through to the executive (of the MIA), where it was thrown out unceremoniously."

By then it was too late to consider other options for the 1992-93 season so the status quo remained in force with quotas allocated on the pro rata share of the companies' estimates of kill for the current season. Even so, the tradeability seed had been sown.

The industry moved back into crisis mode in 1993 partly as a result of the market restraints but also because the procurement war was on again. As far as farmers were concerned there was no problem. Apart from the impact of the strengthening dollar, major markets were holding up reasonably well and, with the procurement premiums, farmers' returns were more than satisfactory. In their eyes there was no financial crisis.

However, the companies and their financiers were not so cheerful. Financial results were expected to be less than adequate again. Some industry leaders had looked at 'improving' the quota allocation systems as a means of establishing 'commercial barriers' to new entrants, but had not gone so far as suggesting them as a means of imposing restraints on the 'last man standing' procurement game.

Two significant factors characterised both the EU sheepmeats and the US beef quotas. Firstly, the responsibility for allocating and monitoring the agreed volume each year was in the hands of New Zealand. The value or 'economic rent' arising from the quotas accrued to New Zealand and be-

cause of the procurement battles most of it was passing through the meat companies to the producer. Secondly, the intervention required to administer the schemes was not an internal New Zealand agri-political matter but a result of decisions of overseas governments or administrations. Even Warren Berryman, who generally opposed any form of interference in the free play of market forces, had to concede in the *Independent* on 5 November 1993: "While the market can generally sort out a clash of commercial interests, this particular quota issue is not for the market". He noted that it was up to New Zealand to decide how the quotas were split or to allow the exporters to fight it out in the marketplace.

He recognised, also, that a market solution could lead to chaos. If exporters fought to be first into the market to get as much of the quota 'premium' for themselves they would drive down prices and destroy the premiums. There was also the danger that the importing countries might react to the market disruption and take over the quota allocation role, with their importers gaining the quota rent rather than New Zealand.

The traditional system for allocating quotas had been based on the estimated production volumes for each company as a proportion of a projected but uncertain level of total production for the current season. Companies earned their quota as the season progressed and the final level was only known when the season had finished.

The quota markets were generally better-priced so companies had an incentive to increase their volumes if they could by bidding stock away from other operators. It forced companies to be procurement and throughput oriented.

Industrial Research Ltd had developed computer models (Prime Cut Meat) for managing market allocation planning for both beef and lamb and proposed they be used to model and manage quota allocation, both for companies and the industry as a whole. Hugh Barr pointed out in IRL Report 56 (June 1993) the uncertainties of the existing system and that operators were forced to chase stock and bid up prices, while there was minimal focus on the markets and marketing. By comparison the Australian system was based on market diversification. Quota entitlements were earned on the basis of sales to non-quota markets and a previous time period was used to eliminate the uncertainty.

Mick Calder took up the theme of basing allocations on market performance and using previous rather than current performance in his reports to the Freesia board and in correspondence and discussions with MPC secretary Don Harwood. Subsequently Bernie Knowles developed the same ideas at the Richmond board and extended them to include the concept of tradeability, which he outlined in correspondence to David Frith. The MPC had received the report of its sub-committee with recommendation for a system of Tradeable Rights (TRs) and had developed the proposal despite the MIA executive's opposition.

In August 1993 the MPC announced its proposals for TRs which were to be market-related rather than production-driven. As they would be held in perpetuity there would only be an initial allocation and new entrants would have to buy their rights from existing holders. The initial allocation was to be based on the percentage of kill owned at the time of slaughter in the 1992-93 production year. The rights were to be tradeable on the grounds that this was "more in keeping with the free market spirit of the meat industry" and much more commercially-oriented than the existing system.

TRs would allow companies to put a true value on markets and encourage maximisation of returns. There were extensive rules governing the management of the system. In keeping with its requirement to consult, the MPC distributed copies of its proposals to all signatories for consideration and comment.

The banks, which had been seriously depressed about meat company viability again, greeted the proposals as the 'best news' they had heard. In their view the tradeable concept was especially welcome. The proposal went down like a lead balloon with the industry, especially the Wairakei Group, and with the farmers.

Quota allocation was furiously debated at the August Electoral Committee meeting with the Board. *Rural News* was in headline heaven as quotas became a cause celebre for both of the groups it was championing, the Farmers for Positive Change and the Wairakei Group.

"There was a lot of groundswell against the council's proposal," said the chairman of the Wairakei Group, Warwick Wilson of Crown Meat Exports, as reported by Glenys Christian in the *New Zealand Herald* on 17 September 1993. The group did not believe the plan was in line with free market thinking and they were concerned that there would be a "very real lack of competition" because of the ownership in perpetuity aspect.

They supported an alternative plan put forward by Waitotara Meat Company for allocations to be reviewed annually and based on the previous season's export-related performance. The allocation would still be tradeable within each year so companies could increase quota for the next season by buying it from others – if others were willing to sell.

There was also provision for 2.5% of the total quota to be set aside for new entrants, though some parties considered the amount was insufficient.

Don Harwood (left) and Bill Joyce photographed by David Frith during a visit to the Middle East. Harwood and Joyce, who each spent time as the Board's Middle East director in Bahrain, also played a significant role in the Meat Planning Council. Don Harwood returned in 1992 and became the MPC secretary. Bill Joyce, who had two terms in Bahrain, put forward the idea of franchising markets.

Hide pulling at the Riverlands Manawatu plant, opened in 1992. In a step back to old ways, individual slaughtermen at this leanly staffed plant took each carcass through all the processes up to boning. However, they had the latest in mechanised assistance. With a new plant and additional capacity, Riverlands was soon plunged into the heat of the quota allocation argument. Originally it was thought most of the contention would be over sheepmeat but the first and fiercest argument came over beef quota, after the US imposed an early quota restriction.

Prime Minister Jim Bolger speaking at the opening of Riverlands Manawatu at Bulls. Company chairman Ken Macdonald does the honours with the umbrella. Mrs Joan Bolger officially opened the plant, in recognition of the contribution of women to the meat industry.

The Wairakei Group members had styled themselves free marketers and then added their own interventionist rules.

The system was reviewed by the MPC in September. This time 130 submissions were received "from farmer groups, meat exporting companies and individuals outside but with a concerned interest in the New Zealand meat industry" – and most of them were opposed. Even so, the existing production-based system was also the cause of some discontent. So instead of reverting to the status quo if their TR proposal was not accepted, the MPC developed a further compromise solution, a modification of the existing system.

The compromise provided for the allocation of annual quotas based on current year's throughput at export plants with up to 3% reserved for new entrants. But to qualify companies had to export more than 60% of their production. This alienated the Abattoirs Association. As well, a clause which required the meat to be exported in standard cartons infuriated Colin Henderson whose Benmore company exported boneless beef in recyclable bins. So another round of bickering broke out, and prompted the *Independent* to headline Warren Berryman's article on the debacle on 5 November 1993: 'What a helluva way to run our biggest export industry'.

By then it was too late to get agreement on a new system for the 1994 quota year. So a variation on the status quo compromise was implemented; allocations were based on ownership at time of slaughter of qualifying export graded production in the current season less "the quantity of product deployed on the New Zealand market that exceeded 5% of the company's total export graded production of that product". There was no mention of standard export cartons. The issue was therefore 'settled' for another season and attention focussed on other matters.

But high level interest in and analysis of the industry's future continued. Much of the initial emphasis of those analyses was placed on the structural, ownership and legislative change that would reduce the corrosive effects of the procurement competition. Eventually attention moved onto quota management as a contributor to industry instability.

One of the outside resource papers that had been considered by the 'Secret Seven' was entitled 'Allocation of Quota Rights in the New Zealand Meat Industry', and was prepared for the Meat & Wool Section of Federated Farmers by Grant Scobie.

In a series of questions and answers Scobie noted that the quota rights to the EU sheepmeats market and the US beef market were scarce and valuable resources. A system for allocation of these rights was required which, in his view, should be based on the following principles. It should be easily understood; announced well in advance; allow competition between existing players and new entrants; reflect the particular needs of each market; provide a stable climate of certainty to encourage new investment and innovation; be administratively straightforward; and equitable, favouring neither one party nor another.

The 'Secret Seven' had by then also focussed on the quota allocation system because of its effect on the procurement competition.

Some of the group – those representing the producers – wanted the existing allocation system retained as the competition it generated passed the quota premium back behind the farm gate. As Peter Harris recalled: "The guy who finally pulled the plug was David Byrch from the BNZ. He said: 'We've made mistakes, we've backed new entrants in the past, when we shouldn't have, and cut our throats. But we've learned from that. We don't want to walk away from the industry; it's a big borrower, a source of significant business to banks, it's a mainstream part of New Zealand's economy. We are prepared to make a contribution, but we're not here to allow you to waste more of our money. We want to bank the industry, but it's not bankable like it is'."

Peter Jackson (left) and Graeme Lowe were part of a large New Zealand contingent which attended the World Meat Congress in Sydney in 1993. Peter Jackson, chairman of AFFCO from 1990-97, was about to embark on a capital restructuring which, although it was temporarily derailed by the quota allocation row, would result in the company being publicly listed in 1995. AFFCO was founded as Auckland Farmers Freezing Company in 1904 and lost its farmer co-operative status when it listed, but the majority of its current shareholders are farmers.

Byrch also noted there were several foreign banks wishing to exit their syndicates. The problem was that if one pulled out then none of the other members of the syndicate could afford to take up the balance. They were either all in or all out. To keep them in they had to have confidence the industry was stable and not bleeding to death.

The view was that a permanent allocation of quotas would remove one of the main causes of the procurement focus and allow companies to concentrate on earning more from the market.

In the end, the 'Secret Seven' proposed allocated quotas which would be held in perpetuity but were tradeable. Allocation for the 1994-95 season would be based on the throughput for the 1993-94 season but 5% of total quota would be set aside in year one for tendering to provide an entry mechanism for new competitors. Subsequent new entrants would have to buy quota from existing operators. Any increases in total quota arising from the GATT negotiations would be tendered among licensed exporters.

The 'Secret Seven's' analysis with its package of solutions was put together as a discussion document entitled 'Securing a Profitable Future for the New Zealand Meat Export Industry' which was circulated to all industry stakeholders for consideration on 27 October 1994. However, almost immediately, the acting Minister of Agriculture, Dennis Marshall, until then a supporter of the 'Secret Seven', completely upstaged their proposals.

In a surprise move he announced that the Government supported tendering some or all of the quota. It was an option that had been considered and largely rejected by the 'Secret Seven', but was apparently supported by the more market-oriented 'dries' among the officials. In Peter Harris's view it was promoted by MAF and Treasury officials.

The officials' proposal was that entitlement would be distributed initially in a once-only process that would combine straight allocation and tendering, with some questions as to where the income from the tendering process would be directed. The volumes to be allocated would be the increased tonnages of beef and sheepmeat recently negotiated in the GATT agreement. "One of the key issues to be resolved is how much of this quota should be assigned to meat companies in accordance with their previous processing history and how much should be tendered so as to allow new entrants to the meat industry the chance to participate, and the existing companies to expand where appropriate." A working party was to meet to consider the issues.

This announcement temporarily derailed AFFCO's capital raising programme, but fortunately the delay did not prove fatal. Peter Jackson, chair-

man of AFFCO was reported in the *New Zealand Farmer*: "We were proceeding down the critical path to producing a prospectus; the deal was largely
underwritten when on 13 October the Minister announced a review of the
quota arrangements. In effect it switched off the underwriters, which switched
off the prospectus which switched off the float."

Bill Garland pointed out that quotas were negotiated at government level
and the Government had the ultimate responsibility to determine the rules
or methods of allocation and any permanent allocation would require legislative backing. The increase in the EU sheepmeats quota under the GATT
agreement "provides a window of opportunity to introduce a new system
without the disruption that would have occurred last year, and given the
inability of the industry to agree on a better method after months of debate,
the Government clearly decided they needed to intervene."

The members of the working party were: chairperson Larry Fergusson
(MAF), Doug Andrew (Treasury), Sir David Beattie (MIA), David Frith
(Meat Producers Board), Graham Robertson (Federated Farmers), Bill Gar-
land (FF Meat & Wool Section), Malcolm Bailey (FF Dairy Section), James
Aitken (Electoral Committee), Colin Henderson (Wairakei Group), and
Norris Everton (Abattoirs Association). Only Bill Garland had been a regular
participant at the meetings of the 'Secret Seven'. The working party was
given two weeks to report to the Minister.

The working party had been set up to consider the quota allocation options separate from the MPC which, it was claimed, had too many vested
interests to reach an agreement on market access.

However farmers, abattoir operators and the smaller meat companies,
including some members of the working party, dismissed the proposed system as they had the two previous attempts to allocate on a one-off basis.
The tradeability and the tendering proposal were perceived to reduce the
level of competition and to disadvantage new entrants who were still building a production record.

Farmers and the Board wanted a system that would pass the maximum
return from the quota markets back to the farmer through procurement prices.
In other words, they wanted procurement competition to continue.

They also queried the suggestion that MAF or another government agency
manage the tender and monitor transfers, and sought information on where
the money from the tender process would end up. MAF apparently favoured
distributing it to farmers via research and development or reducing meat
inspection charges, while Treasury favoured payment into the Consolidated
Fund. There were also concerns that the EU or US might consider taking
back control of the quotas if they could see the Government or some other
agency was determining a value for them through the tendering process.

The working party could not agree on a scheme let alone meet its deadline. In the circumstances, and given the intensity of the opposition to the
proposals, a combined team from the Board, MIA and Federated Farmers
sought a delay in implementation of the Government-imposed scheme and
worked to devise a compromise.

The outlines of the new option were drawn up over a weekend of intense
drafting and discussion with a major contribution from Stewart Barnett of

PPCS. The preferred system of allocation was based on a rolling average of historic export tonnage. The broad outline of the scheme was presented in a joint news release from Federated Farmers, MIA and the Board on 8 November 1994, with the details to be worked through and announced by 30 November.

The Government made it clear that the industry-inspired alternative had to be agreed by all stakeholders and in place by 30 November. There were also indications from bankers that seasonal finance was dependent on the scheme being watertight. The principles were agreed by mid-November and signed off by the MPC in early December.

The industry scheme was designed to at least largely satisfy the requirements of all the parties – producers, processors and exporters – with another set of rules that initially ran to 15 pages. The key features were: the allocations were to be made on annually but calculated on a three year rolling average based on ownership at time of slaughter of qualifying export graded product; companies could earn quota on 5% of qualifying product sent to the domestic market; a percentage of the quota would be reserved for new entrants; decisions regarding the reserved tonnage would be made by an independent tribunal; quotas could be traded.

It was still a production-based system, but some of the uncertainties and the incentive to chase livestock had been ameliorated. However the system was agreed and it stuck – remarkable given the meat industry's history of attempting to circumvent any agreed arrangement. It survived the demise of the MPC agreement in 1996, with control as well as management reverting to the Board.

It may have been a factor in averting some of the worst elements of the procurement wars along with some judicious pressure from the banks, but nature also played its part. The drought conditions of 1995 saw a reversal of procurement factors as drought-affected farmers urgently sought killing space reduced by the Fortex and Weddel closures.

In the following year the BSE scare in the UK pushed market prices up and the market paid for any procurement incentives that may have been necessary. Also, by that stage, the quota pattern had been settled and stock numbers appeared to have stabilised after their previous steady decline.

No matter what the issues are locally, the ultimate influence on the New Zealand meat industry is the state of the global meat market, and forums like the World Meat Congress are an important means of keeping up with trends and developments. Among New Zealand's representatives to the 1995 Congress in Denver Colorado, from left: Board CEO Warwick Bishop, producer representative Gavan Herlihy, trade policy manager Cheryl Craig, chairman David Frith and producer representative Richard Johnstone.

Back on the Marketing Merry-go-Round 1995-97

"If you ever wanted an argument for the advantages of a single seller, look at the history of DEVCO in Canada and the prices that they got – they were the best in the world." Norman McRae.

The ink had barely dried on the quota document when James Aitken, John McCarthy and their mentor Tom Atchison joined forces to propose a radical change to the sheepmeat marketing system. In early January 1995 they circulated a document proposing that all export processors of sheepmeats form a commercially-driven marketing company separate from any processing company. It was essentially a rerun of 'Super Farmco' with some additions such as the suggestion the Board should only promote meat sold by the company or its licensees.

Apparently the idea had sprung from a comment attributed to Richmond's John Foster during a farmers' discussion on the problem of a 'surplus' of lightweight carcasses and the impact on prices in the Middle East and the Mediterranean. He had suggested that a single export gate might be more appropriate than the existing system of nominating special access markets with designated licensees. There was also some dissatisfaction among the farmers over the handling of the quota question and suggestions of a lack of focus on the marketplace.

The proponents for the change faced the usual problem of gaining acceptance and implementation in an industry where managements thrive on competing rather than co-operating.

For the idea to work, it would have required the companies to work together and also relinquish their marketing activities to a central organisation. Statutory backing or Board agreement to provide an exclusive export licence for sheepmeats – world-wide – was also a prerequisite. It was a forlorn hope, but attracted a lot of attention and comment as the promoters persisted valiantly.

Rick Bettle drew attention to the issue in February 1995 in a *National Business Review* interview following the announcement of his retirement from Alliance later in the year. He suggested that while the industry was relatively stable at the time, within two years the participants would forget the upheavals and go back to the old pattern.

"Industries with a high seasonal peak and high fixed costs are kiwifruit, apples, dairying and lamb. Three are regulated and one isn't. Look at which ones are succeeding and which one is in turmoil… There's a huge groundswell of farmers saying that maybe the dairy industry has got it right and maybe Alliance, PPCS, Richmond and AFFCO should form one marketing company so we all stop slaughtering each other offshore.

"But we won't have a single seller because people say it's commercially not correct; it's going in the wrong direction; don't be wet. I can't see anyone being brave enough to bring in the legislation against the howls of the Business Roundtable and others."

Despite this realistic advice interest in the proposal rumbled on with the *New Zealand Farmer* noting in an editorial on 15 February 1995 that meat company chief executives could not afford to ignore the weight of farmer opinion in favour of the proposed new structure. Graeme Harrison advised that marketing consortiums to develop specific markets were not new but that industry executives had traditionally been cautious about them. He listed ANZCO's joint venture with AFFCO, the activities of the Lamb Company in North America and the handling of the Iran contract by the Meat Marketing Corporation, recently disbanded in favour of individual marketing approaches by its principal suppliers Alliance and PPCS.

David Frith commented that there was nothing to stop companies getting together to form a new enterprise but it would require complete commitment from them all. He wondered whether one company was in the best long-term interests of the producers and reverted to the Board's preference for regional marketing companies.

Within New Zealand, almost every aspect of the meat industry was coming in for criticism. But those looking from the outside saw a lot to praise. Miriam Parker, 1996 Waitangi Fellow from the UK to New Zealand, was impressed by the high standards of animal welfare and humane slaughter in this country. The Waitangi Fellowship was established in 1990 to further understanding between the New Zealand and UK meat industries. Winners from New Zealand have included Philippa Stevenson and Malcolm Taylor and from the UK Clive Dibben and Clive Godden.

True to his dictum that "I have always been an advocate that markets should be open" exporter Gray Mathias was opposed to any suggestion of compulsion or the use of regulations to set up a single marketing company. So, too, was John Falloon. The Minister noted there would be major risks and a large capital requirement which should not be provided by the Meat Board. He then trotted out a bogeyman warning that he and the MIA used frequently in debates on producer boards and farmer control. "Any sign of farmer intervention to form a single seller or even heavily controlled marketing would stop people investing in the industry. And that would be bad for farmers."

James Aitken and John McCarthy launched the weak seller argument when they contended the MPC was not able to hold companies to the pricing arrangement agreed to and that they cheated to get around the rules. Eric Cammell, as the representative of the independent meat companies on the MPC, advised that the marketplace would find its own level. "New Zealand cannot control overseas markets."

On 20 February, *Rural News* reported that others in the industry had pointed to the Board's foray into single-desk selling in the early eighties which lost money heavily. "At the same time, processing companies were making a fortune, and farmers were being ripped off in big lumps."

Others agreed that the pricing arrangements were fragile, with Treasury and MAF officials insisting such efforts were futile because New Zealand did not have enough market power to influence prices.

In 'A Personal View' in the *New Zealand Farmer*'s 25 January 1995 issue, South Canterbury farmer David Stanton proposed a separation of the marketing arm of the industry from the processing operations. The Meat Board or 'Meats of New Zealand Marketing Board' would take over the marketing and gradually buy up the marketing arms and brands of the meat processor cooperatives – anathema to any red-blooded meat processing manager.

He made another attempt in June 1995. "Only a collective single desk has the size and security to forego the easy commodity trade to invest in developing markets… If we as farmers and New Zealanders want to break away from

Korean beef buyers take a close look at beef being processed at AFFCO's Manawatu Beef Packers plant in Feilding. Interpreting for them, at right, is Young Mee Nicholls from MIRINZ. From left, two of the visitors: Mr Oh of the Korean Cold Storage Company (KCSC) and Mr Kim of the Korean Meat Industries Association (KMIA).

These organisations and the Korean Tourist Hotel Corporation (KTHSC) and Korean Restaurant Supply Co. (KRSC), represent most of the groups which became able to deal direct with suppliers as the Korean beef market began to liberalise. In a Joint Action Group, the Board and industry have been working to build relationships with the buyers of the future.

commodity cycles and be price-makers not price-takers, if we really want jobs for New Zealanders, we need strong vertically integrated industries, adding value/adding jobs onshore or within New Zealand ownership."

At this stage the debate started to cross over the parallel discussions on the future role of the Meat and Wool Boards and the findings of the survey of farmers undertaken as part of the Scobie report commissioned by Federated Farmers.

The latter suggested farmers supported an open competitive structure for the industry and the powers of the Boards to co-ordinate marketing should be reduced. It was significant, though, that the survey questionnaire did not include an option for any Dairy Board-style centralised marketing, not an alternative as far as the Federation was concerned.

Arising from the survey Bill Garland suggested that farmers as shareholders of the farmer-owned companies held the key to the future marketing structure of the industry. David Frith joined in and suggested that decisions on such commercial matters should be for the companies and their shareholders to decide.

James Aitken and John McCarthy showed that, if nothing else, they were adaptable. Realising that a single company would not gain acceptance, they changed their proposal to the promotion of regional marketing companies, and used ANZCO as a prime example of what could be achieved if the Board, representing producers, and the farmer-owned meat companies got together in the marketplace. James Aitken also declared there was no need for political interference as the proposal was basically commercially driven.

While the promoters claimed growing farmer support the reality hit home at the farmer political level when delegates to the Meat & Wool Section annual conference in June voted against any further investigation of the single-seller proposal. The 'Farmers for Positive Change' group was undaunted, especially following a meeting of farmers in the Wairarapa to discuss the issue with the aid of some industry experts.

In his address to the meeting Rick Bettle suggested that while a single-seller system probably could do a better job of sharing the profits of the industry, he doubted whether it was practical or there was any chance of single-seller legislation for the meat industry. His answer, supported by Warren Larsen, CEO of the Dairy Board, was in the commercial approach. Farmers had to take up shares in their co-operatives and work together to control their own destiny.

Against this negative feedback James Aitken continued to press for an industry study to investigate the option of combined marketing by meat companies. He said in the *New Zealand Farmer,* 20 July 1995: "If the present structure is best then the meat companies should be happy to participate. Let them prove it… What is really disappointing is that the Meat Board is not leading the debate on behalf of the producer."

By August he and John McCarthy were questioning whether farmers were adequately represented by Federated Farmers and promoting the idea of formalising their group and setting up a fighting fund to debate meat issues.

Ian Lawrence, chairman of Bay of Plenty Meat & Wool Section, roundly slated this suggestion. He commented in 'A Personal View' in the *New Zealand Farmer* of 3 August that he admired the way James Aitken had organised his team and "I endorse in principle the concept of co-ordinated marketing for frozen lamb carcasses" which they promoted. But he was horrified they were proposing a separate organisation. "Farmers need another representative group like they need another drop in the schedule… Come on 'Farmers for Change', if you have strong support then you will have no trouble going to Federated Farmers' ballot box and ensuring that meat and wool farmers are represented in the way they should be. That is democracy – you've used it once, why not again?"

Although James Aitken's crusading zeal faded a little, particularly after he was voted on to the board of Richmond, another campaigner Ian Cresswell, president of Wairarapa Federated Farmers took up the cudgels. Cresswell, who twice stood unsuccessfully for the Board, believed in the single-seller concept and had initially suggested use of Section 11 of the Meat Export Control Act to promote a scheme for farmers to contract supply all their stock to processors. Section 11 enabled the Board to act as the agent for the owners of stock and to make arrangements for the slaughter for export. Cresswell was advocating that marketing control should begin to be exercised with intervention at the live animal stage, a task even more difficult than the intervention at the scales.

He took up the call for a study of the meat industry and also sought a delay in the changes to the Board's new legislation limiting its powers of intervention. He considered that some of the powers, such as Section 10, and more particularly Section 11, would be required to put in place his co-ordinated plan for the industry.

Following his retirement from Alliance, Rick Bettle kept the pot simmering. He commented in the *New Zealand Farmer* on 31 August 1995 that, "A single seller offers the perfect mechanism for marketing sheepmeat," but admitted the dynamics of the system made it too difficult to contemplate. He also rehearsed the arguments for some form of intervention. "There is no easy way out of this trap. If they finally agree one day that this is an empty core market, and I suspect they will, they will either have to turn it into a single seller or allow a conference where processors can get together and offer one price."

The Cresswell crusade attracted another stalwart in Lindsay Smith, who issued a press release on 28 September entitled 'A Radical Plan for the Meat Industry.' Lindsay Smith was a Hawke's Bay meat and wool farmer who had branched out into kiwifruit and apple growing. "Getting into apples convinced me that if meat was going to survive it had to go a similar way," he said. The 'Radical Plan' proposal was based on an 'Integrated Marketing' (IM) model for the industry and suggested there was growing interest among farmers in seeing it developed and progressed.

Claims that the opportunity for introducing such a model had passed were refuted by Smith who suggested that the absence of an integrated marketing system was only due to political reluctance and a lack of commitment from farmers and companies. His plan came complete with a vision statement for the industry: "To maximise the sustainable income of the entire meat sector, through the development of efficient structures and through excellence in the global marketing of New Zealand-derived meat products."

The plan relied on the reconstitution of the Board into a new entity called the NZ Meat Marketing Corporation (MMC) to take on all the powers of the

Board and "additionally be responsible for the marketing of all New Zealand beef, sheep and goat meat products". It said a lot about Objectives, Strategies and Pre-conditions, but the section on how the MMC would operate was somewhat tentative.

Smith's proposal got the inevitable lambasting by all and sundry as it conflicted with the political trend towards less regulation and intervention. MIA executive director Brian Lynch immediately suggested that the plan risked a leap backward "by resurrecting a structure that was tried and failed a decade ago, and left the industry burdened with a billion-dollar debt". Of course, the industry had not suffered from the debt, but it was a good debating point. He took the proposal apart for looking backwards and not recognising the current performance of the industry and the changed marketing environment.

Both Lindsay Smith and Ian Cresswell were aware of the opposition they faced from vested interests in the industry, but they were convinced that if they put their plan to farmers, via a referendum if necessary, they would win support.

Initial farmer meetings to discuss the plan appeared to support it or at least require that it be further investigated. However, Graham Hewett, chairman of Marlborough Meat & Wool Section considered the responses in his area were not unexpected "given the level of frustration among farmers over the lack of profit from meat production".

When he took over the reins as chairman of the Board from David Frith in October 1995, John Acland joined the fray. He came down on the side of meat companies being fully integrated in processing and marketing rather than supporting the single-seller system being proposed by Smith and Cresswell. "If companies want to come together and be a single seller in a particular market then that's fine. But it has to be done in a commercial way and not by using a law or power…. What we have got to do is give people the confidence to work within the structure we have now. I don't blame farmers one bit for feeling cross and negative. But I'm saying, hang in there. We're at the turning point for lamb and given a couple of years beef will turn around."

However the debate would not go away. Early in 1996 Smith and Cresswell

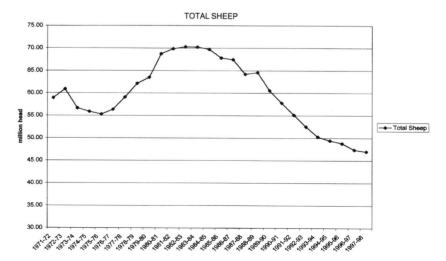

The rise and fall of total New Zealand sheep numbers and lamb kill tell part of the story of the change that has taken place in the meat industry over the past 25 years.

still claimed they had support from a growing groundswell of dissatisfied farmers who were "increasingly nervous of Agriculture Minister Falloon's proposed changes to the Meat Export Control Act 1921-22". They were still lobbying for a delay until their proposal had been fully researched and debated. In a press release of 12 March, John Acland told them they were swimming against the tide with a proposal that was outmoded by 10 years. "The economy has been deregulated and the same is happening to the meat industry."

The simmering weak-seller pot started steaming again early in 1996 when Dr John Morris criticised the export marketing of meat in an address to the NZ Grassland Association conference. In his view New Zealand exporters stole market share to sell their product, and not always from foreign competition.

He gave an example of a meat company that undercut a fellow New Zealand exporter to steal a contract to supply a US cruise liner company. "The price reduction was substantial and so was the loss of returns to farmers, but the deal did nothing to develop the market." If the company had wanted to win long-term business and build relationships with other cruise companies, it could have offered a price that was just a few cents cheaper, Morris said.

The situation had become so confused that Bill Garland pleaded for a stop to calls for political meddling in the meat industry in an article in *Straight Furrow* in July 1996. He argued against the regulated, vertically integrated structure proposed by Lindsay Smith and Ian Cresswell. The 'Secret Seven's' investigation had discounted several suggested intervention measures including a single seller, and "history shows that meat and wool farmers support intervention when prices are down and don't want a bar of it when the going improves".

Unfortunately for the crusaders the farm gate prices for lamb had begun to improve. Although interest waned they were not to be deterred, continuing to put forward remits to each annual general meeting of the Board proposing that the issue be investigated but failing to rouse sufficient support. They are still trying.

The other half of the story is the greatly increased productivity which means that there is almost as much meat for export as at the height of subsidy-boosted production in the early 1980s.

All Together at the Table
1995-97

"Meat Board chairman David Frith says it should be possible to reach agreement, given the level of mutual interest in workable future structures. 'They may be three different organisations, but the Meat Board and Federated Farmers are basically representing the same people, and if you consider the fact that producers are shareholders in the majority of the sheepmeat processing companies and half the beef processors, the Meat Industry Association is also speaking on behalf of the same farmers'." Meat Board News, *2 March 1995.*

Meals and meat cookery at the Board today are very different in style from the years when Andy Andriotis catered to the unchanging requirements ordained by Charles Hilgendorf. Chef and food consultant Janet Lymburn, who joined the Board in 1990, and was a regional Lamb Cuisine Award winner, has cooked meals featuring everything from bull beef to goats' testicles as part of her brief to showcase New Zealand meat products. As well as preparing meals for the many visitors to the Board, Janet Lymburn has also worked with industry promotion teams at the Anuga Trade Fair and, more recently, demonstrated the distinct qualities of New Zealand meat to the food service sector in the Middle East.

The intention to reform producer boards had been made plain in the mid-eighties and had remained constant through the change from Labour to National as government in 1990. But despite all the political will the deadline for effecting the changes was continually extended, and the extra time was used to further debate the ultimate scope and purpose of the legislation.

Producer board reforms based on increasing commercial responsibility and a lessening of government intervention were very much what Minister of Agriculture John Falloon had in mind. His sights were set on the powers relating to licensing, acquisition, freight rates and grading. If an industry board was still needed then the MPC structure was a step in that direction with the final objective being some form of joint producer/industry organisation.

He had originally intended to have new legislation by 1993 but the Government began its second term in office with no definite timeframe for completion, and no let-up in the lobbying and jockeying for position.

New communications manager Eirwen Tulett joined the Board in May 1994, her brief to substantially increase communication with stakeholders. With recent experience working in Minister Falloon's office, and previously with Federated Farmers, she moved to improve the flow of information about the role and functions of the Board to both government and opposition members, and to influential journalists, both national and provincial. One of her toughest tasks was managing the PR fallout from Board secretary Trevor Playford's decision to lead the way in accounting terms by publicising the fact that 10 Board executives were paid over $100,000 and that Warwick Bishop's salary was in the $230,000-$239,000 band.

Eirwen Tulett also dramatically increased the flow of background information to a range of groups including Federated Farmers' provincial offices, many of them holding a different view of the Board from the official national line.

The multi-sector steering committee convened by the Minister was looking at how electoral change would be put into practice. Separately, the Board itself was considering the evolution of its powers, with staff like Cheryl Craig reviewing ways to streamline the licensing process.

It was rather against the run of play when, in July 1994, Federated Farmers Meat & Wool chairman Bill Garland announced the intention to make a "grassroots review" of structures affecting incomes, in order to shape future policy. Later the focus was narrowed to begin with the meat and wool industries, and with a review commissioned from Waikato University academic Dr Grant Scobie. The 'Scobie Report', co-authored by Massey's Frank Scrimgeour, was published shortly after the steering committee's final recommendations for electoral changes.

The report offered a number of different scenarios for future meat industry structures, from complete free-market through to the existing situation. It did not, however, include the option of returning to a single seller. Perhaps it was an unthinkable concept for authors who had both previously been strongly identified with Business Roundtable projects.

David Frith described the Scobie Report as a brave first attempt and said that its "main conclusion seems to be that the functions the Meat Board already carries out are important, and someone needs to do them".

Bill Garland and others from Meat & Wool Section began an exhaustive round of farmer meetings to discuss the report. From the perspective of the Board – which quietly abandoned an already scheduled series of its own farmer meetings and sent at least one representative to each of the 'Scobie' meetings – the project was doomed to add to confusion rather than understanding.

Meals made with New Zealand lamb following a training course run by Terry Brown of the Board's Brussels office in 1996.

Board secretary Trevor Playford complained that meetings consisted of a presentation about the Board's statutory powers with no exploration of what they actually were, or the Board's policy to use them as part of industry agreements. More positively a number of farmers spoke out in favour of retention of the Board's statutory powers, and there was an impressive level of understanding of their importance.

The public disarray and disagreement prevailing at the end of 1994 was great for rural headline writers, but it undoubtedly frustrated the Minister in his drive for a co-operative industry.

If there was any doubt about the cost of the lack of focus on a common strategy, it came with a poor performance for the animal products industries in the latest Public Good Science Funding Round. The figures spoke for themselves. The small but focussed venison industry had secured as much research money as the long-established beef industry.

It was a poor beginning for 1995. Then the Board and Federated Farmers each announced their own proposed amendments to the Board's powers and structures. David Frith pointed out that all organisations representing producers should be able to reach an agreed position.

This was clearly the Minister's view. As the regulations allowing for direct elections were gazetted, he put forward a proposal for new legislation which would remove the Board's powers of control, reduce its licensing role, and make classification a company responsibility. He challenged the Board, the MIA and Federated Farmers (whose Meat & Wool Section was now led by Edward Orr) to come up with an agreed position on this.

There followed a furious round of meetings. At the Board's interim AGM in early May, the Minister made it clear he saw its statutory powers as a bar to industry investment. But the industry-agreed position, outlined in a joint letter to the Minister on 11 May, endorsed a continuing statutory role for what would become an industry board in grading and classification as well as licensing. Processor-exporters would appoint four members to the new Board, and the Meat Planning Council would be formally reconstituted as a Meat Industry Council, the primary forum for industry policy formulation.

David Frith told *Meat Producer* that the Board "already acts in consultation with the MIA and the wider industry, but this has not always been seen to be done… The new structures would give processor-exporters the right to be part of the decision-making process, and also the responsibility to make sure it works… When there is a shared responsibility for decisions, it will be more difficult for any party to backtrack or stand apart and criticise agreed positions."

The legislation which came back from the Ministry in August 1995, and was finally signed off in the expectation that it would go into Parliament before the end of the year, gave more emphasis to the need for "industry agreement". It also provided for one more seat on the Board, a ministerial appointee, lifting membership to 12.

As outlined in the Board's annual report, fittingly titled 'A Year of Change', the Meat Board's new functions would include: increasing the demand for New Zealand meat through promotion and market development; funding research and development; gathering and providing information; accounting to producers for activities and the uses of levy money; encouraging increased efficiency in all facets of the industry; and helping New Zealand attain greater meat market access.

The Board would lose its transport, control and 'other' powers but retain the powers of a natural person and the power to levy. It would continue to license exporters and retain amended powers for quality purposes and grading, and was required to develop mechanisms, in consultation with industry, to allocate access to quota markets, within certain criteria. The Board would only be able to exercise powers relating to meat quality with industry agreement. In other words, it could be very difficult in future to introduce a new technical innovation such as A C & A, if the majority of the industry was against it.

Overall the continuing importance of the Board had been acknowledged. Its role had been endorsed in providing some of the functions the MIA had tried to mirror, such as information gathering and market access. Its role in

The MIA Council, 1995-96. Standing from left: chief executive Brian Lynch, Owen Poole of Alliance, David Evans of Norman Evans Ltd, Graeme Harrison of ANZCO, Graeme Lowe of Lowe Walker, Keith Taylor of Taylor Preston, Richard Cornelius of Phoenix, Gray Mathias of Mathias Meats, Warwick Wilson of Crown Meat Export and Colin Francis of Davmet. Seated from left: John Foster of Richmond, chairman Sir David Beattie, deputy chairman Don Manson of AFFCO and Stewart Barnett of PPCS.

John Foster retired the following year. Warwick Wilson moved into a new gourmet butchery business after Crown Meat Export was absorbed into ANZCO in 1997.

Keith Taylor died in late 1997. Knowing he did not have long to live, he farewelled the industry in style with a series of champagne lunches in Auckland, Wellington and Melbourne.

generic promotion was acknowledged. In the market access area it had won the major argument against the MAF bureaucrats about who should be responsible for quota allocation.

Also, survey evidence from October 1995 – strategically passed on to the appropriate politicians – showed a high level of farmer support for the Board's continued involvement in market access, grading and classification and local promotion.

The MIA had managed to pare back the Board's involvement in quality and classification to a minimum, beyond which all had to be "industry-agreed". They and Federated Farmers had waved goodbye to the powers of control which so worried them, but which the Board had readily conceded were no longer needed. Federated Farmers had, however, not managed to get the Commodity Levy requirements applied to the Board.

Meat Board chief executive Neil Taylor, AFFCO chief executive Don Manson, Board chairman John Acland and Gray Mathias at the launch of the Beef and Lamb Quality Mark in 1997.

Minister John Falloon had got his Industry Board. He said having industry representatives at the Board table breaks with "legacies of the past 75 years of mistrust between farmers and artificially erected barriers between companies and the Board". He had put a personal stamp on the new legislation. As the Board summed up in its annual report: "The Minister of Agriculture is also changing some aspects of the Meat Board's powers and responsibilities. The changes planned by the Minister will remove a number of Board powers with the intent of encouraging industry innovation, but at the same time allow the Meat Board to act in the interests of the wider industry."

It was, as both the Board and the MIA commented in their annual reports, a significant turning point. For the Board itself another turning point had come with David Frith's decision to step down from October 1995, with the new legislation apparently agreed, if not enacted. The day after he announced his decision his deputy Alan Grant was defeated as a ward representative. He was entitled to stay on the Board until the following March, because he held a seat under the old system – and did so – but he could not fulfil expectations that he would become the new chairman, a position for which he had been extensively groomed.

Instead John Acland accepted the job he had not sought, but for which he was well-equipped, as a long-time supporter of the industry board concept and a firm believer in the value of bringing people together to talk through issues. Though not a high-profile Board member he had served three terms, had unmatched networks of contacts and he and his wife Rosemary had widespread respect in both the farming and the wider community. Former chief government whip, and first-term producer representative, Jeff Grant, was elected deputy.

In the Board's annual report John Acland said: "After a decade of infighting, farmers, meat industry players, government and the Meat Board itself have agreed on a set of measures which will enable the Board to meet (the) challenges (of the 21st century)."

Sir David Beattie commented in the MIA's annual report: "From the Association's standpoint, the main thrust of the Government proposals is very acceptable. In summary, they are to give the Board a clearer and reduced focus of activity, by removing powers that are no longer relevant, modifying others, and eliminating responsibilities that are of a commercial nature which in today's competitive environment are more appropriately

Minister of Agriculture Lockwood Smith has got to eat quite a lot of beef in the course of duty. Here he enjoys Quality Mark beef offered to him by Michael Coughlin and Beef and Lamb Marketing Bureau general manager Rod Slater.

left to companies… The Association fully supports the concept of the future Board having the role of 'facilitator' rather than being an 'interventionist' body."

By January 1996, the Industry Board was a reality, despite the fact that legislation was still stalled. AFFCO's Don Manson had become the first processor representative on the Board, appointed under the old regulations with the agreement of the Board (which had to recommend the nomination to the Minister). As little progress was made on legislation until later in the year, this was in hindsight a good move for the proponents of the industry board.

John Acland's Board included the first ward representatives, Brent Rawstron and Tim Brittain.

By April of 1996 the lineup was different again as two more processing industry appointees, Stewart Barnett and Gray Mathias, joined the Board along with another ward member, Jeremy Austin. Ross Finlayson remained as the government appointee.

Over at Federated Farmers, Theo Simeonidis had moved on and his replacement was Tony St Clair, formerly with the Victorian equivalent in Australia.

And there was a new minister of agriculture. As Sir David Beattie described it in the MIA annual report: "Following his decision not to seek re-election, Hon John Falloon was replaced in March 1996 by Dr the Hon Lockwood Smith. During his five years as Minister, Mr Falloon was a good friend of the Association, and I appreciated his ready willingness to meet with us on matters of concern.

"Dr Smith has shown early indications of relishing the challenges of his new portfolio and we look forward to constructive dialogue on his ideas about ways of expanding market returns."

While his predecessor had possibly been too ready to lend an ear to a wide range of arguments, Lockwood Smith, the former Education Minister who was also a proud farmer of Belgian Blue bulls, was a man of firmly formed convictions. Amongst them was the marketing superiority of the dairy industry, as he made clear in one of his first speeches, to the Board's 1996 AGM.

For John Acland's new Board their first informal AGM at Christchurch was a baptism of fire, and not only because proceedings were interrupted by a bomb scare. The day coincided with fresh revelations about the extent of the British problem with BSE. 'Leadership', many at the meeting and the rural media made clear, would have best been demonstrated by taking the maximum advantage of the situation in promoting New Zealand beef and lamb. Those attending didn't want to hear Warwick Bishop's presentations showing the dramatic productivity gains of the sheepmeat sector. The floor was also held by the 'Smith-Cresswell' group presenting their petition for a study into a "fully integrated sheep and beef processing/marketing sector" (aka single-desk seller), but sidestepping John Acland's offer of a vote on the issue.

Despite this rocky start 1996 was to see, as the Board's annual report said later, "giant steps in working together as an industry". Joint initiatives included the start of a major study into international competition in protein supply; a two-day 'Blue Sky' strategic direction meeting, and the formation of the Global Market Development Groups for the long-term planning of sheepmeat and beef marketing.

The Meat Research and Development Council's annual meeting 1996. Standing from left: Bill Bly, representing beef breed societies; Robert Anderson, Massey University; Kerry Dunlop, sheep breeders; Mark Aspin, MRDC programme manager for monitor farms; Joanne Young, administrator.
At front: Graeme Harrison, ANZCO; Craig Hickson, Progressive; Jeff Grant, MRDC chairman and Meat Board deputy chairman; Neil Clarke, executive director, and Dr Jim Ellis. Ben O'Brien, programme manager for off-farm projects, is absent.

The MRDC is now incorporated in the Meat Board and producer-funded research and technology transfer is delivered under the Meat New Zealand brand.

The term of the commercial co-operation agreement for the MPC expired in June and with little support for its retention it was disbanded, with the quota control and monitoring passing to the Board.

Warwick Bishop had said working together with the industry "represents a sea-change from the ways of the past, but it will not come as a shock. In reality we have already made the adjustment to working more closely together."

As Sir David Beattie described it in his 1995-96 annual report the industry representatives on the Meat Board made an immediate impact. "The value of their presence, in terms of bringing hands-on practical experience of the realities and priorities of the marketplace to the Board's deliberations, was soon apparent. There is now mutual recognition by the Board and the Association that we need, jointly, to develop a generic vision for the industry and a set of guiding principles, complemented by a set of specific strategies," Sir David said.

One tangible demonstration was closure of both the Bahrain and Hong Kong offices by year's end, with the Asian region (managed by Liz Francis) and the Middle East (by Kevin O'Grady) in future to be run from Wellington.

In fact work had begun on a major collaborative project to establish research priorities in early 1995. It culminated in June 1996 in the publication of Ernst and Young consultant Dr Andy West's report 'A Future for the Red Meat Industry', linking research priorities with predicted changes in consumer needs.

This was distilled and combined with other research strategies into 'Towards 2006: a 10 year Research and Development strategy for the New Zealand Red Meat Industry', funded by the Board, the MIA and AgResearch and signed off by two Board directors, Stewart Barnett as chairman (and MIA representative) of MIRINZ, and Jeff Grant as chairman of the MRDC.

To the funding providers, it was a clear message of resolve. Further signals were sent when the Foundation for Sheep Production Research was launched in August 1996, followed by a high profile function "celebrating the sheep". Encouraging indications given to beef producers culminated in the Beef Research Foundation in mid-1997. The foundations, whose membership included producer, processor and research providers, were another 'partnership' mechanism to identify and promote research priorities and, incidentally, show sector-

Introducing the MRDC and particularly the concept of farm planning at the 1991 Christchurch Royal Show.

wide solidarity.

In 1996 food scientist Neil Clarke took over from Alan Royal – who became the Board's webmaster – at the MRDC. In 1997 MRDC ceased to exist and the research function was 'mainstreamed' as the research and information transfer division of the Board, with Neil Clarke as its general manager.

Despite the hopes of the new Minister, the Producer Boards Amendment Bill did not get its second reading before the November 1996 election. Nevertheless a commitment was given that it would remain in the system, paving the way for it to go to the Primary Production Select Committee in 1997.

In December 1996, in a further show of commitment to co-operation, John Acland and Sir David Beattie announced plans to produce a joint strategic direction for the meat industry. They said the Meat Board's management of quota markets was central to the new direction and agreed it was important that the Board continue to undertake generic promotion. The statement also reconfirmed a commitment to joint venture promotions, a co-operative initiative by the Board, which had at first struggled to gain the acceptance of industry participants in 1992.

The new-look Board wanted to give an even higher profile to communication. This was echoed in the processing industry. Even the fortress-like PPCS, with its CEO now on the Meat Board, acknowledged the greater need to talk to its suppliers, and did so through farmer meetings.

Within the Board it was reflected in the emphasis on relationships following a comprehensive restructure. For instance, the new division of market and industry services was "responsible for ongoing relationships with farmer groups, exporting companies, government and government advisors", the *Meat Board News* of 12 September 1996 reported. A new recruit to this area, with the title of executive officer industry planning, was Miriam Williams, who had built strong industry respect during her years with the MIA.

In the communications section itself the cupboard was bare, following the 'restructuring out' of the corporate affairs position held by Don Harwood, and later the resignation of Eirwen Tulett. At the end of 1996 Warwick Bishop also resigned, to become chief executive of the Institute of Professional Engineers.

For the first time for a number of years, the new chief executive was appointed from within the Board ranks. Neil Taylor met with almost universal approval, commanding widespread respect throughout the farming as well as the industry sector with experience which included time at the head of the Economic Service and as European director in Brussels.

With the upcoming select committee process, it would have been a coup if Owen Symmans, Prime Minister's Department staffer, and former Federated Farmers policy manager, had taken up the Board's communications position, but he was persuaded to stay where he was. The new external relations position then went to former Telecom government relations expert, Chris Galloway.

PPCS advertises one of its annual meetings with producers. "This day is for PPCS suppliers and all other interested farmers. Media by invitation."

The Producer Boards Amendment Bill had its second reading in Parliament early in March 1997, just before the Board held its AGM, still informally pending the legislation. Lockwood Smith again addressed the meeting. He was now a 'superminister' for the meat industry, having added the portfolio of international trade to agriculture.

Neil Taylor's presentation to the AGM asked for farmer opinion on the future of the Board's reserves, then standing at $137 million. Acknowledging some farmers would like to see at least a proportion returned to them, assuming this could be done equitably, he put the case for maintaining a contingency fund of at least $50 million. He was backed up by the UK Meat and Livestock Commission's Colin McLean who described the vast expenditure needed to restore confidence in British beef following the BSE outbreak. The reserves issue failed to raise passions and the most heated debate, as previously, involved the Smith-Cresswell group now officially known as Meat and Wool Levy Payers (MAWL).

A sign of things to come was the presence of representatives of the Federation of Maori Authorities and the big Maori corporation Mangatu Blocks. Representing the owners of some of the largest livestock holdings in the country, they had an obvious interest in the possibility of proportionate voting. A remit on the subject was closely lost. Their potential for influence was also illustrated in questions to the Board about its accountability and planning procedures.

Subsequently, particular effort was put into consultation with Maori groups and encouraging Maori levy payers to enrol as voters.

A side effect of the saturation levels of communication and consultation was that the Board had a much clearer view of how levy-payers and other stakeholders saw it. This included some welcome news, such as the independent 1997 research showing the enormous impact and uptake of MRDC-funded research, in particular on the relationship of animal stress to meat quality. Later a study would show an almost 20:1 cost-benefit for expenditure on the monitor farm programme.

Spearheaded by Allan Frazer, the Board was separately encouraging involvement in the Ministry of Research Science and Technology's Foresight Project, where a number of industry sectors looked further into the future and its implications for strategy.

1997 was the year of the Primary Production Select Committee hearings on the Producer Boards Amendment Bill. Chaired by Awarua MP (and former Electoral Committee member and unsuccessful Board contender) Eric Roy, its membership also included Otago MP and former Board member Gavan Herlihy, defeated by Jeff Grant at the 1994 election, and ACT MP and former president of Federated Farmers, Owen Jennings. Others were Grant Gillon of the Alliance, longtime deputy Agriculture Minister Dennis Marshall, and opposition spokesman Jim Sutton, Damian O'Connor and Tutekawa Wyllie.

Parliamentary authorities reported unprecedented interest in the submission process. During an extended period the committee heard over 90 submissions, including ones from the Federation of Maori Authorities and from MAWL. It held sessions outside of Wellington and visited Australia, where massive changes to structures formerly centring on the AMLC as an industry board (with appointed, rather than elected, representatives) were taking place.

The Board's own submission, co-ordinated by Miriam Williams, was one of the earliest presented. By and large the Board submission – summarised and sent to all levy-payers – followed the already agreed position. It did, however, suggest that the Bill should be amended to make provision, at the request of the wider industry, for the Board to implement minimum quality requirements for

Miriam Williams, executive officer, industry planning.

John Loughlin became the new chief executive of Richmond in 1997. He has since presided over the rebranding of the company as Richmond Farm Fresh and the acquisition of all the Lowe Walker plants, and been elected a processing industry representative on the Meat Board.

John Acland, who followed a family tradition when he became chairman of a producer board. He was elected chairman of the Meat Board in October 1995.

New Zealand meat products in agreed markets. Echoing ongoing concerns, it also suggested a separate licensing system for quota and non-quota markets.

Chairman John Acland argued strongly for a continued producer majority on the Board. The MIA wanted to have six Board seats – half the proposed number – designated for processing representatives. Certainly, this would have accommodated the Abattoirs Association demand to have a seat at the table.

With the large number of submissions it was not until November 1997 that the Select Committee reported back. Nevertheless, the new Act was a reality before Christmas. Welcoming the 'new mandate' Neil Taylor said its timing was ideal, with challenges, such as food safety and the next WTO trade access talks, facing the meat industry internationally.

Two significant changes were made as a result of hectic last-minute lobbying. The Board would in future consist of 13 members. There would be seven producer directors, with dairy farmers also voting rather than being represented by a Dairy Board appointee. The processing industry would have four representatives and the Minister would appoint two directors on the recommendation of the Board. These appointees were to be nominated bearing in mind the need for Maori and women to be represented.

The Act also introduced a weighted system of voting for representatives, a change which greatly increased the potential influence of larger farmers.

The Board's proposals for more stringent licensing requirements for quota markets were not included and its powers to establish quality requirements were removed. In the words of the select committee "quality is a commercial matter and should be left to the judgement of the parties that carry the business risk". The Board would audit industry-agreed disciplines for quality in quota markets.

The Act also signalled the likely end of compulsory classification systems, with reviews scheduled in a year for beef and two years for sheepmeat. Whether or not carcass classification was mandatory, indications were that a number of customer countries would still require it, and the Board had become the legal owner of the intellectual property of the system.

It also further underscored the requirement for the Board to consult producers and other interested groups as part of its planning process.

By repealing many of the Board's previous powers of intervention, the new legislation turned the tide decisively against any single-seller approaches. The mechanism required to implement the integrated marketing model was excised from the statutes.

This might seem to be a point at which the industry could pause to consolidate. But that would be reckoning without politics.

Full Circle –
Post 1997

"In the South Island, there is now a much closer attitude to companies and more loyalty. When I said at a meeting in the North Island that farmers should get closer to companies so they know what lambs are being produced and when they will be sent for processing, a fellow stood up and said, 'Are you telling me, John, that I can't ring around five companies on Sunday night and get the best price?'

"We are going to have to make the industry board concept work. It's been more difficult than I thought. But the best thing is that the farmer directors and the producer directors are now listening to each other. I think we'll go to some legislation where the farmers have a greater say on how the levy is spent... there are certainly some activities that we do need to collect a levy for and that benefit all farmers. At woolshed meetings, farmers tell me they are happy to pay a levy to the Board for its work on their behalf in market access and research and development. But the big area for debate will be promotion," John Acland.

Meat New Zealand chief executive Neil Taylor, leading the flock into the 21st century.

The August 1996 board meeting of ANZCO, chaired by Mervin Barnett, was held in a ward in Christchurch Hospital.

A week later, Mervyn Barnett was dead. He had been suffering from cancer for some time but in typical fashion maintained his interest and involvement in the company until the last.

Adam Begg, for whom he had been a support and sounding-board during the years from 1979 to 1987 when both were on the Board, had been planning to visit Mervyn Barnett in the hospital, feeling better after a long period of failing health. However, the night before he was to leave, he too died.

As part of the huge contribution he made to the meat industry in its most turbulent years, Adam Begg had been the founder chairman of ANZCO. Begg's funeral was notable for a big turnout from the farming community and other organisations he had been involved with. Barnett's funeral also showed his close links to his local community and church, but was also attended by a large contingent from the commercial side of the meat industry, including prominent members of the Japanese meat business. The New Zealand and international rugby fraternity was also there.

It was in many ways the passing of an era, although this was formalised for the New Zealand Meat Producers Board with the new Meat Board Act of December 1997.

In March 1998, Meat New Zealand became the new trading name of the Board. A new logo in blue-green Pacific colours replaced the red and blue initials and stars of the former identity. The image suggested a fork on a plate, making it clear that the focus was now on food.

Much of the year was involved in actioning what had been set in place

With the Meat Board Act of December 1997, the New Zealand Meat Producers Board became the New Zealand Meat Board. Shortly after it changed its operating name to Meat New Zealand.

*The Global Protein Report,
one of the collaborative efforts
between the Board and the
MIA.*

by the passing of the new Meat Board Act. It was not until the end of 1998 that the regulations governing Board membership were amended.

John Acland summarised farmer feeling from various forums as: "Get on with the job – don't stand for political interference". At the 1998 AGM a remit to abolish the compulsory levy was lost, as was another calling yet again for "a full review of possible options for the structure of the whole sector".

Throughout 1997 stakeholders had been working on the first truly joint strategic plan. When it was published in March 1998, 'Towards 2006, the New Zealand Red Meat Industry Strategic Direction' document included a prominent four-way sign-off by John Acland, David Beattie, Meat & Wool chairman Edward Orr and Norris Everton, chairman of the Abattoirs Association. It was a far cry from the low point of the separate 1993 Strategic Plans.

Building on the Strategic Direction document was the Strategic and Business Plan, first published as a 'consultation edition' for discussion at the AGM, and then a round of 'farmer forum' meetings. It gave more detail of goals and the performance measures for their achievement. It also provided a useful explanation of the Board itself and how it would meet the expectations of industry stakeholders, from livestock farmers and government to consumers, the food service industry and research providers.

But new pressures were already coming on the Board to reinvent itself once again. It began with coalition partner Winston Peters' budget announcement for a review of the trading boards, beginning with the Kiwifruit Authority. Then John Luxton, who had replaced Lockwood Smith as Agriculture Minister and strongly promoted the Government agenda for further producer board reform, set a deadline of 15 November 1998 for each board to indicate how it would operate in a completely deregulated environment.

Once again the trading producer boards were the principal target. The Dairy Board called the Government's bluff, along with Federated Farmers, to force a backdown, or at least a longer timeframe from the Minister. While the Dairy Board deliberately missed the deadline, Meat New Zealand met it, with its November 1998 'Plan for Change'.

This says: "Meat New Zealand's directors see a future requiring few legislative provisions, providing a range of services to benefit livestock farmers and the industry collectively, and with a structure that is effective, cost-efficient, flexible, relevant and accountable." The Board will in future offer a range of services to producers based on functions most effectively carried out on a collective basis, including trade policy and access issues; marketing services; research, development and information transfer; quota administration; and planning, co-ordination and information services.

It argued for continuation of compulsory levies for these core functions, to avoid the problem of 'free riders'. This was acknowledged by Treasury and policy makers as a problem in projects of whole industry benefit as far back as the 1987 restructuring initiatives.

The most appropriate structure, the plan suggested, would be a body corporate operating under the new Meat Board Act. The need for legislation would be minimal. Then, in a statement built on new-found confidence that its core expertise and services were likely to be the preferred choice, the Board said: "We intend to ensure that our activities add value. However if costs outweigh the benefits of any or all of our activities, we want to ensure that there are mechanisms in place to allow our funders to express those views and to either change, or in the ultimate, dissolve the organisation…"

John Acland, nephew of Sir John Ormond, now chairs a Board which his late uncle would find hard to recognise or even locate. The 1998 move by Meat New Zealand means that with the exception of Federated Farmers, a block away down Featherston Street, all the main participants in the meat industry – the Meat Board, the MIA, the Economic Service and the Abattoirs Association – are together in Wool House.

Gina Rudland.

The Board has been expanded by regulation to 13 members, at a time when the organisation itself is shrinking in size, budget and authority and the ideal number is seen as nine or 10.

Among those at the Board table are the first woman member, Maori lawyer Gina Rudland and another government appointee, Hemi-Rua Rapata of Whangarei. The first formal elections for meat industry representatives to the Board brought Graeme Harrison almost full circle – from Board employee to Board director, representing ANZCO. The vote also returned PPCS CEO Stewart Barnett, who had been on the Board since 1996, and brought in Richmond CEO John Loughlin. The elections also marked the end of nine years on the Board for Ross Finlayson, who first joined as a government appointee in 1990, but had maintained a seat, latterly as an industry representative. He was defeated by John Upton of Horizon Meats in a contest for the exporter seat.

John Acland is still a believer in an industry board but admits the concept and the current mix of membership still needs some fine-tuning. Debate at the Board table is often still divided on producer/industry lines and "while I can remember only one or two votes during the whole time David Frith chaired the Board, almost every issue now goes to the vote".

New Zealand is now divided into seven wards, each with a producer representative. Representing the South Island wards are John Acland, Jeff Grant and Alan Grant, who regained his seat from Brent Rawstron in the 1999 election. North Island ward members are Jeremy Austin, Tim Brittain, Bruce Jans and – elected for the new central North Island ward – John McCarthy – who last had dealings with the Board as one of the 'Farmers for Positive Change'.

Whether voters feel more enfranchised with direct elections is still open to question. Many former Electoral Committee members feel much has been lost and there is a real danger of a 'knowledge vacuum' developing among the next generation of potential farming leaders. A new farmer delegate body may be set up, following the passing of a remit at the Board's 1999 AGM. Expenses would be paid for this group, which at three per ward, numbers almost exactly the same as the old Committee.

The reality of the industry Board means that the MIA has had to redefine its role yet again for its very demanding financial members. The industry's ownership structure and control have changed dramatically in the last 25

Hemi-Rua Rapata.

Board members went back to the farm for the 1998 Annual Report. At back from left, Tim Brittain, deputy chairman Jeff Grant, and Alan Grant. In front, Jeremy Austin and Bruce Jans.

years with its fortunes shaped by the tidal changes of political and economic events in New Zealand and internationally, as well as commercial stresses and strains. The oft-predicted scenario, envisaged by Adam Begg and John Neilson among others, of a small number of larger operators with some smaller niche businesses, has come to pass. Producer ownership and control is still a feature but it is not regarded with the same reverence as in the past, particularly in the North Island. The industry is more integrated with most companies undertaking their own livestock procurement and retaining more of the product selling function.

Two major companies, PPCS and Alliance, both co-operatively owned, now dominate processing in the South Island. Two, the publicly owned AFFCO and the public unlisted company Richmond, are the major companies in the North Island. None of them were in a dominant position 25 years ago and neither PPCS nor Richmond owned processing facilities.

Graeme Lowe, who said when he began in the meat processing business that he aimed to have a million-dollar turnover, has regularly made the *NBR* Rich List and early in 1998 sold most of his Lowe Walker empire to Richmond for $27 million. With a 12-year agreement giving him access to Richmond's by-products, and continued ownership of rendering and hide-processing companies, his name is likely to be heard in the meat industry for some time.

Richmond, which 25 years ago was a farmer-owned marketing company, and has grown to a leading position in the North Island, recently announced it will take over the two Waitotara plants at Waitotara and Tirau, giving it a dominant position in both sheepmeat and beef processing. With rationalisation and centralisation, it currently operates six plants, all single-species, and is rebranding itself as Richmond: New Zealand Farm Fresh. It has acquired two bright ideas begun by companies since failed – the former Fortex subsidiary Gourmet Direct, and the Beef Improvement Group.

Some smaller companies like Oceanview have closed, but others like Craig Hickson's Progressive, with three plants, and Peter Egan's Greenlea with two, are thriving, while Taylor Preston continues to defy geography as

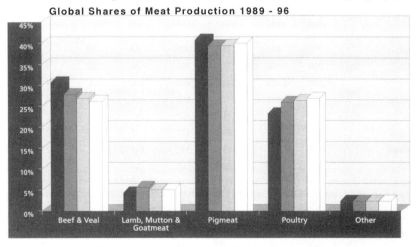

Global Shares of Meat Production 1989 - 96

Production trends show the future potential of the meat business.

| | 1989 | 1994 | 1995 | 1996 |

one of the few remaining multi-species plants, at Ngauranga. AFFCO has also rationalised with the closure of Waitara and Taumarunui and reorganised operations at Imlay, Wairoa and Manawatu. More recently, after two years of disappointing profits, it has reorganised its financial structure once again with the introduction of the Farmers Mutual Group as a cornerstone investor in convertible notes.

Having successfully fended off attempts by PPCS and AFFCO to buy the Freesia shares in late 1997, Richmond fell victim to a typical manoeuvre by PPCS which gained a foothold in major shareholder HKM. Stewart Barnett has proved Ian Jenkinson's faith in him to be justified by maintaining a forthrightly independent stance, the source of grudging admiration and powerful influence in the industry. He has never held an official position on the MIA, but is the chairman of MIRINZ Inc, which has recently sold off its food research business to AgResearch. Robbie Burnside, who chaired PPCS for 25 years, paid the penalty of farmer suspicion that the chairman and chief executive were working too closely together, and was deposed early in 1999. Ian Jenkinson, one of the few people to be able to resist a continued hands-on involvement in the meat industry, still maintains a lively interest in its financial circumstances.

Anzco Foods' Angel Bay Burgers – international award winning products being snapped up on the local market.

As Waitaki once did, PPCS now spans the North and South Island, but it holds fiercely to its farmer co-operative status. Alliance, too, under Owen Poole, is confirmed in its co-operative status and conservative stance, in the southern South Island.

AFFCO, founded in 1916, now has a new chief executive Ross Townshend, ex-dairy industry, and chairman, Sam Lewis. It survives, despite being the company all farmers love to hate, and the gloomy predictions of its many critics and bankers. It now operates six processing plants, and since 1996 its global business has included Mathias Meats.

Many New Zealand farmers would be hard pressed to name the other major meat company with a multi-million dollar turnover. It is ANZCO, which started as a Meat Board marketing subsidiary; its managing director is Graeme Harrison, who first came to the attention of the meat industry with his Master's thesis on market access.

ANZCO has, with few headlines, built itself into a multi-national trading company which operates a feedlot, four meat processing plants and a 'state of the art' food processing facility in New Zealand. In line with one of the long-held principles of the Board's marketing approach, it moved early to make links which would enable it to maintain supply, even though not from New Zealand sources. Apart from the Itoham shareholding in ANZCO, there is now no significant overseas ownership of meat processing facilities in New Zealand.

Any licensed exporters can send product to any market they gain access to. All restrictions were removed with the 1997 legislation. All that is needed to secure an 'Export Licence' (EL) is a mere $30 for registration of name, address and contact numbers, although there are still conditions relating to the quota markets of the EU and US.

The picture of overseas representation is quite different now, with an increasing number of companies having their own offices in the Asian region and making a much stronger and more permanent commitment to marketing through strategic alliances and joint ventures.

Individual company schedules can still be found each week in the media. But other procurement relationships such as contract supply are gradually gaining acceptance.Increased information and forms of traceback are allowing meat companies to identify and reward their preferred suppliers.

The classification system, which formed the foundation of farmer payment and carcass trading, ceased to be mandatory from October 1999, and the supervisory service which managed it has been disbanded. After 75 years of Board control, meat companies are responsible for classification and quality which, along with the negotiation of freight contracts already handed over to the industry, were two of the foundation stones for the Board's original establishment.

The growth area for Board activities – at a time when it has cut its levies and its income – is in research and technology transfer.

For all the high hopes about free trade in agricultural products, the protectionist mood still prevails in many major markets, with the dwindling number of American sheep farmers the most recent group to successfully pressure its government into introducing restrictive tariff quotas, despite the long-standing relationships built by successive Board chairmen and representatives. In his last 'diplomatic' role for the Board, North American representative Bill Joyce has been active, along with Australia, trying to devise counter-proposals that will increase all lamb consumption in the US.

Fears are still expressed about the overall viability of the meat processing business. But it has won international accolades for its cost-effective productivity, and the small number of isolated industrial actions helped contribute to 1997 being the year of lowest overall work stoppages since the war. The industry is still a major employer, with up to 23,000 employed in meat processing, working a smorgasbord of different shifts.

The typical farmer is likely to be managing twice as many stock units as 25 years ago, and a family farm of traditional size struggles to survive. Women are much more visible and play a much more significant role in farm labour and business management.

New Zealand has been able to build on quality and scarcity for its lamb exports, but its beef industry, as part of an increasingly global business, remains vulnerable to consumer backlash from health scares affecting beef, wherever they occur. However, its reputation for safe food has been protected by those very meat hygiene practices so expensively introduced 25 years ago.

While there is still no globally recognised brand for New Zealand meat, the rosette used by the Board has wide international recognition, and most companies draw on the country's clean, natural image in their marketing. For the first time, a campaign has been launched to differentiate New Zealand grass-fed beef for the restaurant consumers of Asia – as "far and away the world's best".

The meat industry of the late 1990s is only half as important to the New Zealand economy as it was in 1972. But its global marketing spread is much wider, both in beef and in lamb. Now it operates in almost 100 markets for lamb, which is increasingly exported chilled; 80% of it is further processed. The UK is still an important sheepmeat market, but the best per tonne returns come from the US and Germany.

Though Prime Minister Jenny Shipley and her predecessor Jim Bolger – now in the front line of access arguments for New Zealand lamb as ambassador in Washington – have both been farmers, rural representation in the National Cabinet is minimal. Even in the All Black front row, farmers are now hard to find. The country's powerbase is urban, and improved roading and communications are bringing many aspects of the lives of all but the most remote farmers closer to their city counterparts.

Meanwhile, New Zealand farmers have turned their subsidy-free status into a virtue to be paraded internationally. Some of the most hard-line free market statements emerge from Federated Farmers.

In so many ways there has been a paradigm shift – in status, expectations, structures, power, products, productivity and people, in mindset and attitudes. In many ways the meat industry's last 25 years mirror the changes in the New Zealand economy and New Zealand society itself. And the only thing predictable about the future is more change.

But the meat industry has always been larger than life, bloodier and more bloody-minded. Nothing is as straightforward as it seems. The best-laid plans have often delivered surprises to those who conceived them as well as those on the receiving end.

In many respects the industry gives all the appearance of having recovered from the frantic rationalisation and restructuring activities of the last 25 years and put in place elements of the 'desirable' structure. Time will tell whether what exists today is really any more stable than what existed 25 years ago. The only certainty is that the industry will continue to operate in interesting times.

The future marketing structure will be a matter for the companies to decide. There is increasing commercial representation in overseas markets and strategic alliances have been forged. There continues to be a degree of co-operation in the co-ordination of supplies to markets such as Iran, but in others the spirit of competitive trading persists despite New Zealand remaining a very small cog in a very large and sophisticated international meat market. The prospect of a complete merger to put in place the 'integrated marketing' dream is probably impossible. As Gray Mathias says: "Egos get in the way of those sorts of things".

Government appointees	
Ansell, Graham (CMG)	1990-95
Begg, Adam	1969-76
Carroll, Thomas	1971-74
Dineen, Barry	1996-99
Dobbs, Fred	1977-85
Dryden, Gordon	1975-76
Finlayson, Ross	1990-99
Kennedy, 'Blue'	1985-89
Macaulay, Jim	1990-96
McRae, Norman	1976-86
Neilson, John	1986-89
Rusk, Reg	1980-85
Ryan, Bruce	1965-68
Rapata, Hemi-Rua	1999-
Rudland, Gina	1999-

Processing industry representatives	
Barnett, Stewart	1996-
Harrison, Graeme	1999-
Loughlin, John	1999-
Manson, Don	1996-99
Mathias, Gray	1996-97
Upton, John	1997-98

Exporter representatives	
Upton, John	1999-

Dairy Board representatives	
Ebbett, Bernie	1976-81
Gordon, Mac	1993-96
Jensen, Peter	1989-93
Mooney, Brian	1981-88

The Board's new logo and identity.

MEAT INDUSTRY TIMELINE

1971
National Government in power: Sir John Marshall PM, Doug
  Carter Minister of Agriculture
Meat Export Control Act changed to permit Board to market lamb
  (October)
Dawn Meats/Richmond form Pacific Freezing Ltd; Board
  approves new beef plant (October)
Board intervenes in lamb market (December)

1972
Board opens Brussels office
Begg Committee on future lamb marketing
Meat Exporters Council (MEC) established
First Board/MEC Iran delegation
Stabilisation of Prices Regulations (January)
Livestock Incentive Scheme - $1 a head for sheep (June)
Labour Government elected (November): Norman Kirk PM,
  Colin Moyle Minister of Agriculture
CFM proposes South Island rationalisation

1973
Oil crisis
Britain enters EC
Industrial Relations Act amendments
Nordmeyer Commission
Minimum prices for beef
Borthwicks takes 24% of CFM, will market all product
Swifts exit: close Ngauranga (May), sell Wairoa to Waitaki
CWS offers Longburn to Board (June)
Waitaki bids against CFM for SOFCO and Nelson Freezing Co
  (November)

1974
Japan shuts out beef imports
Nordmeyer Commission reports (April)
Norman Kirk dies, Bill Rowling Prime Minister (August)
Shah of Iran visits NZ (September)
Board gets Order in Council to buy and sell beef
Board turns down Longburn offer (March)
Board announces guaranteed prices for lamb and mutton
  (November)
South Otago Freezing Company (SOFCO) bought by Waitaki,
  Nelson also bought
Pacific Freezing plant opened (April)

1975
Board opens Teheran office
AFFCO, Alliance, HBFMC form Associated NZ Farmers
NZ Meat Marketing Corporation (MMC) set up
Govt announces agricultural support measures - $1 per head per
  sheep (January)
Stone Committee on producer ownership of meat companies
Thomas committee on NI slaughter facilities
Farm Incomes Advisory Committee (Zanetti Committee)
  recommends additional support (March)
Price Smoothing Scheme development; Meat Industry
  Stabilisation Account MISA
Board guarantees 74-75 and 75-76 beef prices; also intervenes in
  lamb and mutton
SFM, Waitaki and PPCS all bid for NZR
National Government elected; Rob Muldoon PM and Minister of
  Finance, Duncan McIntyre Minister of Agriculture, Peter
  Gordon Minister of Labour (November)

1976
Meat Export Prices Act establishes Price Smoothing Scheme
Waitaki succeeds with takeover bid and becomes Waitaki/NZR
  (January)
Meat Amendment Act establishes Meat Industry Authority (MIA)
Industrial Relations Amendment (No3) Bill
Livestock Incentive Scheme
Electrical stunning compulsory (October)

1977
"Biggest drop ever" in prices for NZ lamb in UK
Meatmark Ltd in UK (February)
US ITC investigates beef imports
MIA first meeting; four plant applications (December)
Board supplements beef prices, intervenes for mutton
Borthwicks/CWS form joint company for processing only; fail in
  bid for Gear
Brierley and HBFMC succeed with Board-approved rival bid but
  Brierley offer for Richmond repulsed

1978
Drought and "intense industrial action"
Muldoon involvement in wages settlement (March)
Government announces SMPs; Board to administer (July)
Meat products qualify for Export Incentives under the Income Tax
  Act 1976
Ravensdown/KP/Farmers Fertiliser - Board funds from MIRA
Peter Gordon's 'five point peace package' settles Ocean Beach
  strife (September)
Board buys 25% of mutton due to lack of Russian orders
MIA approves Hellaby plant at Taumarunui and Phoenix at
  Kokiri; turns down Oringi and Takapau

1979
Oil crisis again
Crawling peg exchange rate (June)
Islamic revolution, Shah in exile
NZ delegation has audience with Ayatollah, agrees to Halal
  slaughter
Iran declared development market (June); contract to supply
  200,000 tonnes (or more) over 4 years signed (October)
Storage Under Board Control to stabilise prices in the UK
New US Meat Import Law, quotas for beef and mutton (December)
Price Surveillance Regulations replace Stabilisation of Prices
  Regulations 1974
PM's conference on the meat industry (April); K & F charges
  removed from price control
Shipping – Board assumes control over Waitaki's meat
Board buys 50% of DEVCO; shares held by Meat Industry
  Research Trust
Board's 'Key works' purchase of NCF Kaiapoi approved
  (September)
Borthwicks UK float fails
Meat Industry Authority approves HBFMC application for
  Takapau, declines Pacific Freezing for Oringi (February)

1980
Beef price collapse in North America (February)
EC Sheepmeats Regulation agreed (May)
NZ signs VRA for lamb to EC (July)
Board supports beef prices for 10 weeks

1981

Lamb for oil deal with Iran
Continuous decline in US beef prices
US CVD petition against imported lamb
Meat Act 1981 dissolves MIA and deregulates the meat industry
Shipping – court rules for Board in Waitaki case (April)
Joint Meat Export Marketing Council (JMEMC, then JMC)
    established (September)
Board supports beef prices
Board intervenes in the mutton market (October)
AFFCO closes Southdown
Waitaki closes Picton
HBFMC opens Takapau (August)
Pacific Freezing opens Oringi (November)
Alliance beats CFM to buy Ocean Beach from CWS (November)

1982

Japan and North Africa declared development markets
Board stores lamb in UK by agreement with JMC (March-May)
Board intervenes in lamb market (April)
Meatmark reactivated (May-July)
LCPAFFP (Buyback) for further processing
Price and wage freeze (June); fixed exchange rate introduced
Manalytics report on shipping (July)
Board decision to take over all sheepmeat, supported by Muldoon
    (October)
Iran contract delayed, lamb-for-oil agreement signed December
    (120,000 tonnes to March 84)
Gear exits, closes Petone plant. Patea (W & R Fletcher) closed;
    Shortland (Hellabys) stops processing lamb and mutton
Fletcher Challenge takes over DMBA
PPCS buys Borthwicks shareholding of CFM (20%)

1983

Glendinning report on UK product and distribution
Board cuts UK importer/agents from 30 to 8
Meat Industry Task Force set up (June) – proposes Meat Industry
    Council and National Pool
Government price and wage freeze extended to February 1984
Board considers using Section 10 to retain control of sheepmeat
    (November)
ANZCO established (December)
PPCS a shareholder in SFM for a fortnight.
FCL and PPCS become controlling shareholders of CFM
Brierleys buys Riverlands beef plant
Waitaki opens new Marlborough plant
Farmers Meat Export Whangarei upgraded
Dalgety and Crown Corporation merge

1984

Subsidised EC beef disrupts world market
Dramatic improvement in UK market (January)
Meat Industry Council meets (February)
Board opens office in Bahrain
Sheep numbers peak at 70 million (June)
Govt announces SMPs will be dismantled, lump sums to replace
Price freeze partially lifted
Snap election brings Labour Government (July); David Lange
    Prime Minister, Colin Moyle Minister of Agriculture, Mike
    Moore Minister of Overseas Trade
20% devaluation costs industry $104 million (July)
Wage controls ended (November); meatworkers award one of first
    to be negotiated
PPCS floats Apex, takes control of CFM from FCL, gets
    controlling interest in Hellabys
SFM exits, Mataura and Makarewa plants taken over by FCL as
    Challenge Meats

Alliance faces major industrial problems at Ocean Beach

1985

North America beef prices 7 year low – dairy reduction pro-
    gramme
US CVD on lamb imports hits DEVCO
Barter trade deals including oil for lamb
Record lamb production and 39 million kill
SMPs dismantled, producer boards to operate own price support
    schemes with Reserve Bank backing
PCEK report recommends closing plants and Tradeable Killing
    Rights to rationalise capacity (March)
MEC, FCA and IMEA combine as Meat Industry Association
    (MIA) (July)
Janmark established
MIA proposes 5 marketing groups to act in co-operation with the
    Board (August)
Board withdraws from ownership (November)
Advanced Foods Waipukurau plant opens (May) 50% Board, 50%
    Advanced Meats owned
Fort Export becomes Fortex

1986

Cairns Group founded
GATT Uruguay Round begins
Spain and Portugal join EC
NZ dollar floated, 28% revaluation, export returns fell
UK importers: Self Appointed Famous Five
Freesia re-established for Board investment in marketing
    (January)
DEVCO renamed The New Zealand Lamb Company (North
    America) Ltd (March)
Farmers march on Parliament (May)
National meatworkers strike – longest in 30 years
Commerce Act; decision to cease publishing national schedule as
    possibly infringing the Act
Repeal of Meat Export Prices Act (October)
SIMCO (South Island Marketing Co) and Farmco among
    marketing strategies considered
Red Meat Promotion Council (later Beef and Lamb Marketing
    Bureau) established
Hellabys taken over by Apex then AFFCO
Borthwicks/CWS taken over by Waitaki
W & R Fletcher (Vesteys) and Dalgety Crown form Weddel
    Crown
AFFCO closes Shortland (July)
Advanced Meats sells AFL shareholding to GFW; gains 25% of
    HBFMC and supply agreement
GFW lifts shareholding in Waitaki to 73%
PCEK and Southpac each recommend reducing capacity
Richmond buys out Dawn Meats so owns Pacific Freezing
    (October 7)
North Island rationalisation takes out 7 processing chains:
    Waitaki, Weddel, Richmond contribute to HBFMC closure of
    Whakatu (October 9)
HBFMC exits: Richmond takes over Takapau
Lowe Walker established: buyout of T H Walker, purchase of Te
    Aroha

1987

Middle East - Gulf War
NZ Lamb Promotion Council (6 importers and Board) formed in
    UK (July)
North American Lamb Market review - Lamb Company loses
    exclusive licence to US, keeps it to Canada
Challenge and Waitaki sell Towers to Hillsdown Holdings
Labour Relations Act 1987

Sharemarket crash (October)

Towards 2000 Meat Marketing Symposium (April)

Freesia funding decided: Govt writes off MISA debt, shares
    MIRA with Board 'for industry investment' (March)

Freesia loans $35 million to AFFCO, takes over Board
    shareholding in AFL

Freesia takes 19% shareholding of Richmond; 25% of Fortex

North Island rationalisation concluded: slaughtering activities of
    Advanced Meat transferred to Gisborne Refrigerating Co

New plants: Blue Sky Meats, Fortex Seafield, Frasertown Meats,
    Paramount Exports

C S Stevens exits: Alliance buys Kaiapoi, Sockburn and Ashley

PML exits: company folds

PPCS buys 50% Brooks of Norwich

Lowe Walker buys Namron Meats Paeroa

Brierleys forms Riverlands Group

1988

GATT mid-term review: EC and US at loggerheads over SPS; EC
    bans growth promotants

Farmers move away from sheepmeat to beef

EC VRA renegotiated

Cyclone Bola (March)

Marketing groups increased to 6

All companies sign Quality of Product Agreement – compulsory
    minimum of AC, A C & A next year

Chilled packaging – commercial launch of CAPTECH

Freesia and GFW establish Garway Meats for Waitaki holdings
    (March)

Garway report recommends further rationalisation – 45 chains

Weddel Crown 'demergered'

PPCS buys Marlborough and Finegand from Waitaki, contributes
    to closure of Islington and Burnside

Challenge Meats merges with Waitaki

Waitaki faces huge loss; Waitaki Trade Finance established

New plants: NZ Beef Packers, South Pacific Meats, Ventec,
    Waitotara, Wallford

1989

Fall of the Berlin Wall

EC agrees 4 year derogation from VRA (December) 10%
    sheepmeat levy reduced to zero, backdated to January

Board moves US office to Washington, re-opens in Brussels

Port and Local Government reform

Meat Export Control Amendment Act redefines Board functions,
    composition (December)

Meat Industry Freight Council and Special Access Markets
    Committee

Meat Workers Union claim for national redundancy agreement

Waitaki North Island assets sold to AFFCO (November)

Freesia Meat Holdings (Freesia, FCL, GFW) established for
    negotiations with Alliance

Freesia sells Fortex shareholding

Record profit for Alliance

ANZCO joint ventures: Southern Nissui and Five Star Beef

Weddel closes Westfield

Cavalier Meat Co takes over Ventec

1990

Iraq invades Kuwait

Big downturn in beef prices, first half, following heavy Australian
    supplies

New major lamb contracts with Iran and Jordan

MRDC established (October)

Alliance takes over remaining Waitaki assets (March)

AFFCO closes Waingawa, leaves Longburn closed

Fortex lists on SX, opens Silverstream plant

Waitane Meats new plant

1991

Japan's beef market fully liberalised (April)

Employment Contracts Act

Resource Management Act

Procurement war

MIHC established

MPC established, 'Wairakei Group' formed (October)

Weddel Crown becomes Weddel New Zealand; opens rebuilt
    Feilding plant

Fortex wins top business award; eyes UK plant sites

Alliance closes Ocean Beach, Kaiapoi, Ashley Lean; becomes the
    Alliance Group

AFFCO opens Singapore, Tokyo office; with ANZCO forms NZ
    Beef Japan; Affco plans staggered closures

Richmond buys Dalgety Lonsdale

Lowe Walker hot bones beef at Hawera

Lowe Walker buys NZ Beef Packers and Ngauranga Meat
    Processors, sells NMP to Taylor Preston

Richmond buys Paramount Te Kauwhata

Weddel opens rebuilt Feilding plant

Waitangi Fellowship established

1992

Snow decimates sheep flock

MIRINZ wins Rutherford award for A C & A

Weir Committee to review Electoral Committee

Board establishes 'arm's length' subsidiaries: Freesia Investments
    to PRL, ANZCO to MEL

24 MRDC monitor farms established

AFFCO opens Manawatu Beef Packers (rebuilt Feilding plant)

Five Star Feedlot opens (February)

Brierleys lists Huttons Kiwi/Riverlands

New plants: Clover Exports, Hill Country Beef, King Country
    Lamb, Cromwell Meats, Riverlands Manawatu

Waikato Beef Packers buys South Pacific

1993

Single market – EC becomes EU

Uruguay FMD clear

Board opens Hong Kong office

MPC debate over quota allocation including tradeable rights.

Farmers for Positive Change majority on Electoral Committee
    (August)

ANZCO ownership changes, merger with Janmark

Benmore, Wilson, Hellaby buy Auckland Meat Processors

Fortex buys into Phoenix

New plants: Greenlea, Hill Country Beef, Lowe Walker
    Dargaville, rebuilt Affco Moerewa

Phoenix, Alliance and Atas in joint venture in Stoke plant

1994

GATT agreement signed (April)

Board opens Korea office

EU access rolled over, but ceiling on chilled lamb raised to 13,500
    tonnes

Referendum indicates direct elections; Cullwick Committee
    reviews electoral process

PRL sells AFL shareholding

Fortex exits: company collapse

Canterbury Meat Packers (ANZCO) buys Seafield plant

Weddel funding collapse, Tomoana, Feilding, Aotearoa,
    Whangarei and Kaiti closed.(August)

1995

Uruguay Round decisions implemented from January (US) and

July (Europe)
WTO replaces GATT
Sweden, Finland and Austria join EU; access increase 850 tonnes.
US lifts CVD on lamb; lamb producers want check-off
Food safety concerns (E coli) in US; Mega-Reg mooted
Commerce Commission investigates price fixing
Restructured Beef and Lamb Marketing Bureau funded by
    processors levy and Board grant
Electoral Committee abolished; first direct elections for Board
Trial Run Holdings consortium disperses Weddel assets
AFFCO public float
Alliance shareholders approve capital plan
ANZCO purchases Huttons Kiwi; Board sells ANZCO
Canterbury Meat Packers builds beef plant
Universal Beef Packers new plant Te Kuiti

1996
Bad year for beef: BSE in Britain, E coli in Japan, peak cattle
    numbers and high stocks in US
Board closes Bahrain, Hong Kong offices
Board challenges US lamb checkoff
Processing industry representatives replace commercial appoint-
    ees on Board
Lamb Promotion Council ended (December) Board responsible
    for generic promotion; joint ventures with exporters and
    importers
Producer Board Acts Reform Bill introduced (August)
Foundation for Sheep Research established
Board funds local promotion, 'the iron campaign', through
    BLMB
29.6% of levy spent on R and D through MRDC
PRL sells shareholding in AFL, Lamb Company
ANZCO sold to Janz; sets up Pacific Beef
New plants: Lamb Packers Feilding
Trial Run Holdings wipes debt
AFFCO buys Mathias

1997
Lobbying successfully defeats US Sheep Promotion Order
    (checkoff)
MPC wound up
Joint strategic directions paper and foresight project
Quality Mark launched (September); Board commits $10 million
    over 3 years
Board holdings in Alliance and Richmond sold
Beef Research Foundation launched
Board 75th anniversary (October)
MRDC 'absorbed' into Board as Research and Information
    Transfer Group.
Meat Board Act 1997 (December)
ANZCO buys NZ Casing Co
Benmore exits: in receivership
MIRINZ forms strategic alliance with AgResearch

GLOSSARY

3 CVD: Third country veterinary directive - EC
AC&A: Accelerated conditioning and aging – technique for improving the tenderness of frozen meat
Ad valorem: Import duty or tariff according to the value of the product
c&f: Costs of product to market including shipping freight
cif: Costs of product to market including insurance and freight
Classification: The description of meat carcasses according to specified characteristics (also known as grading)
Cold shortening: When muscle fibres contract if meat is frozen before the muscle has had time to 'condition' (and becomes tough)
Countervailing duty: A duty or tariff imposed to offset production or export subsidies
fob: Free on board – price of product delivered on board ship, ie cost of production
GATT bound: A duty or tariff rate written into GATT
Halal: Slaughter according to Islamic religious requirements
K & F charges: Killing and Freezing Charges
Key works: A Board concept of having farmer-owned meat processing plants in each major livestock-producing area
National Pool: Central procurement system proposed for lamb
On the hoof: Buying stock for slaughter by visual assessment
Open door policy: A provision under the Meat Act that obliged meat processing companies to accept stock for slaughter
Owner's account: Having stock slaughtered, processed and marketed at the farmer's risk with the market return credited to them
Per head selling: Selling stock for an average price for each animal
pH: A measure of acidity/alkalinity linked to tenderness of meat, its eating quality and storage life
Pool: Where farmers opt to sell stock for an initial payment with the prospect of further payment depending on the outcome of the marketing of the product
Premium: A price offered in excess of a previously advised price offer
Primals: Cuts from the initial processing of a lamb carcass – shoulders, racks, loins and legs
Processing capacity: The estimated volume of stock that can be processed by a meat plant in a specified period
Procurement: Buying livestock for slaughter from farmers
Quota rent: A premium over normal market prices for product supplied under quota
Schedule: The range of prices announced weekly for each weight and grade of carcasses by meat companies
Single buyer: A government buying agency responsible for the importation of a particular product
Single-desk seller: An organisation responsible for the marketing of all of a particular product for export
Special access markets: Markets determined to need special development and therefore conditional export licences
Tariff: A duty or charges to be paid on the import of goods
Tariff rate quota: A quota with one tariff rate for shipments within the quota volume and a higher rate for shipments in excess of quota
Tradeable Killing Rights: Killing quotas allocated to individual companies as a means of rationalising slaughter capacity
Toll processing: Slaughtering and processing stock for a fee
Weak selling: Selling a product at prices considered by some to be less than the market is prepared to pay

INDEX